Frank

ugh!

MODELS, METHODS, AND ANALYTICAL
PROCEDURES IN EDUCATION RESEARCH

# MODELS,
## METHODS,
# AND ANALYTICAL
## PROCEDURES IN
## EDUCATION RESEARCH

JOSEPH E. HILL
*Wayne State University*

AUGUST KERBER
*Wayne State University*

*1967     Wayne State University Press     Detroit*

# Contents

*List of Tables*       vii
*List of Figures*       ix
*Glossary of Symbols*       xi
*Preface*       xiii

PART I  INTRODUCTION TO RESEARCH AND MODELS       2

*1*    *Inquiry and Research*       3
*2*    *Models: Structure and Function*       14

PART 2  THE GENERAL ANALOGUE MODEL OF EDUCATIONAL RESEARCH: DESIGN AND PROCEDURES       22

*3*    *Problem and Hypothesis*       23
*4*    *The Universe and the Sample*       37
*5*    *Data Collection—Conditions and Methods*       46
*6*    *Data Collection—Instrumentalities*       61
*7*    *Data Processing*       70
*8*    *The Research Decision*       79

PART 3  ADAPTING THE GENERAL MODEL TO PROBLEMS IN THE BASIC TYPES OF RESEARCH       90

*9*    *Models of Experimental Research*       91
*10*   *Descriptive Research*       108
*11*   *Action Research*       117
*12*   *Historical Research*       125
*13*   *Field Research*       134

PART 4  STATISTICAL TECHNIQUES AND MODELS       145

*14*   *Basic Concepts*       149
*15*   *Probability and Frequency Distributions*       173
*16*   *The Normal Distribution*       189
*17*   *Numerical Aspects of Sampling*       203
*18*   *Numerical Aspects of Sampling* (Sequential Sampling)       220
*19*   *Estimation*       240

20    *Further Methods of Correlation and Regression*     259

21    *Non-Linear Regression and Correlation*     267

22    *Multiple Correlation and Regression*     275

23    *Statistical Inference*     292

24    *Nonparametric Statistical Tests—*I     300

25    *Nonparametric Statistical Tests—*II (The Kolmogorov-Smirnov Statistical Test Model)     311

26    *Nonparametric Statistical Tests—*III (Tests Employing Related Samples and *k* Independent Samples)     323

27    *Parametric Statistical Tests—*I (The Normal and *t*-Distributions)     334

28    *Parametric Statistical Tests—*II (The *z* or *F*-Distribution)     355

29    *Parametric Statistical Tests—*III (Analysis of Variance Multiple Bases of Classification)     375

30    *Parametric Statistical Tests—*IV Analysis of Covariance     418

31    *Numerical Procedures* (Factor Analysis)     459

32    *Numerical Procedures: Further Considerations* (Linear Programming and the Theory of Games)     500

*Notes*     529

*Bibliography*     533

*Index*     547

*Colophon*     551

# Tables

1   Discriminative Power of Test Items in Per Cent of Success by Superior and Inferior Groups   68

2   Classification of Experimental Designs in Educational Research   95

3   Height to Nearest Inch of 300 Male Students Involved in Study Associated with the Model of Field Research   149

4   Chi-Square Table (Single Classification)   305

5   A Contingency Table Showing Responses of Graduates   308

6   Selected Critical Values of $D$ for the Kolmogorov-Smirnov One-Sample Test   312

7   Rankings of "1" for Three Categories in Connection with Ten Administrative Problems Considered by Twenty-five "Successful" Elementary Principals   315

8   Selected Critical Values of $K_D$ for the Kolmogorov-Smirnov Two-Sample Test   318

9   "Scores" of Twenty Elementary School Principals and Twenty High School Principals Indicating Weight Given to the Dimension of "Community" in Administrative Decision-Making   320

10  Data to Illustrate the Wilcoxon Signed-Ranks Tests for Paired Observations   325

11  "Flexibility" Scores of Three Groups of Teachers   332

12  Selected Percentiles of the $t$-Distribution   338

13  Initial and Final Scores of Ten Children Participating in Remedial Reading Laboratory Program   349

14  Selected Critical Values of $F$ for the 5 Per Cent and 1 Per Cent Levels of Significance   357

15  Scores $(X)$ and Squares of Scores $(X^2)$ on a Particular Test for Materials Taught by Laboratory, Lecture, Project, Discussion, and Teaching Machine Methods   361

16  Variance Table of Results of Analysis of Data from Table XV   365

17  Analysis of Variance for Two-Way Classification Factorial Design   376

18  Summary of Analysis of Variance for Data of Table XVII   377

19  Fictitious Data Illustrating Zero Interaction   381

20  Fictitious Data Illustrating Maximum Interaction   381

21      Fictitious Data Illustrating Interaction for More Than One, But an Equal Number of Values Per Cell      382

22      A $2 \times 3 \times 5$ Factorial Design Experiment in Mathematics Instruction —$n = 3$ Observations Per Cell      392

22(S)   Tables for the Calculation of the Interactions
        Sums of Squares
                Table 1      396
                Table 2      396
                Table 3      396
                Table 4      397
                Table 5      397
                Table 6      397
                Table 7      397

23      Summary Table of Interaction Sums of Squares Equations      405

24      Sum of Squares Equations and Accompanying Degrees of Freedom for Error Term and All Interactions of a Six Factor Research Problem, with $n$ Equal Entries in each Cell of Original Table      410–14

25      Summary of Analysis of Variance for Fictitious Data of Table XXII      415

26      Equations for Sums of Squares and Sums of Cross Products of the Interactions and Main Effects Involved in the Research Problem      450–51

27      Tests of Significance of Interactions and Main Effects      452

28      Correlation Matrix of Nine Test Variables      469

29      First Factor Product Matrix      473

30      First Residual Matrix      473

31      First Residual Matrix (With Reflections)      477

32      Second Factor Product Matrix      479

33      Second Residual Matrix (With Reflections)      481

34      Third Factor Product Matrix      482

35      Third Residual Matrix      482

36      Factor Loadings Before Rotation      483

37      Factor Loadings After One Rotation      491

38      Factor Loadings After Rotations      493

# Figures

1     General Model of Educational Research     20

2     Examples of Testing Null Hypotheses Involving Population Means     34

3     Histogram of 300 Male Student Heights to Nearest Inch in the Model of Field Research     150

4     Histogram of 300 Male Student Heights to Nearest Half-Inch     151

5     Smooth Curve of 300 Male Student Heights     152

6     Height in Inches of 300 Male Students Involved in Study Associated with the Model of Field Research     153

7     Three Frequency Distributions with Same Mean ($\overline{X} = 4.0$)     158

8     Examples of Skewness     171

9     The Normal Probability Curve     189

10     Three Types of Normal Distribution     192

11     Area from $z = -\infty$ to $z = -1.00$     193

12     Area from $z = 0$ to $z = +1.00$     193

13     Area from $z = -1.96$ to $z = +1.645$     194

14     Operating Characteristic Curve     227

15     Sequential Analysis Graph of Proportions Example     229

16     Sequential Analysis Graph of Methods Example     238

17     Graph of "Incorrect" Regression *Line* and "Correct" Regression *Curve*     270

18     A Two-Tailed Critical Region     295

19     Graphic Illustration of a Beta Error     296

20     Portion of the Probability Table of Chi-Square     303

21     The *t*-Distribution for $n = 4$, or $n - 1 = 3$ Degrees of Freedom     337

22     Sample of Work Tables for Determining Values of Sums Appearing in Sums of Squares and Sums of Products Equations     444–47

23     Vectors and Cosines of $\theta$     462

24     Scatter Diagram and Vector Representation of Correlation     462

25     Spatial Model of Test Vectors, Clusters, and Factors     463

26     Three Intercorrelations Not Resolvable into the Two Factors (Dimensions) of a Plane Area     466

27     Centroid of a Geometrical Figure of a Set of Correlating Variables     471

28    Reflection of Vectors with Respect to First Factor (Centroid)    474
29    Test Projections Before and After Rotation of Factor Axes    485
30    Reference Axes and Graphs    501
31    A Polygonal Convex Set of Feasible Points    503
32    Saddle-point S—Maximum Point of Curve $C_1$, and Minimum Point of Curve $C_2$    513
33    Payoff Matrix to the Research Group    516
34    Payoff Matrix of a Mixed Strategy    517
35    Payoff Matrix to "Concept (Topic) Presentation-Player"    524
36    Plots for $g$ in Interval $0 \leqslant x_1 \leqslant 1$    525

# Glossary of Symbols

NOTE: This presentation does not include all of the symbols employed in the book. The set includes only those symbolizations that are associated with certain mathematical definitions found in the text.

| SYMBOL | READING AND MEANING | EXAMPLE |
|---|---|---|
| $\equiv$ | is identical with | $A \equiv A$ |
| $=$ | is equal to | $3 = 2 + 1$ |
| $\approx$ | is approximately equal to | $3.76 \approx 3.8$ |
| $\neq$ | is not equal to | $3 \neq 4$ |
| $<$ | is less than | $3 < 4$ |
| $\leq$ | is less than or equal to | $X \leq 8$ |
| $>$ | is greater than | $5 > 4$ |
| $\geq$ | is greater than or equal to | $X \geq 9$ |
| $\not<$ | is not less than | $5 \not< 4$ |
| $\not>$ | is not greater than | $3 \not> 4$ |
| $\therefore$ | therefore | $A > B; B > C; \therefore A > C$ |
| $\infty$ | infinity | Area under curve from $X = -\infty$ to $X = b.$ |
| $\sqrt{\phantom{x}}$ | square root | $\sqrt{36} = 6$ |
| $\vert\ \vert$ | absolute or numerical value | $\vert -5 \vert = \vert 5 \vert = 5$ |
| $\Sigma$ | summation operator | $\sum_{i=1}^{3} X_i = X_1 + X_2 + X_3$ |
| $!$ | factorial product | $4! = 4 \cdot 3 \cdot 2 \cdot 1$ |
| $\tilde{X}$ | tilde $X$, criterion value | $\tilde{X}_0 = b_1 X_1 + b_2 X_2 + b_3 X_3$ |
| $n'$ | $n$ prime | $n' = n - 1$ |
| $n''$ | $n$ double prime | $n'' = n' - 1$ |
| $X^2$ | $X$ square | $X^2 = X \cdot X$ |
| $\hat{Y}$ | Adjusted mean score, $Y$ | $\hat{Y} = \overline{Y} - b(X - \overline{X})$ |
| $X_i$ | $X$ subscript $i$ | $X_3$-third value in a set of $X$ scores |
| $\sin \theta$ | sine function of angle $\theta$ | $\sin \theta = \sin 30 = \frac{1}{2}$ |
| $\cos \theta$ | cosine function of angle $\theta$ | $\cos \theta = \cos 90 = 0$ |
| $\ln$ | natural logarithm to base $e$ | $\ln 2 = .693$ |
| $e$ | the constant $e$ | $e = \lim_{n \to \infty} \left(1 + \frac{1}{n}\right)^n \approx 2.71828$ |
| $\log$ | common logarithm to base 10 | $\log_{10} 100 = 2$ |
| $_nP_r$ | the permutation of $n$ different things taken $r$ at a time | $_5P_2 = \frac{5!}{(5-2)!} = 20$ |
| $_n C_x$ | the combination of $n$ different things taken $X$ at a time | $_2^5 C = \frac{5!}{2!(5-2)!} = 10$ |
| $\pi$ | Greek letter Pi, either a constant, or $\pi$ radians | $\pi \approx 3.1416$, or $\pi$ radians $= 180°$ |

## GREEK ALPHABET

| LETTERS | | READING | LETTERS | | READING | LETTERS | | READING |
|---|---|---|---|---|---|---|---|---|
| 1 | α | Alpha | 9 | ι | Iota | 17 | ρ | Rho |
| 2 | β | Beta | 10 | κ | Kappa | 18 | σ | Sigma |
| 3 | γ | Gamma | 11 | λ | Lambda | 19 | τ | Tau |
| 4 | δ | Delta | 12 | μ | Mu | 20 | υ | Upsilon |
| 5 | ε | Epsilon | 13 | ν | Nu | 21 | φ | Phi |
| 6 | ζ | Zeta | 14 | ξ | Xi | 22 | χ | Chi |
| 7 | η | Eta | 15 | o | Omicron | 23 | ψ | Psi |
| 8 | θ | Theta | 16 | π | Pi | 24 | ω | Omega |

# *Preface*

THE SUBJECT OF EDUCATIONAL RESEARCH includes information from each of three broad and highly interrelated areas: (1) research design, (2) methods and conditions of collecting data, and (3) analytical and numerical procedures of processing data. In order to avoid the erroneous impression that a research process is composed of procedures, drawn as needed, from three distinct and separate categories (i.e., design, methods, and numerical analyses), a general analog model of education research has been suggested.

The development of the general model is the result of the authors' long experience in working with advisers, graduate students, administrators, and other school personnel on various types of problems in educational and behavioral sciences research. It is not the intent of the authors to advocate the "only" way of conducting research through the use of the general model. The main purpose of the model is to provide the researcher with one of many integrated and systematically synthesized approaches to solving the various types of problems found in educational research.

Although the approach employed in the book has been intentionally geared to graduate students and school personnel with limited backgrounds in mathematics, statistics, and research design, the selection of topics and their development has been carried out in a manner that will also make the book helpful to individuals possessing what might be termed an "intermediate" level of competence in these areas. For example, the topic of factor analysis is discussed in terms of the rationale underlying each of the phases of factor extraction, factor rotation, factor identification, and the use of the specification equation. Through this type of approach the person with little background in the subject can follow the step by step development of it, while the person with an "intermediate" knowledge can choose from the sequential offerings those elements he wishes to investigate.

It is hoped that the book is multi-purpose in meeting such needs as:

(1) a basic textbook in introductory courses in research;
(2) a textbook for classes in methods of educational research;
(3) a textbook for an integrated course in statistics and research design;
(4) a resource book for doctoral students and advisers involved in dissertation research; and
(5) a resource and guide-book for educational research conducted by personnel in school systems.

The book includes four parts, each part complementary to all of the others, and each synthesizing the demands of a suggested general model of research for treatment of problems at both the theoretical and the applied levels of concern. This approach necessitates a flexible but still unified treatment of the topics included in the presentation.

Part I of the book deals with a brief search of selected, philosophical movements for elements of inquiry common to each of the approaches. Through the use of these common elements, and the concept of the isomorphism of sets, the rationale for the development of the general analog model of educational research is presented. The model is then presented in terms of the research process, which in turn is expressed by means of the previously defined common elements of inquiry. The completed model shows that the general sequence of steps employed effectively to produce good educational research procedures is: (1) the problem; (2) the hypothesis; (3) the universe of data; (4) the sample(s) of the study; (5) the processes of data collection; (6) the procedures of data processing; and (7) the research decision.

Part II deals with a detailed explanation of each of the elements composing the general model. Throughout the discussion reference is made to many concepts covered in Parts I, III, and IV. In similar fashion, reference to Part II, for a more detailed discussion of the elements composing the models, is made throughout the other three parts of the book.

Part III covers five different types of research and illustrates the "adaptation" of the general model to a problem classified under each of the respective "types." The five arbitrarily defined basic types of research covered are: (1) experimental, (2) descriptive, (3) action, (4) historical, and (5) field studies. Although skeletal forms of various "adaptions" of the general model are employed throughout Parts I and IV, five models are accorded a complete treatment in Part III, one for each type of research covered.

Part IV is concerned with explanations and applications of basic statistical concepts; sampling procedures; procedures of estimation; selected types of nonparametric and parametric statistical tests; factor analytic approaches; decision theory involving "certainty" decisions (linear programing); decision theory involving "risk" decisions (theory of strictly determined games); and theory involving "uncertainty" decisions (theory of non-strictly determined games).

In preparing the final content and format of this book, the authors were the beneficiaries of many sources and individuals. These sources include: previous literature on topics related to the text; and the advice, suggestions, corrections, and other types of assistance provided by students, colleagues, anonymous reviewers, and the publisher's editors. It is impossible to acknowledge individually the authors' indebtedness to all of these contributors. All comments and criticisms were greatly appreciated, and should the book prove to have merit, credit, in no small part, will be due those many individuals who found time from busy schedules to be helpful.

J.E.H.

A.K.

# PART I

## *Introduction to Research and Models*

THE PROCESS OF INQUIRY is the foundation of research. Inquiry, as the term is used here, began when man's reason asserted itself and his blind belief in the supernatural yielded to the powers of observation and living experiences.

In Part I of the book we offer a brief discussion of selected major philosophical movements to show the existence of certain "common" elements of inquiry around which the general model of educational research is to be developed. After identifying the "elements," the concept of "isomorphism of sets" is defined and utilized to construct the general model. It should be pointed out immediately that there is no attempt here to formulate the "ultimate" process of inquiry for educational research. To be sure, the process of inquiry can never be ultimately formulated because the creativity and flexibility of human thought defy description in terms of a rote or a catechism. There are many ways of determining "truth." To present *all* attempts and *all* plans of approach is impossible. The suggested general analog model of educational research is but one presentation of the many possible approaches to the problems associated with conducting good research in the vast and relatively unprobed area of education.

### Chapter One

# Inquiry and Research

BASIC INQUIRY is as old as man. Human beings begin to learn by trusting the authenticity of senses, feelings, and experience. As a natural consequence of sense perception, basic inquiry is inseparable from human life. It is a persistent quest for knowledge and truth. A curiosity without beginning or end.

Philosophical inquiry began when man's reason asserted itself and his belief in the supernatural yielded to the power of observed facts and living experiences. Greek philosophers successfully shed the yoke of the supernatural by fusing human curiosity with the tools of logic and wisdom. Natural scientists adapted certain methods of philosophical inquiry to their empirical investigations and thus developed a net of scientific modes of inquiry. Social, behavioral, and educational scientists, in turn, have by similar canons of delineation adapted selected methods of inquiry from philosophy and the natural sciences to the study of various aspects of human behavior.

Development of appropriate methods of inquiry for the social, behavioral, and educational sciences has been a difficult task because of the multivariate nature of problems extant in the respective disciplines. Thus, the social scientist confronts problems that the natural scientist need not consider. Test tube contents can be controlled, whereas human behavior frequently refuses to be isolated or compartmentalized for purposes of experimentation. Experimentations in a natural science laboratory, under controlled conditions, can be repeated frequently and yield expected results. Human behavior, however, frequently exhibits unexpected variables at unexpected times, despite the fact that all foreseen precautions might have been included in the design of the experimentation. These types of differences suggest that the social scientist cannot predict results with the same degree of accuracy expected of the natural scientist.

It should be noted, however, that as the complexity of the physical world and universe is unfolded by modern science, the natural scientist is finding an increasing need to parallel the methods of inquiry employed by the social scientist. For example, the field of modern physics exhibits the need for the scientist to be keenly aware of the fact that the observer and his frame of reference are integral parts of what might be observed. Despite the amazing variety and unpredictability of variables extant in the physical world, the universe has shown itself amenable to many generalizations, and scientists are encouraged to develop summative laws like the unified field theory. On the other hand, some areas have defied description or solution, and in some of those cases where solutions have been derived, other problems have burgeoned in geometrical profusion. It is oversimplification to say that there is rapprochement between the social sciences and the natural sciences. It is true that the matter of social science is different from that of the natural sciences—that many of the axioms, laws, and methods of the natural sciences do not apply explicitly to the social sciences. What has happened through a general increase in knowledge, with many failures and many successes, has been the establishment of an awareness that inquiry, in its broadest sense, is an adaptive process which must continually be employed to extend the frontiers of all human knowledge.

RESEARCH

The word "research" is a derivative of the French word "recherche" which means: quest, search, pursuit; the search after truth, the search for truth, to make searches into; close investigation or *inquiry*. Considered in this context, the meaning of the term "research" is general and abstract with no connotation of method, procedure, direction, or value. In Good's *Dictionary of Education*, "research" is defined, in part, as follows:

> RESEARCH—careful, critical, disciplined *inquiry*, varying in technique and method according to the nature and conditions of the problem identified, directed toward clarification or resolution (or both) of a problem. Philosophical dimensions or aspects of research have to do with locating hidden assumptions, presuppositions, and value judgments implicit in the treatment of problems; with criteria of evaluation and admissible evidence; with selection of methods appropriate to various investigations. . . .[1]

Although both definitions differ in degree of precision, one concept fundamental to each of them is that of *inquiry*. The process of inquiry, that is, the process of asking and answering questions, of formulating and solving problems, is vital to all scientific research. Thus, the problem of what constitutes an inquiry, and what makes one inquiry better than another, is a critical one in both natural and social science research.

What is the difference between scientific and common sense inquiry? Is it the control of the inquiry? What constitutes the control of the inquiry? What processes are employed in both common sense and scientific inquiry? What is the process of deriving a conclusion, or making a decision? These questions are not new. They have plagued mankind since the sixth century B.C., which marks the beginning of Western philosophy. With the founding and development of each influential philosophical movement, answers to these old questions were sought. As a cumulative result of these endeavors to derive answers to the questions, a set of what we choose to term "common elements of inquiry" were evolved. It is proposed here that it is possible to construct a general model for behavioral, and more particularly, educational research in terms of these "common elements." Before proceeding to the construction of such a model, however, we discuss briefly the contributions of each leading philosophical movement to the evolution and refinement of the "elements."

*Early Greek Philosophers*

The first formulations of meaning arrived at by the reflective thought of individuals, independent of the idols of the tribe, came from the Greeks. Their historic contributions culminated in the works of Plato and Aristotle. Plato divined that *ideas* were most important for men. His architectonic system of ideas, however, caused knowledge to be defined as a static body of ideational forms, and thus limited critical inquiry to the acceptance of the teachings of the oracle. Aristotle had a more practical approach to classifying and expanding knowledge. He was greatly concerned with empirical details, and as a result, he placed *idea* inside of the material habiliments. But he rigidly separated *teoria* and *praxis*, reflecting the aristocrat's contempt for labor—an outlook which debased the actual and active work so vital to the fulfilment of inquiry. Euclid's "self evident" system of axioms from which geometry was rigorously derived stands as a model and product of idealistic thinking—in which the true and the good had immutability and a fixed existence above the hurly-burly market place, which, in turn, was governed by ideas but always fell short of perfect consummation in practice.

*Rationalism*

The basic notion of rationalism can best be surveyed in the approaches presented by René Descartes, and Benedict Spinoza. Descartes tried to sweep away all the truths that mankind recognized as valid. He accepted as true only that which was presented to his mind so clearly and distinctly that he could have no occasion to doubt it. In essence, Descartes made the judgment of truth an individual and internal process. This type of truth was to be the starting point of knowledge and the means of knowing other truths.

Although Descartes' contribution was one of the most outstanding of his time, and earned for him the title, "Father of Modern Philosophy," a better statement of rationalism is found in the works of Spinoza. Spinoza aimed to apply the Euclidean technique of reason or proof to the problems of man, the universe, and God. His system, despite its severe scientific form, was of a practical character, and represents rationalism's concept of a perfect science. Spinoza's concentrated effort, to define rigorously the criteria for choosing elements of a system of deduction, forced a revision of thought concerning the theory of deductive systems. While the rationalists struggled with developing a process of inquiry which would lead to the determination of a true system, empiricism began to evolve.

*Empiricism*

Empiricism has its roots in certain phases of Greek philosophy and has continued throughout the ages. During the medieval period, when faith and intuition were almost totally dominant, thinkers like Roger Bacon argued for *empiricism*, a philosophy of experience. Empirical science was scanty in the medieval period, and it was not until the Renaissance that many of the scientific truths that the Greeks had known were rediscovered and verified.

The works of Francis Bacon and Thomas Hobbes established a crude departure for a well-planned empirical philosophy. Full stature came to empiricism in the great systematic effort of John Locke, who brought recognition to empiricism as the philosophy of knowledge.

Opinions are divided as to the greatness of Locke, but his comparison of the human mind with a *tabula rasa* (blank tablet), and his thesis that experience could be the starting point of all knowledge, stirred the imagination of his contemporaries. Locke refused to recognize the Platonic concept of eternal ideas that could be discovered by thought. Each mind, he insisted, was a white sheet of paper, as it were, devoid of all characters, symbols, or ideas. Through sensations of external things and perceptions of internal mental operations, the individual supplies the tablet of knowledge with content. Thus, through these sensations and experiences, coupled with mental reflection, the mind develops.

The empiricists placed a great restriction on the realm of human knowledge by attempting to account for reasoning in terms of simple sensations and reflections. Knowledge, they said, arises out of direct observations. All that can be gained from experience are perceptions. Thus, the empirical theory of knowledge does not begin by positioning transcendental aspects of the world as causality and substance. Material substance, according to empiricism, cannot be shown to exist, because all knowledge is limited to perceptions which can only occur in the mind. Similarly, it cannot be shown that mental substance exists, because introspection shows that it is impossible to perceive directly the substance of the mind. Empiricism finds extra experiential substance of any kind neither relevant nor necessary for understanding. It is impossible to show that the universe is governed by some causal plan, because the proof of such a law would demand going outside of all perception known to man.

Thus, the reasoning of the empiricists enforced dubiety upon the number of things which man could know with certainty. What man could know depended upon intuition and the mind's ability to jump from its empirical findings to general laws about the natural world. This ability, or process, came to be termed "induction," and was the vehicle by which David Hume and John Stuart Mill attempted to explain cause and effect from the empiricist's point of view.

Hume's concern was to account for causality on purely empirical grounds. To explicate his view, he exhaustively discussed the definition of the causal relations and the presumption of necessary connections between events. He showed that previous reasoning used the conjunction of events based upon repetition of occurrences, and took for granted that association or concomitance of occurrence was the basis of belief. He classified occurrences into two kinds: (1) beliefs free from doubt, and (2) beliefs attended by uncertainty—the latter occurrence requiring an understanding of probability, a combination of causality and chance.

Although Hume's work on "cause and effect" was in some ways monumental, it was Mill who most cogently described the necessary connection between events based upon observations. Mill disagreed with Hume's insistence on repetition as the essential element in beliefs of causality. Mill suggested that belief in a connection of events could be established by prescribing the appropriate ways of making observations rather than by repetition. The designs which would accomplish this end Mill called the "Canons of Induction." Categorically, the canons are as follows: (1) The method of agreement; (2) the method of difference; (3) the joint method; (4) the method of residues; (5) the method of concomitant variations. These canons are widely used as a basis of scientific inference, and their creation has been recognized as a clarifying formulation of the conditions of a scientific method of inquiry. Criticism of the canons lies in the question of whether the validity of the canons rests on purely empirical grounds, or, at least in part, on non-empirical principles.

The point to be established here is that proper experimental design is more than mere observation. It is the means of establishing particular purposes of the experiment, and causal connections in general. These developments showed that the empiricists' ideas of establishing a method of science on the basis of observation alone was doomed to failure. Immanuel Kant attempted to synthesize empiricism and rationalism in order to develop a method of scientific inquiry based upon the process of observation alone. In general, his effort has been considered a failure, but it should be noted that Kant's work provided the framework for the development of a method of inquiry which recognized the necessity of starting the observation cycle of inquiry only after general assumptions underlying the study had been defined.

*Criticism—Synthesis*

Kant attempted to show how both observation and general understanding were essential to an individual's experience. Kant held that there was no denial of sensations, and/or perceptions, but sense data by themselves had no meaning. In order to understand "sense" data, frameworks had to be defined, or as Kant stated the situation, "forms on which to place them." Time and space were forms of a priori experience that were necessary to the establishment of contextual background in the individuating of objects. Because the natural world had order, the principle of regularity was necessary for the mind to be able to grasp sensations (intuitions). Proceeding along this line of inquiry, the problem arises as to which theory of time, which theory of space, and which theory of regularity is the valid one? Although Kant made a valiant effort to synthesize rationalism and empiricism (commonly called the Criticism movement), there remained many geometries, mechanical systems, and methods of inquiry other than those he upheld or could "explain." In addition to this situation, the problem of which system (rationalism or empiricism) portrayed the actual truth was still unsolved. The only conclusion ultimately derived through the Kantian approach to the "problem" was that the selection of "true" factors was completely arbitrary. Thus, it became necessary to make the a priori factors analytic rather than synthetic as Kant had attempted. The conversion of a priori factors from the synthetic to the analytic stage was the main work of logical positivism.

*Logical Positivism*

As a result of Kant's attempts to combine the philosophies of rationalism and empiricism, in order to overcome their weaknesses and buttress their strengths, it became increasingly clear that science could not start without certain general principles. One modern solution of this problem led to the notion that the essential part of the method of scientific inquiry was logical analysis of language.

The logical positivists were the precursors of analytic and linguistic philosophy. Symbolic logic deals with proof of truth values of statements by systematized use of technical symbols. This approach is a very limited form of philosophical discourse. A more comprehensive philosophical system must deal with the broader problems of ethics, epistemology, and the development of a philosophy of science. The basic problem has been to bridge the gap between logical and factual problems, and to attempt a synthesis or a reconciliation of "formal science" and "empirical science."

Formal science depends upon factual statements, but is somewhat independent of the syntactical structure of the statement. In mathematics, one exception disproves the rule, whereas in physics a prediction is derived and then compared with the results of observations.

In logical positivism, sentences and expressions are classified under the following headings: (1) logically true, or analytic, sentences; (2) logically false statements, or contradictions; (3) factually true assertions, corresponding to observed facts; (4) factually false assertions, not corresponding to observed facts; or (5) emotive expressions having no cognitive meaning—pictorial, figurative, poetic, emotion-releasing phrases and, in general, most metaphors. It should be noted here that a distinction has been made between logical problems and factual problems; the former leading to a "formal science" based upon logical problems through analytic statements and the latter to an "empirical science" based upon factual problems of synthetic statements.

Logical positivism is a fruitful source of common language and formulas in universalizing the scientific method of inquiry. Since it is language centered, it demands rules of formation and transformation, elements of language, rules of designation and meaning (semantics), rules of practical application of language (pragmatics), determination of the factors of explanation, prediction and induction, rules of confirmation of a theory, a definition of simplicity, and procedures of analysis, to mention only the fundamentals of the system.

Despite the rigorous approach of the positivists to establish a definitive, independent formal science and an equally independent empirical science, the problem of developing the "simple" element made it difficult, if not impossible, to sharpen the distinction among the methods of scientific inquiry. Formal science still required the aid of nonformal methods to establish truth. Thus, the attempt to construct a scientific procedure of inquiry, based upon rational or sensory origins seems to have been inadequate, and a new approach was necessary to avoid an enforced termination of thought concerning the matter. At this point, pragmatists such as Peirce, James, Schiller, and Dewey furnished a methodological reorientation. The reorientation was effected by shifting the point of concentration from the "first things, principles and supposed necessities" to "last things, fruits, consequences, and facts." In this context, the scientific method of inquiry became a means, or an instrument, for obtaining answers and objectives. Theory and observation are justified only to the extent that they provide vehicles to connect experiences, simplify work, and provide a security and confidence in the findings.

*Pragmatism*

After Kant's criticism had failed to provide "answers," pragmatism came into being. According to the pragmatist, reason examines the relationship between suggested solutions and the facts (settled aspects) of the case. From the first and most tentative suggestions there is a movement toward more precisely formulated ideas which are capable of directing further activity in the problematic situation. In a scientific method of inquiry, as opposed to a common sense inquiry, the final form of the suggested problem solution is an hypothesis. A good hypothesis is determined by evaluating possible suggestions in terms of past experience, to utilize what is already known about related situations. Familiar concepts are used for framing hypotheses thus making knowledge additive and avoiding creation of a new scientific language whenever a new experiment is conducted. Reason connects the present definition of the problem with the past knowledge, thus resulting in the formulation of the hypothesis.

The reconciliation of observed facts and reasoned ideas within the framework of pragmatic theory denies that facts are "given," but insists that they be utilized towards the solution of the problem under consideration. They serve as evidence for an indicated solution and its test. The observed facts bear a strong relevancy for the problematic situation. For example, if a structure were crumbling and in dire need of reinforcement or additional support to remain standing, the color of the structure, whether it be brown, white, or yellow, would be irrelevant to the problem situation. However, the size of steel beams, wooden props, and the amount of load they could support would be relevant facts of observation. Isolated facts have no meaning by themselves, and cannot be used as evidence. Thus, only related facts can test an hypothesis. As the facts become evidence, the hypothesis becomes a solution.

The process of moving from description or narration of problem situations, to explanatory principles (causal laws) is commonly called "induction." Moving from principles to facts is conversely called "deduction." The pragmatic approach obviously leads to the establishment of the interdependence of induction and deduction. That is, in any scientific inquiry the deductive process may direct observations, but this deduction is composed of general principles and facts that in turn were based upon the results of earlier investigations. The principles were induced from earlier observations. Therefore, inquiry is continuous, and grows out of past inductions and deductions, and can only be carried on by the continued interrelated use of both.

Pragmatic theory introduced the notion of problem solving as the fundamental aspect of the scientific method of inquiry. It showed that inquiry works from indeterminate (problem) situations to determinate ones (solution). No particular part of the process has meaning in and of itself. Observed facts and reasoned ideas (theory) are valid only in terms of the continuing process of problem solving. This approach answered the problems of the reality of the external world, causal determination, and validity of prediction; which the rationalists, empiricists, and Kantian movement were unable to solve. The successful accomplishment of the end purposes determines truth for the pragmatist. Emphasizing ends and means rather than beginnings, pragmatism forced a new look at the scientific method of inquiry.

## Experimentalism

Experimentalism, like the Kantian and logical positivism movements, is basically a synthesis. This synthesis is the culmination of the historical analysis of the scientific method of inquiry. History has demonstrated that the scientific method is not necessarily rational, empirical, critical, positivistic, nor pragmatic.

Experimentalism, therefore, has certain characteristics in common with antecedent schools of philosophical thought. For example, experimentalism agrees with rationalism, i.e., that questions of fact cannot be answered immediately. It is necessary to assume answers to certain general questions in order to make certain basic assumptions.

Similarly, experimentalism is in agreement with empiricism that laws cannot be known immediately, particularly scientific law, which requires that certain facts must first be known. Therefore, if experimentalism agrees with rationalism and empiricism on these points, it must agree with the Kantian synthesis (criticism) that to answer any question, certain laws and facts must be assumed relevant, and thus are presupposed.

Positivism and experimentalism recognize that explanation requires an interdependent inductive-deductive system of reasoning. Experimentalism also concurs with pragmatism in the belief that a scientific method of inquiry has no fixed beginnings, since the beginnings are relative to the ends.

Two basic themes can be seen in the historical development of scientific method. First, scientific inquiry requires an integrated effort. None of the facets of the inquiry are meaningful in and of themselves. They acquire meaning only as they form an interrelated and well-integrated endeavor.

Second, evaluation of a scientific method of inquiry can be made with respect to a criterion of progress which is independent of particular individuals or societies, thus providing an ethical point of view for experimentalism. This condition permits more freedom of inquiry than that which is associated with each of the other approaches, because it bases the measurement of scientific progress on the ultimate objectives of all scientific effort, not upon what the eminent scientists of today are doing, nor upon what a given society feels should be done.

In order to explicate basic concepts of experimentalism, certain definitions are necessary. For example, the observed differences between ideal and actual responses are necessary. The tentative replies are defined as "responses," while the ideal replies are "answers." Thus, our knowledge of "answers" can only be provided after all possible observations have been obtained in absolutely exact form. If this condition is true, how do we know whether "answers" exist, or whether there exists a series of more exact "responses"?

If we can define "error" as "risk," based upon the notion that risk is a combination of the probability of making a mistake and the "importance" of the mistake, then the aim of science is to provide replies to questions that are free of risk. Now the ideal (the "answer") and the tentative (the "response") are functionally related. "Responses" are deviations from the "answer" (the ideal truth). "Answers" are the limits that "responses" approach as the risk they involve decreases. This is circular definition, but in experimentalism there are no "basic" concepts; all scientific definition has a circular aspect. In fact, it is the task of scientific inquiry to show how all scientific concepts can be interrelated, and still permit progress in scientific endeavor. By analogy, this approach means that science is "cyclical" rather than "circular," science is something like a spiral which itself is spiralling upward toward perfection; notions developed in one field give meaning to, and get additional meaning from, notions developed in another field. This situation, however, is not to be interpreted as "metaphysical," as though it lay outside the realm of experimental science. Actually, the concept of truth conditions what the scientist does in an experiment.

In order for experimentalism to have meaning for scientific inquiry, it must offer some improvement in the method of carrying out the process of inquiry. Experimentalism accomplishes this improvement by constructing criteria of adequate "design" in experimentation. Modern scientific inquiry is the cooperative task of many different interests and kinds of experts, for no one individual is equipped to determine the "best" design for an experiment. In order to carry out the cooperative endeavor most effectively, some pattern of design should be followed. This pattern is general in the sense that it is applicable to any type of scientific inquiry, but specific in regard to the particular steps in the experimental design.

An outline form of the experimental design is herewith presented. A point which should be emphasized is that the steps listed as they are do not indicate temporal priority. All of the steps are interrelated. The result of performing one has an effect on the performance of the others.

I. The Criteria of Relevance
   A. State basic assumptions.
   B. Define terms.
   C. Determine which observations are pertinent.

II. Formulation of Responses (Experimenter's Replies)
   A. Construction of alternative hypotheses.
   B. Risks relative to the acceptance of the alternative hypotheses.
   C. Determination of the starting point based upon background and context of the problem.
   D. Precision of the experiment.
   E. The number of observations necessary for a reliable response.
   F. Methods and procedures of making observations.
   G. Analytic techniques to be employed.
   H. Method of drawing an inference.

III. Formulation of an Answer (Ideal Replies)
  A. Specify conditions that will allow responses to be more precise (approach "answers" more closely).
  B. Report conditions that should contribute to a greater completeness of the experiment.

IV. Formulation of Progress Criteria
  A. Determine purposes of experiment, in terms of progress of mankind.
  B. Evaluate results of experiment.

Obviously, progress in science is possible without the rigorous formulations proposed by the experimentalists' outline of the design of an experiment. If it is desirable to know how to carry out the differentiation of the good and the bad in science, however, or the direction in which scientific inquiry is leading, the formulations of experimentalism provide an adequate method for accomplishing these objectives.

OPERATIONS RESEARCH

A science which has evolved and emerged from a convergence of interests in the application of models in the process of solving particular types of problems, is that of Operations Research. Operations Research witnessed its greatest early development in Great Britain during World War II. American industry quickly adopted it, and by 1951 industrial Operations Research was firmly entrenched and was in the process of expanding rapidly.

A basic objective of industrial Operations Research is to provide the management of an organization with a scientific basis for solving problems involving the interaction of components of the organization. The ideal condition is attained when an "optimum" decision is reached. An optimum decision is one which is best for the total organization. A suboptimum decision is attained if the decision is best for only certain components of the organization. Thus, Operations Research attempts to locate the best decisions possible relative to situations involving the largest part of a total organization.

Operations Research closely parallels a "systems" approach, to the extent that a system is an interconnected complex of functioning components. Examples could be a business organization, a school, or for that matter the educational system operating at any level of the social or human machine system. The human machine is in contrast to the mechanical system which is well illustrated by the automobile. We do not concern ourselves with mechanical systems here, hence we shall not discuss them further.

The procedure for conducting Operations Research is particularly useful in the study of problems involving machine systems. In a generic sense, the school is a complex human machine system. Therefore, the procedures of Operations Research can be applied to many of the problems that exist within the educational system known as the "school."

Churchman, Ackoff, and Arnoff suggest the following as major phases of Operations Research: (1) formulating the problem; (2) constructing a mathematical model to represent the system under study; (3) deriving a solution from the model; (4) testing the model and the solution derived from it; (5) establishing controls over the solution; and (6) putting the solution to work; implementation.[2]

Each of these phases, and its relationship to an Operations Research analysis of school system's "problems," could be discussed in some detail here, but this is not our objective. The point to be made is that Operations Research, a problem-solving device, which already exists in industry, demonstrates that inquiry can be channeled through a "models" approach. It also demonstrates that research of a human machine system, like that of education, for example, can be carried out with the rigorous standards of scientific research if the "models" approach is employed.

We conclude our discussion by re-asserting that it is possible to construct a general model for educational research based upon elements of inquiry common to each of the philosophical schools of thought described. Before exploring this possibility, however, we should examine what is meant by the term "model." This task we undertake in the next chapter.

*Chapter 1—References*

See Bibliography: 3, 20, 21, 24, 32, 36, 38, 59, 66, 79, 80, 125, 129, 142, 188, 191; 6a, 9a, 17a, 65a, 77a, 89a, 93a, 97a, 102a.

# Chapter Two

# Models: Structure and Function

THE BASIC CONCEPT of a research model is that of *isomorphism*. The science of logic states that two sets are isomorphic if the following two conditions are satisfied: (1) there exists a one-to-one correspondence between the respective elements of the sets, and (2) certain structures of the sets are preserved. These two conditions are *necessary* if isomorphism of the sets is to exist. Based upon this understanding of isomorphism, a meaning of the term "model," precise enough for our purposes, is now possible. We merely consider two sets that are isomorphic, and allow that either set may serve as the model of the other. This notion of "model," as an isomorphism of two sets, implies that the two sets are symmetrical. Symmetry, however, is not a *necessary* condition for the employment of one set as a model for the other. To illustrate the foregoing:

A miniature automobile is a model of a real automobile if it is isomorphic with the real one. The concept of isomorphism used in this sense means that for every detail in body design of the actual automobile, there is the same detail in the miniature's body design; i.e., every wheel has its replica, every window its replica, and every other feature its counterpart. In other words, there is a one-to-one correspondence between the respective elements of the "sets." This is a necessary condition for isomorphism, but not the only one. We also find that a certain structure is preserved between the miniature and real automobiles. For instance, if the speedometer is located above the steering column on the dashboard of the real car, the replica is similarly located and constructed to scale in the miniature automobile. Thus, the second necessary condition of isomorphism, the preservation of certain structures of the "sets," is met. To this point we have used the miniature car as a model of the real car; naturally, the converse condition could exist. The real car could be the produced model of the miniature automobile. In this context the symmetrical aspect of isomorphism is important, and is employed. It has been noted, however, that symmetry is not a *necessary* condition to the employment of a model. If this statement is true, then under what conditions can a model be employed when symmetry does not necessarily exist between the isomorphic sets?

Symmetry is relegated to a secondary role when an area about which a great deal is known is used as a model to *suggest* theory or laws for an area about which comparatively little is known. This approach was employed during the early study of electricity, when much of the confirmed theory of the better-understood field of hydrodynamics was used as a guiding model for the development of electrical formulas and theory.

Viewed in its broadest sense, a scientific model might be thought of as a representation of some subject of inquiry (e.g., objects, processes, systems) to be utilized for purposes of controlling predictions and decision-making. Based upon the definition of a model in terms of isomorphism, it should be obvious that if the laws and theory of one discipline are isomorphic with the laws and theory of another discipline, either one of the "sets" may be used as the model (representation) of the other. We also know that if isomorphism is *considered to exist* between two disciplines, the laws and theory of the more familiar discipline may be used as a model *to suggest* laws and theory for the comparatively little-known discipline. Thus, the set chosen as the model mainly serves an explanatory purpose, and facilitates the discovery of how alterations in certain aspects of its components affect certain other aspects of the set, or how these alterations affect the total system. In short, the model is manipulated to determine effects of change, rather than imposing the changes directly on, or over, the system of the subject of inquiry itself.

Models can be broadly classified as one of three basic types, namely: iconic, analog, or symbolic. Employing the approach of general characterization once again, we could state that:

(1) *the iconic model* is a pictorial or physical representation of certain parts of, or the total, system under inquiry. A photograph, or our earlier illustration of the model automobile, are good examples of iconic models;

(2) *the analog model* is a diagram, flow chart, or a similar type of representation resulting from employing the properties of a familiar system to represent those of the system under inquiry; where the "sets" of properties of the respective systems are considered to be isomorphic. The previous example of the study of electricity by means of employing the properties of the then more familiar field of hydrodynamics is a good example of analog model utilization;

(3) *the symbolic model* is a "formula" representation resulting from the employment of symbols to *designate* properties of the system under study. A good example of the symbolic model is the mathematical equation, or set of equations, which represents the problem situation under study. The symbolic model is employed in those cases where the laws and theory of mathematics, or symbolic logic, are isomorphic with the laws and theory of the system under inquiry.

It should be noted once again that these descriptions are only general characterizations of three basic types of models. Precise definition and discussion of relationships that might exist between the respective types have been purposely omitted. This approach is employed in order to avoid complex discussions involving topics of symbolic logic and formal semantics that otherwise might tend to becloud the basic understanding of the term "model" as it is to be used in the process of formulating a general model for educational research.

From our earlier descriptions it should be evident that the iconic model is usually the simplest to construct, and the most specific and concrete of the three types of models discussed. An iconic model is most frequently employed where a descriptive function is necessary. Rarely is the "iconic" employed to determine causal relationships, or generally speaking, to serve an explanatory function. Thus, its facility for prediction or inference, in connection with alterations imposed on the system which it represents, is limited. At the other extreme we find the symbolic model, which is frequently difficult to construct, and usually the most general and abstract of the three basic types. It usually serves an explanatory function, and has good facility for prediction or inference in connection with the effects of alterations on, or in, the system under study. The middleground of the two extremes represented by the functions of the iconic and symbolic models is occupied by the analog model.

## ICONIC MODELS

The educator's life is filled with iconic models. Most classrooms contain the inevitable sphere as an iconic model of the earth. Many of the school's scientific laboratories include iconic models of parts of the solar system; what are purported to be iconic models of atoms and molecules; models of insects, animal-life, and even certain mycological structures. Art rooms display paintings, sculptures, and frequently photographs, all of which are iconic models of persons, places, or things.

The iconic model is used mainly to describe a static condition, a thing, or a dynamic system at a particular instant of time. The "iconic" is a representation resulting from a metric transformation, a scaling up or down, of properties of the static system or things it represents. Although this feature has already been discussed in the illustration involving the miniature and real automobiles, it has its counterpart in the geography classroom globe serving as an iconic model of the earth. In the latter case, the diameter of the earth is scaled down to the diameter of the globe, and the same metric transformation is preserved for all other properties of the earth so that the relative size of continents, oceans, and other important geographical features are approximately correct. A model of a minute growing mycological structure, possibly constructed for the purpose of depicting a particular moment in the organism's development, would necessarily be scaled upward, if it were to be visible to the naked eye in a classroom setting. The transformation of the scale of properties represented is a feature of models which contributes greatly to their utility. A scaled-down, or scaled-upward, iconic model, under usual conditions, can be worked with more easily than the thing, or system, it represents.

Iconic models are particularly useful for the description of static systems, but they are not very useful as representations of dynamic systems. Because of their general inadequacy in representing dynamic systems, iconic models are not particularly useful in situations calling for the study of the effects resulting from the altering of certain elements of a system.

Although the iconic model might closely resemble the thing which it re-presents, like the other basic types of models, it preserves only a *certain* structure, and need not include a *total* one-to-one correspondence between its elements and those of the set which it depicts. To the extent that the model does not represent the *total structure* and *all of the elements* of the "original," the representation will differ slightly from that which it is to represent. The purpose for which the model is constructed determines the essential properties to be included in the representation. Those properties which are considered to be unessential are usually omitted from the model. It is in the selectivity feature that a good share of the economy associated with the use of models is found. To illustrate, in most cases the geography classroom globe need not show details of elevation, slope, and other similar features of the earth's surface. The continents and seven seas, however, are almost never omitted.

ANALOG MODELS

In constructing a model we always seek a "sufficient" amount of one-to-one correspondence between the elements of the "original" and those of the model set, in order to serve the purpose at hand. We also attempt to preserve certain structures in order that the model may represent, as closely as possible, the various properties of the original entity under consideration. It may be concluded from these statements that it is not necessary that we reproduce *all pertinent* properties with exactness in the model. While we could not conveniently produce with precision the geological structure of the earth in an iconic model, the various types of geological structure could be represented, however, by different colors on a chart. This approach employs the substitution of one property (color) for another (geological structure), based upon certain rules of transformation. Since the chart was constructed on the basis that one set of properties (geological structure) was represented by another set of properties (color), the resulting representation would not be an "iconic," but instead an *analog* model. To further clarify the issue, let us consider another example. We might desire to use the biological theory of cell growth as a model for social growth. Relatively precise meaning has been given to anabolic and catabolic processes in cell growth theory. If we are able to give correspondingly precise meaning to the building and deteriorating processes of human institutions, a one-to-one correspondence is approximated, and a certain general structure is preserved. Thus, we have the necessary conditions for using cell growth theory as a model for human institutions theory. Similarly, nutrition is connected with growth in biology. Can we discover social concepts that cause human institutions to grow and at the same time are similar enough in nature to nutrition to preserve the one-to-one correspondence and approximate a certain general structure? If these notions could be accomplished, the biological theory of cell growth could be used as an *analog model* for social growth.

The question of how rigorously the conditions of a one-to-one correspondence and the preservation of a certain structure need to be observed in order to establish the isomorphism of sets, is a problem area in model construction. Suffice it to say, that scientists accept the fact that models are not *exact* replicas of the problem area under study. There are always certain aspects of the model that do not apply completely to the subject under inquiry. In other words, there are always certain features of a model that are more appropriate to the inquiry than others. In any case, if certain elements and general structures of two respective "sets" correspond, and the connections between the structures can be reasonably preserved, either set can be employed as an iconic, analog, or symbolic model, whichever the case might be, of the other.

Probably the simplest form of the analog model is that of the graph. Graphs may be used to represent distance, time, force, learning rate, number, per cent, and many other concepts. From graphs we are able to determine how a change in one property will affect another property. Flow charts are other forms of analog models that have great utility in prediction and inference regarding changes in a system.

Where the iconic model shows great effectiveness in description of static systems, comparatively speaking, the analog model shows the same type of effectiveness in representing dynamic systems. Where the iconic model shows little value in predicting and inferring results due to changes in a system, the analog shows good capability for prediction and inference regarding the effect of changes in dynamic systems. Finally, the analog model is more general than the iconic model, and as such can usually be made to represent many different processes of the same type. For example, the flow chart is an analog model which is simple to construct, and effective for the work of representing many different processes of the same type.

### SYMBOLIC MODELS

It is frequently possible to establish a modified isomorphism in those cases where two empirical theories might not share a common structure. This condition often exists when an empirical theory (or set of propositions) might have the same form as a set of mathematical truths. Symbolic models, wherein the components of what is represented and their interrelationship are given by symbols, are frequently this sort of mathematical representation of an empirical theory. For example, one axiom of arithmetic is the relation "less than," among integers. We can readily state that "five is less than six." If we choose, we might well replace the integers by names of animals and replace the arithmetical relation by the empirical relation "smaller than." Since the arithmetic relationship proved to be *transitive*, i.e., $5 < 6$; and $4 < 5$; $\therefore$ $4 < 6$, if the statement resulting from the translation of integers to names of animals is true, the empirical relation of one animal being smaller than another is also transitive. Thus, if we desired we could use the arithmetic model above as a representation of the empirical relationship of the names of the animals involved (e.g., a rat is smaller than a cat; a cat is smaller than a particular breed (collie) of dog; therefore a rat is smaller than a collie dog).

If the properties of a particular discipline are capable of quantification, or capable of measurement, then these properties can be expressed by a set of empirical laws which is isomorphic to a set of certain laws of mathematics. By virtue of this isomorphism, we have many quantified empirical laws. Thus, these particular parts (usually equations) of mathematics may serve as models for these types of empirical properties. For example, an aspect of mathematics which is frequently employed as a symbolic model for empirical properties is that of probability theory.

When a symbolic model is used as a source of hypotheses about the relationships among the properties of empirical areas, it does not explain these empirical hypotheses. The model is merely a representation of the form of the hypotheses. When these empirical hypotheses are confirmed by the mathematical (symbolic) model, however, they then may be used to explain and predict new empirical knowledge associated with the area under inquiry.

The symbolic model enjoys a decided advantage over the analog model in the study of the effects of change in, or on, a system. If the system can be represented by a symbolic model, i.e., in the form of a mathematical equation, the effects of change can be determined in a few steps of mathematical deduction. The analog model is more efficient than the symbolic model, however, in studying the effect of changes in a highly complex system where the *construction* of a symbolic model would require a prohibitive amount of work and time. In such cases, the analog model is preferred.

The type of model employed, and its characteristics, determines the procedure for deriving a solution to the problem under inquiry. The procedures, in turn, may be categorized broadly as analytic and numerical. Analytic procedures are basically deductive, while numerical procedures are essentially inductive.

In light of our earlier discussion, we are now prepared to present a general model for educational research. The proposed model involves a method of inquiry and a set of elements that are isomorphic to a set of elements of inquiry common to the philosophical movements discussed in Chapter 1. The basic elements of the general model are: (1) problem, (2) hypothesis, (3) universe, (4) sample, (5) data collection, (6) data processing, and (7) decision.

Figure 1 shows the suggested general analog model for educational research. It should be noted, however, that this is not an attempt at "reductionism," nor is it an attempt to show "the only way" to do educational research. To be sure, there are manifold ramifications of the general model, each one devised to satisfy the demands of the particular problem under study. Examples of modified forms of the general model of educational research are presented later, but before proceeding to them we should discuss in some detail the basic elements of the general model.

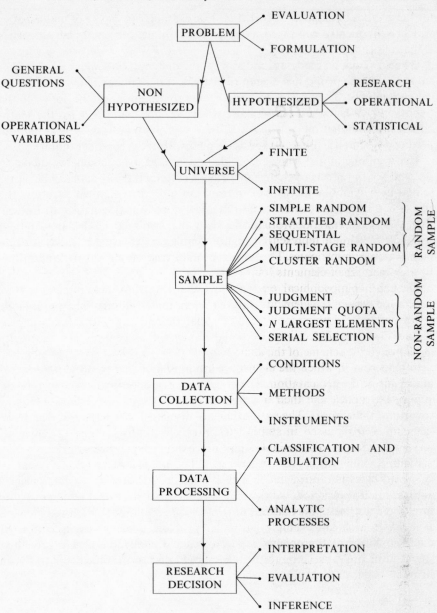

*Figure 1*
*General Model of Educational Research*

*Chapter 2—References*
See Bibliography: 3, 20, 21, 24, 32, 38, 59, 66, 80, 81, 82, 125, 142, 188, 191; 1a, 6a, 9a, 14a, 16, 17a, 18a, 19a, 20a, 29a, 35a, 56a, 65a, 69a, 70a, 77a, 89a, 93a, 97a, 102a.

# PART II

## The General Analog Model of Educational Research: Design and Procedures

THE GENERAL ANALOG MODEL of educational research is developed on the basis of its being a representamen of "common" elements of inquiry drawn from selected philosophies. The "model" is a set of elements which is isomorphic to a defined set of elements found throughout methods of inquiry associated with certain philosophical orientations. The analog shows clearly the relationships between the elements which are: (a) the problem; (b) the hypothesis; (c) the universe; (d) the sample; (e) data collection processes; (f) data processing, and (g) the research decision.

Although the scheme of the analog would imply a chronology in connection with the order in which the elements of the model are considered, such is not the intent of the presentation. The order of presentation of the elements composing the model, and their arrangement in the model, are but the arbitrary choices of the authors. The various aspects and interrelationships between the elements are discussed in some detail in this section. Intentionally omitted are the numerical and analytical procedures associated with the elements of: sample, data collection, data processing, and the research decision. Discussion of these topics is carried out in Part IV. It should also be pointed out that examples of applications of the "general" model are not presented in this section of the book. Part III of the presentation is devoted to a discussion of types of research, and examples of "adaptations" of the general model to actual educational research problems.

# *Problem and Hypothesis*

IN THIS CHAPTER, cardinal features of the first two elements of the general model for educational research will be discussed. Included in the discussion of the *problem* element are descriptions of the processes of *problem evaluation* and *problem formulation*. The discussion of the *hypothesis* element of the model evolves around the development of an *hierarchy of hypotheses*, and the problem of *testing certain types of hypotheses* included in the hierarchy.

In essence, the processes of: (1) determining a problem, (2) evolving hypotheses from the problem, and (3) testing the hypotheses, compose the basic approach of most research efforts. Scientists for several hundreds of years have attempted to develop and improve methods and conditions associated with processes of research. Despite the attempts to perfect these methods, conditions, and processes, the fundamental element of any research effort is the capability of the mind to make its own leap somewhere in the bounded area of the problem under study. The involvement of the mind in "honest" inquiry is guaranteed by the fact that problems are never "given to," but rather are "taken by" the researcher. Even in those cases where problems are held to be "obvious," some persons will comprehend more quickly and clearly than others. Having taken a problem, however, the researcher invariably follows certain canons of procedure, and observes, despite his philosophical orientation, certain elements of inquiry in conducting the research effort. It is precisely these elements that we have found "common" to the various modes of philosophical inquiry, and the ones that are used as the basic elements of what we term "a general analog model of educational research."

In earlier discussions, the basic elements of the general research model were defined to be: (a) the problem; (b) hypothesis, or general questions; (c) the universe; (d) the sample; (e) data collection; (f) data processing; and (g) the research decision. The discussion here will be confined to the first two elements listed above . . . (a) the problem, and (b) hypothesis, or general questions.

## THE PROBLEM

Problem evaluation and formulation is one of the most difficult and important phases of the research process. In constructing the final statement of the problem, the evaluation and formulation stages of the process should be carried out so thoroughly that the resulting statement almost suggests the solution. Such productivity is almost impossible without careful and critical evaluation of all aspects of the problem followed by a simple and precise formulation of the statement.

Though the sequence is not to be considered rigid, evaluation of the problem may be accomplished by giving thorough consideration to each of the following five areas:

*Evaluation (Need)*

1. Discover the nature of the problematic situation. Who has the problem? Is it capable of solution through the use of research?

2. Determine the desired end-objectives. What is gained by solving the problem? Is it significant to society, or only to relatively few people?

3. Logically exhaust the possible courses of action open to the problem-solution. Has there been earlier research? Where can the investigation begin? How can the data be collected? From what source? Is there more than one means of collecting the data?

4. Eliminate methods of solution not feasible to the setting. Does the method of arriving at a solution create a greater problem than the one under investigation? Is it financially possible to effect the method? Is the research worker, or team, competent to carry out the method? Estimate the sensitivity of the problem. Does the method strongly conflict with the social mores of society? Is the method too time consuming?

5. Investigate the setting of the problematic situation. Would the problematic situation exist in another setting? (Example: The problem might be that of calling members of a community together to tell them of the danger of an epidemic of a particular disease that is present in the locality, yet their congregation would increase the possibility of an epidemic. The problem, therefore, actually is how to prevent the epidemic, rather than how to call a meeting of the community members.) Would a change of setting affect the possible approaches to the solution? Would the solution be more easily obtained in a different setting? If so, can the setting be changed without affecting the problematic situation to any major extent?

Upon completing what might be termed the "five-step procedure of problem evaluation," the "problem" element of the model is ready to undergo the process of formulation.

## FORMULATING THE PROBLEM *—(STATEMENT) & (Definition)*

The process of formulating the problem may be considered to be composed of two phases: (1) the development of a statement, and (2) the definition of the problem.

The statement of the problem can be in the form of a question, several questions, a declarative statement, or a declarative statement composed of a series of statements. Regardless of the form, every effort should be made to avoid vagueness or undue broadness of scope as well as extreme specificity and localization. The focus of the statement should be concentrated on a clearly defined objective, and should be limited in scope so that a definite conclusion concerning the problem is possible and feasible. The statement should be presented in simple terms, avoiding unscientific, argumentative, or emotional language. The statement of the problem should also define and preserve an appropriate universe of discourse which is based upon the body of prior knowledge concerning the subject matter. Many excellent examples of the type of "problem statements" referred to here may be found in Good and Scates.[1]

The definition of the problem, which is the second phase of problem formulation, should include the significance of the problem, definition of terms, underlying assumptions, and limitations of the scope of the problem. In the discussion of the significance of the problem, implications and possible applications resulting from the solution of the problem should be discussed in order to show the comparative worth of the problem under study. Any terms that might be misinterpreted, or not clearly understood, should be defined. This course of action makes for clearer interpretation of the findings, and frequently prevents misuse and misquotation of the data. Assumptions underlying the study of the problem should be described in detail to prevent misinterpretation, misunderstanding, and in some cases, misapplication of the findings. The limitations aspect of problem definition provides a description of the scope and depth intended for the study of the problem.

## SUMMARY OF PROBLEM EVALUATION AND FORMULATION

Our discussion of problem evaluation and formulation has focused upon the constituent parts of these two aspects of the "problem" element of the general research model. Problem evaluation can be resolved into five steps: (1) discovering the nature of the problem, (2) determining the end-objectives, (3) specifying possible courses of action, (4) eliminating infeasible courses of action, and (5) investigating the problem setting for possible alteration and simplification of the problem.

Problem formulation is composed of two parts: (1) statement of the problem, and (2) definition of the problem. The statement of the problem can be in declarative or interrogative form. It should be clear, and of such a scope that a definite conclusion is possible. The definition of the problem should include the significance of the problem, the definition of terms necessary for a better understanding of the problem, the assumptions underlying the study of the problem, and the limitations of the scope of the problem area.

With this background established we are now prepared to discuss the element of "hypothesis," or "general questions," in the suggested general model.

## HYPOTHESES, OR GENERAL QUESTIONS

The basic notion underlying the definition of an hypothesis, simply stated, is that a "hunch," or "educated guess," is advanced for the purpose of being tested. The basis for an hypothesis is found in the need to solve a problematic situation. The elements of the hypothesis come from the problematic situation and the needs of the researcher to solve the problem. To understand completely the importance of the hypothesis element in the research model, it will be necessary to approach the discussion of this element not only from the beginning of the hypothesizing process (need and problematic situation), but from the end (conclusion, or solution of the problem) of the process as well.

The term "inference" must be defined here. An inference may be considered to be any probability conclusion drawn on the basis of experience. Inferences are made continuously throughout our daily living. For example, a certain person looks like another person whom we consider to be honest, hence we might conclude that the "certain" person is probably honest. A particular man is tall and appears to be muscular. From past experience, we might conclude that he is probably strong. From these examples, it should be clear that an inference is a probability conclusion drawn on the basis of experience. But how does this knowledge of inference contribute to a better understanding of the term "hypothesis"? The relationship is clarified by the fact that the hypothesis is inherent in the inference process. In fact, the advancing of an hypothesis is the first step of a systematic approach (the inference process) to testing the advanced proposition. Considered in this light, the hypothesis plays an unusual role in the process of inquiry. It is an "antecedent," to the extent that it gives direction to, and imposes limits upon, the inquiry, and it is a "consequence" of the process in that it terminates the inquiry by being accepted or rejected by the data collected in the process of conducting the study.

### Establishing An Order of Hypotheses

In order to achieve a better understanding of the subject, we must examine the process known as "testing the hypothesis." This process of examination might best be accomplished by considering, in a sense, a form of "hierarchy" of hypotheses. In this context we would find, first, that the hypothesis of the inquiry (the research hypothesis) is stated. The inference to be drawn from a proposition, however, frequently cannot be accomplished on the basis of the research hypothesis alone. It is often necessary to determine elements of the hypothesis of inquiry, or related factors, and "map" the research hypothesis into operational hypotheses, i.e., hypotheses that lend themselves more readily and easily to testing than does the research hypothesis. To illustrate, suppose the research hypothesis of a particular study is: Reading ability bears a close relation to value-attitude structure among sixth-grade children.

In order to test this research hypothesis, the research worker could "map" it into the following operational hypotheses:

1. The group of sixth-grade children who have reading comprehension scores of 6.2 or higher on standardized reading test A, will have a significantly different group mean value-attitude structure score on standardized instrument B, from those children who have scores below 6.2 on test A.

2. The group of sixth-grade children who attain rate-of-reading scores of 50 or higher on standardized test C, will have a significantly different group mean value-attitude structure score on standardized instrument B, from those children who have scores below 50 on test C.

A question which might arise at this point is, "Why not make the so-called operational hypotheses the research hypotheses, i.e., the hypotheses of the study?" Considered from the analytic or strictly logical point of view, nothing prevents the use of this form of the hierarchy of hypotheses. From the synthetic point of view of scientific inference, however, the utilization of the rather well-defined operational hypotheses in the place of the more general research hypotheses might well negate the testing of a whole series of operational hypotheses which would have otherwise been considered. Put in another way, use of the rather restricted operational hypotheses might place limitations on the scope of the study that the more generally stated research hypotheses would avoid by allowing for the possibility of mapping other operational hypotheses within acceptable boundaries of the problem under study. Without further laboring the point, it is preferable to employ research hypotheses with their potentials for greater possibilities of exploration, and proceed to work with the scheme that provides for mapping them into a series of accompanying operational hypotheses.

After the operational hypotheses of the study have been stated, the sources of data, i.e., the measurements described in the operational hypotheses, are automatically defined. In order to employ these types of data efficiently, however, it will frequently be found convenient to change the statement form of the operational hypotheses into that of the statistical hypotheses. Since a statistical hypothesis is defined to be a *mathematical* statement of the stated proposition of a given operational hypotheses, we map each operational hypothesis into a particular type of mathematical statement known as "the statistical *alternative* hypothesis $(H_1)$." Once the statistical alternative hypothesis $(H_1)$ is defined, it is possible to form the statistical hypothesis known as "the *null* hypothesis $(H_0)$." With the null hypothesis defined it is then possible to employ the theory of probability in the process of deriving a decision to reject or not reject the "null" $(H_0)$ on the basis of the data provided by a sample of elements selected from the population (universe) of the problem under study. The process of deriving a decision to reject, or not reject, the null hypothesis in this fashion is called: "statistical inference."

### Resolving Operational Hypotheses Into Statistical Hypotheses

In order to employ statistical inference in the process of deciding whether to accept, or reject, an *operational* hypothesis, it is necessary to map the operational proposition into two related forms of a *statistical* hypothesis. First, the operational hypothesis, which in original form is stated in non-mathematical terms, is analyzed into a simple mathematical statement known as: "the statistical alternative hypothesis $(H_1)$." For example, suppose the operational hypothesis under consideration is the first of the two presented earlier:

> The group of sixth-grade children who have reading comprehension scores of 6.2 or higher on a standardized reading test A, will have a significantly different group mean value-attitude structure score on standardized instrument B, from those children who have scores below 6.2 on test A.

The appropriate *statistical alternative* hypothesis associated with this operational proposition would be $H_1 : \mu_H \neq \mu_L$ where $H_1$ indicates the statistical alternative hypothesis; $\mu_H$ indicates the population mean score on test B for sixth-grade pupils with a reading score of 6.2 or higher on test A; $\mu_L$ denotes the population mean score on test B for sixth-grade pupils with a reading score of less than 6.2 on test A; and $\neq$ indicates that the respective means are "not equal." It should be pointed out that the operational hypothesis merely stated that the one group of students would have "a significantly different group mean value-attitude structure score on standardized instrument B" from that of the other group. No *direction* was stated, i.e., it was *not* stated that the one group would have a mean score significantly higher (or *lower*) than that of the other. Had *direction* been involved, the hypothesis ($H_1$) might have been stated as: $H_1 : \mu_H > \mu_L$; the mean score of the "high" group is greater than that of the "low" group; or: $H_1 : \mu_H < \mu_L$; $\mu_H$ is less than $\mu_L$; according to whichever statement was appropriate.

After the statistical alternative hypothesis ($H_1$) is stated, the null hypothesis ($H_0$) is formulated. In our example, since the statistical alternative hypothesis was $H_1 : \mu_H \neq \mu_L$; the accompanying "null" would be: $H_0 : \mu_H = \mu_L$. It is the null hypothesis ($H_0$) which is submitted to test by the process of statistical inference. Since this process is accorded detailed discussion later, it will not be treated further at this time.

Statistical inference can be classified as one of two basic types: (1) deductive, or (2) inductive. In deductive statistical inference, the probabilities and characteristics of a population (universe) are known, and the problem is one of drawing inferences about the expected probabilities and characteristics of a random sample taken from that population. Inductive statistical inferences are employed in those cases where the probabilities and characteristics of a population are unknown and a random sample, drawn from the population, is used to make inferences about these probabilities and characteristics. The inductive inference approach is required most frequently in practice, because rarely are the probabilities and characteristics of the population under study known, and in many cases the population undergoes a change of extent and composition over the period of time covered by the study.

## THE STATISTICAL HYPOTHESES

Statistical hypotheses are mathematical statements that, depending on their form, are amenable to classification under one of three categories: (1) hypotheses of magnitude, (2) hypotheses of difference, or (3) hypotheses of relationship. Each of these three types of statistical hypotheses may be cast in the form of a "null" ($H_0$), and be tested by an *appropriate* statistical inference process. Before attempting to explain what is meant by the phraseology, "an *appropriate* statistical inference process," we shall find it convenient to have definitions, or explanations, of certain terms that are fundamental to the process. The explanations and illustrations of the respective terms are as follows:

1. An *hypothesis of magnitude* is one in which a statement of the number, size, or value of an entity is stipulated. For example, the proportion of persons voting "yes," where only a "yes" or a "no" vote was possible to cast, is not equal to some predetermined value of *P*. The *statistical alternative hypothesis* of such an "operational" would be $H_1 : P \neq P_0$; and the accompanying "null" would be: $H_0 : P = P_0$. As another example, the mean score of a particular group of persons on a given standardized test is greater than some predetermined value. The appropriate "statistical alternative" would be $H_1 : \mu > \mu_0$; and the accompanying "null" would become $H_0 : \mu \leq \mu_0$.

2. An *hypothesis of difference* is one which deals with the difference between quantified expressions of items being compared. For example, suppose the operational hypothesis states: the students in the "experimental" group will have a significantly higher mean score on a given test than those in the "control" group. The appropriate statistical alternative hypothesis of difference would be: $H_1 : \mu_E > \mu_C$; and the accompanying "null" hypothesis would become: $H_0 : \mu_E \leq \mu_C$. Had the "operational" stated that the "group mean scores of the experimental and control groups would be significantly different," the appropriate statistical alternative hypothesis would be: $H_1 : \mu_E \neq \mu_C$; and the accompanying "null" would be: $H_0 : \mu_E = \mu_C$.

3. An *hypothesis of relationships* is one in which the degree of relationship, or association, between two variables assumed to be causally related and forming a bivariate population, is stated. For example, the height and weight of a given population of persons may be hypothesized to be directly related. The appropriate statistical alternative hypothesis of relationship would be $H_1 : \rho > 0$; i.e., rho, the population correlation coefficient, which is the measure of relationship employed in this case, is positive and significantly greater than zero. The accompanying null hypothesis would be $H_0 : \rho \leq 0$: i.e., rho is significantly negative (indicating an inverse relationship between height and weight), or is zero (no relationship between height and weight exists in the population).

4. A *statistic* is a calculable characteristic of a sample, derived from the set of values included in the sample which has been drawn from the population. The arithmetic mean (average score) of scores realized on a mathematics test by a sample group of twenty-five children would be an example of a "statistic." The statistic in this case would be the arithmetic mean, calculated by summing the twenty-five scores, and then dividing that total by twenty-five. Another example of a statistic is the median score of a sample group of, say, eleven persons (the middle score, after the scores have been arranged according to descending or ascending values; the sixth score in this case).

5. A *sample* is defined to be any subset of a given population, or universe. A sample of five pieces taken every hour out of the hundreds being produced by a machine during that hour is an illustration of the concept. Another illustration is that which results from first testing all school children in a *particular grade* of a *particular school district*, and then computing the arithmetic mean score for each grade and hence each school in the district. We now have a finite

population of "school averages." If there were twelve schools in the district we might choose one, two, three, or four, or any number less than twelve for that matter, as a *sample of schools' averages* for the particular grade level involved.

6. A *population* or a *universe*, is defined as the totality of objects under consideration. The totality may be composed of persons, physical objects, or operations. Examples of populations are: the weights of people from a certain area; the annual incomes of American families composed of three persons, during a given year; or the kilowatt hours of life of 50-watt bulbs being produced by a particular company. A population may be composed of an infinite, or finite, number of objects. The "size" of a population depends upon the specification of time, place, and conditions in the process of identifying the population.

7. The term *distribution* refers to a series of data plotted on ordinary graph paper with the values of the variable (the statistic in this case) measured horizontally, and the corresponding frequencies of occurrence measured vertically. In statistical literature such an arrangement is called a "frequency distribution." The frequency distribution shows the range of values over which the variable is distributed. It also indicates the values of the variable which occur most frequently and those that occur least frequently. When used for probability estimates, the distribution shows the most probable (high frequency of occurrence) and least probable (low frequency of occurrence) values of the variable.

With these explanations in mind, we can now discuss "appropriate inference processes" in some detail. There are four statistical inferences that can be drawn from the three statistical hypotheses. The four inferences are: (1) inferences of magnitude, (2) inferences of difference, (3) inferences of relationship, and (4) inferences of appraisal. The *inferences* of magnitude, difference, and relationship are effected by submitting *statistical hypotheses* of magnitude, difference, and relationship, respectively, to a test involving a *statistic* which can be reliably calculated from the data of the *sample*, under the condition that the *distribution* of that *statistic* is known when the statistical hypothesis (the "null" $H_0$) under test is considered to be true. Testing the null hypothesis ($H_0$) under these conditions allows the researcher to decide, on a probability basis, whether to reject, or not reject, the "null" ($H_0$), and accordingly to decide whether to accept, or not accept, the statistical alternative hypothesis ($H_1$).

The *inference of appraisal* is effected by evaluating the results of the other three inference processes in terms of determining the degree to which a priori objectives of the entity under consideration have been attained. For example, if an automobile tire is to be evaluated, it can be appraised in terms of: (1) the degree to which it showed wear for, say, 25,000 miles (measured in terms of an inference of magnitude); (2) its demonstration of superiority when compared with a competing tire (determined by an inference of difference); and (3) its capability of emulating "desirable characteristics" of a tire known to be of superior quality (determined by an inference of relationship).

Although "research" and "evaluation" (appraisal) are terms that are frequently confused, and erroneously used interchangeably, when considered in terms of statistical hypotheses and inference processes their definitions become clear, and differentiation between the terms is a simple matter. To be sure, evaluation (appraisal) is an integral part of the research process, and therefore highly involved in the general model of educational research. But other than providing for the necessary "rigorous" or "systematic" approach demanded by the research process, it is relatively unnecessary to our discussion. For this reason we shall not accord the topic of "evaluation" further treatment here, other than to reinforce the fact that "evaluation" and "research" are two *different* processes with different purposes and objectives in the area of scientific study.

The statistical hypotheses and inferences of magnitude, difference, and relationship are extremely important in the numerical procedures associated with the general model of educational research, and thus we shall accord these topics further, limited treatment at this point.

### Statistical Alternative Hypotheses ($H_1$) vs. Null Hypotheses ($H_0$)

Statistical hypotheses are classified as either "alternatives" ($H_1$), or "nulls" ($H_0$). The null hypothesis is developed from the statistical alternative hypothesis, and is a hypothesis of "no difference," i.e., it must contain a statement of equality somewhere within its framework. The "null" is a "void" or "empty" hypothesis stated for the purpose of rejection. In other words, it is a hypothesis advanced with the hope that the data will present sufficient evidence to reject it. If the data reject the "null," it is possible to accept the "statistical alternative" with a stronger probability of it ($H_1$) being true than otherwise would have been possible. Thus, the process of testing the null hypothesis in this fashion is, in essence, the process of testing it *against* its accompanying statistical alternative hypothesis ($H_1$). If the data reject the "null" ($H_0$), the researcher may accept the accompanying "statistical alternative" ($H_1$). If the data do not reject the "null," the experiment, study, or project must be dismissed, or repeated under similar conditions. *It should be noted that the null hypothesis is never accepted*, it is either *rejected*, or *not rejected*. The "null" cannot be accepted because, at best, it is one of many "alternatives" to the statistical alternative hypothesis ($H_1$), and, in any event, is not a hypothesis which has been given *careful study* by the researcher before it is advanced for testing. Actually, the null hypothesis ($H_0$) is developed as an "opposite" to the "statistical alternative," it must contain a statement of equality (no difference) somewhere within its framework, and it cannot be stated (in terms of mathematical symbols) until the "alternative" ($H_1$) is known. For this reason, the statistical alternative hypothesis is cast from the operational hypothesis which is under consideration, and if the accompanying "null" ($H_0$) is rejected by the data, the researcher may accept $H_1$, the "alternative," and hence the *operational* hypothesis from which $H_1$ was derived. If the operational hypothesis can be accepted, then the research hypothesis can be accepted in the dimension(s) covered by that "operational."

To illustrate the foregoing, suppose a certain treatment is applied to a group of twenty-five students with the hope that it is effective. Before administering the treatment to the random sample of twenty-five students, it was known that the *mean score of the population* (in the universe of discourse under study) from which the sample was taken was $\mu_0$. The operational hypothesis to be tested is: the mean score of the population to which the sample subjects will belong, after the treatment, is greater than $\mu_0$. The appropriate statistical alternative hypothesis for the "operational" is: $H_1: \mu > \mu_0$; hence the accompanying "null" will be: $H_0: \mu \leq \mu_0$. Suppose now that the treatment is administered, and the group is tested. The mean score of the sample group of twenty-five is found to be $\overline{X}$. The null hypothesis, $H_0: \mu \leq \mu_0$, is tested against the "statistical alternative," $H_1: \mu > \mu_0$; by determining whether the value of $\overline{X}$ occurs in the "critical region" of the sampling distribution of the mean for sample size, $n = 25$. If the value of $\overline{X}$ does occur in the critical region, the null hypothesis, $H_0: \mu \leq \mu_0$, can be rejected in favor of the statistical alternative hypothesis, $H_1: \mu > \mu_0$. If $H_0$ is rejected and $H_1$ is accepted, the operational hypothesis, from which $H_1$ was derived, can also be accepted, and hence the research hypothesis can be accepted in the dimension covered by the "operational." If the value of $\overline{X}$ does not occur in the critical region of the sampling distribution, the null hypothesis ($H_0$) cannot be rejected, and thus $H_1$ cannot be accepted. If $H_1$ cannot be accepted, the operational hypothesis from which it was derived cannot be accepted, and hence the research hypothesis cannot be accepted in the dimension covered by that "operational."

The testing of statistical hypotheses of magnitude, difference, and relationship is a broad topic, of which space limitations and continuity preclude extended discussion at this time. Certain basic details of the subject, however, were covered at this point in order to provide the basis for a better understanding of how the general model of educational research might be modified and applied to different types of research problems. For those readers who, at this point, are interested in a detailed discussion of the topic, see Chapter 23.

TESTING THE NULL HYPOTHESIS

The statistical alternative hypothesis $(H_1)$ is not tested directly in the statistical inference process. The approach employed is that of first examining $H_1$ in order to determine the appropriate form of the null hypothesis $(H_0)$, and then submitting it to test. If the "null" is *rejected* by the data, the "statistical alternative" $(H_1)$ can be accepted. If the "null" is *not rejected*, the experimentation should either be repeated, or abandoned.

The testing of the null hypothesis in the statistical inference process necessitates the formulation of an objective criterion by which the appropriate decision to reject or not reject the "null" can be derived. In order to establish an appropriate objective criterion, portions in the end(s) of the probability distribution of the statistic being employed in the testing procedure (e.g., the sampling distribution of the mean for sample size $n$, see page 41), are designated as forming the *critical region* of the distribution. Whenever a random sample of the population under consideration yields a value of the statistic which falls in the critical region of the distribution, the null hypothesis ($H_0$) under test is rejected, thus allowing acceptance of the statistical alternative hypothesis ($H_1$).

The critical region of the probability distribution being employed is determined in the following fashion. First the sampling distribution (probability distribution) of the statistic being used for the test must be known. Second, the *supposition is made that the null hypothesis ($H_0$) is true*. Third, the values stipulated in the supposedly-true "null" are those that would occur most frequently in the distribution. Fourth, the critical region is established in the end(s) of the distribution where values of the statistic would occur with low frequency, if $H_0$ were actually true.

With the critical region of the curve (distribution) defined in the fashion described, "extreme" values (i.e., values in the ends of the distribution) of the statistic calculated from the data of the random sample employed would make the "truth presumption" of the null hypothesis ($H_0$) suspect, and thus lend credibility to the possibility that the statistical alternative hypothesis ($H_1$) was actually the "true" state, or condition, extant in the population under study. This condition does not negate the possibility that an "extreme" value of the statistic might arise purely by chance when actually the null hypothesis ($H_0$) is true. The researcher is actually gambling at this point, when he chooses to reject the "null" ($H_0$) on the basis of the occurrence of the "extreme" value of the statistic being employed. He, in effect, is stating that he does not believe that the "extreme" value of the statistic occurred by chance under the condition of $H_0$ being true, but instead, that the value of the statistic occurred because the "statistical alternative" ($H_1$) is true and the "null" is not, i.e., the "null" is false.

The amount of risk (i.e., of concluding wrongly about the null hypothesis when, in fact, it is true) is based upon the size of the critical region. If the size of the "region" is too large, the risk of rejecting the null hypothesis when it is actually true is high. The act of rejecting a hypothesis when, in fact, it is true is called a "Type I," or "alpha ($\alpha$) error." If the critical region is defined in such a fashion that it involves only small portions of the distribution, the risk of not rejecting the null hypothesis when it is actually false and should be rejected is high. The act of not rejecting a hypothesis when, in fact, it is false is called a "Type II," or "beta ($\beta$) error."

In most research practice, either one of two levels of significance (sizes of critical regions) are employed: (a) the 5 per cent level, or (b) the 1 per cent level. If the 5 per cent level ($\alpha = .05$) is employed, then 5 per cent of the total area under the "curve" of the probability distribution of the statistic being used as the measuring device, (and located in its end(s)), is defined as composing the critical region of the distribution. If the 1 per cent level ($\alpha = .01$) is employed, then 1 per cent of the total area located in the end(s) of the appropriate probability distribution is defined as the critical region of the curve.

There are two types of critical regions, depending upon the statement of the "null" ($H_0$), which may be employed: (a) the type associated with one-tailed tests, and (b) the type associated with two-tailed tests. If the null hypothesis does not state direction, i.e., does not employ "greater than" or "less than" statements, then a two-tailed test is to be employed, and the critical region is composed of two equal portions of the distribution, one located in the upper end of the curve, the other in the lower end of the distribution. If the null hypothesis does state a direction (e.g., $H_0: \mu \geq \mu_0$), then a one-tailed test must be employed, and the critical region is composed of one portion of the distribution located in the appropriate end of the curve.

If the sampling distribution of the mean ($\overline{X}$) for sample size $n$ is being used to test certain null hypotheses pertaining to population means, the critical regions would appear as shown in Figure 2.

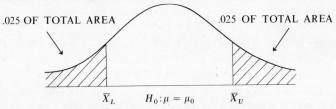

.025 OF TOTAL AREA          .025 OF TOTAL AREA

$\overline{X}_L$     $H_0: \mu = \mu_0$     $\overline{X}_U$

EXAMPLE 1. Illustration of a two-tailed test of the null hypothesis: $H_0: \mu = \mu_0$; with $\alpha = .05$. If the value of the statistic ($\overline{X}$), calculated from the data of the random sample drawn from the population under study, is less than $\overline{X}_L$, or greater then $\overline{X}_u$, then the null hypothesis is rejected in favor of $H_1$.

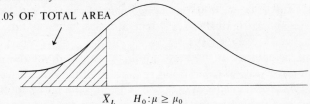

.05 OF TOTAL AREA

$\overline{X}_L$     $H_0: \mu \geq \mu_0$

EXAMPLE 2. Illustration of a one-tailed test of the null hypothesis: $H_0: \mu \geq \mu_0$; with $\alpha = .05$. If the value of the statistic ($\overline{X}$), calculated from the data of the random sample drawn from the population under study, is less than $\overline{X}_L$, then the null hypothesis is rejected in favor of $H_1$.

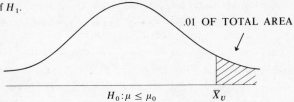

.01 OF TOTAL AREA

$H_0: \mu \leq \mu_0$     $\overline{X}_U$

EXAMPLE 3. Illustration of a one-tailed test of the null hypothesis: $H_0: \mu \leq \mu_0$; with $\alpha = .01$. If the value of the statistic ($\overline{X}$), calculated from the data of the random sample drawn from the population under study, is greater than $\overline{X}_U$, then the null hypothesis is rejected in favor of $H_1$.

*Figure 2*
*Examples of Testing Null Hypotheses Involving Population Means*

Each example in Figure 2 discusses the course of action to pursue if the value of the statistic, $\bar{X}$, calculated from the data of the random sample falls in the critical region. If the value of $\bar{X}$ *does not* fall in the critical region, the null hypothesis ($H_0$) cannot be rejected. *This result does not mean that the null hypothesis is accepted.* The null hypothesis is *never* accepted, it is either *rejected* or *not rejected*. If the data cannot reject the "null," the researcher has the option of re-designing the experiment, or study, and testing the null hypothesis derived under the conditions of the "new" study; or replicating the original study after carefully investigating the three major sources of biased error; (a) sampling, (b) data collection instrumentalities and procedures, and (c) data processing techniques. Naturally, the option of abandoning the research effort is also a possibility.

With this background on the topic of hypotheses, we are now prepared to discuss what is meant by the terminology "General Questions."

GENERAL QUESTIONS

Many times in the process of carrying out the methods and procedures of descriptive research, particularly in the process of conducting survey studies, general questions to be answered are advanced, instead of hypotheses. Performing the same function in "non-hypothesized" research that hypotheses do in hypothesized research, general questions to be answered provide the means of directing and limiting the descriptive, or survey, study. It is not the intent here to leave the impression that the interrogative statement cannot be used as a convenient form for stating the hypothesis of a study. Hypotheses may be advanced as declarative or interrogative statements. The point to be made is that the *spirit* of the hypothesis is frequently lacking in exploratory, survey, and/or descriptive types of studies. Thus, the general questions approach is frequently employed to frame, bound, and direct research efforts that are not envisioned as hypothesis-testing types of studies.

The general model of educational research is altered slightly to accommodate the "non-hypothesized" research effort. The element of the general model which must undergo alteration to modify it so that it may be employed in "non-hypothesized" studies is that of the hypothesis. The inclusion of the general questions element in the model alters its design so that non-hypothesized inquiry can be conducted by its application to those problem areas susceptible to such inquiry. The term "non-hypothesized" is introduced at the risk of its being a misnomer; however, it cannot be denied that, particularly in educational research, many studies are of an exploratory nature, and truly are about the process of answering questions instead of testing advanced hypotheses.

Despite the lexical meaning of the term "non-hypothesized," we shall find it to be an element of the general model for educational research which is most convenient and useful in discussions of modified forms of the general model that are applicable to certain descriptive, historical, action, and field study types of research. Where the general-questions-to-be-answered approach is used, the model employed will be referred to as the "non-hypothesized research" type. With this discussion as background, we are now prepared to discuss the elements of the model known as the *"universe and the sample."*

Chapter 3—References

See Bibliography: 6, 38, 49, 54, 66, 79, 82, 102, 104, 113, 143, 148, 155, 183, 188; 16a, 42a, 46a, 47a, 57a.

### Chapter Four

# The Universe and the Sample

THE UNIVERSE (population) and the sample are elements of the model that are of critical importance to the research process prescribed by the model. The universe and sample are obviously related, and it is difficult to discuss one apart from the other. The population or universe is the source of data for the inquiry. It is defined on the basis of the problematic situation and the hypothesis, or general questions, of the inquiry. A sample selected from the population must be representative, adequate, and free from bias, so that the data gathered from this source can provide reliable estimates and inferences about the characteristics of the population that are under study.

## THE UNIVERSE: FINITE AND INFINITE

If the population is finite (objects are countable and limited in number), and used in its entirety as the source of data, the selection of a representative sample for the purpose of estimating population characteristics is unnecessary. In the majority of cases that involve finite populations, however, and in all cases of infinite populations (objects unlimited in number), sampling is necessary. Thus, the selection of the sample becomes an important part of almost all inquiries. In fact, in many instances the methods and conditions of selecting the sample are considered to form the operational "design" of the inquiry or research. With this information as background, we shall now discuss the factors and elements of universes (populations) and samples that are fundamental to productive methods of inquiry or research.

## UNIVERSE (POPULATION)

In an abstract sense, we can consider the universe separately from the sample. We recall from earlier treatment that a population (universe) is defined to be the totality of objects under consideration. The universe can be specified in terms of an entity and/or defined characteristics of the entity.

Examples of population (universe) entities and characteristics are:

| *Population Entity* | *Population Characteristic* |
|---|---|
| School Children | Number, Height, Weight, Test scores |
| Cigarets | Nicotine content, Number defective |
| Social Institutions | Number, Methods of operation, Size |
| Grain in a Storage Bin | Moisture content per pound, Flour yield per pound |
| Sound | Volume, Frequency, Amplitude |

A population entity may have an infinite list of characteristics, but interest under a particular problematic situation usually centers in one, and at most, a few of the characteristics.

In order to provide an adequate description of the population under consideration, factors of time, place, conditions, and other similar features should be included in the definition of the universe.

*Population Limits*

The limits (boundaries) of a population are determined by the problematic situation, the hypothesis of the inquiry, and the resources available to the researcher. It is frequently necessary to limit the population deliberately so that adequate results may be obtained from the sample to be employed. The rationale here is that it is better to obtain adequate and more reliable results from a smaller population than less reliable and less adequate results from a larger population. The *relative* nature of a population can be illustrated by considering an example in which the population is to provide data for the study of oil. Under these circumstances the data may deal with oil fields, oil wells, tank cars full of oil, or quarts of oil composing the supplies of certain types of gasoline stations. The boundary and definition of the population depends upon the circumstances of the problematic situation, the hypothesis of the inquiry, and the availability of the resources.

A ramification of the problem of determining the population is that of real, artificial, and hypothetical populations. A real population is one which actually exists. An artificial population is created by the researcher in order to illustrate a principle, or to make for more convenience and ease in carrying out the study of a problematic situation. A hypothetical population is an artificial one devised on a purely theoretical basis. The hypothetical population permits, for example, the researcher to work with an infinite population of entities, when the real population under study is much smaller.

Of importance at this point are the meaning of "known" and "unknown" populations. A known population is one for which the frequency distribution, and/or the parameters thereof (e.g., mean, mode, median, standard deviation, etc.), are known for the variable under consideration. An unknown population is one for which no such information is available. In most practical research problems the population frequency distribution, and/or its parameters are not known. Because of this condition, estimation of the values of these population parameters, by means of computing values of comparable statistics (mean, mode, median, standard deviation, etc.) from random samples, becomes necessary. Such an operation is one of the chief functions of statistics.

*Population Stratification*

Frequently it is desirable to "stratify" a population. Stratification may be carried out by dividing the population into groups on the basis of the variability of the characteristic under study. The groups so formed are called "strata." The purpose of stratification is to obtain groups *each of which is more homogeneous in the characteristic under study*, than is the population *in toto*. If stratification can be accomplished, sample units may be selected from each of the strata; and because of the homogeneous nature of each stratum, less numbers of sampling units will be needed to obtain the same precision in the estimation of a value of a parameter as that which would have been yielded by a sample of larger size taken from the total (unstratified) population.

The basis of stratification may be any factor judged to be causal to the variability of the characteristic under study. Some examples of factors upon which stratification could be effected are: weight, age, height, class, status, source, location, or time. A combination of factors may be used for stratification if each accounts for significant variability of the characteristic under inquiry. The selection of factors upon which the stratification is to be based, depends upon the experience of the researcher and statistical tests of the variability of the characteristic under study due to these factors. It is well to remember that although a certain basis for stratification may appear to be obvious, a statistical analysis of variability should be employed. It is not unusual in such cases to discover that the factors upon which the stratification is to be carried out do not contribute significantly to the variability of the characteristic, and therefore do not accomplish the purpose of the process. When this situation occurs, other factors should be sought for stratifying the population. If other factors are not available, there is no reason for attempting to effect stratification.

In the discussion of the stratification of the population, the term "sampling unit" was employed. This is an important concept in sampling theory. The sampling unit is defined as that population element, or group of elements, which is used as the basis for selection of the sample. To illustrate, in estimating the number of people present at a huge outdoor rally, the *population element* is the individual; however, the *sampling unit* may be the individual, a group of ten individuals, a roped-off section of individuals, or some area filled with people. In sampling a population of grade-school pupils, the *population element* is the individual pupil, but the *sampling unit* may be the pupil, a class, a particular grade, an entire school, or a school district. In production processes, the *element* is the individual item being produced, but the *sampling unit* may be a package, bale, or "lot" of the produced items.

The units comprising a sample must be selected from the population. A "random sample" has been drawn if the selection occurs in such a fashion that every unit has an equal opportunity, or chance, of being selected. This definition demands that selection be independent both of the selector and of the methods used to effect the drawing of the sample from the population. If the units are affected by the selection procedure, a biased sample results. For example, suppose that in sampling public opinion on a particular issue, the poll is limited to persons who were listed in the telephone directory. Those homes not having a telephone would be omitted from the sample. This omission would mean that those persons who could not afford a telephone, or for some other reason did not have a telephone, would not have the same chance of being selected as those persons with telephones. Thus, a biased sample relative to economic, health, or retirement status would result. Random selection avoids this type of bias.

A *simple random sample* is chosen when every selection of a sampling unit involves every unit in the population. A stratified random sample is chosen when the selection of a sampling unit is restricted to the units in a stratum (rather than selecting units from the whole unstratified population), and one or more sampling units are selected randomly from each stratum until all strata are included. It should be noted that the number of units drawn from each stratum need not be the same.

### Random Numbers and Sample Selection

In order to facilitate random selection, lists of random numbers have been published. Two of the more popular lists are those of Fisher,[1] and those of Kendall and Babington-Smith.[2] These lists have been carefully tested, and present numbers arranged in random order with each of the ten digits 0, 1, 2, 3, 4, 5, 6, 7, 8, and 9 appearing approximately equally often in the lists.

The method of using random numbers is comparatively simple. First, the population must be finite. Second, the population elements are numbered in order. Third, the random numbers list is employed, by first determining the number of digits required in the random numbers, and then selecting random numbers from the list until the desired sample size is realized. Let us demonstrate a typical case. Suppose a finite population is composed of two hundred elements. The elements are numbered : 000, 001, 002, 003, . . . , 197, 198 and 199. A random numbers table is consulted. Starting at any point in the table, and reading in any direction; up, down, across, or diagonally; three digit numbers are sought between the values of 000 and 199. If a sample of forty items were desired, the table of numbers would be examined until forty different random numbers from the array 000 to 199 were found. Any random number which has occurred once in the selection process, and is a number which has been assigned to one of the population elements, is ignored after its initial occurrence. For example, if number 099 were to occur three times in the process of carrying out the selection of a sample of elements on the basis of a random numbers table, only the element selected as the result of the first occurrence would be used. The element represented by 099 would *not* be included three times. A sample which is drawn by means of a random numbers table is considered to be a random one.

### Probability Sampling

In recent statistical literature the term "probability sampling" has come into use. Basically there are three types of probability sampling now employed in research. One is the random sample, in which every sampling unit is given an equal probability of selection. A second one is that in which sampling units do not have equal probability of selection, and finally one in which the sampling unit is selected with a probability proportional to its size.

### Pertinent Considerations Under Actual Sampling Conditions

Sampling may be carried out with or without replacements. Most research sampling is conducted without replacement. In this form, the drawing of sampling units diminishes the population in size, and the probability of selection changes (particularly if the population is finite and not too large). If the drawing changes the population proportion of a characteristic being studied significantly, then a correction must be made to adjust for the fact that the population is finite.

*Sample Size*

The size of a sample is determined by the number of sampling units composing it. A small sample usually is considered to be one of thirty sampling units or less. This figure is derived under the assumption that the selection of the sample will have been made from an infinite population. If the selection of the sample were made from a finite population composed of fifty elements, however, a sample of thirty sampling units would be considered a comparatively large one. On the other hand, a sample composed of forty or forty-five elements might be considered a small one under other types of conditions.

The necessity for distinction between small and large samples is based on the fact that certain statistical operations can be applied to large samples but not to small samples. The solution of the problem of estimating the values of population parameters from random samples also demands a knowledge of the different capabilities, or power, of large and small sample sizes.

*Sequential Sampling*

Sometimes it is necessary to take more than one random sample from a population. If the size of the *total sample* to be drawn is not determined beforehand, but it is possible to take a number of small random samples of one or more units each from the population until an estimate can be made, or a decision reached, then a sequential sample is said to have been taken. Another hallmark of sequential sampling is the decision that must be made after each drawing to determine if further sampling is necessary to draw a conclusion about the matter under study. Sequential sampling has its greatest application in statistical quality control processes of industry. It also can be employed in certain types of problems occurring in educational research.

Sequential sampling should not be confused with the process of replication. Replication is said to occur when repeated random samples are drawn in the same experiment. For example, if a random sample of sixteen students is taken in one school, the data are processed and a conclusion is drawn, and if the same design is repeated in five or six other schools, the experimental design is said to have been replicated.

*Sampling Distribution*

Of extreme importance to sampling theory is the concept of the *sampling distribution*. A sampling distribution is a theoretical one composed of all of the values of a particular statistic (e.g., mean, median, mode) that are derived from each of all of the possible random samples of a given size, $n$, which can be drawn, with replacement, from a given population (see Chapter 15). Thus, it is possible to have sampling distributions of means, medians, modes, standard deviations, differences of two group means, and many other types of statistics.

*Theoretical and Actual Sampling Distributions*

The statistic (mean, etc.) used to establish a sampling distribution is an estimate of the value of its related population parameter (mean, etc.). The standard deviation of a sampling distribution is called "the standard error of the particular statistic" upon which the sampling distribution is based. For example, if all of the possible samples of size $n = 25$ are drawn, *with replacement*, from a given population, and for each sample a mean ($\overline{X}$) is calculated, a frequency distribution of these means (statistics) could be constructed. If the mean ($\mu_{\overline{x}}$) of this sampling distribution of the mean for sample size 25 were calculated, its value would be an estimate of the mean ($\mu$), a parameter of the population. The standard deviation ($\sigma_{\overline{x}}$) of the sampling distribution is called "the standard error of the mean."

The sampling distribution of a particular statistic for sample size $n$ employed in practice is a *theoretical* distribution to the extent that it is *assumed* to be based upon the values of the statistics derived from *all possible samples* of size $n$ that could be drawn *with replacement* from the original population of data. This hypothetical distribution is in contrast to an *actual* sampling distribution of a particular statistic based upon the values derived from a limited number of samples of size $n$ drawn *with replacement* from a comparatively small finite population. An *actual* sampling distribution rapidly approaches the *theoretical* sampling distribution if the population is composed of a reasonable number ($N$) of elements, and the sample, drawn *with replacement*, is composed of a comparatively small number ($n$) of sampling units. The explanation of the latter statement is obviated by the formula for finding the number of *possible different samples* of size $n$ which can be drawn with replacement from a population of size $N$: Number of samples $= N^n$

To illustrate, suppose a population is composed of $N = 5$ elements, and samples of size $n = 3$ are to be drawn. The number of possible different samples, and therefore the number of possible values (all of which are not different) of the statistic to be used to construct the sampling distribution for sample size $n = 3$, is: $5^3 = 125$. If there had been $N = 10$ elements in the population, and the sample size was to be $n = 5$, there would be: $10^5 = 100,000$ values of the statistic upon which to base the sampling distribution. Obviously, when the population is numbered in terms of hundreds of "objects," and the samples are to include more than five elements, the assumption of a *theoretical* sampling distribution for the *actual* sampling distribution is performed with little risk of introducing "damaging" errors in the processes of estimation and inference about the values of the population parameters under consideration.

DEFINITION OF TERMS FUNDAMENTAL TO SAMPLING

The elementary principles of sampling cannot be explained adequately unless certain statements and definitions of terms are presented. The "definitions" in question are listed below to provide basic knowledge of the concepts and their relation to the processes of sampling. Since the fourth section of the text has been devoted to a detailed discussion of sampling, the definitions and descriptions provided here are intentionally brief.

### 1. *A Population*

A population is defined to be the totality of "objects" under consideration.

### 2. *A Sample*

A sample is defined to be a subset of a population, where a set, in turn, is described as a carefully defined collection of things.

### 3. *Allocation of a Sample*

The allocation of a sample is performed by allocating a certain portion of the total sample size *n* to each of the strata into which the population may have been divided. The basis for allocation may be the size of each stratum, the variability of the data included in each stratum, or a combination of size and variability of each stratum. When the latter combination is utilized as a basis for allocation, the process of *optimum allocation* is said to have been effected.

### 4. *Subsampling*

Subsampling is of two basic types : (1) a random sample of a random sample, and (2) a random sample of a group-type sampling unit. The first type is illustrated by taking a random sample of fifty persons from an original random sample of, say, ten thousand. The second is found by choosing random sample "lots" of a product, and then inspecting a random sample of, say, bundles of twenty-five, from the random "lots." Thus, in subsampling, random selection is applied two or more times to the sampling units.

### 5. *Design of a Sample*

The design of a sample is accomplished by a definite statistical plan formulated before the research is begun. It should specify an acceptable error in estimates, and the probability of error in the inferences. Minimally, the sample design should include the stratification of the population, acceptable error in the estimates, sample size necessary for adequacy, procedure of allocating the sample to the strata, method of selection of the sample, methods of estimation, and various tests to keep biased sources of error to a minimum. The basis for the design must include the most variable characteristic of the population, out of the group of characteristics that might be under investigation.

### 6. *Non-random Selection*

Non-random selection is said to occur when the selection of the sample is either based upon human judgment or upon some quantitative rule.

### 7. *Judgment or Purposive Sample*

When the selection of a sample is based upon human judgment, it is called "purposive" or "judgment" selection. Such selection is determined on the basis of what the research worker might consider from his past experience to be a typical, or representative, sampling unit. It may also be based upon the findings of an analysis of the statistical population relative to physical, psychological, sociological, or economic characteristics. Sometimes it is a haphazard selection of accessible population elements—persons who pass a particular corner in a certain city, for example. Frequently "purposive" selection is considered "segmental" selection, to the extent that the selection is restricted to certain segments of the total statistical population.

### 8. *Controlled or Quota Samples*

Naturally, purposive selection is frequently subject to bias. When an attempt is made to control this bias, the sampling is referred to as "controlled" sampling. One frequently, and successfully, used method of controlled sampling is that of "quota" sampling which is used in opinion poll work. In this process, persons with particular characteristics, located in a particular locality, are interviewed for their opinions on a particular issue. The results are considered to be representative of that particular type of cross section of the community. Such quotas are calculated before the research is undertaken, and frequently are based upon census and/or election statistics.

### 9. *Serial Samples*

Two types of quantitative rules in non-random selection, are termed "$n$ largest elements," and "serial" selection. Selection of $n$ largest elements is a form of segmental selection. Correction is made for bias by covering certain estimated proportions of the total statistical population, or by relating known pilot study sample values to known sample values. Let us consider, as an illustration of the "$n$ largest elements" approach, a particular voting precinct's constituency which forms a sizable part of the total community, and is further judged to be representative in racial distribution of a particular city. Suppose the precinct is composed of 50 per cent Democrats, 25 per cent Republicans, 15 per cent Socialists, and 10 per cent "others." The vote will be most affected by the Democrat and Republican elements. The voting trend of these two groups might be examined in this precinct in order to predict the selection results for the city.

Serial selection, which is a process of selecting every $i$-th population element, is a restricted type of random selection if the population elements are thoroughly mixed and the starting point for selection is chosen at random. It is restricted in the sense that not every element, or group of elements, has an equal chance of being selected. Obviously, selection depends heavily upon the determination of the starting point.

### 10. *Causes for Variation in Samples*

Non-random sources of variation in research are important to consider because they cannot be controlled by the sampling design. These sources of variation could be due to the unfelt and unknown biases of such participants of the research effort as: observers, investigators, respondents, and interviewers. To these sources must be added those of: ambiguity in instructions to the sample subjects, defective measuring instruments, faulty construction of data gathering instruments, and faulty techniques of data processing. Although these additional sources of variation cannot be controlled by the sampling design, they require careful planning if other phases of the inquiry are to maintain the reliability and validity of the inquiry.

A detailed discussion of biased and unbiased error (variation) is presented in Chapter 5. Supplementing these materials are the demonstrations presented in the modified general models discussed in later chapters. Many of the sampling designs are illustrated by the sampling procedures employed in these models. For additional descriptions of these topics beyond those included in this text, the interested reader may consult the sources listed in the references of this chapter.

*Chapter 4—References*
See Bibliography: 18, 23, 37, 40, 48, 49, 50, 53, 63, 65, 67, 78, 80, 82, 83, 91, 93, 94, 100, 109, 116, 120, 127, 137, 148, 150, 152, 155, 161, 178, 183, 194, 195; 7a, 8a, 12a, 22a, 23a, 28a, 43a, 54a, 57a, 62a, 63a, 66a, 76a, 78a, 87a, 101a, 108a; 1b, 2b.

*Chapter Five*

# Data Collection—Conditions and Methods

THE ELEMENT OF DATA COLLECTION in the suggested general model for educational research may best be discussed in terms of: (1) the conditions under which observations are to be made, (2) the methods, or procedures, of making observations, and (3) the instrumentalities of data collection. These arbitrarily defined categories are not mutually exclusive facets of the data collection process, and frequently research situations exist wherein these aspects are intermingled, and differentiation, or classification, as "condition," "method," or "instrumentality" rely upon the value judgments of the researcher. The classifications are employed, however, in order to provide a relatively direct and simple means of discussing the data collection element of the research model. In addition to contributing to the facility of the discussion of the element of data collection, the reader will find that the approach provides a means by which he can retain the material pertaining to the functions of this aspect of the model in relation to the research process.

## OBSERVATIONAL CONDITIONS AND HISTORY

The *first* condition of data collection which the researcher should examine is the history of the problematic situation. This history is composed of the many antecedent problems and solutions connected with the problem area. It is important as a reference frame and general orientation for evaluating the relevancy of data. Previous problems and their accompanying solutions are links forming a constantly lengthening chain of information concerning the discipline or area in which the research problem is found.

The condition calling for the examination of the history of the problem is also important to the processes of delineating and defining relevant data. The history of a problematic situation provides the meaning of concepts involved in the problem. This condition is restrictive to the extent that the researcher cannot arbitrarily define the concepts with which he might be forced to deal. To illustrate, the scientist cannot define such terms as "time," "intelligence," "culture," and other generally used concepts, sufficiently well to meet only the needs of his *argument* while denying the generally accepted meaning and historical use of these terms in other universes of discourse.

Every scientific term has a background and a foreground. The term's background is composed of the historic trends from all of the disciplines that have employed the term. Its foreground is composed of the purposes the term is to serve. Thus, the *second* condition of data collection deals with predicting the best way in which the problem's historical trend can help solve the research problem. This prediction is based upon what is termed the "prior knowledge" of the researcher. Prior knowledge is built upon knowing the historic trends of the problem, having interdisciplinary knowledge, and recognizing the inter-relatedness of the problem with its setting and elements of other disciplines.

Prior knowledge is not easily acquired. The researcher is not omniscient, and it is physically impossible for him to read all of the literature and investigate all of the other sources that might be relevant to the research problem. There is also another limiting factor. It is impossible to conduct an exhaustive investigation of the problematic situation, because the problem might well be undergoing change with the passage of time. Finally, the financial capability of the researcher sets definite limits on the magnitude and scale of the investigation into the prior knowledge aspect of the research problem. Few, if any, researchers could afford, in time and money, a truly *exhaustive* search of the problematic situation. Thus, we must recognize that good research is not accomplished on the basis or the adeptness of *one* research worker and his knowledge of only one discipline. Prior knowledge is only acquired *by the researcher* if he is willing to depend upon the findings of other sciences, and the previous work completed within the discipline of the research problem's contextual setting. The following illustration will help clarify the point of the discussion.

The aneroid barometer is an instrument which measures atmospheric pressure. Its main use, at one time, was in the field of meteorology. With the invention of aircraft, it became necessary to develop some means of determining the altitude of the craft during flight—an instrument was needed. The aneroid barometer was adapted to the problem situation, and in its new form came to be known as the "altimeter." Considering this situation in connection with the historical trend of the problem and the necessary prior knowledge of the re-searcher, we find basically two important facts: (1) the researcher had to know something about atmospheric pressure, meteorology, the mechanics of the aneroid barometer, the effect of motion on a barometer, certain aspects of mechanics, instruments, hydrostatics, chemistry, biology, physiology, and anatomy; and these are but a few of the host of scientific facts that were necessary to the invention of the instrument; and, (2) if the inventor had not been willing to accept certain facts from other scientific fields, not to mention the previous findings in the field of instrumentation, the problem would have probably denied solution.

The historic trend of the problematic situation is also the source of information for determining the reliability and validity aspects of data collection, the third and final condition of the process. By "reliability" we mean the consistency of the data as evidence for a solution of the problematic situation when the situation has repeated occurrence, or when similar situations have repeated occurrence. By "validity" we mean that the data are authentic, that they measure what they are supposed to measure. How do we determine if this third condition of data collection is being satisfied? In the process of answering this question it will become apparent that the categories of "conditions," "methods," and "instrumentalities" are not mutually exclusive.

### Determining Reliability and Validity of Data

The process of investigating the reliability and validity of the data involved in the inquiry is carried out by seeking a pattern of consistency and authenticity of the data in the historical trend of the problem. It is necessary to investigate this pattern not only within the discipline of the problem setting, but in related disciplines as well. For example, the data of the historical trend of a problem in psychology should be checked for consistency and authenticity not only in the field of psychology, but in, say, sociology, education, physiology, biology, and any other disciplines that might have a pertinent connection with the problem and its data. Briefly, all related knowledge relevant, or conceivably relevant, to the problem should be reviewed. Admittedly, no one human being can investigate all of the original scientific endeavors that might have involved the data under consideration, but a positive solution to this problem is to analyze pertinent and *relatively recent* previous attempts, including those which have ended in failure, confusion, or inconsistency of results.

How does the researcher investigate patterns of consistency and authenticity of the data involved? This end is accomplished by answering questions of: who, what, when, where, why, and how about the data. More specifically, the researcher should:

1. Examine the historical trend of the problem, and related disciplines, asking himself: "What elements are important here? Which of these elements show consistency and authenticity throughout the historical trend of the problem, and remain so when tested within related disciplines?" These questions help the researcher determine what to observe on the basis of his prior knowledge.

2. Re-examine the evaluation and formulation of the problem, the statement of the hypothesis, the definition of the universe and the determination of the sample, in order to know what, when, where, who, why and how to observe reliably and validly. In other words, the method of inquiry itself determines objectives of the research problem, gives guidance to the investigation, and determines in large part data that can be considered to be reliable and valid.

3. Determine the availability of reliable and valid data. In essence, the researcher is answering questions of: when, where, who, and how, about the data. The problem of data availability can be analyzed into three categories: (a) an availability, (b) availability, but difficult observation, and (c) availability, but possible error observations.

The problem of unavailability of data is resolved by either modifying the problem, hypotheses, universe, and sample, or rejecting the problem as unsolvable. These are clear courses of action, and will not be discussed further.

Those cases that require special equipment, or those where the subject refuses to respond, compose the main part of the category of "availability, but difficult observation." When special measuring instruments or equipment are necessary to data collection, instrumentation or special equipment experts should be consulted. Consultation with such personnel is the most efficient, and in the long run, economical, course of action that the researcher can pursue. If suitable instruments cannot be developed, problem reformulation might be necessary.

## GATHERING DATA FROM RESISTANT SUBJECTS

Subject refusal to respond demands that the alert researcher exercise his ingenuity and be ready to act. In such cases, prevention is worth far more than an after-the-fact solution. Some of the better preventive measures are:

1. Providing publicity for the research project which emphasizes the importance of the research to the individual and society. To illustrate, the importance of mental health may be urged, not only to the individual, but to the nation. The tremendous financial gains of preventive medicine and mental health, and the possibility of making non-productive persons in society productive, are valid arguments. "Help do your part in obtaining better mental health for the nation," might be a publicized slogan. Such publicity should tend to make persons more willing to participate in research projects associated with mental health.

2. Employment of keen and alert observers who have a good knowledge of the problematic situation, and the ingenuity to adapt to the unexpected.

3. Assurance to every respondent that he will not be embarrassed or inconvenienced by his participation in the research project.

4. Compensation for participation in the research.

5. Performing pilot studies and trial experimentations to gain prior knowledge of the situation and the potential respondents.

6. Framing the research so that it does not create animosities or antipathies in the respondent. Avoid using emotional or sensationally descriptive language about the research. Emphasize the sincerity of the research effort. Impress the respondent with the fact that his answers are important. Point out that his responses are representative of a particular cross-section of the universe under study, and are treated as the "answers" of that cross-section.

Where after-the-fact, or remedial, measures are necessary to collect data, it might be necessary to: (a) offer greater financial inducement for cooperation, (b) employ more astute observers, (c) find a secondary source of information to check on the response of the "difficult" responder, and (d) select suitable replacements. In most cases, the best methods for handling refusals are indicated by the situation, and the researcher should be prepared to act accordingly. It is at such points of the data collection process that behavioral science research meets its greatest difficulty.

## ERROR: DEVIATION, DIRECTION, AND MAGNITUDE

We shall discuss the category of "*data available, but possible error observations,*" by considering what we mean by the term "error." An error can only be determined in terms of the deviation of an observed value from a "true" or "expected" value. Obviously, such a deviation cannot be determined if an antecedent definition of "true" or "expected" value has not been set forth. Thus, error is defined as the deviation of an obtained value from a true or expected value of the variable under study. Symbolically, if $v$ symbolizes the observed, or obtained value, $V$ symbolizes the true or expected value, and $e$ denotes error, we can write:

$$e = v - V \tag{1}$$

From (1) we see that an error has both magnitude and direction, that is, $v$ can be greater, or smaller, than $V$.

Regardless of form, all variables are subject to error. Errors can be made in counting objects (enumeration), measuring objects (instrumentality error), deriving values (computational errors), originating values (errors of estimate), and drawing conclusions about objects or values (errors of inference). The types of errors which occur most frequently, in terms of these classifications, are: errors of measurement (instrumentalities), errors of estimation, and errors of inference. A major problem in the research process is the control of these three sources of error.

If we consider the error $e$ to be the sum of two error components; the biased error ($e_b$), and the random, or unbiased error ($e_u$), then:

$$e = e_b + e_u \tag{2}$$

From equation (1) we know that any error has magnitude and direction. Therefore, in equation (2), if the biased error, $e_b$, and the unbiased error, $e_u$, are in the same direction, we have a *maximum error possibility condition*; and if these components have opposite direction, a *minimum error possibility condition* exists.

The most desirable research situation eliminates the biased error component (i.e., $e_b = 0$). If $e_b$ cannot be eliminated, the next most desirable condition is to account for its magnitude and direction. If $e_b$ can be eliminated, or if it is known, a statement of the reliability and validity of the data can be made on a probability basis.

*The main characteristic of a biased error is consistency. A biased error* exists when observations yield data values that are constantly higher, or lower, than the true value of the characteristic under study.

Algebraically, a biased error is consistently positive, or consistently negative. Biased error may arise from many different sources, e.g., methods of data collection, poor analytic techniques, unrepresentative samples, samples of inadequate size, faulty data collection equipment or instrumentalities, and response error (deliberate, or unintentional, inaccuracy of response). Biased error is difficult to account for under any circumstance, and the researcher should be continuously aware of its possibility of occurrence, and attempt to eliminate it wherever possible.

*Unbiased or random error* can be accounted for on a probability basis. Mathematicians have long known that if there is a relatively large number of values involved, chance deviations from a true value (random errors) tend to distribute themselves normally. Thus, the normal probability distribution can be used to provide an account of the unbiased error.*

## BIASED ERROR SOURCES

The most common sources of biased error are: (1) sampling, (2) response, (3) interviewing, (4) observing, (5) measuring (instruments and techniques), (6) processing, and (7) interpreting (inference) the data.

### Sampling

Faulty sampling is a common source of biased error in research. The bias usually arises because elements are selected in a way which systematically underestimates, or overestimates, the value of the characteristic under study. When this situation exists, a *group error* occurs. *Group errors* refer to those situations where the entire group of measurements is in error relative to the true value of the population characteristic under study. *Individual errors,* in contrast, are those errors that are attributable to individual measurements. Individual errors do not possess the systematic, or constancy of error, quality that group errors do.

Factors which contribute most frequently to faulty sampling are: (a) selection of the most accessible population elements, (b) selection of "typical" elements, (c) selection of only the large, or more predominant, elements, (d) selection of elements without regard to proper weighting, (e) selection from unrepresentative sources, (f) not accounting for inaccessible sample elements, and (g) not accounting for changes in the population during the inquiry.

The factor of "most accessible elements" frequently causes faulty sampling. In sampling both animate and inanimate populations, it is easy to fall prey to the error-causing cooperating groups, man on the street, "random" audiences, college groupings, and similar entities of various kinds. Usually such samples are not representative nor of adequate size to furnish reliable and valid data. In the case of inanimate populations, *the top elements* in a pile of lumber, a tank of liquid, bales of cotton, or a bin of grain are usually selected and contribute unknown biases to the data. Telephone directories, automobile registrations, and organizational memberships frequently provide samples that are biased in social and economic data. A well-designed sample may fail to provide reliable and valid data if the elements mentioned here are not considered during the sampling phase of the data collection process.

Many of the sampling pitfalls previously described can be avoided by careful pre-planning. In those cases where they are unavoidable, every effort should be made to account for the magnitude and direction of the introduced biased errors. For example, three ways of correcting for the bias of inaccessible elements (non-response) in mail surveys and interview samples have been applied successfully.†

---

* Random error is not a difficult problem in research, and further time will not be spent on the topic here. For further discussion, see Normal Probability Distribution, Chapter 16.

† For actual example of a correction pattern see model, Chapter 10.

Hansen and Hurwitz[1] have developed a follow-up method of interviews of a random sample of the non-respondents in a mail survey. The data are treated as two strata of a stratified random sample, one stratum composed of the original respondents' data, the other of the interviewed non-respondents' data. Sampling errors are computed for each stratum, comparisons made, and a combination effected to account for an estimation of the total sampling error involved in the operation.

Politz and Simmons[2] have developed a mathematical method for correcting for "not-at-home" elements of an interview sample. The method consists of four steps:

1. Call on each person in the interview only once.
2. Determine from those who are contacted what number of the interview periods of the preceding week they were at home. For instance, if the interviews were being conducted from 3 to 5 P.M., Monday through Saturday, the respondent is asked to recall how many days of the previous week he, or she, was home between 3 and 5 P.M.
3. The respondents contacted are grouped according to whether they were home 6/6, 6/5, 6/4, 6/3, 6/2, or 6/1 evenings.
4. Compute the *weights* for the number of eligible interviewees who were at home, to give an *adjustment number* for the responses in the sample. This method corrects for much of the bias, but does not account for those who are not at home during the period on any of the six nights.*

The Politz–Simmons method is not necessarily the best one to use for every situation of "not-at-home" elements. Sometimes call-backs may be more efficient. Comparative evaluations of these two methods must be based upon not only bias, but the amount of variability in the estimates of the values of the population characteristics involved, and the operating costs of data collection. The Politz–Simmons method is advantageous where there is little money available for call-backs, where the survey must be conducted rapidly, and where the population is widely dispersed thus making call-backs too expensive to carry out. A combination of both methods is possible, and where neither of these two methods is feasible, the pilot study approach can be used to provide information for the establishment of criteria for reliability and validity of the interview sample data.

A method for accounting for biased error resulting from non-respondents in mail surveys has been suggested by Hendricks.[3] The rationale of the method is that the number of mailed requests required to obtain an answer is a measure of the "resistance" to participate. The logarithm of this "resistance" is assumed to be normally distributed, so that the following equation may be employed:

$$\log X = \sigma z + \log \overline{X} \qquad (3)$$

where $X$ is the number of mailed requests necessary to get the answer, $\sigma$ (sigma)

---

* Politz and Simmons (88a), suggest a method for taking account of this group.

is the standard deviation of the total number of mailed requests necessary to get the answer from all of the sample elements, $z$ is the normal deviate, and $\overline{X}$ is the average resistance of all the sample elements. The main disadvantage of this method is the difficulty of estimating $\overline{X}$ and $\sigma$, and the somewhat rigorous mathematical approach to the problem.

## Response

Measurements depending upon response are often biased because of misunderstanding, ignorance, carelessness, or intentional misstatement by the respondent. This type of error is "individual," in contrast to the "group" error caused by faulty sampling.

Response errors depend heavily upon the content and clarity of the questions being asked. For example, women tend to be more vague than men respondents concerning age. Other categories that cause considerable response error are: nationality, marital status, income, job information, employment status, educational background, years at a particular residence, and data of leaving last job—to mention only a few.

In certain situations respondents tend to exaggerate or minimize. Mechanics frequently describe themselves as machinists, bookkeepers become accountants, and time-study personnel become industrial engineers. Large corporations and small businesses are as guilty of perpetrating response errors as are individual respondents. Fear of material shortages, tax assessments, adverse "profits" publicity, and many other factors, often cause business firms to "color" their responses to questions. Such misrepresentation was discovered during World War II, when it became necessary for the War Production Board to determine true needs of certain businesses for "control" materials, such as rubber, oil, and coal.

To reduce response errors, checks and balances should be included in data collection methods and instrumentalities. Questionnaire data can be checked by follow-up interviews. Other useful cross-check sources of responses made in interviews, questionnaires, and other data-gathering methods and instruments might be: income tax reporting forms, Social Security office information and report forms, and files of other governmental agencies. In the interview, the response error includes a dimension due to the interviewing condition and the interviewer.

## Interviewing

Biased error can be introduced into the data through incomplete and misleading interviewing. Incomplete interviewing can occur when the interviewer does not have sufficient knowledge of the research to know all of the possible sources of pertinent data. To illustrate, suppose it is necessary to determine, by interviewing, the average yearly personal incomes of presidents of a selected sample of small business concerns. Unless the interviewer has some background in, possibly, investment banking and accounting, the interview session may omit discussions of many possible sources of personal income and result in a constant underestimation of the true income of each sample member. Therefore, it is important that interviewers be selected and trained carefully.

Another way to account for interviewing errors is through statistical design and analysis. To check whether interviewer bias is occurring, an appropriate factorial design can be constructed, and the analysis of variance treatment of the data and conditions involved can be employed. Such an analysis would show whether some or all interviewers introduce bias, and to what degree they supply such error.

### Observing

Biased error may be introduced by certain habits, or practices, of the observer. A study of a statistical quality control operation showed that there were three main sources of observer bias present: (1) even values were favored when the measuring instrument was scaled in units of "2," (2) readings were "centered," no values were reported below a "lower limit" and none above an "upper limit," although such values actually existed, and (3) different standards of "defectiveness" were employed from one random sample to another (inconsistent quality standard).[4]

Where observations must be made of groups, two or three observers should be used. This approach provides a means of determining the reliability of the data, and any observer bias that might be present. Correlation, and analysis of covariance are statistical techniques that can be employed to determine such factors.

### Measuring Instruments and Techniques

Another source of error arises from the measuring instrument and/or the observational techniques employed. In mechanical instruments, calibration may be poor, points of reference inaccurately placed, or the instrument may be affected by heat, light, magnetism, electricity, or any number of physical forces.

Tests, questionnaires, and scales must be carefully prepared. The language employed in the items composing such instruments frequently is the source of biased error. Emotional content, or ambiguity, might lead respondents to an answer. For example, in asking, "Do you agree with the useless spending for athletic programs by the Board of Education?", the question bids for a "no" response, because if the respondent answers "yes," he admits to approving "useless spending." In order to avoid this source of bias, it is necessary to design tests, questionnaires, and scales carefully. This important topic is covered further under "instrumentalities" in Chapter 6.

### Processing of Data

One of the chief sources of biased error occurs in the processing of data. Two phases of data processing significantly affect the results: (1) preparation of the data for observation, and (2) data tabulation and computation.

Data obtained from samples may be influenced by the way materials are processed before measurements are made. Generally, these processes include: handling, transporting, and treating the data. These operations can significantly affect the measurement of a characteristic to be estimated from a sample. Knowing these facts, every effort must be made to standardize these processes. Standardizing the handling, transporting, and treatment of the data should result in producing measurements—obtained at different times by different persons—more consistent, and thus more comparable, than they might otherwise be.

To avoid, or minimize, the second type of error, that which is associated with the operations of tabulation and computation, it is necessary to create cross-checks throughout each of the respective processes. Tabulation covers enumerating, categorizing, and recording the data. Cross-checks in tabulation may be provided by: (1) having the same data tabulated by more than one person, for two or more operations; (2) including intermediate checkpoints prior to final tabulation, and (3) including "checking" procedures in the tabulation programs of automated tabulating machines and equipment. Although the cross-check in (3) may prove to be more costly than a usual program, tabulation accuracy is of such importance that it is well worth the additional expenditure.

In computation processes, hand or machine placement of the decimal point is one of the chief sources of error. Mathematical "precision" and "accuracy" in performing the four fundamental operations of arithmetic is another. These points are treated in most elementary statistics books, and will not be discussed further here, except to point out that errors in computational processes may be reduced by including "proof systems," and other forms of cross-checks, or by employing a properly programed computer to process and analyze the data.

*Interpreting the Data*

Data interpretation is a process of integrating the results of the study into a meaning which "answers" the research question. This activity is accomplished by relating the data to the problem's historical trend and to fields that are complementary or supplementary to the problematic situation. The attempt to compose a general proposition, or theory, from the integration of specific data, provides the opportunity and means for biased error.

The biased error caused by the process of interpretation can be greatly reduced by planning the research inquiry on the basis of the analysis and interpretation of the data. In other words, true research inquiry cannot be planned without anticipating what should be done when the data are in, and what the possible interpretation of the findings will be. If those points are not considered, the relevancy or pertinency of the data cannot be determined. These considerations alone, however, cannot eliminate the total amount of biased error due to the interpretation of the data. The researcher's knowledge, imagination, and wisdom are elements of data interpretation which, while vital and creative, are unavoidable sources of bias. While impossible to eliminate, these biases can be controlled to a great extent by the researcher's early concern for framing the interpretation of the data.

The interpretation and analysis of the data will tend to vary with the type of research being performed. It is safe to say that there is greater difficulty with biased error due to data interpretation in Action, Descriptive, Field, and Historical research than in Experimental research. If the basic principles of data interpretation are observed, however, then biased error can be reduced in all types of research.

The process of interpretation is an attempt to find the broadest possible meaning of the research data, and the process is composed of two parts. First, there is the establishment of "continuity" by relating the data to the historical trend of the problem. For example, interpretation is employed in the transition from exploratory to experimental research. Second, interpretation of data leads to the development of "explanatory concepts," not only for the problematic situation, but for other fields or disciplines where such concepts might exist. Interpretation increases the meaning of findings of a given research by perceiving them not as bits of empirical information, but as a basic body of knowledge for developing a set of more abstract propositions. The aim and belief of this approach are that general concepts provide a better basis for prediction and discovery of theories than do specific orderings of particular data from certain studies. This dimension of the interpretation of data makes it all the more important for the researcher to attempt to counteract the possible sources of biased error within it.

*Unbiased Error Sources*

The three main sources of unbiased error are: (1) random sampling, (2) repeated measurements, and (3) "rounding-off" data. Mention of these sources of error is made only to emphasize their existence, and to provide the potential researcher with an awareness of them.

In random sampling we occasionally find a value that deviates widely from the population value which it purportedly estimates. It is a known fact, however, that the average of several random sample values will tend to fluctuate about the population value being estimated, and that the error involved will decrease as the size of the sample being employed is increased. Thus, random sampling is a source of unbiased error that tends to correct itself under the condition of adequate sample size. This condition emphasizes the need for determining "adequacy" of the size of the sample to be employed in a research project.

Some research efforts require *repeated* measurement(s) of the variable(s) under study. When this condition exists another source of unbiased error is present, the "repeated measurements" error. This type of error is not too serious, and may be accounted for by establishing a distribution of the values yielded by the research. From this distribution, "weights" can be calculated and the repeated measurements error can then be corrected. Where proper attention has been given to the methods and instrumentalities of data collection, the error of repeated measurements is inconsequential and tends to be self-corrective. The condition is not a serious one, but the researcher should be aware of all possible sources of unbiased error.

Measurements at best are approximations of the true dimension of the variable(s) under study. Some measurements are more precise and accurate than others, but still only approach the actual value(s) of the variable(s) involved. In view of this fact, and because of the limitations of calculating methods and computing instruments, researchers frequently "round-off" data values. This rounding-off procedure provides another source of unbiased error.

The source of error due to "rounding" is not a serious one, if the researcher provides for precision and accuracy of the data beyond the needs of the research. For example, when "units" precision and accuracy is necessary for the research findings, but the measurement and computation is carried out to "tenths" precision and accuracy, any rounding employed throughout the procedures would yield a negligible error.

When the researcher is working with data that are not as precise and accurate as he would like, rounding must be done carefully. In fact, under such conditions, the researcher should avoid rounding off as much as possible. If rounding is required, it is best to make it as accurately compensatory as possible, that is, if one value is rounded to the next higher unit, the next case which demands rounding should be decreased to the next lower unit. By following this procedure the researcher does not control the source of error, but enters an effect which tends to keep the error to a minimum. Still, we must re-emphasize rounding-off data should be avoided whenever possible, so that another possible source of unbiased error is nullified. With high speed computers and excellent automatic desk calculators as readily available as they are in the modern research center, the error of rounding can be avoided completely by employing "raw score" computational procedures, i.e., not bothering to round any of the data, thus performing calculations with the data in their original quantified forms.

OBSERVATIONAL METHODS

*Methods* of data collection are differentiated from *conditions* of data collection on the basis of *collection procedures*, as opposed to *manipulating, analyzing, summarizing*, and *generalizing* procedures.

Whether the type of research is action, descriptive, experimental, field, or historical, the methods of making observations (methods of data collection), can be classified into four general categories:

1. Observations made under actual, or real, conditions.
2. Observations made under artificial, or arbitrarily created, conditions.
3. Interviewing methods.
4. Correspondence methods, including letters and mailed questionnaires.

Of these four, the most desirable method is that of "observation by the researcher under actual, or real, conditions." Frequently the problematic situation is such that observations must be made under artificial or arbitrarily created conditions. This situation implies a laboratory setting, which though not as desirable as observation under actual conditions, can through careful consideration and an accounting of the controlled environment and variables, result in good data collection procedures. The interview method is the next most desirable, and although the data are being received through the mental screening processes of the respondent, an alert interviewer should be able to avoid many possible misunderstandings and misinterpretations. The correspondence method reaches more individuals in a given length of time for a given amount of money, but is the least desirable of the four procedures. There is greater room for misinterpretation and misunderstanding by both the respondent and the researcher in this method than in any of the other three.

The success of any data collection method depends greatly upon the ability of the researcher. Thus, it is important that the researcher understand what is meant by "observation" and "interview." An excellent explanation of "observation" is made by J. F. Rummel,[5] thus a summary of his principles is presented here.

*Summary of Rummel's Principles of Observation*

1. Obtain prior knowledge of what to observe. If the researcher knows what specific things he is to look for, he will observe and remember the significant details.

2. Examine general and specific objectives of the research problem to determine what to observe. Many suggestions for observations may be obtained from previous related studies.

3. Devise a method of recording results. Standardized methods of recording save time and help make for accuracy. For example, relatively complete check lists, designed to keep the amount of writing to a minimum, can be used at the time of observation, or soon thereafter.

4. Establish and define the various levels of proficiency, categories, or ratings to be used. When it is necessary to make qualitative observations and interpretations at the same time, use a two-way table, with kinds of behavior on one axis and qualitative ratings on the other. The researcher can easily record data that would otherwise be difficult to handle. This method is especially important where two or more observers are collecting the data.

5. Observe carefully and critically. Determine what to observe and record, then concentrate on specifics from the beginning of the observation.

6. Rate specific phenomena independently. Each qualitative value should be rated independently of others by use of a well-defined rating scale. This approach will help to reduce the halo effect.

7. Become well acquainted with the recording instrument and the procedures in its use prior to making observations. Preliminary training conferences and discussions for those who are to use the instrument will increase the reliability and authenticity of the data.

These basic principles make it clear that observation is specific in nature. It is systematic in its control of setting, recording, and checking of results. Finally, *good observation demands expert personnel.*

The *interview method* depends upon the ability of two or more persons to communicate well. It is a face-to-face relationship in which one participant seeks information from the other(s). The interview method has a definite objective, hence a certain functional unity. The interview method can be used for fact finding, and to determine attitudes, beliefs, and opinions of respondents. It should not be used to obtain information about a situation which has been factually reported, or authentically documented.

Rummel, in his discussion of basic guides to the interview, advises the following procedures which we present in summary form:[6]

*Summary of Rummel's Guides to Good Interviewing*

1. Determine who is to be interviewed. Select an adequate number of interviewees who have the information sought by the research. These individuals must be chosen with care, and must be representative of the group being studied.

2. Make preliminary arrangements for the interview. The time and place of the interview should be definite. The atmosphere should be one of privacy and comfort, and be conducive to soliciting the interviewee's responses.

3. Determine the plan of the interview and questions to be asked. In addition to having his problem well formulated, and a schedule of questions prepared, the researcher should know the objectives of the interview and what information, attitudes, motivations, and actions to solicit.

4. Conduct a preliminary tryout of the interview plan. The researcher should try out his interview plan with persons not in the interviewing sample. This activity will improve his techniques, reduce ambiguity or misunderstanding of the questions, and give an indication of the kind of responses and experiences awaiting him.

5. Become familiar with various interviewing processes and techniques. Three major techniques of interviewing are: (a) creating a friendly atmosphere, (b) asking questions, and (c) obtaining responses.

Use care in getting a cordial setting for the interview. Try to establish a sincere relationship of friendliness and mutual confidence. Link the topic of the inquiry to the interests of the person. Avoid making it an oral questionnaire.

Ask questions first which are "easy" and help establish confidence. Emotionally colored ones, not apt to be answered easily, should be left until the end of the interview when the interviewee might be more willing to answer. Be straight-forward and frank rather than shrewd and clever.

To facilitate responses, role play the interviewee. Direct him through each question, and consider only one at a time, allowing him free expression and taking careful note of everything about him as he answers. Avoid cues to answers. Keep control of the interview without being domineering, and listen carefully for casual remarks that might be revealing. Do not portray surprise, shock, or emotional tensions at the disclosures. Be professional and friendly, but avoid sentimentality or antipathy.

6. Check the accuracy and reliability of the information obtained. Errors in response might occur as a result of sight and hearing defects, or because of the duration of time of the interview. People tend to make loose statements and practice deceit; learn to separate truth from falsehood, fact from opinion. Constantly check yourself to see if you are causing colored responses.

7. Make a written record of the interview as soon as possible. Whenever notes are taken during the course of an interview, a certain skill is essential so that the interview is accurately recorded. It is better to get responses without the use of pencil and paper than to get no responses at all. Record data as soon as possible after an interview in which notes were not taken.

Develop an interview schedule precoded in such a way that the interviewer can check the code that comes closest to the interviewee's response. Check the schedule soon after the interview to be sure the entries are correct.

The following errors often occur in reporting interviews: (1) the error of *recognition*—failing to recognize, or overlooking, or minimizing significant facts; (2) the error of *omission*—omitting some facts, expressions, or experiences that are significant (this error is more often made in note taking than in the coded or mechanically recorded reports); (3) the error of *addition*—elaborating on, or exaggerating the respondent's remarks when the report is written from memory; (4) the error of *substitution*—the interviewer does not recall exactly what was said and substitutes words having different connotations than the ones used by the respondent; (5) the error of *transposition*—this error occurs when the interviewer does not recall the proper sequence of events or the proper relation of facts to each other.

These basic guides to the interview method of collecting data demonstrate that the method depends greatly upon the interviewer's abilities to establish rapport, make judgments, constantly analyze the situation, and report accurately. *The interview method requires trained personnel*, and the expert researcher will employ it only if he himself is trained, or can get experienced interviewers.

*Correspondence*

*Correspondence, the last method listed,* involves the use of personal letters and questionnaires. Since the topic of questionnaires will be discussed at length under the category of the instrumentalities of data collection, our remarks pertaining to the instrument at this point are limited to the fact that the primary use of the questionnaire in the correspondence method is in conducting follow-up studies, opinion polls, or attitudinal inquiries.

The correspondence method is a popular one, but has frequently been misused. Such misapplications as requesting information which is available in other more reliable sources, failing to motivate the respondent, and requesting too much information for the amount of time and space in which to answer, may be cited. Coupled often times with poor letter and questionnaire construction, the correspondence method of collecting data is probably the most overworked and poorly productive method of the four procedures listed. It may be the only method available, however, and therefore is a vitally necessary and useful technique. This data collection method, properly applied, is demonstrated in the modified general model discussed in Chapter 10.

*Chapter 5—References*
See Bibliography: 13, 14, 18, 25, 61, 75, 81, 82, 83, 102, 124, 135, 137, 139, 148, 150, 151, 188, 196; 54a, 57a, 61a, 63a, 88a, 92a, 101a, 106a.

# Data Collection—Instrumentalities

THE BASIC PHASES of any method of inquiry are highly interrelated, and the consideration of one phase to the exclusion of the others is impossible. Accordingly, the method of inquiry associated with the general model of educational research is no exception and thus the instrumentalities of data collection rely upon the problematic situation, the hypotheses, the universe, the sample, the type of data being collected, and the possible conclusions to be drawn from the research effort.

In the planning stages of an inquiry the researcher investigates the historical trend of the problematic situation. Frequently his investigations uncover existing data-gathering instruments that have been successfully employed in past research efforts directly related to the problem under study. When this situation occurs, construction of an instrument is unnecessary.

Various types of data-gathering instruments published by commercial establishments are readily available in almost any quantity.[1] Other data-gathering instruments have been published and are described only in professional journals. Although these instruments might be only partially validated and standardized, they are frequently worthy of application to a particular type of research problem. The researcher should therefore be equipped to evaluate data-gathering instruments.

There are many types of data-gathering instruments, each type particularly appropriate for certain kinds of research problems and data. Each kind, or type, can be evaluated in terms of four criteria: (1) the reliability of the instrument, (2) the validity of it, (3) its objectivity (in terms of "scoring"), and (4) its capability to discriminate between subjects. In the selection of available instruments, or in the construction of new ones, the researcher should always be concerned with the *reliability, validity, objectivity*, and *discriminatory* powers of the instrumentality under consideration. A good data-gathering instrument should: (a) measure consistently over repeated trials (reliability), (b) measure what it purports to measure (validity), (c) furnish data that are capable of consistent evaluation and interpretation by more than one individual (objectivity) and, (d) differentiate between subjects in terms of the data produced, so that the subjects may be classified easily and consistently by more than one individual.

## RELIABILITY

Although the reliability of a data-gathering instrument is fundamentally concerned with the consistency of data produced by repeated applications of the instrument, the purpose underlying the collection of the data also plays an important part in determining the reliability of the instrument. In other words, the reliability concept differs with the purpose for which the data-gathering instrument is being used. For example, the consistency of measuring instruments used in a physics experiment being conducted in a laboratory should be higher than those of instruments used in behavioral science research where variations in time of administration, in subjects, and in a multitude of other possible effects would have bearing on the data-gathering situation.

The concept of instrument reliability in behavioral science research depends upon fluctuations in performances during (a) a period of time, (b) a sample of test tasks, or (c) both. These fluctuations are expressed by three coefficients: (1) the coefficient of equivalence; (2) the coefficient of stability; and (3) the coefficient of equivalence and stability, respectively. The aforementioned coefficients are described concisely in the following definitions:

(1) *The coefficient of equivalence.* The coefficient of equivalence shows the extent to which scores on two forms of the same test fluctuate when administered at one sitting. It shows how the individual's performance fluctuates when he is measured on two different samples of the same behavior. If the individual's accomplishment on one form of a test is similar to his performance on another, the test is reliable.

The coefficient of equivalence is frequently calculated by using what is known as the split-half method, in which the individual's success on odd-numbered items of a test is correlated with his success on the even-numbered items of the same test.... Inasmuch as one half of a test is correlated with the other half, it is necessary, when using this procedure, to determine by the Spearman–Brown formula the reliability of the entire test.... Best results are obtained from the Spearman–Brown formula if the means and standard deviations of the two halves are approximately equal.... Similarly, the halves should also be comparable with respect to content and difficulty of test material.

A variation of the split-half method is the *parallel-split* method. When using this procedure the investigator makes no assumptions regarding the equivalence of odd and even-numbered items but empirically determines the comparability of the two samples of behavior. A number of test papers are examined to determine the number of persons passing each item. The items are then classified into two groups in such a way that the two halves are approximately equal in content and difficulty. Another group of papers is then scored on the two half-tests and the appropriate formulas are applied. The Kuder–Richardson formula and its variants provide dependable estimates of test reliability when the *parallel-split* procedure has been arranged.... This is a method of "rational equivalence," which is basically a measure of internal consistency in items. The formula takes into account the intercorrelation of the test items.

(2) *The coefficient of stability.* The coefficient of stability provides an estimate of the degree to which an individual's score varies in the case of identical sets of test items during a time period. These estimates of reliability tend to vary inversely with time intervals.

(3) *The coefficient of equivalence and stability.* The coefficient of equivalence and stability.... shows the extent to which an individual is consistent in his performance on two comparable forms of a test over a period of time. Reliability is estimated by what is called the *delayed parallel-test* method. The coefficient reflects both the fluctuations in performance of the individual and his choice of specific items of the test. Two forms, comparable in difficulty and content, are administered to the same persons on two different occasions. By correlating the two sets of scores we arrive at a coefficient.[2]

Needs of the research indicate which of the three coefficients should be applied. If a speed test is administered, the coefficient of equivalence would be used only if parallel test forms are administered immediately. Thus, the

Kuder–Richardson formula and the "split-half" method should not be used in calculating the reliability of speed tests.

Where fluctuations from day to day provide the source of difficulty concerning consistency, the coefficient of stability is applicable. If the research involves the reliability of intelligence and aptitude tests, wherein the content requires immediate reactions to problem situations which are considered "environment free," either the coefficient of equivalence and stability or the coefficient of stability may be used.

## DETERMINING RELIABILITY OF TESTS

We now discuss factors impinging upon reliability in testing situations. Since the reliability of the test depends upon the reliability of the test items, each item should be composed only after it has been tried out on a sample of subjects as similar as possible to those for whom the test is intended. This phase of test construction should be conducted along rigorous lines. It is most important that the test question or item be able to discriminate between high ability and low ability students. If the researcher can successfully frame a question which causes wide variability among the scores of the examinees, where the good students obtain high scores, and the poor students, low scores, the item is probably a reliable one.

Beyond such factors as item construction, editing and revision of items, consideration of item difficulty, and item discrimination power, there are other factors to consider in the construction of a reliable test. The length of the test, that is, the number of items included in the test, the range of difficulty of the test items, the level of ability for which the test is being devised, the format of the instrument, the time limits for certain types of timed instruments, all affect test reliability and must be considered in the construction of the instrumentality.

It is generally agreed that longer tests are more reliable than shorter ones, if they contain items of equal difficulty. Longer tests decrease the opportunity for guessing, and provide a greater opportunity for measuring the subject's true ability over a wider range of the test topic. In other words, a test of fifteen items will not be as reliable as one containing thirty items, providing the items on each test are of equal caliber.

The range of difficulty of test items has a decided effect on the reliability of the instrument. Items should be neither too difficult, nor too easy. A suitable range of difficulty, determined by past experience, pilot studies, or trial runs, must be provided if the reliability of the instrument is to be preserved. Closely related to the "difficulty" factor is the level of ability of the group for which the test is being constructed. The decision of "too difficult" or "too easy" concerning a test item is mainly a function of the ability of the group for which it is being devised, i.e., a highly reliable item for one group could prove to be highly unreliable for another.

The format of a test affects its difficulty and, therefore the instrument's reliability. The format of a reliable test depends greatly upon clear directions, legibility, attractiveness, and the arrangement of items according to their difficulty. The grouping or "bunching" of items of high difficulty tends to decrease the reliability of a test. The format which seems to provide the best opportunity for high reliability is one which arranges test items in ascending order of difficulty. This statement should not be interpreted to mean that the easiest item must be first and the most difficult one last on the instrument. It can be interpreted to mean, however, that in a ten-question test, for example, that the easiest item should be included somewhere in the first three and the most difficult one somewhere in the last three.

Any timed test should be put to a thorough trial to determine precise time limits, as opposed to rough estimates by the test constructor. Time limits on items must be carefully determined if the reliability of the instrument is to be kept high.

RELIABILITY OF QUESTIONNAIRES

To this point, the discussion has been concerned only with the reliability of tests. The reliability of questionnaires, scales, and other types of rating techniques is also a problem frequently confronted by the researcher.

The reliability of the questionnaire depends upon the length of the instrument, the subject, the wording of items, the format, and how the instrument motivates the respondent. Pilot studies, trial runs, and precautionary methods of construction based upon factors affecting questionnaire reliability are courses of action available to the researcher who wishes to construct a reliable questionnaire. Best discusses the characteristics of a reliable questionnaire, which we shall present in summary form.[3]

*Summary of Best's Characteristics of a Good Questionnaire*

1. It deals with a significant topic. The significance should be clearly stated in the questionnaire or in the letter that accompanies it.

2. It seeks only that information which cannot be obtained from more factual sources (school records, etc.).

3. It is as short as possible, and requests only essential data.

4. It is arranged efficiently, and is clearly duplicated or printed.

5. Directions are clear and complete; important terms are defined; each question deals with a single idea; categories provide for unambiguous responses.

6. The questions are objective with no hint of desired responses.

7. Questions are presented in good psychological order, proceeding from general to more specific responses. Embarrassing questions should be avoided.

8. It is easy to tabulate and interpret the data yield.

These remarks conclude our treatment of the reliability of a questionnaire. Readers desiring further information on this topic may consult references listed at the end of this chapter.

RELIABILITY OF RATING METHODS

The reliability of rating methods is most frequently determined by computing intercorrelations among ratings made by a "jury" or "panel" of persons considered to be experts in the field that is being rated. For example, if the Thurstone Technique of scaled values or the Lickert Method of Summated Ratings are to be employed in rating a particular field, they can be submitted to a panel of "judges" for a trial test. Items that the judges rated approximately the same would be considered the "consistent" ones in the field. If a new rating scale is constructed and includes only those items which were previously determined to be "consistent," the new instrument is considered to be reliable. An intercorrelation of the judges' ratings of the "new" instrument should tend to be high, i.e., in the direction of $r = +1.00$, where $r$ denotes the Pearson product-moment correlation coefficient.

There are other means of establishing the reliability of a rating scale; for example, determining the "norms" of items by "test runs" on samples similar to that to be used in the study, or employing standardized instruments with reliability established on the basis of the population which has employed the instrument. These methods are adequate, but the "jury" or "panel" method is easier to employ in most cases, with the added prestige of experts having been involved in the construction of the scale.

## VALIDITY

Some measurement experts feel that validity is the most important characteristic of a data-gathering instrument. This attitude is based upon the judgment that unless the test, questionnaire, scale, or whatever instrument is being used, is valid, it serves no useful purpose. The validity of a data-gathering instrument depends upon how effectively the instrument measures what it purports to measure. It must satisfy the purpose the user had in mind. Validity, then, is a specific rather than a general criterion of a data-gathering instrument. Data-gathering instruments cannot be completely described as valid in general terms, but only in connection with intended use on a population of a particular maturity, level of ability, and experiential background.

Validity can be defined basically in three different ways. First, *logical validity* implies that the data-gathering instrument measures what it is designed to measure, or is specifically related to the characteristic for which it was designed. Errors frequently are made in determining this type of validity. For example, a test designed to measure reading comprehension of high school seniors cannot be considered a highly valid instrument for testing the reading comprehension of high school freshmen, nor would it be highly valid for judging the reading habits of high school seniors. Note that a change in the group or a moderate change in the field affects the validity of the instrument.

Second, a data-gathering instrument will have high *empirical validity* if it successfully predicts or diagnoses performance or whatever characteristic it is intended to measure. For instance, if the results yielded by a particular rating scale, questionnaire, or test are highly correlated with successful on-the-job performance of clerk-typists, the instrument can be considered highly valid for predicting that performance. If the results yielded by an instrument are highly correlated with certain classifications of emotional disorders suffered by particular types of patients in a mental hospital, it can be considered a highly valid instrument for diagnosing those disorders.

Third, the *comparison validity* of a data-gathering instrument is determined by comparing the instrument with others of a similar nature which have established validity ratings. If the results yielded by a newly developed instrument are highly correlated with those of an instrument of known validity, the validity of the new instrument can be determined.

The comparison method of determining validity is very helpful in those cases where the characteristics being measured are not clearly delineated or defined. For example, the validation of an intelligence test is difficult because no adequate criterion of "intelligence" actually exists. If a "new" intelligence test is administered to elements of the same population as that of an intelligence test of established validity, and if the results are highly correlated with those of the "known" instrument, the validity of the new instrument can be determined.

When the validity of a newly developed instrument is to be determined by the comparison method, the "new" one should be attempting to measure the same thing under the same conditions as the criterion instrument. For example, if the *criterion* instrument was a test designed for measuring mechanical and numerical aptitudes of 12- to 14-year-old *boys* and the *new* instrument was designed to measure these aptitudes in 12- to 14-year-old *girls*, the test measuring the boys' aptitudes *could not* be used as the criterion for establishing the new instrument's validity by comparison.

DESIGNING VALID INSTRUMENTS

The crucial problem in validating data-gathering instruments is that of obtaining satisfactory and adequate criteria. In general, a valid instrument can be constructed if the following points are kept in mind:

1. For what purpose (or purposes) is the data-gathering instrument being designed (purpose)?

2. For whom is the instrument being designed (population)?

3. Under what conditions can the instrument be administered (experiential background of population)?

Each data-gathering instrument mainly constitutes its own definition of its validity. If the instrument constructor keeps in mind the three points listed above, he can establish good criteria of validity for the instrumentality being developed. The criteria chosen on these bases will also be in keeping with the purpose of the research effort.

The discussion presented here does not exhaust the topic of validity. There are many other aspects of it. The material covered here includes only the basic notions or fundamentals of the concept. Readers desiring a more detailed treatment may consult the references found at the end of this chapter.

OBJECTIVITY

A data-gathering instrument is considered to be objective if the personal judgments or individuals' ratings, classifications, or scorings of it are eliminated.

Objectivity in scoring an instrument depends greatly upon the objectivity of the items composing the test. If more than one interpretation of an answer is possible, the item is not an objective one. If the item is free of ambiguity, and is worded so that only one answer satisfies it, then it is considered to be objective.

The advantage of employing objective items in an instrument is that, with the exception of chance errors, there should be no variation in the scoring of the results by different persons, or by the same person on different occasions. Ambiguity in test items should be determined through "trial runs" of the item on appropriate populations. This approach makes it possible to determine if the item under study is capable of attaining high objectivity in both scoring and meaning.

The objectivity of a questionnaire differs slightly from test objectivity. Questionnaire objectivity is based upon the extent to which respondents agree upon what facts are sought. Where questions are of a personal nature, responses tend to be unique, and agreement among respondents should not be expected. In those cases where items require expression of opinion or judgment expressed in rankings or ratings, the extent of agreement of individual responses can be checked. A method which is frequently used to determine the extent of inter-agreement of individuals on items that require ranking is that of the "rank" correlation coefficient $\rho_s$ (see Chapter 20).

Questionnaire objectivity may also be determined on the basis of the extent of agreement of group with group. In composite responses (group), however, individual variations in one direction may be offset by other individual variations in the opposite direction. Thus, the average interagreement of groups is usually closer than the inter-agreement of individual with individual. In determining questionnaire objectivity it is assumed that individuals are using similar standards in objectively deriving opinions.

The objectivity of rating scales is more easily insured than that of questionnaires and tests because the traits, characteristics, or skills to be rated are described in such a manner that each rater knows what they include and exclude. Raters also profit by performing the rating under supervision. Hence, variability in opinion tends to be reduced. By the same token, objectivity in observational methods is increased through the training of observers to differentiate qualities or distinctive features in the observational situation.

A situation similar to that of adequacy of sample size prevails in the case of objectivity. The objectivity of an item or an instrument cannot be determined on the basis of the performance score of one individual on one occasion. In general, the greater the number of different occasions, the greater the confidence in the objectivity determined for the item or instrument in question.

DISCRIMINATION

The basic purpose of employing a research instrument is to place or categorize individuals along a defined scale in accordance with differences in the amount of the characteristic under study which they possess. The instrument which can successfully fulfil this function is said to have "high discriminative power." The discriminative power of an instrument depends greatly upon the reliability and validity of the instrument. In other words, the characteristic of discrimination is more apt to exist in a valid and reliable instrument than in one which is not.

The theory underlying the discrimination power of test items is based on the belief that a different quality or magnitude of response should be expected from different individuals or groups of the population under study. For example, pupils of superior ability should answer a difficult item correctly more frequently than inferior pupils. A procedure for determining the discriminatory power of a test item is illustrated by a modified example taken from Green, Jorgensen, and Gerberich:

> An experimental test was given to a class of 100 pupils having the normal range of ability in the subject. The tests were corrected and scored. On the basis of these scores, the pupils were divided into three groups.
>
> The 27 per cent of the pupils making the highest scores constituted the superior group; the 27 per cent making the lowest scores formed the inferior group. The 46 per cent of the class in the middle were not considered in computing the index of discrimination. The use of the 27 per cent comprising each of the extremes followed a proposal made by Kelley and further exploited by Flanagan [John C. Flanagan, "General Considerations in the Selection of Test Items and a Short Method of Estimating the Product-Moment Coefficient from the Data at the Tails of the Distribution," *Journal of Educational Psychology*, 30: 674–80 (December 1939)] for this purpose. The next step involves an item count for all of the items in the test showing the per cent of pupils in the superior group and the per cent of pupils in the inferior group that answered the respective items correctly. A *summary* of a brief *sampling* of items from a typical test is given in Table I.

Table I

Discriminative Power of Test Items in Per Cent of Success by
Superior and Inferior Groups

| Item | Superior Group High 27% | Inferior Group Low 27% | Index of Discrimination |
|------|------|------|------|
| 1 | 12 | 4 | .23 |
| 12 | 6 | 4 | .08 |
| 23 | 8 | 14 | −.13 |
| 44 | 10 | 18 | −.15 |
| 55 | 24 | 13 | .15 |
| 76 | 42 | 22 | .23 |
| 97 | 52 | 12 | .46 |
| 108 | 80 | 36 | .46 |
| 129 | 90 | 66 | .08 |
| 140 | 92 | 40 | .59 |

This table indicates that Item 1 was answered correctly by 12 per cent of the superior and 4 per cent of the inferior pupils. The index of discrimination can be found by the two × two table method of computing the $\phi$ (phi) coefficient (see Chapter 20). Item 1 thus shows great difficulty and a limited power to discriminate between good and poor achievement. The fact that the item is answered correctly by such a small proportion of all pupils (average 8 per cent) indicates that its difficulty is great. Item 44, however, is correctly answered by a smaller per cent of superior pupils than of inferior pupils. This is shown by the negative discrimination index of −.15. The negative value of the index indicates that the item is at fault or the wrong facts have been taught in this subject. The item should probably be eliminated from the test. Items 97, 108, and 140 with positive indexes of .46, .46, and .59 are probably good enough to retain in the test.

This method of determining the discriminative power of test items is widely used in the critical analysis of test items for standardized tests. . . .[4]

Discrimination is an important property of a data-gathering instrument. It is the basic reason for measurement and classification. The method of determining the discriminative power of test items varies from common sense to the method illustrated above.

The researcher must collect data that are valid, reliable, and objective, but these properties are comparatively meaningless if the data do not possess discriminative power. Data-gathering instruments must not only be reliable, valid and objective, but must have discriminative power if the research demands predictions and/or inferences of difference, magnitude, and relationship.

Throughout the discussion of data-gathering instrumentalities there has been no special effort made to discuss particular instrumentalities such as: intelligence tests, aptitude tests, performance tests, achievement tests, attitude scales, personality tests, inventories, schedules, psychological tests, rating scales, questionnaires, score cards, check lists, and other particular types of instruments. It was the aim of this section to discuss only the basic or fundamental elements of the instrumentalities of data collection. For those readers who desire more specific information about particular types of instrumentalities, the topics of reliability, validity, objectivity, and discrimination; and other related information, the references found at the end of this chapter are recommended as excellent resources.

It should also be noted that no special effort has been made to discuss particular statistical techniques at this point of the presentation. This material is presented in the statistics section (see Chapter 19).

*Chapter 6—References*
See Bibliography: 1, 2, 5, 6, 18, 23, 30, 43, 56, 70, 79, 80, 81, 82, 83, 86, 87, 89, 94, 102, 116, 120, 134, 139, 145, 146, 150, 151, 152, 153, 163, 166, 168, 169, 185, 187, 192, 200; 2a, 25a, 26a, 29a, 30a, 33a, 36a, 37a, 39a, 41a, 42a, 43a, 46a, 47a, 48a, 53a, 61a, 68a, 71a, 73a, 74a, 79a, 91a, 92a, 94a, 95a, 96a, 99a, 100a, 101a, 103a, 109a, 111a, 112a, 114a, 115a.

*Chapter Seven*

# Data Processing

THE SUGGESTED GENERAL MODEL of educational research has as its elements those components of inquiry that were found to be "common" to the approaches of certain leading philosophies. The purpose of the model is to provide a process or method of scientific inquiry into the complex problems of education that demand further study. The method of scientific inquiry associated with the model relies heavily on the processes of statistical inference and decision theory. Essentially, these processes are composed of four parts:

1. Research hypotheses are advanced and are mapped into operational hypotheses, which in turn, are translated into statistical hypotheses, or some other forms of mathematical statements, for the purpose of confirmation or rejection.

2. Empirical data are collected to determine whether the statistical hypotheses can be rejected or accepted; or if other processes of decision theory are employed, sets of logically constructed propositions are analyzed to determine *best* solutions to the problems under consideration.

3. A statistical inference model is chosen on the basis of the nature of the population, the manner of sampling, and the level of measurement employed in the data collection process; or if analytical procedures are to be employed, such as linear programing or theory of games, reference frames suitable to the analyses of the form (level of measurement) of the data are logically constructed.

4. The data are classified and analyzed by the appropriate procedures (statistical inference processes or analytic procedures of linear programing and/or theory of games), and a decision is made to reject, accept, or revise the advanced hypotheses, or propositions.

Whether statistical inference processes, or the analytic procedures associated with certain methods of decision theory, are to be employed in deriving a decision concerning the advanced hypotheses, the level of measurement of the data must always be considered. Ultimately, then, the level of measurement of the data is fundamental to the classification and analysis of data, i.e., to the data processing element of the research model. Put in another frame of reference, the processes of statistical inference and/or decision-theory are fundamental to the method of inquiry associated with the general educational research model. The primary determinant of the appropriate statistical inference or decision theory model to be employed is the level of measurement of the data to be processed. Since the classification and analysis of the data are actually carried out under the analytical procedures of the statistical inference or decision-theory model, the level of measurement, then, indirectly determines not only the appropriate method of classification but the analytical techniques to be employed in the research. Thus, the element of data processing in the general research model can be discussed, essentially, in terms of the level of measurement of the data involved in the research effort.

## LEVELS OF MEASUREMENT OF DATA IN EDUCATIONAL RESEARCH

There are four levels of measurement of data that are of primary interest in educational research. The four measurement levels in question are: (1) the nominal scale, (2) the ordinal scale, (3) the interval scale, and (4) the ratio-interval scale.

### The Nominal, or Categorical Scale

The nominal scale, or level of measurement of data, is considered to be the most basic type of measurement. It is used when classification of a characteristic is desired. When symbols are used to denote classifications, categories, or groups under which the characteristics of the study are placed, these symbols form a nominal scale of measurement. For example, the eye color of a certain group of people may be of interest in a particular research project. The researcher designates categories of eye color: blue, brown, black, and green. A survey of the group is made and tallies of the frequency of occurrence of each of the four eye colors are recorded under the appropriate category.

The nominal, or categorical, scale of measurement leads to a field of statistics known as *enumeration statistics*. Enumeration might also be thought of as counting. Counting is frequently thought to be a simple method for quantifying a variable. This is a fallacious notion. Counting requires the identification of items to be counted. Depending upon the situation, identification can be simple or quite complex. For example, suppose a questionnaire item seeks information concerning marital status by asking the respondent to check the "appropriate" category of "married" or "single." How does the processor identify the response of a check appearing next to the word "single," if an added note of "widow," or "widower," or "divorcee" has been inserted?

The counting process demands that the items being counted be carefully identified and then matched with elements of the real number system. There are many possible errors of "underenumeration" and "overenumeration," that is, failing to count an item that should be counted, and counting an item that should not be counted, or counting an item more than once, respectively. Difficulties in counting can only be controlled by concise definition of the conditions and characteristics of objects under study.

The nominal scale of measurement yields data that result from the partitioning of a given set, or class, into a set of mutually exclusive subclasses. In other words, a class is subdivided into a set of parts, and any item belonging to the original class can fall into one and only one of the subclasses. When classification is properly effected, it is impossible for an item to be counted under more than one subclass. To illustrate, if hair color (the original class) is partitioned into the three subclasses of blond, brunette, and redhead, it would be impossible to classify one person's hair coloring under more than one of the subclass designations, providing the permissible operations of scaling associated with the nominal scale of measurement are observed. The point to be made is that the only relationship involved in the nominal scale of measurement is that of equivalence.

In short, the members of a subclass must be equivalent in the characteristic being measured. Mathematically, the equivalence relation is: (a) reflexive: $X = X$ for all values of $X$; (b) symmetrical: if $X = Y$, then $Y = X$ and (c) transitive: if $X = Y$ and $Y = Z$, then $X = Z$.

*The Ordinal Scale*

The nominal scale of measurement of data involves only equivalence in the original class and demands that the subclasses of the original class be mutually exclusive (different from each other). If all of the subclasses of a scale are not only mutually exclusive, but stand in a "greater than" ($>$) or "less than" ($<$) relationship to each other, depending upon the point of reference, we have another scale of measurement known as the "ordinal scale." If it happens that the "greater than," "more preferred," "higher than," ($>$); or "less than," "less preferred," "smaller than," ($<$), relationships hold for some but not all of the equivalence classes (subclasses), then a *partially ordered* scale is formed.

The ordinal scale, by definition, differs from the nominal scale because it incorporates *not only the notion of equivalence; but also that of relative magnitude or degree*. There are further contrasts. The nominal scale must be reflexive ($X = X$ for all the values of $X$). The ordinal scale may be reflexive; but it includes the irreflexive property as well. It is not necessarily true that for any given $X$, that $X > X$, or that $X < X$. While the nominal scale is symmetrical (if $X = Y$, then $Y = X$), the ordinal scale is asymmetrical; because if $X > Y$, then $Y \not> X$, or if $X < Y$, then $Y \not< X$. Both the nominal and ordinal scales of measurement are transitive; for the nominal scale; if $X = Y$ and $Y = Z$, then $X = Z$; and for the ordinal scale; if $X > Y$, and $Y > Z$, then $X > Z$, or if $X < Y$ and $Y < Z$, then $X < Z$.

We might use as an example of the ordinal scale the system of academic rank employed by most universities, i.e., professor, associate professor, assistant professor, and instructor; or if we wish to change the point of reference: instructor, assistant professor, associate professor, and professor.

As another example of the ordinal scale of data, suppose that a data-gathering instrument instructs the respondent to "rank" each of four items under a question from 1 to 4. If the rank of 1 signifies "most desirable," and no two items are allowed the same ranking; then for a given question an item ranked 1 is more desirable than an item ranked 2 (i.e., $1 > 2$). Similarly, an item ranked 2 is more desirable than an item ranked 3 ($2 > 3$); and $3 > 4$. If we choose to change our point of reference, then an item ranked 4 is less desirable than an item ranked 3 (4 < 3). An item ranked 3 is less desirable than an item ranked 2, (3 < 2); and 2 < 1.

An important fact for the reader to remember at this point is that most of the data collected in behavioral science and educational research is either of the nominal or of the ordinal scale of measurement.

*The Interval Scale*

The interval scale of measurement incorporates all of the characteristics of the ordinal scale, i.e., *equivalence* and the relationships *"greater than"* and *"less than."* The interval scale has the added feature that the interval of distance between any two objects on the scale is constant and of known size. In a broader sense, the interval scale includes a unit of measurement which is common and constant, and hence assigns a real number to the interval formed by a pair of consecutively scaled objects in the ordered set of such objects. We emphasize that although the unit of measurement is common and constant, the length of the unit, and the original point of reference, or zero point, are arbitrary. In the interval scale of measurement, the ratio of any two intervals with a given zero point and unit of measurement on one scale will yield a value equal to that of a ratio of two equivalent intervals on another scale which measures the same thing as the first, but has a different zero point, and a different length of unit of measurement. To illustrate this point, and the general idea of the interval scale of measurement, we borrow from Siegel:

We measure temperature on an interval scale. In fact, two different scales—Centigrade and Fahrenheit—are commonly used. The unit of measurement and the zero point measuring temperature are arbitrary; they are different for the two scales. However, both scales contain the same amount and the same kind of information. This is the case because they are linearly related. That is, a reading on one scale can be transformed to the equivalent reading on the other by the linear transformation:

$$F = 9/5C + 32$$

Where

$$F = \text{number of degrees on Fahrenheit scale}$$
$$C = \text{number of degrees on Centigrade scale}$$

It can be shown that the ratios of temperature differences (intervals) are independent of the unit of measureme:t and of the zero point. For instance, "freezing" occurs at 0 degrees on the centigrade scale, and "boiling" occurs at 100 degrees. On the Fahrenheit scale, "freezing" occurs at 32 degrees and "boiling" at 212 degrees. Some other readings of the same temperature on the two scales are:

| Centigrade: | 0 | 10 | 30 | 100 |
|---|---|---|---|---|
| Fahrenheit: | 32 | 50 | 86 | 212 |

Notice that the ratio of the *differences* between temperature readings on one scale is equal to the ratio between the equivalent differences on the other scale. For example, on the centigrade scale the ratio of the differences between 30 and 10, and 10 and 0, is: $(30 - 10)/(10 - 0) = 2$. For the comparable readings on the Fahrenheit scale the ratio is: $(86 - 50)/(50 - 32) = 2$. The ratio is the same in both cases: 2. In an interval scale, in other words, the ratio of any two intervals is independent of the unit used and of the zero point, both of which are arbitrary.[1]

From Siegel's discussion it is apparent that the interval scale of measurement of data is different from the nominal and ordinal scale of measurement in some properties, and like them in other properties. A brief comparative analysis of the three scales is indicated.

The interval scale of measurement includes the property of equivalence as does the nominal scale, and it includes the properties of "greater than" and "less than" of the ordinal scale of measurement. It is different from the nominal and ordinal scales in the properties of: (a) presenting a defined unit of length as a standard, and (b) presenting an arbitrarily selected zero point.

The nominal scale of measurement yields information of an enumerative character, such as the "number of persons with blue eyes," and the "number of books with red covers." The information yielded by this scale is collective —a sum of elements. The ordinal scale of measurement yields information of a comparative character in terms of the characteristics themselves. That is, if a characteristic $A$ is approximately twice as long as a characteristic $B$, and $A$ and $B$ are each longer than $C$, we could if we so desire rank $A$ as 1, $B$ as 2, and $C$ as 3. What would happen if we dropped $B$ from consideration? Naturally, we would still rank $A$ as 1, but now $C$ would be ranked 2. Through our knowledge of the background of the situation we realize the ranking of 2 for $C$ is different than the rank of 2 accorded $B$, originally. This example shows that the ordinal scale of measurement orders data within a class, under a particular set of conditions. As such, it yields data that are capable of limited interpretation.

If, instead of having "ranked" $A$, $B$, and $C$, we had developed a measuring scale with a defined unit of length as a standard, we could compare $A$, $B$, and $C$ directly without defining the condition each time a different comparison was to be made. This latter condition is accomplished by employing the interval scale of measurement. It contains all the properties of the nominal and ordinal scales plus the property of isomorphism with the structure of arithmetic. That is, data yielded by the interval scale can be identified with numbers, and the operations of arithmetic can logically be performed to draw conclusions about the data. Thus, the interval scale of measurement is a "quantitative" scale in the true sense of the word.

### The Ratio-Interval Scale

We recall from earlier discussion that the selection of a zero point and a unit of measurement in the employment of the interval scale is arbitrary. Now, if the characteristic being investigated is of such a nature that the selection of a zero point is not arbitrary—weight for example—then a new scale of measurement is needed. *This new scale can allow an arbitrary unit of measurement, but not an arbitrary zero point. Such a scale is termed a ratio-interval scale.*

The ratio-interval scale contains all the properties of the interval scale, and beyond that is independent of the unit of measurement. To illustrate, suppose we weigh two different objects on a scale which measures in units of pounds only. The first object weighs 6 pounds, the second weighs 2 pounds. The ratio of the weight of the first to that of the second object is: $6/2 = 3$. Now, suppose the same two objects are weighed on a scale which measures in ounces only. The first object would weigh 96 ounces, the second object would weigh 32 ounces. The ratio of the weight of the first object to that of the second object is: $96/32 = 3$. If we were to weigh the same two objects on a scale which measured in units of grams, or drams, or tons, or any other unit for that matter, we would find that the ratio of the weight of the first object in a given unit to that of the second object expressed in the same unit would be 3. Thus, the ratio-interval scale of measurement features a true zero point and an arbitrary unit of measurement.

The ratio-interval scale is of interest only to the behavioral scientist if he wishes to make use of statistics which demand a true zero point. The geometric mean is such a statistic. This statistic finds application in particular types of time series analysis. Since the ratio-interval scale of measurement has limited application in the behavioral sciences and educational research, and space priorities preclude further treatment here, we refer the reader who is interested in further information concerning this topic to the references listed at the end of the chapter.

This discussion of the levels of measurement of data is necessary to understand those aspects of the scales which set limits and determine permissible operations for data processing in the inquiry (admissible operations). Since all of the scales of measurement are functions of rules under which some number, or symbol of value, is assigned to the observations, the resulting data must be related to some form of numerical structure. This condition being true, certain arithmetical operations and manipulations can be performed on the data. The operations and manipulations that are admissible depend upon the level of the scale of measurement. They prescribe the limits for the data processing phase of inquiry, and thus are of fundamental importance to the discussion of the data processing element of the suggested general model of educational research.

## LIMITATIONS AND USES OF SCALES OF MEASUREMENT IN DATA PROCESSING

In the case of nominal data, the essential operation is categorization, or classification. The nominal scale of classification can be represented by any convenient set of symbols. For this reason, mathematicians term this scale to be "unique up to a one-to-one transformation." Thus, the symbols chosen to identify the subclasses, or categories, may be interchanged, if the change is carried out consistently and over the total class. To illustrate, suppose that in a given year the teams of a particular football conference have agreed to have all "ends" wear uniform numbers in the "90's," all "tackles" wear uniform numbers in the "80's," and all "guards" wear numbers in the "70's," for easier and more immediate player identification by spectators. The following year, the conference officials decide that it would be better if all ends wore uniform numbers in the 80's, all tackles in the 70's, and all guards the 90's. The nominal scale is preserved because the exchange of numbers was carried out uniformly and consistently over the subclasses of the class of football players known as "linemen."

Thus, we see that in the nominal scale, the symbols designating subclasses may be interchanged without altering the essential data yielded by the scale. The only admissible analytic techniques for data yielded by the nominal scale are those statistics which would be unchanged by the type of transformation described earlier. Examples of such statistics are frequencies and counts. When these data are yielded by the research, proper null hypotheses regarding the distribution of them (the data) over the categories may be advanced and tested by statistical tests known as "nonparametric tests." Nonparametric tests are appropriate for nominal data because they analyze enumerative data (e.g., frequencies, "counts"). Such tests as "Chi Square" ($\chi^2$), Kolmogorov–Smirnov, and the Phi($\phi$) coefficient are good examples of the types of analytical techniques permissible for data yielded by the nominal scale of measurement. (See nonparametric statistics, Chapters 24, 25, and 26). In summary, then, data of the nominal scale can only be analyzed categorically through examination of frequencies, counts, and such which in turn can only be analyzed correctly by nonparametric statistical tests.

### Uses of the Ordinal Scale of Measurement

The ordinal scale of measurement permits the use of any symbols or numbers that preserve the ordering of the class. More specifically, it does not matter what symbols we assign to the sub-classes, or members within the sub-classes, as long as a higher number is assigned to the members of the class of the "greater than," or "more preferred" categories. Of course, it should be understood that a lower number could be assigned to the "more preferred" group, as long as such assignment is carried out consistently over the range of classes, and it is understood that the "more preferred" category is identified with a lower number. Thus, any transformation which does not affect the ordering of the classes is admissible because "it does not involve any loss of information" —the "more preferred" classes maintain their appropriate and same identification in the newly assigned symbol system.

Theoretically, the only admissible techniques for ordinal data are nonparametric ones. When data are in the form of ordinal scaling, null hypotheses can be tested by using the nonparametric statistical tests sometimes known as "ordinal" or "ranking" statistics (see chapter on non-parametric statistics and estimation).

The error of using parametric statistical tests on ordinal scale data results from the fact that ordinal data are erroneously considered to be on an interval scale of values, when actually they are categorical. That is, in the ranking of objects as 1, 2, or 3, some objects ranked 2 are closer to 1, and others of that class are closer to 3, but in the nonparametric analysis of the data this fact need not be taken into account, because the analysis is concerned with the category, or class, of 2 as related to the other categories, 1 and 3. When the data are analyzed by a parametrical statistical technique (in error), however, the distribution of the rankings within the respective intervals, and for that matter, the length of the intervals themselves, must be taken into account.

To be more specific, the parametric statistical tests employ "means," "standard deviations," and other related statistics that require treating the "rankings" as though they were measuring a precisely defined interval of a continuum of scores, and calculating these "parameters" (e.g., mean, or standard deviation) from them. The properties of the ordinal scale, however, are not isomorphic to those of an interval scale (how far the interval of rank 1, or that of 2, and so on, extends over the continuum of rankings, is not stipulated). The absence of this isomorphism shows that the calculation of "means," for example, is a liberty which the form of ordinal data does not permit. When parametric techniques are applied to the ordinal scale (which is an error), any decisions about the null hypotheses that have been advanced prior to the undertaking of the analysis are definitely in doubt.

### Uses of The Interval Scale

The admissible operations associated with the interval scale are those that preserve not only the order of the objects, but the relative differences between the objects. We use distances along a line to exemplify:

| $(X)$ | ı | ı | ı | ı | ı | ı | ı | ı |
|---|---|---|---|---|---|---|---|---|
| | 0 | (0.5) | 1 | (1.5) | 2 | (2.5) | 3 | (3.5) |

Scale A

| $(Y)$ | ı | ı | ı | ı | ı | ı | ı | ı |
|---|---|---|---|---|---|---|---|---|
| | 7 | (8) | 9 | (10) | 11 | (12) | 13 | (14) |

Scale B

On Scale A, the selection of the zero point is arbitrary, but the interval of 1 runs from (.5) to (1.5) and is a *fixed distance*. The interval of 2 runs from (1.5) to (2.5), is a *fixed distance* and is *equal to the distance* designating interval 1. In similar fashion each interval would have a fixed value and length, and the length would be equal to the length of each of the other intervals measured on that scale. Mathematically, the interval scale is "unique up to a linear transformation," which means that all the identifying characteristics of the interval scale may be maintained even though the original data of a given interval scale were transformed to a new interval scale by the formula: $Y = aX + b$. In this formula, $Y$ is the new value on the new interval scale. The positive constant $a$ multiplies each of the values of the original scale, $X$, and $b$ is a constant which has been added to each product $aX$ formed. To illustrate, Scale B has been formed by the transformation equation: $Y = 2X + 7$. For the arbitrarily selected zero point, we have: $Y = 2(0) + 7 = 7$; for $X = .5$, $Y = 2(.5) + 7 = 8$; for $X = 1$, $Y = 2(1) + 7 = 9$; for $X = 1.5$, $Y = 2(1.5) + 7 = 10$; and so on. Thus, the new scale ($Y$-form) has not affected the information yielded by the scale, because the order of the objects has been preserved (the object which was 2 becomes 11, and is still "greater than" the object

1 which becomes 9). Each *fixed interval* on the new scale ($Y$) designates a value which is consistently seven plus twice the original value ($X$). Thus, the information yielded by the original scale has not been affected by the application of the linear transformation: $Y = aX + b$.

The interval scale is seen to be a truly quantitative scale, and as such, all common parametric statistics (e.g., mean or standard deviation), and all common parametric statistical tests (e.g., *t*-test, or *F*-test) are applicable to data yielded by measurement carried out in it. Interval scale data should be analyzed by parametric tests, because under such conditions parametric tests are more "efficient" and "powerful" than the nonparametric tests. Either parametric or nonparametric tests *may* be used, however, on statistics yielded by interval scale measurement.

### Uses of the Ratio-Interval Scale

The ratio-interval scale has both a *true zero point*, and a common interval which is arbitrary. Information of the ratio scale is "unique up to multiplication by a positive constant." This statement means that the ratios between any two numbers are preserved when all of the values in the scale are multiplied by a positive constant. To illustrate, suppose the transformation $Y = 2X$ is employed; $X$ being the values on Scale A, and $Y$ the values on Scale B, shown below.

| ($X$) | | | | | | | |
|---|---|---|---|---|---|---|---|
| 0 | (0.5) | 1 | (1.5) | 2 | (2.5) | 3 | (3.5) |

Scale A

| ($Y$) | | | | | | | |
|---|---|---|---|---|---|---|---|
| 0 | (1) | 2 | (3) | 4 | (5) | 6 | (7) |

Scale B

The analysis is very similar to that associated with the interval scale. The order of the objects has been preserved, the true zero point has been preserved, and the interval is consistent and regular throughout.

Any statistical test, parametric or nonparametric, is permissible when data have been yielded by ratio-interval measurement. Parametric tests are preferred, however, because of their efficiency and power in comparison with nonparametric tests under these conditions of measurement.

*Chapter 7—References*

See Bibliography: 1, 2, 18, 35, 36, 63, 78, 82, 88, 100, 102, 118, 119, 124, 143, 150, 155, 160, 161, 162, 166, 170, 187, 196, 199; 2a, 3a, 4a, 5a, 36a, 49a, 71a, 87a, 115a, 119a.

# The Research Decision

THE PROCESS OF DRAWING a "probability conclusion," be it associated with
the suggested general model of educational research or an individual decision,
involves the same basic process. This process is called "inference."*

Much of man's life is devoted to making inferences. You are introduced to a
person. He has brown eyes, well-groomed hair, uses good grammar, and has
a pleasant voice. Depending in some part on your past experiences with persons
possessing the same features and characteristics, you might infer from these
data that you like (or dislike) the man.

Man's whole pattern of survival and progress depends upon inference of
some kind. The making of sound inferences, of arriving at "best" answers to
questions or, in a research sense, of rejecting false hypotheses and accepting
true ones, is vital to human progress.

## PREDICTION AND INFERENCE

The important activity of prediction, or prognostication, is mainly based
upon the process of inference. An example of this activity is the prediction
of weather events. The meteorologist analyzes pressure patterns, wind directions,
barometric tendencies, isobaric configurations, temperatures, dew point
temperatures, and precipitation patterns, makes an inference and then attempts
to predict the weather for a particular locality for a certain time period. A
simpler example is the prediction that man can be sure of two things in his
lifetime, death and taxes. From these examples, it is apparent that prediction
is basically an inference regarding the future.

### *"Sound" Inference*

Inferences regarding the future (predictions) are not the only ones that man
makes. Frequently it is necessary to infer events that have happened in the past.
When one reads a history book he infers that certain events actually happened
as described. Sometimes it is necessary to infer what is going on at the present
time in some other place. Military intelligence problems are good examples
of this application of inference. Intelligence personnel must often infer conditions
that exist in certain sectors of action that are not directly observable.

---

* An inductive logical process (e.g., statistical inference) produces a probability conclusion.
A deductive logical process (e.g., syllogistic reasoning) produces an irrefutable conclusion within
its defined frame of reference (universe of discourse).

The process of inference involves an aspect of correctness. In other words an inference can be a "good" one or a "bad" one. When we think of a "good" inference, we are not demanding that it be a "perfect" one, an inference in which no possible loopholes exist. Experience has taught that perfection in anything is rarely, if ever, obtained. There is no perfect cure for ills. When we purchase automobiles, television sets, radios, and refrigerators we do not expect them to be perfect. Similarly, there are no perfect solutions to our economic and political problems. Pursuing the same dialectic, a good inference is not a perfect one, but rather the best one available under the prevailing conditions.

A researcher cannot be condemned for making a wrong inference, providing he went about the inference-drawing process in the best possible way under the existing conditions. Wrong inferences, as well as good ones, help man to progress. The researcher's moral obligation is to attempt to make the best inferences (research decisions) possible, not necessarily perfect ones.

Looking for the *best available* (not the perfect) inference leads to the problem of inference evaluation. Obviously some inferences must be relatively bad and others relatively good. How do we decide whether an inference (decision) is good or bad?

*Inference Evaluation*

Inference can best be evaluated by considering the following phases of it: (1) beginnings, (2) ends, and (3) the manner of getting from beginnings to ends. This approach implies that an inference process (research decision) produced by the suggested general model for educational research can be evaluated by deciding what are its "beginnings," and its "ends"; ascertaining the amount of certainty which can be assigned to these aspects of the process; and then listing the relative values of the various ways (possible specific models) of getting from the beginnings to the ends.

The best research decision is made when valid and reliable data have been collected and analyzed. The evaluation of inference (research decision), then, must necessarily concern itself with the process by which valid and reliable data are collected and analyzed. This conclusion, in effect, means for us that inference evaluation becomes a focalized summary of the various elements of the suggested general model for educational research.

Beginnings of Inference

The "beginnings" of inference associated with the suggested general model include the following elements: (a) problem evaluation and formulation; (b) hypotheses, or general questions; and (c) the universe and the sample of the inquiry.

*Problem Evaluation and Formulation*

That part of the "beginning" phase of inference evaluation which deals with problem evaluation can be conducted by answering the following questions:

1. Has the true nature of the problematic situation been discovered?
2. Have the desired end objectives been determined?

3. Have the possible courses of action open to the attainment of the solution to the problem been specified?
4. Have the alternative methods of solution that are not feasible to the setting been eliminated?
5. Has the setting of the problematic situation been investigated thoroughly, that is, would a change of setting affect the possible approaches to the solution?

After these questions have been answered, the phase of inference dealing with problem formulation must be considered.

Adequate problem formulation depends upon the statement of the problem and the *definition* of the problem. The features of *problem statement* important to inference evaluation can be examined by posing the following questions:

1. Does the statement of the problem seem to be vague, or too broad in scope?
2. Is the statement of the problem too specific, or too localized?
3. Is the focus on a clearly defined objective, so that a definite conclusion is possible?
4. Does the statement of the problem avoid unscientific, argumentative, emotional language? Is it stated in simple terms?
5. Does the statement preserve a reasonable consistency with the body of prior knowledge available on the subject matter?

The *definition* of the problem, the last part of problem formulation, should be examined for:

1. The significance of the problem.
2. The definition of terms to be employed.
3. The underlying assumptions of the inquiry.
4. The limitations of the inquiry in terms of the depth of the investigation, the implications and the possible applications of the findings of the inquiry.

These considerations complete the initial phase of inference evaluation associated with the "beginnings" aspect of the general research model.

*Hypotheses or General Questions*
Another important part of inference evaluation deals with the hypotheses or "general questions" phase of the "beginnings" aspect. The evaluation at this point must take account of the following:

1. The hypothesis is simply a tentative conclusion, proposition, or a "hunch" which is to be tested.
2. The hypothesis gives direction and limit to the inquiry.
3. There is a hierarchy of hypotheses associated with the inquiry:
(a) The hypotheses of the inquiry, formulated on the basis of the problematic situation;
(b) The operational hypotheses that are based upon elements of the hypotheses of the inquiry, and that make the testing of the research hypotheses easier by providing for the collection of more tangible data than otherwise possible;

(c) The statistical hypotheses, which are mathematical statements of the operational hypotheses, and which make possible the employment of statistical inference in deciding whether to reject or accept them. Statistical hypotheses are statements of magnitude, difference, or relationship involving a statistic that can be reliably computed from the data of the sample, if the distribution of the statistic is known when the hypothesis is considered to be true. Statistical hypotheses are classified generally as null hypotheses and statistical alternative hypotheses. The null hypothesis is tested against the statistical alternative hypothesis. When the operational hypotheses are cast as the statistical alternative hypotheses, rejection of the null hypotheses permits acceptance of the operational hypotheses. Acceptance of the statistical alternative hypothesis, or hypotheses, permits the acceptance of the associated operational hypotheses. The hypotheses of the inquiry, in turn, depend upon the acceptance of the operational hypotheses, that is, the research hypothesis is accepted to the extent that the various operational hypotheses may be accepted.

4. When the hypothesis "spirit" is not present in an inquiry (exploration, survey, or descriptive study), the "general questions-to-be-answered" approach may be employed. Arbitrarily, this approach has been termed "non-hypothesized" inquiry. Evaluation of this type of inquiry is conducted by searching for: a clear and concise statement of the questions, the power of the questions to guide and bound the inquiry, their power to provide specific definition of the universe and the sample which determines pertinency of data; and, finally, their capability of indicating possible methods of collection and analysis of data.

When these steps have been thoroughly considered, the second part of the "beginnings" aspect of inference evaluation has been completed.

### The Universe and the Sample

The evaluation of the inference process must consider the universe and the sample. The population (universe) as the source of data for the inquiry is defined on the basis of the problematic situation and the hypotheses, or general questions, of the inquiry. Investigation to determine whether the population is finite or infinite, and whether the selection of a sample is necessary, is a fundamental step of inference evaluation. If a small finite population is under study and it is possible to employ all of its elements, a sample is unnecessary. If the population is large or infinite, a sample must be employed, and inferences about selected population parameters must be drawn from the data of the sample. The evaluation of such inferences depends in large part on: (1) how the sample was selected; (2) the representativeness of the sample; and (3) the adequacy of the sample. The "beginnings" aspect of inference evaluation in our model is completed with the consideration of these three points, and we are now ready to consider the "ends" aspect of the process.

### Ends

The "ends" of the inference process include the following elements of the general model: data collection, data processing, and the research decision (conclusions). Despite careful problem evaluation and formulation, clear statement of hypotheses, or general questions, and good definition of universe and sample, the procedures and techniques of data collection and data processing may lead to incorrect or poor conclusions concerning the subject of the inquiry.

## DATA COLLECTION

Inference evaluation must include three arbitrarily defined categories of data collection:

1. the conditions under which observations are to be made,
2. the methods, or procedures, of making observations, and
3. the instrumentalities of data collection.

These categories are arbitrarily defined, and are not mutually exclusive. They are but a means of approach to the area of data collection.

### Observational Conditions

Three observational conditions should be considered in connection with the "ends" aspect of inference evaluation.

(a) *The history of the problematic situation* provides the true meaning and general orientation of concepts involved in the problem. It is an internal and external consistency check on the subject of the inquiry.

(b) *The prediction of the best way the historical trend of the problem can serve the solving of the problem of the inquiry.* This prediction is based upon the researcher's "prior knowledge" of the problem. Prior knowledge is composed of specific knowledge of historic trends of the problem, and the interrelatedness of the problem with its setting and elements of other disciplines.

(c) *The reliability and validity of the data.* The reliability is determined by considering the consistency of the data as evidence for a solution to the problematic situation when the situation has repeated occurrence, or when similar situations have repeated occurrence. The validity of the data is determined by ascertaining their authenticity.

Observational conditions can be evaluated by:

1. Examining the historical trend of the problem, and asking: "What elements are important here? What elements found in the problem situation maintain consistency and authenticity throughout the historical trend of the problem, and at the same time are consistent and authentic within related disciplines?" Answers to these questions will determine if the inference has been drawn from pertinent data defined on the basis of the researcher's prior knowledge.

2. Re-examining the evaluation and formulation of the problem, the statement of the hypotheses (or general questions), the definition of the universe and the design of the sample, will determine if the inference has been drawn under adequate conditions of: what? when? where? who? why? and how?

3. Examining the availability of reliable and valid data will help in deciding if the inference is a good one (if reliable and valid data are readily available, it is

highly probable that the inference is a good one). Consideration of these points cover the "observable conditions" associated with data collection as they affect the "ends" aspect of inference evaluation.

*Methods of Making Observations*

Questions to be answered in evaluating the "methods" phase of the "ends" aspect of the inference process are:

(a) Was the researcher able to make personal observations of phenomena under actual or real conditions? If so, did he?

(b) If the methods of part (a) were not possible, was the researcher able to make personal observations of phenomena under artificial or arbitrarily created conditions? If so, did he?

(c) If the inquiry required interviewing, were the interviews conducted by trained personnel?

(d) If interviews were not possible, were mailed questionnaires employed to gather the data? Were the instrumentalities carefully constructed and tested before they were used?

In answering these general questions, certain specific questions are also answered. Some of the specific questions are:

(a) Did the researcher have prior knowledge of what he was to observe? If he did, the data should reflect a refinement of observational method which would otherwise not be present.

(b) Were the general and specific objectives of the research problem stated clearly, before the data were observed?

(c) Were the methods of recording results free of as much bias and error as possible?

(d) Were the various ratings, categories, and levels of proficiency that were employed clearly established and defined?

(e) Were all of the observations made equally carefully and critically?

(f) Were the phenomena under observation the only items to enter into the ratings?

(g) If instruments were used, was the researcher well acquainted with their operation and function?

(h) If interviews were called for, how did the researcher determine who was to be interviewed?

(i) Were proper arrangements made for the best atmosphere in which to conduct the interview?

(j) Was the plan of the interview carefully prepared so that the objectives of the interview were best realized?

(k) Was a pilot study effected to improve techniques and reduce ambiguities?

(l) Were the best interviewing processes and techniques employed for the circumstances and setting of the inquiry?

(m) Did the interviewer check the accuracy and reliability of the information obtained? Were there cross-checks in the interviewing schedule?

(n) Was a written record of the interview made at the time of the interview, or at least as soon thereafter as possible?

Upon completing the answers to these questions, the process of inference evaluation has been completed through the "conditions" and "methods" phases of the "ends" aspect of inference.

INSTRUMENTALITIES OF DATA COLLECTION

The "ends" aspect of inference evaluation is also concerned with the instrumentalities of data collection. In conducting the evaluation of this phase, there are four basic properties of instrumentalities to be considered: (a) reliability, (b) validity, (c) objectivity, and (d) discriminating power. The *reliability* of a data-gathering instrument is fundamentally concerned with the consistency of data yielded by repeated applications of the instrument. The reliability concept differs with the purpose for which the data-gathering instrument is to be used. The error in the consistency of measuring instruments used in a laboratory setting might be relatively small. This situation is in contrast to the instruments used in behavioral (educational) research where the situation is highly variable.

Any evaluation of instrument reliability in educational research must take into account fluctuations in performance during: (1) a period of time, (2) a sample of test tasks, or (3) both. Items affecting instrument reliability, such as length, difficulty, and format must be taken into account to complete this phase of the inference evaluation.

The validity of a data-gathering instrument depends upon how effectively, or efficiently, the instrument measures what it purports to measure. Validity is more specific than the other general criteria of a good data-gathering instrument. Data-gathering instruments cannot accurately be described as valid in general terms, but only in connection with intended use on a population of a particular maturity, level of ability, and experiential background.

Evaluation of the validity of an instrument can be conducted along three lines of inquiry. First, *logical validity* implies that the data-gathering instrument measures, or is specifically related to, the characteristic for which it was designed. Errors are easily made in determining this type of validity. Second, *empirical validity* is determined on the basis of the degree to which the instrument depends upon its usefulness in prediction or diagnosis of the characteristic for which it was designed. Third, the validity of a data-gathering instrument may be evaluated on the basis of *comparison*, that is, instrument validity is determined by comparing its results with those of existing instrumentalities.

Crucial in the process of validating data-gathering instruments is the establishment of satisfactory and adequate criteria. Criteria can be examined by asking three questions:

1. For what *purpose* has the data-gathering instrument been designed?
2. For *whom* (population) has the instrument been designed?
3. Under what *conditions* can the instrument be administered (experiential background of population)?

Thus, we see that the validity of a data-gathering instrument is a rather difficult feature to evaluate. Yet following the prescribed questions above, and being aware of the points made previously in the discussion, the validity of an instrument can be evaluated for the part it plays in the process of inference.

The *objectivity* of a data-gathering instrument is considered to be high, or good, if the personal judgments of persons rating, classifying, or scoring it are eliminated. If the instrument produces results that can be scored approximately the same by persons of widely different interests and experiences, with a fair degree of consistency (high correlation between the scorings of the judges), the instrument has good objectivity.

The basic purpose of employing a research instrument is to place, or categorize, individuals along a defined scale in accordance with differences in the amount of the characteristic under study which they possess. The instrument which can successfully fulfil this function possesses *high discriminative power*. This is a feature of data-gathering instruments which is easily determined, and one that must be considered in inference evaluation.

This discussion of the "data collection" element of the suggested general model, which is included in the "ends" aspect of inference evaluation, completes our treatment of this particular phase of the inference process. We are now prepared to discuss the element of "data processing" in the general model as it relates to inference evaluation.

DATA PROCESSING

The element of the suggested general research model which deals with the processing of data is composed of the sorting, classifying, handling, and analyzing of data. The most fundamental part of data processing is the level of measurement employed in obtaining the data. This is also a key point to be considered in the evaluation of inference. The research effort should be investigated to determine if:

(a) *The data are of nominal scale value.* Data yielded by the nominal scale is categorical in nature. The analytical techniques that may be employed are those of the nonparametric family (enumerative statistical tests).

(b) *The data are of ordinal scale level.* Ordinal scale data are rankings, or orderings of classes. Although symbols of "greater than," "less than," as well as simple 1, 2, 3, 4 ratings may be employed, the data are not intervalized. This type of data requires a nonparametric statistical technique for analysis.

(c) *The data are of interval scale level.* Interval scale data are truly mathematical data. This level of measurement not only categorizes and compares, but intervalizes objects as well. Although its zero point is arbitrary, it is a level of measurement which provides data that are amenable to analysis by parametric statistical methods.

(d) *The data are of ratio-interval scale level.* Ratio-interval scale data have the added feature of a true zero point. Either parametric or nonparametric statistical tests may be employed with ratio-scale data. The parametric tests are somewhat more desirable, because of their greater power and efficiency, than the non-parametric tests under this scale of measurement.

We are now prepared to enter the discussion of the general model element which is the final part of the "ends" aspect of inference evaluation, namely: "the process of decision-making (conclusions)."

DECISIONS (CONCLUSIONS)

The *decisions* phase of the "ends" aspect of inference evaluation can be examined by investigating; (1) the interpretation of the findings of the inquiry, and (2) the inference process which was employed to derive conclusions. In evaluating the interpretation of the findings, the following questions should be asked:

(a) Is there a bias present?
(b) Has the inquiry been conducted objectively and thus avoided errors in the interpretation of the findings?
(c) Have the limitations of the findings been realized in the interpretation?

After these questions are answered we are ready to evaluate the inference process.

The evaluation of the inference process is accomplished by considering its three aspects, namely: (1) beginnings, (2) ends, and (3) the manner or method of getting from beginnings to ends. Since we have just completed a discussion of the beginnings and ends evaluation of inference, nothing further need be said about these two points. The final stage of inference evaluation concerns itself with the manner of getting from beginnings to ends. With the discussion of this point we shall not only be aware of how to complete the last step of evaluating the "ends" aspect of the inference process, associated with our general model, but we shall also know how to evaluate the last phase (getting from beginnings to ends) of the decision-making process.

THE MANNER OF GETTING FROM "BEGINNINGS" TO "ENDS"

The manner of getting from "beginnings" to "ends" of the research inference process is the problem to which we have addressed ourselves throughout this effort. We have attempted to show that a model of a method of inquiry can help determine objectives of the research problem, give guidance to the investigation, and determine what data are reliable and valid for drawing the "best" inference.

We advance the proposition that if a general model of inquiry is followed, the "best" inference for the situation, or subject, under study will be made. Evaluation of the general model of inquiry should be conducted as the summarizing action of inference evaluation. The question that should be asked is: "Does the model withstand vigorous evaluation; and does it produce the 'best' inference under the circumstances?" The proposed general model of inquiry is composed of seven basic parts:

1. The Problem (Evaluation and Formulation).
2. Hypotheses, or General Questions.

3. The Universe.
4. The Sample.
5. Data Collection.
6. Data Processing.
7. The Research Decision (Conclusions).

If each of these parts is evaluated as previously suggested, the model as a whole is evaluated. With the evaluation of the general model of inquiry, the validity and reliability of the research decision is ascertained. The determination of the validity and reliability of the research decision completes the process of inference evaluation. The research decision will be found to be the "best" one to the degree that it is valid and reliable. It will be a valid and reliable one only if the inference process employed was valid and reliable.

*Chapter 8—References*
See Bibliography: 3, 8, 18, 22, 24, 34, 36, 64, 66, 81, 82, 83, 98, 102, 104, 113, 125, 143, 148, 155, 162, 166, 188, 191; 56a, 65a, 69a, 77a, 85a, 105a, 119a.

# PART III

## *Adapting the General Model to Problems in the Basic Types of Research*

THE PURPOSE OF THIS SECTION is to illustrate how the suggested general model of educational research can be adapted to problems found in the basic types of research. The basic types of research are defined to be: (1) experimental research; (2) descriptive research; (3) action research; (4) historical research; and (5) field research.

The five types of research are "defined" entities, or abstract categories, and not realities. These classifications have been defined in order to provide a form of taxonomic structure through which discussions of research projects may be facilitated. The definition of basic types of research makes it possible to provide a broader orientation for the problems than otherwise would be possible. Accordingly, each of the next five chapters will deal exclusively with the basic characteristics of one of the fundamental types of research, and illustrate through actual models how the general model may be adapted to the demands of the particular research approach under consideration.

It is not the intent of this section to present "ideal" or "perfect" models of the basic types of research. Nor is it the intent of this section to present models that include all of the sampling techniques and statistical procedures that have been covered in other sections. The approach employed merely attempts to adapt the general model of educational research either to studies that have already been completed, or to proposed studies that have come into the purview of the authors in their teaching and direction of research. In each case where the general model has been adapted to studies already completed, modifications of the designs of these studies, *in minor detail*, were permitted by the authors of the studies in order that a "patterned" presentation of the resulting models could be made.

### Chapter Nine

# Models of Experimental Research

THE SUGGESTED GENERAL MODEL of educational research can be modified in a variety of ways to accommodate different types of investigations. In order to transform the general model into one designed specifically for a given experimental situation, it is necessary to know the fundamental elements of experimental research. For this reason, we shall now discuss certain basic concepts of experimentation and the experimental method as they are employed in behavioral sciences and educational research.

Experimentation can probably best be defined as a process involving controlled systematic inquiry into a given area of knowledge. The scientist must be active in the conducting of an experiment and must be able to manipulate, observe, and control variables, treatments, subjects, conditions, and certain methods involved in the process. Speaking in a broad sense, the experimenter is one who deliberately and systematically introduces change into "usual" (natural) processes and then observes the consequences of these changes. In educational and behavioral sciences research of a non-experimental character, the researcher is a passive observer who is mainly interested in keeping records of the behavior of objects or organisms in an undisturbed "usual" (natural) setting.

The term "experiment" is not synonymous with that of "scientific method." The scientific method embraces a great variety of activities, while the experimental method is designed to determine causal relations and factors. The determination of causation and relationship demands that variables, treatments, subjects, and conditions be controlled, or accounted for, throughout the experimentation. The experimental approach is intended to deal with dynamics, forces, and interactions; and is not intended to give merely a descriptive picture of a static situation or a "usual" (natural) growth pattern.

In its broadest sense, experimentation may include an informal approach of "trial and error." It should be noted, however, that even under conditions of "informal experimentation" the researcher is, in effect, still manipulating and accounting for at least some of the conditions, variables, and treatments involved in the problem. To some researchers, trial and error investigations are not experiments because the experimenter does not know enough about the conditions and influences affecting his observations. According to Beveridge, however, we find that: "An experiment usually consists in making an event occur under known conditions where as many extraneous influences as possible are eliminated and close observation is possible so that relationships between phenomena can be revealed."[1] If Beveridge's definition is accepted, it would appear that, providing the essentials to which he refers are maintained, the particular "form" of the experiment does not matter. The problem of "knowing enough" about the conditions and influences affecting the event under observation, in order to determine with any degree of confidence the causation present, is still not solved by Beveridge's approach to experimentation.

If all aspects of experimentation are considered, the "best" definition would be: Experimentation is the systematic process associated with testing a hypothesis under known conditions where: (1) as many extraneous factors as possible are eliminated, (2) careful and critical observation is effected in a controlled setting, and (3) by means of a comparative analysis, involving experimental and "contrast" (control) sampling units, evidence is sought to establish the presence, or non-presence, of causation factors for the phenomena representing the presupposed effects.

The "controlled setting," referred to in the definition of experimentation, is usually produced in a laboratory by means of special equipment. In those cases where laboratory experimentation is impossible, "controlled settings" may be simulated through application of an analog model or a symbolic model, where the latter frequently incorporates the theory of probability.

## METHODS AND PROCESSES OF EXPERIMENTATION

Consideration of the basic elements of the general model of educational research indicates that the experimenter is confronted with difficulties in: (1) defining the problem; (2) framing the hypotheses of the study; (3) delimiting the universe of potential data; (4) selecting a representative, adequate sample; (5) gathering the data with reliable, valid, objective, and discriminatory instrumentalities while employing procedures that are free of *biased* error; (6) sorting, classifying, and analyzing the data with processes that avoid biased error; and, finally, (7) reaching a research decision based upon only the factual data produced by the experimentation. Of primary concern to the scientist in conducting an experiment is the type of manipulation of variable(s) needed to solve the research problem. The meaning of "manipulation" is fundamental to knowing how to conduct an experiment properly. The operation performed by the experimenter in the manipulation of an experimental variable is a physical and not a conceptual act. It is a real and objective action. The operation necessitates overt action on the part of the experimenter, and cannot be achieved by a covert action which occurs only in the thought processes of the researcher.

Experimental error is the basic concern of the experimenter. Researchers readily acknowledge the presence of error in all experiments, and accept its presence as inevitable. In attempting to solve the problem of error, scientists have partitioned the phenomenon into two parts: (1) biased error, and (2) unbiased error. The matter of unbiased error is accounted for by probability theory. That of biased error, unless it is introduced purposely through the experimental variable, is accounted for by noting carefully such potential sources as: (1) the source of data, (2) sampling techniques, (3) data collection instrumentalities and procedures, (4) data processing techniques, and (5) the experimenter himself. The acceptance of unavoidable error, in biased and unbiased form, has implications for the evaluation and interpretation of the results of an experiment. In some cases, the analysis of error (variance) in the measures of an experiment provides the means of evaluating the experimental results. In other cases, the acceptance of the presence of unavoidable error makes the researcher astutely aware of the fact that he cannot rely upon a single experiment for the demonstration of a natural phenomenon, that he cannot even interpret repeated research results without error, or in other words, that the knowledge of any phenomenon is always provisional and partial.

When error (variance) is analyzed to evaluate the results of an experiment conducted in either educational or behavioral sciences research, two factors are considered: (1) the *unbiased* error due to differences among subjects, and (2) the *biased* error introduced to the experiment through the manipulation of the variable(s) of the experimentation by the researcher. The differences among subjects represent unbiased error on the basis of the assumption of "heterogeneity of experimental materials." The *assumption* of *unbiased* error existing in differences among subjects does not mean that the experimenter need not consider the possibility of *biased* error existing in the source of data and the sample of the study. The assumption of "heterogeneity" can only be made after the experimenter has given careful attention to potential *biased* error in: (1) the source of data, (2) the technique of sample selection, (3) the representativeness of the sample, and (4) the adequacy (sufficient number of subjects) of the sample. If the experimenter is satisfied that these sources of biased error are adequately controlled, he can *assume* that *unbiased* error will occur because of differences among subjects, and evaluate the results of the experiment in terms of probabilities associated with either the analysis of variance (error), or the analysis of covariance (see Chapters 28-30) technique.

*The Formal Experiment*

The experiment, as employed in educational research, embodies the study of the effects of a treatment plan administered by means of a uniformity trial to a control group and an experimental group. The experimenter performs the operations of the uniformity trial by imposing a treatment on the experimental group which does include the experimental variable. The uniformity trial is effected only after the experimenter is satisfied that biased error from the source of data, sampling techniques, data collection processes, and analytical techniques are controlled (i.e., taken into account).

A conceptualization of the formal type of experiment as conducted in educational research is as follows: Subjects selected at random from the population of the study are assigned by methods of random selection to form a control group and an experimental group. Condition *X* (the "usual" condition) is imposed upon the control group, and condition *Y* (the "usual" plus the experimental condition) is imposed upon the experimental group to form a treatment plan involving a single, independent variable. The conditions are imposed, and the responses of the subjects in both groups are measured, by means of a uniformity trial. The uniformity trial can be effected through a criterion measurement of the treatment made at the beginning of the experiment on both groups. The measurement of the criterion variable is repeated after the imposition of the treatment plan during the course of the experimentation. After these measurements have been corrected for any *initial* variation between the groups on the criterion, the "adjusted" measures are examined for differences in magnitude. Hypothetically, only an *expected* change (e.g., natural growth or maturation) should occur in the control group because it has not received the experimental factor treatment.

The magnitudes of changes in the adjusted criterion measures of the experimental group, providing the experimenter has incorporated the operations of the uniformity trial correctly, are assumed to be composed of two parts: (1) the expected change, and (2) the change due to the experimental treatment. Since the effect of the experimental treatment can be negative or positive, the change in the criterion (single variable) measures must be examined for significance in either direction, i.e., in either a "positive" or a "negative" direction.

The "significance" of a change in the criterion measures is determined on the basis of chance factors at work. Chance factors are considered in terms of probability and are accounted for as follows: In the uniformity trial, the magnitudes of change, or difference, in the criterion measurements "before" and "after" the experiment are assumed to be the direct consequence of a random sampling of the population as it existed prior to the experiment, and then to the random sampling of the population conducted after the experiment. This assumption provides the measure of *expected* change associated with the control group. In the case of the experimental group, it is assumed that the influence of the experimental treatment will be reflected in the magnitudes of change of the criterion measurements as well as those due to random sampling.

The component of variability (change) ascribed to random sampling is used as a "standard" in evaluating the significance of the magnitude of changes found in the criterion measurements of the experimental group. The magnitude of the "sampling" component of variability indicates the magnitude of the error which affected the experiment in the selections of materials (samples) from a heterogeneous source (population). The final evaluation of the results of the experiment involves the comparison of the component of variability ascribed to the experimental treatment with that ascribed to random sampling, or chance variation. If the comparison shows that the magnitude of the experimental component is so much larger than that of the random sampling component, and that such a difference would occur only less than 5 per cent of the time due to chance, the change due to the experimental treatment is considered "significant."

Differences among the subjects in the samples (control group and experimental group) will be reflected in the criterion measures (dependent variable). If conditions $X$ (control) and $Y$ (experimental) have different effects on the responses, they (the effects) will also be found in the measures. Both kinds of differences will be obtained by the experimenter in the total variability of the observational data of the experiment. If the variability due to differences in the subjects (sampling error) is isolated and removed from the *total* variability of the measures, that which remains is due to the differing effects of the treatments (conditions). If the treatment component of variability is partitioned appropriately, the effect due to condition *X* and that due to *Y* can be determined and compared. On the basis of the results of the comparative analysis, a decision concerning the significance of the effects of conditions *X* and *Y*, respectively, on the measures can then be derived.

### Control by Deliberate Selection

Experimental designs in educational research can be classified broadly under one of three categories: (1) cross-sectional, or the present, (2) before and after, or present and future, and (3) ex post facto, or the past. Table II shows the three types of designs and some of their outstanding characteristics. It should be noted that each category (column) in Table II is capable of accommodating: (1) a single variable of classification experiment, i.e., only one independent variable being manipulated; and/or (2) a multivariate experimentation, i.e., factorial and matched-group factorial designs where, in the first case, two or more independent variables are manipulated simultaneously and independently of each other, including "block" designs; and in the second case (matched-groups), two or more variables, dependent in terms of matching factors, are manipulated simultaneously under uniform conditions with adjustments being made by the analysis of covariance technique, or some other method of similar purpose.

The cross-sectional experimental design includes those experimentations that are being conducted at a given point of the present time-slice. The design can accommodate hypotheses of: (1) magnitude, (2) difference, and (3) relationship, involving a single variable, block multivariate, and matched-group factorial approaches. The before and after design includes those experiments that are

Table II
Classifications of Experimental Designs in Educational Research

| Cross-Sectional | Before and After | Ex Post Facto |
|---|---|---|
| 1. Study at a point in present time. | 1. Begin a longitudinal study at a point in present time with termination date defined. | 1. Present effects traced to hypothesized causes that occurred in past. |
| 2. Hypotheses of magnitude, difference, and relationship are usually examined. | 2. Hypotheses of magnitude and difference (for related groups) are usually examined. | 2. Hypotheses of magnitude, difference, and relationship are usually examined. |
| 3. Data collected during and immediately after experimentation. | 3. Data collected before and immediately after experimentation. | 3. Data collected from complete records of past. |
| 4. Testing techniques and forms of analysis: parametric and nonparametric; significant differences, correlational techniques, analysis of variance and covariance techniques, content analysis, categorical analysis, etc. | 4. See column (1). | 4. See column (1). |

considered to be "longitudinal" studies, and thus must involve present and future time-slices, respectively. Like the cross-sectional design, it is amenable to analyzing single variable and factorial (multivariate) situations, but usually involves only hypotheses of: (1) magnitude, and (2) difference. The relationship aspects of the before and after design are employed as means of "adjusting" statistics prior to testing them in hypotheses of magnitude and/or difference. The ex post facto design accounts for those types of experiments in which present effects are traced in terms of hypothesized causations that occurred in the past time-slice. The ex post facto design usually involves hypotheses of magnitude, difference, and relationship, and employs methods of analysis that can accommodate single variable and factorial (multivariate) approaches.

### Cross-Sectional Design

The cross-sectional experimental design is a method of study which makes systematic comparisons for a single date by controlling procedures of subject and treatment selection. The statistical methods most frequently employed with this type of design are those associated with determining significant differences between group means (see pages 341–51), and those concerned with the measurement of relationships, i.e., methods of correlational analysis (see pages 242–66). In many cross-sectional designs, partial and multiple correlational analyses have been found to be powerful tools (see pages 275–84). Partial correlation should be used only if conditions of the experiment can assure, *relatively* speaking, that: reliable measurements are attainable, homogeneity of subjects in the bivariate population prevails, appropriate sampling techniques can be employed, and the distribution of the measurements is approximately normal. In other words, partial correlation can be used as an analytical technique in cross-sectional experimental designs if it is possible to stratify the sample into homogeneous sub-groups, and the scale of measurement of the data is such that simple correlations can be calculated within each sub-group (stratum).

The basic purpose of the cross-sectional design is to compare two homogeneous groups, i.e., the experimental group which receives the program of treatment(s) is compared with the control group which is denied the treatment(s) program. Control of the measurements of the variables being investigated in the experiment can be achieved by "matching" subjects in the respective groups on the basis of factors selected by the experimenter. The factors upon which the matching of groups is effected are determined by the experimenter on the basis of their (the factors) potentials for affecting the results of the experiment. For example, in a cross-sectional experimental design dealing with reading achievement, factors upon which the matching of subjects could be based are: age, intelligence, educational background, and physical stamina.

If the matching of subjects approach is not employed, the control of known factors may be achieved by the process of *adjustment*. The technique of *adjusting* the experimental and the control group's measurements on the basis of their initial variation from the "grand" mean is the approach employed in the analysis of covariance method (see Chapter 30). After the measurements of the respective groups have been adjusted for initial variation, the resulting data can be analyzed for causation factors and relationships.

The analysis of covariance is a statistical technique which provides for the adjustment of *final* measurements in terms of initial variations existing in known factors that are related to the variable (measurements) under study. The worth of matching subjects has been brought under serious challenge with further refinements in the analysis of covariance technique, and the easy availability of electronic computers and data-processing equipment. Under these conditions, the adjustment method, which is more exact in producing ascertained corrections in factors highly related to the variable under study than is the technique of matching, is enjoying extensive use in the current practices of educational research, while the method of matching subjects is being discarded. If the process of matching does not seriously limit the size of the groups being compared, the "best" approach to employ is one in which the methods of matching and adjustment are both involved. Under this "combination" approach, subjects in the experimental group are matched with counterparts in the control group. A test, or battery of tests, is administered to each group to provide before measures in the variables covered by the tests. After the experimental treatment(s) have been imposed on the experimental group, parallel forms of the tests employed are administered to both groups, in order to provide after measures. The resulting measurements on the after tests are then adjusted for the initial variation in the before scores. The adjusted measures are then examined for probable causation.

*Before and After Design*

A classical pattern of the before and after experimental design is found frequently in sociological research and is called the "projected" design. The projected experimental design is used to represent a relationship between causation factors and effects in a time sequence, where the relationship is not established by rigid determinism, but rather on the basis of a determinable probability of occurrence.

In the projected experiment the researcher establishes a controlled situation for the exposure of a control group and an experimental group to a given stimulus. The experimenter has the subjects before him and is in a favorable position to control the situation while collecting data on the relevant factors. He can hold back the exposure of the respective groups to the stimulus, until he is satisfied that the participating groups are ready for it. For example, if an experiment of this type is being conducted to test hypothesized cause-and-effect relationships that are operating in the societal situation, quite apart from those that might be investigated through the study of changes made by *enforced* social reform, the researcher can withhold the "suspected" stimulus, until he can be sure that the respective groups (control and experimental) possess information necessary to the production of measurable responses.

A projected experimental study conducted by Dodd,* in the field of rural

---

* *A Controlled Experiment on Rural Hygiene in Syria*, by Stuart Dodd, a research effort described and analyzed by (35) F. Stuart Chapin, *Experimental Designs in Sociological Research*.

hygiene and the hygienic practices of families that were supposed to benefit by the program illustrates our previous discussion. During the interval from 1931 to 1933, a traveling clinic of the Near East Foundation conducted a program of education in hygiene in the Arab village of Jib Ramli in Syria. Dodd wanted to test the hypothesis that this program would result in an improvement in hygienic practices. He therefore selected three other villages which resembled Jib Ramli on nine relevant factors: geographic, demographic, historical, economic, religious, domestic, educational, recreational, and sanitary conditions. In this manner, factor control was provided. These three cities received no hygienic propaganda and were so located that there was little likelihood of hygienic practices spreading to them from Jib. At the end of two years, the hygienic practices of the contrasting villages were evaluated and compared. Employing the findings of only one comparison for our example, it was found that the experimental village (Jib) increased its score from 253 points in 1931 to 304 points in 1933, a gain of 51 points at the close of the period of hygienic instruction. The control (contrast) village also increased its score from 241 points in 1931 to 286 points in 1933, a gain of 45 points without visible instruction in hygiene.[2]

These data were analyzed as follows: The village of Jib and the control village were symbolized by $A$ and $B$, respectively. Under the conditions of the experiment, group $A$ had been exposed to a stimulus which was withheld from group $B$. The data collected were to indicate how many of the $A$'s and $B$'s exhibited the effect $X$ (improved hygienic practices), and how many did not. In the form of a table, the situation would be depicted as follows:

|  | Group $X$ | Group $Y$ | Totals |
|---|---|---|---|
| Group $A$ | $AX$ | $AY$ | All $A$'s |
| Group $B$ | $BX$ | $BY$ | All $B$'s |
| Totals | All $X$'s | All $Y$s | Grand Total[3] |

Where the $A$'s are those who have been exposed to the stimulus (the program of education), the $B$'s are those who have not been exposed; the $X$'s are those who exhibit the effect (improved practices), and the $Y$'s are those who did not exhibit it. Thus, $AX$ denotes all those exposed persons who showed the effect.[4] $BX$ represents those who showed the effect even though they were not exposed; and $BY$ indicates those unexposed persons who did not exhibit the effect. If a projected experiment were to present *conclusive* results, it would be necessary for the $AY$ and $BX$ cells of the table to be empty, that is, all of the experimental group would show the anticipated effect, while none of the control group would. The results of the Dodd study were inconclusive, and in order to prove the relationship between instruction in hygiene and progress in hygiene, further similar experiments were required.

*Ex Post Facto Design*

The procedure of the ex-post factor design is like that of the projected design except that the roles of the independent and dependent variables are reversed. In the "facto" design some present effect is traced backward to an assumed causal complex of factors or forces extant at a prior date. Since in the ex-post facto design the experimenter comes upon the scene after the cause has achieved its effect, he must reconstruct his experiment from records. He does not rule out in advance, with any confidence, that the effect was caused by some other factor that is correlated with the presumed causal factor. The situation, unlike that of the projected design, is not a created one. The experimenter is almost totally dependent upon the written word for data concerning relevant factors of the nature of the hypothetical cause, and the extent of these factors' hypothetical effects.

Without complete records of possible related facts, there can be no ex post facto experiment. Hence it is important to have good records of the factors hypothesized to be relevant to the effect that is being examined. It is also important to point out the great dependence which ex post facto experimentation places on measurement. In the Christiansen study, the experimenter claims that after all her data were gathered and ready for manipulation, fully 295 cases had to be discarded because the records were incomplete.[5] Experimenters who have engaged in the after-the-effect studies, necessitating the resurrection of data from past records, are familiar with the feeling of frustration resulting from the discovery that the records upon which the investigation is to rest are scanty, sketchy, and generally inadequate for the solution of the problem at hand.

In the effect-to-cause experiments (the ex post facto design) the situation is, in a sense, the reverse of that described in the projected experiment. The investigator examines all those who do (Group $X$) and who do not (Group $Y$) exhibit a factor, classifying them as to whether they were (Group $A$) or were not (Group $B$) exposed to the stimulus, that is, whether they are $A$'s or $B$'s. There is a group of "lost" persons whom the investigator cannot identify as either $B$'s or $A$'s. They are a third group, Group $C$. The results in the form of a table are shown below:

|          | Group $X$ | Group $Y$ | Totals |
|----------|-----------|-----------|--------|
| Group $A$ | $AX$ | $AY$ | All $A$'s |
| Group $B$ | $BX$ | $BY$ | All $B$'s |
| Group $C$ | $CX$ | $CY$ | All $C$'s |
| Totals | All $X$'s | All $Y$'s | Grand Total[6] |

The numbers of persons to be classified under the cells symbolized as $AX$, $AY$, $BX$, and $BY$ are known, and these are the data that are analyzed. The numbers are not known in the "cells" symbolized as $CX$ and $CY$. Since Group $C$ is composed of those persons for whom there are inadequate records, it is impossible to know how the group is distributed over columns $X$ and $Y$. There can be no speculation about the distribution of Group $C$ over $X$ and $Y$, because it is not possible to know who in the group was, and who was not, exposed to the stimulus; hence no tracing is possible.

### SINGLE-VARIABLE DESIGNS

The single-variable design, in which one independent variable is manipulated, is the classic reference design used by numerous experimenters. Two conditions or treatments are required for this design. The treatments or conditions are imposed on a selection of experimental materials. In the case of an experiment being conducted in educational or behavioral sciences research the experimental conditions would be imposed on human subjects. Measurements are made on a response variable after the treatments or conditions are imposed on the subjects.

A valid test of significance with independent random samples can be made for the single-variable type experiment. In educational research, however, the single-variable experimental design is not very useful. The extreme heterogeneity of experimental materials occurring in educational research makes it almost impossible to delimit an effect to a single-variable cause. On the other hand, if no attempt is made to delimit, and a single-variable cause is "assumed," the resulting experimental design (utilizing random samples from a population of heterogeneous materials) will be subject to errors of large magnitude; i.e., the experiment will be lacking in precision. *Small treatment* differences under conditions of extreme heterogeneity will seldom, if ever, be discovered. The single-variable design will be satisfactory, at best, if *large treatment effects* are produced and if large random samples are employed. Under these conditions the power of a test of significance could be utilized. The problem here is two-fold, however. First, how to produce the *large treatment* effects, and second, how to employ large random samples without introducing other variables, such as teacher differences, school differences, and other related matters, into the experiment.

The problem of reducing the influence of heterogeneous materials on experimental results can be solved to a certain extent by employing the process of *matching*. The experimenter should carefully choose subjects who, prior to the experiment, give evidence of being exactly comparable, in a single-variable experiment involving two conditions. Matching can provide a practical solution to the problem of heterogeneity when there is a large supply of subjects who have a good probability of being as nearly alike as possible. Since this matter is discussed in some detail under the topic of matching, further treatment will not be accorded it here, except to point out that, despite the mitigating effect of matching under the most suitable conditions, the single-variable type experiment has limited application in educational research.

If the single-variable design is to be applied to a problem in educational research, and whether matching is to be employed or not, precautions must be taken when assigning subjects to treatments. The assignment of subjects to treatments is one of the most critical aspects of conducting an experiment, regardless of the number of variables involved, and must be performed with absolute care and judgment. Despite the care and judgment put forth by the experimenter, a strong possibility of biasing the experimental comparison still exists. This problem may not be the same in all experimental situations, but usually if subjects are assigned at random to the experimental and control groups, after it has been ascertained that they are as nearly alike as possible in all factors relevant to the experimental treatment(s), the experiment will have been placed on a strong foundation.

## MULTIVARIATE (FACTORIAL) DESIGNS

When two or more independent variables are manipulated simultaneously and independently of each other, multivariate or factorial designs result. Each independent variable is considered to be a set of two or more conditions, and various combinations of these conditions can be imposed on the subjects. The effect of the manipulation is measured in terms of a response variable. The measurements may be in the form of test scores, attitude scalings, rankings, or personal observations of the experimenter, to mention but a few. Depending upon the scale, or level of measurement, of the data, an appropriate analytical technique should be selected. If the data are of nominal or ordinal scales of measurement, a non-parametric technique should be employed. If the data are of interval or ratio-interval scales of measurement, a parametric method should be employed. Since in most cases factorial designs employ interval scale data, the methods of analysis of variance and analysis of covariance are frequently utilized as analytical techniques.

### Factorial Designs with Matching

Whenever two levels of a single independent variable are utilized, the matched group is a pair. Prior to the experiment the choice of two subjects for any pair is guided by the ranks of measures obtained under uniform conditions. The greater the correlation existing between the matching variable, and the dependent variable, the more homogeneous the members of each pair will be.

The number of subjects in a matched group is determined by the number of combinations of treatments prescribed by the design in the matching procedures for a factorial design. Each subject in a group is assigned one combination of treatments. A complete set of comparisons within each homogeneous group of subjects is then possible. The inequalities not completely eliminated by the matching can be estimated from the variation in the comparisons from one matched group to another.

### Factorial Designs with Adjusting

In educational experiments combining precision and comprehensiveness the analysis of covariance can be incorporated in the factorial design. Usually the experimenter gathers a large number of random samples of subjects. The actual number of subjects needed is determined in factorial design, by the number of combination of treatments, or cells formed in the factorial grid. Then a response variable which is linearly correlated with the dependent variable is chosen as an adjusting variable. All subjects are measured under uniform conditions on the adjusting variable in the several samples. Next, the treatment combinations are assigned to the samples randomly. The experimenter imposes the treatments and obtains the final observations on the dependent variable. He removes that part of the variability in his observations associated with initial differences among his subjects by using the regression of the dependent variable on the adjusting variable. Then the variability which remains is carefully analyzed and apparent treatment effects are evaluated by comparison with an estimate of the errors which might have produced them.

*Extensions*

Experimental designs vary with respect to : (1) the number of factors and the number of levels of each of them, (2) the way in which a preliminary set of measures is used to indicate precision, and (3) the specific comparisons that are appropriate to a design. The reader should realize that all experimental designs have certain common characteristics, from previous comparisons and discussions. The reader can assume that : (a) the experimenter had only one population or supply which he wished his experiment to be based upon, (b) the experimenter deliberately selected his levels or qualities to suit his purposes, and (c) any given attempt at evaluation judged from the experiment was performed only once.

With this background in single-variable and factorial designs we are now prepared to discuss in somewhat more detail the topics of : matching, adjusting, replication, and evaluation of experiments.

## MATCHING

In carrying out the process of matching, the experimenter selects pairs of subjects who are as alike as possible with respect to the characteristics of the response being studied in the experiment. A condition is then imposed upon the one set of subjects, and then the same condition is imposed upon the other set of subjects. The next step is to measure the responses of each group. After the responses of the groups are measured, a comparison of the two sets of measurements is made. The comparison will probably be biased to some degree, since it is improbable that all of the pairs of subjects in the experiment will have been matched without some error. If the matching or selection has been effective in yielding pairs of subjects very nearly alike, then the magnitude of the value of the measure of error will be smaller than it would have been had no attempt been made to match the groups.

The experimenter must repeat his selection of pairs of subjects and the imposition of treatments if he is to gain some insight into the magnitude of error that still remains in the comparison. Members of each pair are matched so that they will be as much alike as possible. The experimental condition is then imposed on only one member of each pair. The control condition in the design is imposed on the other member. Within each pair the assignment of subjects to the experimental and control conditions should be random. After the assignment of the respective conditions to the appropriate subjects (experimental to experimental and control to control), a measure of response is obtained on each subject.

The experimenter can compare the two conditions as many times as there are matched pairs. By computing a difference ($d$) for each pair, a measure for comparison is available. The differences may vary in magnitude and direction. The differences between the treatments (conditions) imposed on each group can be determined by comparing the group mean difference score ($\bar{d}_e$) for the experimental group with that of the control group.

The variability of the differences ($s_d$) will reflect the magnitude of errors which arise from failures in matching when the assignment of conditions to the subjects within each pair has been done randomly, and when treatment effects are additive and constant.

Errors can be judged as follows: If the differential effect of the two conditions were the same on every pair and the members of each pair were matched perfectly, then the obtained differences ($d$) would be identical and would also show little if any variability. Once completed, the experimenter could state that there were no errors in the experiment. The differences would vary if the members of each pair had not been properly matched and the direction of influence of the failure in matching had been determined randomly in each case. It would be reasonable to assume the poorer the matching, the more variable these differences. There is then available in the variability of the collection of differences, information which concerns the magnitude of errors affecting the experiment.

The experimenter will have greater confidence that the treatments have actually produced differences when the apparent treatment differences are large relative to the variability of these differences. The experimenter should question the validity of his results if the treatments have not really had different effects, and he should also consider the possibility that the apparent treatment effects are due to errors when the treatment differences are small relative to the variability of the differences.

The experimenter needs a systematic procedure for decision-making concerning the results of the comparison. Also, in a design which does not involve matching, a plan is needed to conduct the experiment in a manner that makes it possible to compare the apparent treatment effects with a rough estimate of the errors which may have produced them.

The experimenter can analyze variability in data from matched pairs, and components of variability can also be compared. The component of variability that includes the affects of treatments, and a component that represents error, can be easily located and identified with a proper design. When all of these tasks have been completed, a valid test of significance is readily available for the comparison of the two sources of variability for the experimenter to judge (e.g., analysis of variance).

## ADJUSTING

The repetitious treatment of subjects and the constant matching of them are not the only means by which an experimenter can achieve precision.

The analysis of covariance is another way in which the experimenter can achieve adequate and valuable results. This method results in an increase in precision and does not require the experimenter to arrange his materials in a special way, as is the case in matched group designs, to further reduce the magnitude of errors in the final comparisons of the experiment. The medium of a response variable that is known to be correlated with the dependent variable results in an increase in precision for the experimenter.

A number of random samples corresponding to the number of conditions is required for the "adjustment" design. Prior to the imposition of treatments, measurements on the correlated response variable are obtained under uniform conditions. The adjustment is deferred until the final statistical analysis of the data, and no matching or ranking is needed for the design.

In the experimental data the adjustment involves the elimination of a component of error variability (variance). The variability eliminated from the design is the initial differences among subjects, and can be estimated by the experimenter from the response measurement obtained prior to the experiment on a parallel form of the measuring instrument to be used for the final response measures. By means of the correlation between the dependent variable (e.g., after scores) and the adjusting variable (e.g., before scores), a regression equation can be determined by which the "final" scores (dependent variable) are adjusted for initial variance in the before scores (independent variable). The final adjusted scores are then analyzed for significant differences between experimental and control groups. This technique is illustrated in a model found in the statistics section, see Chapter 30.

### REPLICATION

In experimentation associated with educational research, a major source of error (variance) is the pre-experimental differences among subjects. Other sources of error are those associated with data collection and data processing (computation) as the experiment progresses. Since experimental comparison requires observations on subjects treated differently, the experimenter frequently finds it difficult to identify, with a sufficient degree of certainty, significant differences due to the experimental treatment (variable) alone. One method frequently employed to help resolve this problem is that of *replicating* the experimental design on another sample of subjects drawn from the same population which produced the sample of the earlier experimentation. The magnitude of pre-experimental differences among subjects, differences that are potential errors or biases, are more easily discovered after replication of the experiment has been employed than prior to its application. Further examination of errors due to data collection instrumentalities and procedures, and those due to computational errors and the handling of data, is also possible under the replication of the experimental design. Since the precision of the experiment will be greatly improved, and the decision concerning causation will be greatly refined, an experiment should be replicated as frequently as the data will permit. If the experimenter is satisfied with his "proof" after, say, *n* replications, there is no need to continue the activity beyond that point.

### EVALUATION OF EXPERIMENTS

The knowledge of any phenomenon is only partial and incomplete, therefore the presence of error (variance) in observations made by an experimenter is inevitable. Attempts by the experimenter to reduce error in the basic observations on which the experimental findings ultimately depend is to a considerable extent a function of the experimenter's efforts to acquire new knowledge. In evaluating experiments, two types of erroneous decisions concerning the acts of rejecting or not rejecting the hypothesis under test can be identified. The first type of error, identified as the $\alpha$ (alpha) error, or Type I error, occurs when the null hypothesis is true, but is rejected. The probability of committing this error is determined by the choice of a value for the level of significance by the experimenter (e.g., if $\alpha = .05$ is the level of significance set by the experimenter, there is a 5 per cent chance of rejecting the null hypothesis, when actually it is true and should not be rejected). The second type of error, identified as the $\beta$ (beta) error, or Type II error, occurs when the null hypothesis is actually false, but is not rejected. The probability of making the Type II error depends, in part, on the size of the sample (*n*) being employed, and the possible values that the population parameter under examination might assume with a given probability.

Reducing the size or amount of the error due to sampling, data collection, and data processing, decreases the probability of a Type II error, and in so doing, increases the *power* $(1 - \beta)$ of the test of significance. This condition could also be stated as, "increasing the precision of the design."

The researcher needs, and must seek, a solution to the problem of evaluating the experiment after it has been completed. Since observations by researchers do contain errors, and research is also subject to bias, the experimenter must employ some method which makes it possible to get a valid estimate of the evaluation of his findings. Recent developments in the theory of statistical inference provide the basis for a reasoned systematic procedure for making a valid decision as to the outcome of an experiment, and presenting an acceptable method of evaluation. These types of statistical inference models have been of great value in the evaluation of research in agriculture, labor, finance, education, and the behavioral sciences.

The experimenter must remember that the statistical model is an abstract generalization and only a symbolic representation of an experiment. The decision can be used, trusted, and defended only if the model corresponds closely to the actual experiment. The experimenter must remember that this condition might not be true in all cases. No one can lay claim to the infallibility of an experiment, even with the most exacting statistical procedures and methods available. Sometimes the experimenter's enthusiasm or decision may provide positive results that may be incorrect, but the relative frequency or probability of his making an erroneous decision in a given number of experiments can be stated. The uncritical use of the model in tabulating or evaluating results can lead to decisions whose probability of being erroneous cannot be specified when the properties of the statistical model do not correspond to the properties of the experiment.

The use of a statistical model in decision-making about the results of an experiment presupposes the fulfilment of certain requirements with respect to the correspondence between the experimental situations and the working model. The fulfilment of the requirements for the use of a statistical model is a challenging task to the experimenter, and rarely can the model be expected to meet these requirements exactly. In many instances approximate fulfilment of the requirements must be accepted. The investigator should carefully think, plan, conduct, evaluate, and report his investigations to establish and justify confidence in his work and in himself.

### ADAPTATIONS OF THE GENERAL MODEL TO EXPERIMENTAL RESEARCH PROBLEMS

The principles of experimentation have wide application in the fields of communications, physical, biological, sociological, psychological, and educational research. When a problem is to be "researched" in any of the aforementioned fields, it must of necessity be simplified. One of the most efficient methods for simplifying the research problem and the methods of investigating it, is through the use of some kind of model representing those features considered most important to the problem under study.

The classical model of experimentation was built upon the concept of varying only one factor at a time, while other conditions were kept as uniform and constant as possible. R. A. Fisher and others designed a symbolic model for modern experimentation, which provides for investigation of all factors that arise in "natural" (usual) situations, Fisher's model, based upon probability theory, permitted more complex experiments to the extent that a number of factors could be introduced simultaneously into the same inquiry, and the effects of each factor, as well as the effects of the interaction of factors, could be measured and determined. This "modern" experimental model also covered such essentials of experimental design as replication, randomization, and control of variability. The best analytical techniques for the modern experimental model were found to be the analysis of variance and the analysis of covariance. These techniques made it possible through numerical procedures to account for experimental error, and variation due to the influences of the variables and treatments under study.

The general model of educational research can be modified in certain phases of its elements to satisfy not only the requirements of educational experimentation but to accommodate Fisher's model as well. The phases of the general model dealing with selection of sample, procedures of data collection, and the analytical techniques employed in data processing, are the elements that are modified to accommodate the modern experimental model previously described.

The model of experimental research presented in Part IV, Chapter 30, illustrates the resultant form of the suggested general model after it has been adapted to the type of experiment involved, which is a before and after. The models of the cross-sectional and ex post facto classifications of single-variable and multivariate designs are not illustrated, because the before and after experiment is the one most frequently employed in educational research, and incorporates all of the analytical and numerical procedures involved in the other models.

*Chapter 9—References*

See Bibliography: 2, 4, 8, 16, 18, 24, 29, 35, 38, 49, 54, 56, 58, 62, 64, 65, 66, 77, 94, 100, 102, 104, 113, 116, 141, 143, 148, 149, 150, 155, 158, 159, 170, 172, 175, 183, 188, 191, 200; 5a, 35a, 38a, 84a, 90a, 98a, 101a.

## Chapter Ten

# Descriptive Research

DESCRIPTIVE RESEARCH is a broad category which includes those efforts that describe and interpret certain sets of facts concerned with situations, communities, individuals, groups of individuals, relationships, attitudes, objects, events, classes of events, systems, trends, conditions, processes, or phenomena as they exist at a given time. Particular classifications found under the heading of descriptive research are: normative-survey research, survey research, case study research, community research, comparative analysis research, content analysis research, and trend analysis research. There are undoubtedly other study efforts that could be so classified, but suffice it to say that any research devoted to the gathering of information about prevailing conditions or situations for the purpose of description and interpretation, can be classified as descriptive research.*

Obviously, descriptive research is not merely amassing and tabulating facts.

For example, in judging the work we do, we need not only information describing the work itself, but we must have standards with which to compare the level of work. The goals which direct effort toward a new level are as important (basic) as the starting point or the present status of progress.[1]

Normative-survey research, after collecting data, makes possible the establishment of standards or "norms" for the condition or situation as it is defined to exist.† Such action implies a methodology devoted to the determination of values of particular parameters, or characteristics that might be employed as representative of the "normal" situation, or condition. In the case of survey

---

* The descriptive method of research is fact-finding with interpretation. It may take forms, such as the school or community survey; the genetic or continuity check; the case or case-group study; job and activity analysis, including difficulty analysis; documentary or informational analysis; legal research; and other forms and types of reflective thinking.

The purposes of conducting descriptive research can be: (a) To secure evidence concerning the existing situation or current condition. (b) To identify standards or norms with which to compare present conditions, in order to plan the next step. (c) To determine how to take the next step.

† Three types of normative-survey research are: (1) survey testing, (2) questionnaire inquiries, and (3) documentary frequency studies. Survey testing is used to ascertain the general level of a group with respect to school achievement, intelligence, or personality. Survey testing is carried on widely within school systems. Questionnaire inquiries are adapted to gathering both opinions and attitudes, and have a wide range of application. Documentary frequency studies represent quantitative analyses of written or printed material by counting the frequency with which specified characteristics occur. This method has received extended use as a basic step in curriculum construction, through analyzing uses or goals, errors or shortcomings. This method offers a survey of what is going on or what has taken place in the field of written and printed materials.

research, data are not only gathered, but must be presented in cogent and relative form, in order that the research be meaningful. In some cases, normative and survey research are synthesized or carried on concurrently, and thus normative-survey research describes and interprets data in terms of the standards or normals imposed upon the situations or conditions by the surveyor. Furthermore, in the study of any science, whether it be physical science or social science, one must always be concerned with structures and properties. Descriptive studies often provide valuable clues to causal relationships by revealing the coincidence of certain phenomena or the occurrence of certain apparent consequences.

## Case Study Research

Case study research is frequently termed "descriptive research" because it describes and interprets all pertinent data from a particular case or a limited number of cases. The case under study may relate to one phase of the life history of an individual, an organization, or a situation, or may relate to the entire life history of the subject under study. It usually provides greater depth to the research, and as such contributes to a better and more complete interpretation of the situation or condition than otherwise might have been possible. When the case under study is a community, the community research concerns itself with the description of the individuals, social groups, institutions, economic conditions, physical environment, power, and value structures existing in that community unit. Although it would appear that interpretation of the data is lacking in connection with a community research effort, a moment's consideration of the factors to be described will quickly show that interpretation is essential to any good description of these facets of a community structure.

Case study research is the initiatory phase of the case-study case-work cycle: "The five major phases of the case-study, and case-work cycle ... constitute ... : (1) status of the situation or unit of attention; (2) collection of data, examination, and history; (3) diagnosis and identifications of causal factors; (4) adjustment, treatment, and therapy; and (5) follow up of the adjustment program."[2]

## Comparative and Content Analysis Research

*Comparative analysis* research might be considered extended descriptive research. This statement is based upon the notion that comparison provides a means of discovering additional information to supplement and complement the description and interpretation of data uncovered in the initial stages of an investigation. It also enables us to re-examine our norms and criteria as other conditions change and place them in a new light.

*Content analysis* research deals with systematic examination of current information—be it written, spoken, mechanical, or portrayed in an art form— to provide data that might be categorically classified and evaluated, and thus provide a description and interpretation of a situation or condition not otherwise describable.

*Trend Analysis Research*

Trend analysis research is frequently employed in the fields of economics, sociology, psychology, and education. In essence, trend analysis concerns itself with a longitudinal (time) approach to the study of data. It is a means of connecting comparatively immediate past happenings with current prevalent occurrences in order to prognosticate, within an allowable relative error and at a predetermined level of risk, future events pertaining to the situation or condition under study.*

Thus, descriptive research concerns itself with describing and interpreting data about a situation or condition. This statement implies that descriptive research involves more than merely amassing and tabulating data. Interpretation demands that some type of analysis and evaluation be involved in the process of descriptive research.†

Although the treatment accorded descriptive research here has been little more than elementary, such was the intent at this point of the discussion. For a more profound treatment and discussion, it is recommended that the sources indicated at the end of the chapter be investigated by the reader.

Before proceeding to the adaptation of the general model to a situation calling for descriptive research, the reader is advised to review Figure 1 of the suggested General Model of Educational Research.

---

SURVEY RESEARCH MODEL             MAILED SURVEY TYPE

AN EVALUATION OF A PRE-SERVICE
PROGRAM OF TEACHER EDUCATION BASED
UPON THE OPINIONS OF IN-SERVICE TEACHERS‡

EVALUATION

| PROBLEM |

FORMULATION

*Evaluation of the Problem*

The resourcefulness needed by modern-day teachers demands effective programs and practices in pre-service education. Some authorities believe that a major weakness of pre-service teacher education lies in the discrepancy between theory and practice.

---

* Another type of descriptive research is continuity description. Valuable as a complete status survey may be at any point of time, it is obvious that this check represents only a cross-section report of factors operating in the natural or the human activity realms. A more complete and valuable knowledge about the operation of natural or social forces may be obtained by watching them analytically at stated intervals in their development, over as long periods of time as seem desirable and possible. If detailed and valuable data are desired about progressive changes in development factors in any situation, more frequent steps should be made along the pathway to get pictures of status.

† Descriptive research is reflective thinking actuated and sometimes directed by well-considered objectives and hypotheses. Some criteria are: (1) Descriptive research has a distinctive form with a description of the methodology, sources, and other technical details. (2) Original observations are taken. (3) Each step in the work proceeds with meticulous care and with consideration for the large plan and purpose of the work. The data are verified and evaluated. (4) The data are organized into more general terms and are related to a single, over-all thesis. The data are summarized as systematically as possible. What is done with the data is a definite part of the contribution of the study. (5) The background and general competence of the investigator as well as the spirit with which he works are vital elements.

A teacher education institution cannot know how successful its program is unless the educational product of the institution is taken into account. The analysis of the opinions, attitudes, and performance of the direct consumers of teacher preparation programs should prove significant to the teacher education institution to the extent that the expressed opinions and values held by graduates are realistic assessments of the effectiveness of their preparations in performing the duties and tasks associated with their present teaching assignments.

There is a need to conduct a survey of in-service teachers in order to gather information concerning: (a) the effectiveness of their teacher preparation programs in equipping them to perform adequately the duties and responsibilities of their present positions; and (b) the effectiveness of the predictive measure of "successful teaching" by the selective admission procedure of the teacher education institution.

*Formulation of the Problem*

The purpose of this study is to conduct a mailed survey of a selected group of graduates to gather information for analysis pertaining to:

1. General information and background data.
2. A personal evaluation of the teacher preparation program in terms of course content, course sequence and distribution, student teaching contacts, guidance, selection and admission practices.
3. A personal evaluation of "common" courses that all students are required to take, in terms of: (a) practical value, (b) general professional value, and (c) personal and social value.
4. An analytical evaluation of selected courses using ten prescribed criteria as a guide.
5. Check-list information relative to possible difficulties encountered by beginning teachers.
6. Appraisal of attributes and factors basic to successful teaching.
7. Self-rating of teaching success.
8. Administrator-rating of teaching success.
9. Six factors considered to have a positive relationship to teaching success.

(Comment: *The need and purpose of the study are stated clearly and adequately. The significance of the study is implied, but not stated forthrightly. The reason for the existence of this latter condition undoubtedly lies in the fact that the survey was designed to gather information from the graduates of a particular teacher education institution. Under these conditions the significance of the study is limited, but would be "understood" by the reader.)*

QUESTIONS

NON-HYPOTHESIZED
GENERAL QUESTIONS

STATISTICAL HYPOTHESES (as needed)

*Questions to be Answered*

Questions to be answered by the survey study are:

1. How do graduates evaluate their teacher preparation programs in terms of course content, course sequence and distribution, student teaching contacts, guidance, selection and admissions practices? (1) Superior? (2) Above Average? (3) Average? (4) Below Average? or (5) Weak?
2. What is the value of the "common" courses in terms of practical values, general professional values, and personal and social values?
3. What is the profile of an analytical evaluation of selected courses using ten prescribed criteria as evaluation guides?
4. What are the possible difficulties most frequently encountered by the beginning teacher?
5. What attributes and factors are considered basic to successful teaching by the comparatively "new" in-service teacher?

---

‡ Unpublished doctoral dissertation by Don Davis, Wayne State University, Detroit, 1952. In order to illustrate all elements of the survey research model, certain aspects of the dissertation have been modified with the author's permission.

6. What are the results of a self-rating of teaching success by the respondents participating in the survey?

7. What are the results of an administrator-rating of the teaching success of respondents participating in the survey?

8. Does the survey show that the participating respondents feel that a certain six factors have a positive relationship to teaching success?

*Statistical Hypotheses*

In those cases where statistical inference can be employed in deriving answers to general questions, statistical hypotheses will be employed. Similar to the case of operational hypotheses, the statement of the question to be answered will serve as a basis for deriving the statistical alternative hypothesis ($H_1$). After $H_1$ has been determined, the corresponding null hypothesis ($H_0$) can be cast and then submitted to test.

(Comment: *The following assumptions were considered fundamental to the study:* (1) *The effectiveness of a teacher preparation program is best demonstrated by the degree to which it meets the needs of those individuals who have followed it and are being called upon for services that the preparation program was designed to teach;* (2) *Recent graduates are in a strategic position to evaluate critically and reliably the strengths and weaknesses of their programs of preparation. Definitions of key terms have been omitted.*)

The source of data for the study is a finite universe composed of graduates from a given teacher education institution during a defined period of time. Each graduate included in the population must have followed one of the four major programs listed as: (1) a four year program for elementary school certification; (2) a four year program for secondary school certification; (3) a five year program for certification and a master's degree in certain fields of secondary education (e.g., business education, or mathematics education); or (4) a post degree program leading to either the elementary certificate or the secondary school teaching certificate.

Specifically, the population is composed of 946 individuals who had graduated from a particular teacher education institution during the period of August, 1947, through February, 1950, inclusive. Since a mailed questionnaire was to be the main vehicle of data collection, the sample of the study was to be composed of those persons who responded to the mailing request.

(Comment: *Further description of the universe is omitted here in the interest of discussing the adaptation of the general model to this type of research effort.*)

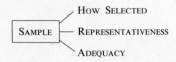

*How Sample of Study was Selected*

The method of selecting the sample for this study is highly related to the processes of data collection. The first step was to mail the questionnaire to each of the 946 individuals composing the population of the study. The mailing of the questionnaire was timed so that each person would receive the instrument during the week following Christmas day. It was assumed here that the graduates would have more free time to respond to the questionnaire during a vacation period than otherwise would be possible. The questionnaire was mailed on a Wednesday in order that it might be delivered to the potential respondents well toward the end of the week. This procedure was followed because research revealed that "questionnaires tend to be filled out during weekends by respondents." The document was also mailed as fourth-class matter, including all mimeographed materials containing instructions, letters of request, and other similar printed matter.

The return of the questionnaire was provided for through first-class mail. A postal permit from the United States Postal Department was required. An envelope bearing the statement "return postage will be paid by the sender" was used for the return of the questionnaire. The advantage of this procedure is that neither the respondent nor the sender need bother with a stamp. A disadvantage in the procedure occurs with the delay associated with the weighing of each envelope by the postal authorities for "postage due."

Since a follow-up letter was planned to be sent by first-class mail, thus guaranteeing its being forwarded or returned, the original "mail-out" was effected through the more economical fourth-class mail procedures. A slight disadvantage of fourth-class mail, however, is that the sender has no way of knowing whether the questionnaire reaches its destination, since forwarding and returning privileges are not accorded fourth-class materials.

In carrying out follow-up procedures, a graph of daily returns was maintained. Follow-up letters were first sent when 39 per cent of the original questionnaires and self-rating scales were received. The results of the first follow-up were held separate from the original returns. A second follow-up letter was sent after 89 per cent of the total number of questionnaires and self-rating scales had been received. The results of the second follow-up were held separate from the other data. The cut-off date for receiving questionnaires was 104 days after the original mail-out. The usable returns composed 49.9 per cent of the total number of questionnaires mailed originally. This per cent return compares very favorably with the majority of mail surveys which tend to range between 5 per cent and 20 per cent of *usable* returns. The term "usable" is included here to define the fact that unless a completed questionnaire and self-rating scale, accompanied by an administrator-rating scale, were available for a respondent, his file was considered incomplete and unusable.

Approximately 473 questionnaires, each accompanied by a self-rating scale and an administrator-rating scale, made up the total sample of the study. The data of the usable sample associated with the original mail-out, those of the one associated with the first follow-up, and those of the one associated with the second follow-up, were analyzed separately for differences in responses. After the separate analyses, the data of the total usable sample were analyzed for total findings of the survey.

### Representativeness of Sample

In the original distribution of potential respondents, 752 of the 946 were graduates of the four-year elementary or secondary certificate programs. If the proportionate quota method of sampling were to be employed, the smallest representative sample of this stratum would be composed of approximately three hundred cases drawn from that segment of the population. Many of the curriculum areas with very few graduates could be represented by one case, and others by a small number of cases that would prove difficult to analyze statistically. In view of these facts, it was decided that the samples resulting from the "returns" would be allowed to represent those strata of the population that, in fact, they did represent. Put in another way, if an area showing few graduates was not represented in the returns it was considered to be non-existent in the population.

(Comment: *Fortunately each stratum of the population was represented in each of the response samples.*)

Differences between the original returns, those accruing to the first follow-up, and those associated with the second follow-up letter are as follows:

1. Graduates who made the highest honor point averages showed a strong tendency to answer questionnaires sooner, and in greater numbers, than those who achieved comparatively low grade point averages.
2. An average age differential of 3.3 years was found between the early and late (follow-ups) respondents. The younger persons answered early, and in greater numbers, than did the older group.
3. More males responded early than did females.
4. Teachers whose self-rating and administrator-ratings were below average tended to return questionnaires during the second follow-up stage more frequently than in either of the first two stages.

*Adequacy of Sample*

If the researcher assumed a dichotomous population composed of responses that could be broadly classified as either favorable or unfavorable, an adequacy of sample size formula for estimating the population proportion ($P$) of the "desirable" characteristic present, with an allowable sampling error of $d$, would be

$$n = \left[\frac{z\sigma}{d}\right]^2$$

where $n$ denotes the size of the sample, $z$ denotes the standard normal deviate associated with the desired confidence interval, and $\sigma$ is an estimate of the standard deviation of the dichotomous population. Under such conditions, it is desirable to set $\sigma = .5$ (the most variable condition of a dichotomous population). If a 95 per cent confidence interval for the estimate of $P$ to the nearest 5 per cent were desired, the formula would become:

$$n = \left[\frac{(1.96)(.5)}{.05}\right]^2 = [19.6]^2 \approx 385$$

This result shows that a sample size of $n \approx 385$ is adequate to establish a 95 per cent confidence interval from $(p - .05)$ to $(p + .05)$, for an estimate of $P$, where $p$ denotes the proportion of the "desirable" characteristic found in a sample of size $n$.

(Comment: *The foregoing describes one method of establishing the size of an adequate sample for the study. For other methods, see Chapter 17.*)

DATA COLLECTION ⟨ CONDITIONS / METHODS

*Conditions of Data Collection*

The conditions of data collection existing in the study are:

1. Graduates included in the unverse of the study were distributed over a wide geographical area.
2. A relatively large number of graduates were to be involved in the study.
3. A three-year time period since graduation allows the graduate the establishment of sufficient experience upon which to base the appraisal of his preparation program.
4. A three-year time period is of relatively short duration and permits the graduate to recall significant experiences in his preparation program.

*Methods of Data Collection*

The methods of data collection involve the instrumentalities employed and the procedures followed in collecting the data.

*Instrumentalities.* The instrumentalities used in the study were: (1) the questionnaire; (2) the self-rating scale; and (3) the administrator-rating scale. The questionnaire was composed of seven parts and collected the following data: (a) general information and background data; (b) evaluation information concerning teacher-preparation programs in terms of course content, course sequence and distribution, student teaching contacts, guidance, and selection admission procedures; (c) information concerning courses all students were required to take, in terms of: practical value, general professional value, and personal and social value; (d) information concerning analytical evaluation of selected courses using ten prescribed criteria as a guide; (e) check-list information about possible difficulties encountered by beginning teachers; (f) information pertaining to attributes and factors considered basic to successful teaching; and (g) information resulting from an analysis of one's own teaching. The self-rating scale and the administrator-rating scale were parallel instruments containing six factors considered to have a positive relationship to teaching success. Each question pertaining to the factors was "scaled" in terms of five divisions: (1) Superior; (2) Above Average; (3) Average; (4) Below Average; and (5) Weak.

(Comment: *The establishment of the reliability and validity of the data-gathering instruments were effected by means of a pilot study. These factors were checked throughout the study by the separate analysis of data associated with each of the stages of the study: original, first follow-up and the second follow-up.*)

*Procedures.* The procedures of data collection are essentially those described under the element of the model dealing with how the sample of the model was selected.

DATA PROCESSING
CLASSIFYING
ANALYTIC TECHNIQUES

### Classification of the Data

The data produced by the study are of three types: (1) those of the nominal scale of measurement; (2) those of the ordinal scale of measurement; and (3) those of the interval scale of measurement. The data of primary importance to the study are those associated with the nominal scale of measurement. These data pertain to evaluation of courses, analysis of student teaching contacts, and other similar matters. Data of secondary importance are those of the interval scale associated with honor point averages, test scores, and quantitative analyses of certain aspects of the teacher preparation program. Of tertiary importance are the ordinal data (scales) associated with the self-rating and administrator-rating of teaching merit and success.

### Analytic Techniques Employed

Arrangements made with the tabulations department permitted the transfer of the data to Hollerith cards. A total of 2,724 cards were needed to record the coded information produced by the study. Analytic techniques employed were: (1) content analysis; (2) $\eta$ (eta) the correlation ratio coefficient, see Chapter 21; (3) the $t$-test of significant difference of group means; and (4) the $t$-test for determining the significance of a correlation coefficient, see Chapter 27.

(Comment: *In addition to the statistical techniques described above, simple arithmetical and logical analyses were employed. Some of these analyses involved simple per cents, differences, and qualities of statements.*)

RESEARCH DECISION
INTERPRETATION
INFERENCE
EVALUATION

### Interpretation of the Data

The interpretation of the data produced by a survey study results in many of the inferences of the study. For this reason the interpretation aspect of the research decision element of the model, when adapted to survey studies, is integrated with the inference aspect of the decision element.

### Inferences

The interpretations of the data, and inferences drawn from them, are as follows:

1. In the main, the graduates seemed to be reasonably well-satisfied with the amount of course work required and the electives made possible by the teacher preparation curriculum.

2. Of the 473 respondents involved in the study, 222 felt the need for additional instruction in the methods courses. Approximately 40 per cent felt there was little correlation between methods courses and student teaching.

3. Approximately 53 per cent desired further freedom in the choice of courses.

4. Sizable minorities expressed desire for more extensive experiences in the area of basic education courses, student teaching, cultural courses, and specialized courses.

5. Approximately 21 per cent of the sample could discern little or no functional sequence in the courses.

(Comment: *A grand total of fifty-seven inferences were drawn as answers to the general questions posed in that element of the model of the study. The purpose of this section is to show how the general model can be adapted to the "interpretations" and "inferences" aspects of the survey type of research. For this reason only five of the "interpretations-inferences" have been shown. From this short example, the reader may attain a rough idea of the format of the "decision" element of the general model when adapted to a survey type of study.*)

*Evaluation*

The evaluation of the study can be effected by employing the procedures found on pages 80-88. This activity is left as an exercise for the reader.

(Comment: *The general questions raised as guide lines to the survey were answered very adequately. The principal findings and conclusions of the survey were amply and clearly stated. The study, as a survey effort, including a matching survey, was well done.*)

## Chapter 10—References

See Bibliography: 1, 2, 15, 17, 22, 23, 33, 50, 56, 63, 73, 78, 81, 82, 83, 88, 90, 97, 100, 102, 116, 122, 134, 137, 140, 145, 149, 150, 151, 152, 155, 161, 194, 195; 2a, 3a, 28a, 33a, 36a, 47a, 54a, 57a, 76a, 86a, 87a, 88a, 90a, 94a, 112a.

# *Action Research*

ACTION RESEARCH is employed by many educators throughout the United States. It is considered to be a scientific method whereby educators can define, guide, correct, and evaluate their problems and make decisions wisely. Action research, used widely, can assist educators in developing a "scientific-practical" approach to understanding individual and group behavior, solving various types of problems, and implementing research findings more rapidly than heretofore possible.

The significant elements of a design for action research are:

1. The identification of a problem area about which an individual or a group is concerned.
2. Selection of a specific problem.
3. Selection of a working hypothesis or prediction that implies a goal and a procedure.
4. Careful recording of action taken and accumulation of evidence.
5. Generalizations from this evidence regarding relations between actions and desired goals.
6. Continuous evaluation and retesting in action situations.

The best way to learn to engage in action research is to try it. According to Blum, action research, as employed in the social sciences, concerns itself with the diagnosis of a social problem from the viewpoint of helping improve the situation.[1] He further claims that all action research can be resolved in two stages:

1. A diagnostic stage in which the problems are being analyzed and the hypotheses are being developed.
2. A therapeutic stage in which the hypotheses are tested by a consciously directed change experiment, preferably in a social "life" situation.

In a different type of setting, that of education, Corey defines action research to be that particular type of research which is undertaken by on-the-job practitioners in order that they might improve their practices.[2] The action researcher attempts to improve the educational practices in which he is engaged. The hope of the researcher is that he will be able to improve the practices of his situation on the basis of the findings of his research. In short, the purpose of action research is to effect action by practitioners in order to affect the actions of the daily, on-going situation. The intent is to improve the current practices in a specific school or community setting wherein the practitioners are not satisfied with their achievement. Self-evaluation is a basic feature of the action research process. Action research may be conducted by a single individual or a team.

When action research is conducted by an individual, the researcher must be interested in improving the educational practices in which he is engaged, as well as in adding to that body of educational research knowledge which he already possesses. The researcher must desire to improve his task of educating, and be willing to employ an "action" method to measure whether he accomplished his purposes. The action researcher needs to have a great deal of experience in the cooperative study of educational problems. He must be able to work effectively with others who are also involved in the situation he is trying to improve.[3] Most proponents of the "action" type of inquiry believe that it is doubtful that many of the improvements that should be made in teaching, supervising, or administering can be achieved if only one person is involved in changing his ideas and practices. Thus, cooperative action research is more greatly emphasized.

Cooperative action research involves the combined efforts of a group of persons. In an educational setting, the group is usually composed of teachers, administrators, pupils, parents, boards of education, and other community people. The object of cooperative action research, in this context, is to obtain whatever data might be necessary in order to determine whether certain practices actually lead to anticipated results.

The Michigan Association for Supervision and Curriculum Development describes the steps in such cooperative action research as follows:

1. The people are concerned about a problem, realize they will be affected by the solution, and decide to do something about the problems.
2. They set up better directions (hypotheses) than those being used.
3. The plan of courses of action is tried out. Data regarding how it worked or didn't work are collected.
4. Evaluations are made by the group. Decisions are made as to whether the persons concerned have better ways of dealing with the original problem.[4]

It is true that some doubts have been expressed as to whether action research can be called a separate and modern methodology to be contrasted with traditional methods of inquiry.[5] In order to clarify this point we present Corey's impressions of the distinctions between individuals interested in fundamental research and those interested in action research.[6]

| *Traditional or Fundamental Research* | *Action Research* |
|---|---|
| Purpose: To establish new generalizations, explanatory principles, or scientific laws. Hypotheses tested so as to justify conclusions extending beyond the populations and situations studied. Makes extensive use of sampling theory and describes population or situation universes. | Purpose: Not immediately concerned with adding truth to body of knowledge found in books. Researcher wishes to improve practices in which he is engaged. |

| *Traditional or Fundamental Research (cont.)* | *Action Research (cont.)* |
|---|---|
| Researcher doesn't work directly to get data and generalization into action, unless they pertain to his own methods of work. Researcher is a student of educational phenomena. | Researcher is a participant in educational activities—a practitioner. No research function without the practice function. |
| Is concerned about the slowness with which research findings affect practice. Says the problem is one of communication. | Contends the difficulty is deeper than one of communication and involves principles of learning. Claims teacher likely to change his practice with pupils due to information accumulated in order to work more effectively with them. |
| Places high value on sampling procedures. | More interested in specific students. |
| Inviolability of design. Study is carefully planned before launching. Design meticulously followed throughout study. | Initial design not inviolable. Problem definition, hypotheses, and method undergo modification as results are validated in practice. Impossible to know in advance what will develop. |
| Great competence is required in the type of logical analysis represented by mathematical statistics. | Less significant for action researchers since they are not extending generalizations beyond their particular populations. Skills in cooperative study and in team work needed. |
| Judged to be superior in the degree to which the method and findings warrant generalizing to persons and situations beyond those studied. Should add knowledge to that already recorded. | The value is determined by the extent to which the methods and findings make possible improvements in practice. |
| Believes that the establishment of enduring laws and principles will improve educational practices. | Knows he must generalize beyond his data. Is interested in applying his findings tomorrow. |

In summarizing the description of action research, it can be pointed out that in addition to contributing to problem-solving, action research has the characteristic of involving the practitioner. This characteristic lends action research the added strength of serving as a vehicle of in-service research training on the job.

There is no way of defining "official" researchers and non-researchers. It is not an all or nothing classification but a continuum containing all shades of grey ranging from black to white. We all have hunches about how things might be made better. When we act on these hunches and then observe the results we are doing research. Granted, not at a high level of sophistication, but none the less research. The sophistication usually lies in the refinement of the hypotheses or theories and the techniques employed, but the basic models do not change. All too often, as the development of hypotheses and refinement of techniques reach a high level of sophistication in a study, emphasis is shifted from concentration on the problem under study to the means used in solving the problem. Action research remains problem centered and is not restricted by sophisticated means and theories.

Different research methods require different frames of reference for their evaluation. Some types of research emphasize one part of the research model more than other types do. Action research does not add necessarily to that body of knowledge previously recorded nor must it apply to situations beyond those studied. These areas are criteria for evaluating fundamental research and play a much lesser role in evaluating action research. Action research, to have value, must be determined by the extent to which findings and methods make improvement possible in actual practice. Corey further states: "Action research is justified when it adds to the practitioner's functional knowledge about phenomena with which he must deal. This type of research cannot be considered apart from social or educational aims."[7]

Action research functions best when it is cooperative action research. This method of research incorporates the ideas and expectations of all persons involved in the situation. Cooperative action research has the concomitants of beneficial effects for workers, and the improvement of the services, conditions, and functions of the situation. In education this activity translates into more practice in research and problem-solving by teachers, administrators, pupils, and certain community personnel, while the quality of teaching and learning is in the process of being improved.

A demonstration of action research is now presented to show how the suggested general model of educational research can be adapted to one of these types of situations.

---

ACTION RESEARCH MODEL                                              GROUP TYPE

(Data are Fictitious)

### A CURRICULUM IMPROVEMENT PROJECT

*Evaluation of the Problem*

The need for the study was found in the necessity for a teacher-administrator group to work together to effect a curriculum improvement project in a particular subject area of an urban junior high school. The significance of the study was confined to the members of the faculty of the school who participated in the action effort, and any benefits that might have accrued to student learning through the change in the curriculum.

*Formulation of the Problem*

The purpose of the study was to establish a teacher-administrator group, which in turn would initiate, organize, conduct, and evaluate a curriculum improvement project in a given department of a certain urban junior high school over a period of forty weeks. Specifically, members of the group were to employ a variety of instructional methods; exchange suggestions with each other; try, test, and develop new methods, techniques and courses for the area of instruction; increase their self-confidence in defining problems; modify their classroom practices; work closely with the head of the department of the curriculum area involved; and work closely with the principal of the school where the study was being carried out.

(Comment: *The need and purpose of the study are stated, but its "true" significance, at best, is implied.*)

*Questions to be Answered*

General questions to be answered by the group action research project are as follows:

1. Under what conditions can curriculum change best be effected?
2. What are limiting factors to bringing about effective curriculum change?
3. What strong points of the group action research method and work-group-conference technique can be employed in effecting curriculum change?
4. Where did weaknesses occur in the employment of group action research methods in bringing about curriculum change?

*Statistical Hypotheses*

In conducting analyses for statistical differences between "control" and "experimental" groups, statistical alternative hypotheses ($H_1$) of difference were cast, and their accompanying "nulls" ($H_0$) were submitted to test.

(Comment: *Two basic assumptions were made by the action research group:* (1) *The curricular experiences of pupils are determined in large measure by the values, goals, skills, and attitudes held by teachers;* (2) *In order to change the curriculum it follows that there must be undertaken an attempt to change the values, goals, skills, and attitudes of the people involved in respect to education, but more specifically in respect to interpersonal relations among members of a working group.*)

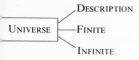

The source of data for this group action study is, for all practical purposes, an infinite one composed of: (1) the twelve members of the study group; (2) the methods and techniques of instruction employed by the group members; (3) the materials of instruction (new and old) used by the members of the group; (4) interactions between the members during group planning and discussion sessions; (5) the modifications of the curriculum tested and examined by the group members; (6) the methods and techniques of evaluation employed by members in class and in group planning and discussion sessions; (7) the various aspects of group action research examined by the group members in the attempt to determine the strong points and weaknesses of this approach to curriculum change. Under the conditions of an infinite universe, it was necessary to adopt a sampling procedure.

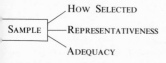

*How Sample of Study was Selected*

The samples of the study were "self-generating," so to speak, i.e., they "evolved" out of the activities of the group members, and the operations of the group. In terms of its operation, the project was organized around two focal points: (1) the regular group meetings held after school, every other week, over a period of forty weeks; and (2) the instructional change experiments involving methods, materials, testing situations, and classroom operations. Samples of various "activities" of the group were selected from the universe by means of factual records made by the secretary. Other samples were drawn in the form of test scores, anecdotal records, and progress reports.

### Representativeness

The sample of the study was assumed to be representative of the population from which it was drawn. Actually, the sample of any situation involved in the project was a judgment-purposive one. The purpose of the group tended to direct the selection of the activity to be recorded by the secretary. The judgment involved was that exercised by the recorder. In the case of test scores and other measurements of students, the samples involved were also taken to satisfy the purposes of the group, and were drawn on the basis of judgments made by the teachers who were participating in the project.

### Adequacy

The adequacy of the "sizes" of the samples drawn throughout the course of the study were not considered by the group members. All samples were assumed to be adequate for the purposes of the project.

(Comment: *Although the sampling procedures of group action research tend to be defined more precisely than those associated with individual action research projects, the sampling designs of each type are poor compared to those associated with fundamental research designs.*)

CONDITIONS

DATA COLLECTION

METHODS

### Conditions of Data Collection

The conditions of data collection associated with the action study were:

1. The biweekly group meetings were aimed at planning, discussion, and evaluation of methods, processes, materials, pupil interactions, and modifications of curriculum that were "tried" by teachers in their classrooms.

2. All members of the action research group worked on the same problem: the improvement of the instruction of English in a particular junior high school.

3. Each teacher who was a member of the group was free to work on a problem in the teaching of English which he considered most important to the improvement of instruction of the subject.

4. The average length of time of the biweekly group meetings was approximately two hours.

5. The members of the group focused their attentions on the following topics: reading, grammar, composition, spelling, handwriting, and speech, in the actual teaching of English.

6. In the group sessions, the major concerns were: interactions between group members; group processes; amount of participation by each group member; and notice of the continually evolving "situational frame of reference."

7. A factual record of each meeting was kept by the secretary.

### Methods of Data Collection

The instrumentalities and procedures of data collection employed in the project were:

*Instrumentalities.* The instrumentalities employed in the study were locally constructed and standardized tests designed to measure achievement in: reading, spelling, grammar usage, composition, and speech. An "opinionaire" was administered twice, during the course of the study, to all members of the group. The opinionaire sought to discover: (1) what the teacher-members of the group perceived the roles of the principal, department chairman, supervisor, and coordinator to be, in effecting the curriculum change sought by the action project team; (2) what data, ideas, opinions, or impressions the group members realized by their participation in the study; and (3) what effect the study, through its group sessions and "experimentations," had on the teacher-members' approach to the instruction of English.

The focus of the data-gathering instrumentalities was: (1) attempting to determine the "growth" of the participants in communication skills, interpersonal relations, and the utilization of group processes; (2) attempting to measure the "growth" of group members in research techniques and appreciation of such tasks; (3) measuring changes in self-perception; (4) measuring awareness and understanding of power structures in groups; (5) appraisal of methods and materials of instruction employed in the teaching of English.

*Procedures.* The data of the action project were collected by the following procedures:

1. The secretary maintained factual records of each of the twenty biweekly group sessions.

2. Group members were asked to submit "meeting notes" at the end of each session.

3. Each teacher submitted five "progress reports" throughout the course of the study (forty weeks). The progress reports were used to keep the group informed about the various "research" projects being conducted by the members.

4. During the last week of the project, each member of the group submitted a final written report on the projects that he had carried out during the course of the study.

5. The opinionaires were administered during the nineteenth and thirty-ninth weeks of the project.

6. Tests were given to pupils, in the various topics previously mentioned, throughout the course of the project. These data were used to explain and embellish topics covered in the members' reports to the group.

7. Members of the group were asked to submit self-evaluation and group-evaluation reports during the thirty-sixth week of the project.

(Comment: *The report of procedures of data collection is difficult to organize for group action research projects. Data are continually being collected, and sometimes group members are unaware of these procedures.*)

CLASSIFYING

DATA PROCESSING

ANALYTICAL TECHNIQUES

### Classification of the Data

The data collected by the study were of two types: (1) the nominal scale of measurement; and (2) the interval scale of measurement. The data of the nominal scale of measurement were those resulting from content analyses of the multitude of written materials produced by the study. Much of the written material was left in its report-form style, thus producing "statement" data. The data of the interval scale of measurement were those in the form of pupil test scores.

The primary data of the study were those associated with the description of the solution of problems confronted in the teaching of English. Data of secondary importance were those connected with the description of how action research affected understandings and operations of group members. Data of tertiary importance were those collected by the opinionaires.

### Analytic Techniques Employed

Since little of the data collected in the study could be quantified, written materials were analyzed for meaning. Content analysis was employed where possible, and simple chi-square statistical treatment of "evolved" categories was employed in certain situations.

(Comment: *The analytic techniques employed in action research are usually dictated by the existing need at a given time.*)

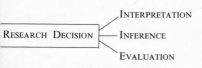

INTERPRETATION

RESEARCH DECISION — INFERENCE

EVALUATION

### Interpretation of Data

The interpretation of the data associated with group action research is usually closely associated with the inferences drawn for the project. In the study reported here the interpretation of data was accomplished by means of logical analysis of written materials; comparisons between written materials and oral presentations made during group meetings; analysis of behavior patterns of individuals in the group setting; and the noting of patterns of change in operation of the group.

### Inferences

Based upon reports of the participating teachers, plus those of the teaching department chairman, there was good evidence of modifications in classroom procedures employed by seven of the ten teacher-members of the group. In the other three cases, changes of significance were not observed.

The data showed that a variety of instructional approaches had been tried and tested. Many of the teachers realized an increase in self-confidence as the result of these "experimentations."

The ability of the teacher-members to define problems and confront issues "squarely" was improved in almost all cases. The candidness of members of the group at the termination of the project reflected a more objective approach to problem-solving than that which existed prior to the "experiment."

The principal's role permits him the freedom to become an "instructional" leader if he so desires. The role of the department chairman does not provide such flexibility.

Group action research can be employed effectively to change curriculum and improve classroom instruction. The improvement of classroom instruction varied from teacher to teacher over the forty week period, but each teacher reported that the project afforded more opportunities to improve instruction than did the conventional approach to teaching.

A total evaluation of the project would show that: (1) over a forty week period the attitudes and skills of teachers changed sufficiently to permit a democratic, experimentation-oriented approach to classroom instruction to exist; and (2) although *great* curricular changes did not occur in the project, the insights and skills acquired by each teacher during the course of the study should make for better action research in the school in the future.

### Evaluation

The evaluation of the study is left as an exercise to the student. The evaluation should be conducted by means of the procedures stated on pages 80–88, tempered by Corey's remarks found on pages 118–120.

(Comment: *Some of the inferences associated with this study are fictitious. The fictitious inferences were provided to "round out" the decision element of the model.*)

### Chapter 11—References

See Bibliography: 11, 16, 17, 39, 51, 79, 82, 92, 94, 114, 138, 150, 154; 1a, 4a, 10a, 16a, 27a, 51a, 52a, 80a, 118a.

### Chapter Twelve

# *Historical Research*

IT SHOULD BE NOTED that any recorded history will usually tend to be both selective and accumulative. By its very nature, however, a history must always be more than just a collection of a series of disconnected and unrelated chronological events—it must also account for the "pieces" that do not seem to fit the puzzle. Were it merely a collection of events, there would be no real way of correlating the apparent contradictions that seem to exist in every age. Without the points of view that seem to grow out of the contradictions, borrowing aspects of the preceding contradictory points and discarding others as well, a history would not be an integrated account of past events. Should this ever be the case, the history could not be rightly considered as being in the true spirit of critical inquiry.

## DEFINITION AND USES

Historical research, which is also referred to as "documentary research," is basically that method of systematic inquiry which seeks data from personal experiences and observations, documents and records. It may be thought of as being the method of inquiry which attempts to encompass and then explain the whole realm of man's past in a perspective that greatly accents his social, cultural, economic, and intellectual development. It places much more emphasis and value upon the evaluation of the total effect of the given condition than it does upon the specific events and/or conditions that may have caused it to occur. The historical method, then, is concerned with a broad view of the conditions and not necessarily the specifics that helped to bring them about.

What is the value of historical research? Many answers could be given to this question, but they would all probably fall into one of the following categories: (1) to inquire into the past for solutions to contemporary problems; (2) to shed light upon present and future trends; (3) to stress the relative importance and the effects of the various interactions that are to be found within all cultures; and (4) to re-evaluate data in the light of proving (or disproving) the hypotheses, theories, and/or generalizations that are presently held about the past. The ability of history to employ the past to predict the future, and to use the present to explain the past, gives it a dual and unique quality which makes it especially useful for all sorts of scholarly study and research.

Historical research is frequently used in the attempt to prove theories and/or perform functions that rightly are not within its realm or scope of operation. At times, it is mistakenly thought that research alone can produce real historical information by delving into old newspaper articles, records of legislative proceedings, recorded eye-witness accounts, or biographical writings. Unless such historical accounts as do exist are actually factual, unbiased ones, describing *all* aspects of the specific situations under study, they are of little real worth. Eyewitnesses giving only a limited or biased description of a happening were as prevalent in the past as they are in the present. Obviously, biased informational sources also tend to lack a *critical* inquiry into the *whole* truth. It is obvious that any conclusions derived under such circumstances would not be wholly valid.

The evaluation and formulation of the problem associated with historical research involves the personality of the researcher to a greater extent than do the other basic types of research. Personal factors of the investigator such as interest, motivation, "historical curiosity," and educational background for the interpretation of historical "facts," tend to influence the selection of the problem to a great extent.

Historical research demands intensive investigation of all details associated with the problem. The details, including those that are relatively obscure, are not investigated for their individual worth, but for the contributions they make to the historical condition under study.

The specific source of data is highly important to the performance of good historical research. Data employed in documentary (historical) research can be classified under one of two sources: (1) primary, or (2) secondary. Primary sources of data are those items that are "original" to the problem under study. Remains or relics of a period, records of oral or written evidence, a written account composed by an author who actually witnessed the events he describes, original art objects, manuscripts, documents, or any other information which is (intentionally or unintentionally) capable of transmitting a first-hand account of an event are all considered to be primary sources of data. Secondary sources are composed of all data pertaining to the condition under study that cannot be classified as "original." Such items as quoted material, prints of paintings, replicas of art objects, reports written by persons who were not actually in attendance of the events being described, textbooks, and other reproductions of material or information are all considered as secondary sources of data.

The importance of using primary sources of data in historical research cannot be over-emphasized. In the process of conducting historical research the investigator should never be satisfied with copies of documents that can be obtained in original form. Photostatic copies of documents, however, are considered to be primary sources of data. Relatively insignificant errors in reproduction processes may, through additive or multiplicative effects, produce a resultant error of comparatively great magnitude in the final form of the data. This condition is particularly well-illustrated in reporting census data in various forms and indexes, where these final forms are derived through the operations of addition, subtraction, multiplication, and/or division.

Although the primary sources of data produce the most reliable and valid information, the value of secondary sources should not be discounted too greatly. For example, if the nature of the historical study is such that the geographical and/or physical setting might possibly have significance for the determination of events under consideration, a visit to the locale could possibly provide the investigator with more insight concerning the matter than could months of study involving many documents from primary sources of data. Secondary sources of data like the one just described can be highly contributory to more valid and reliable historical research efforts than otherwise might be possible.

HISTORICAL CRITICISM

The mere collection of volumes of historical data concerning a given problem area has little significance unless the data are subjected to historical criticism. The criticism of historical data is dichotomous and is composed of: (1) external (lower) criticism; and (2) internal (higher) criticism.

External historical criticism concerns itself with the authenticity of the data, i.e., the determination of whether the data are true representations of the facts. By using the methods of external criticism, the investigator engaged in historical research attempts to ascertain the degree to which the data are free from inadvertent errors, frauds and forgeries, distortions, and inventions. External criticism, then, is more concerned with analytic forms of the data than it is with the interpretation or meaning of them for the condition under study.

Internal historical criticism is concerned with the meaning and reliability of the data that pass the external test. The emphasis of internal criticism is on the determination of the validity of each datum within its source, i.e., transferring the concern from the form of the data to the meaning of each datum and its implication for the condition under study. In reality, then, internal criticism becomes a test of the credibility, literal meaning, and real meaning of each datum for the condition under examination, and a test for bias, prejudice, competence, and accuracy of the source (contributor).

Although criticism is very important to good historical research, it need not be carried to the extreme where the researcher becomes cynical and hypercritical. For further discussion of criticism and its application in historical research see Good and Scates.[1]

After the data have been collected, processed, and subjected to the various tests of criticism, the researcher can proceed to prepare the historical manuscript. In preparing the manuscript, consideration must be given to all of the principles generally employed for the presentation of data associated with the other types of basic research. The following guide-lines are valuable for preparing the report associated with historical research:

1. The historical research report cannot be any better than the scholarship and data that went into its formulation.
2. A good system of notes can help to:
   (a) master and digest the material,
   (b) speed the classification of data, and
   (c) form a working outline for the actual writing.

3. History can be written in a simple and concise manner if:
   (a) all unnecessary data are deleted,
   (b) good literary judgment is employed,
   (c) emotional dramatization is avoided,
   (d) flowery and/or exaggerated rhetoric is not used, and
   (e) "simplicity" is the guiding factor.
4. There should be some major themes, or a guiding thesis, readily evident throughout the presentation.
5. Good history always has progression—the story must have sufficient forward movement.
6. A certain amount of narration may be necessary to fill in certain gaps that may exist in the history.

To illustrate how the general model of educational research can be adapted to a historical research project, James Ross Irwin's doctoral dissertation, *Wayne University—A History*, is modified and presented in the form of the model.

---

HISTORICAL RESEARCH MODEL                          INSTITUTIONAL TYPE

### WAYNE UNIVERSITY—A HISTORY*

PROBLEM — EVALUATION
         — FORMULATION

*Evaluation of the Problem*

The story of Wayne University is replete with information and incidents that, properly compiled, should be of interest to all persons concerned with educational activities. Wayne University is unique in that its establishment in Detroit in 1933 saw for the first time in America a university in the fullest sense of the term existing within a public school district and under its jurisdiction.

The recording of the steps in the evolution of such an institution will not only be valuable to students of education but also to city and university officers who may contemplate the organization and administration of a similar university in other communities. This study will enable them to profit by the experience of Wayne University.

Furthermore, the need for a complete history that provides an accurate, comprehensive, and current treatment of the university is obvious. By tracing the history of Wayne University a significant chapter in the story of the rise of the municipal university will have been recorded. As such, the study should make further contributions to existing educational knowledge.

*Formulation of the Problem*

The purpose of the study is to present: (1) the principal facts that led to the establishment of a municipal university in Detroit; and (2) the roles of the several individuals who were largely responsible for the founding of the university.

The study will be limited to an analysis of the data pertaining to the development of the university from its founding date, 1933, to a point in time six months prior to the writing of the study report. As a result of this approach, an analysis and evaluation of the present administration is not included in the study. The delimitation imposed by the "six months" time restriction is not a serious one, however, because it is impossible, at the present time, to analyze and evaluate, with any degree of

---

* Unpublished doctoral dissertation by James Ross Irwin, Wayne University, Detroit 1951; modification of the form of the dissertation with the permission of the author.

accuracy or precision, the long-range development program of the present University administration.

(Comment: *The need and purpose of the study are clearly stated. The significance of the study is well-established.*)

NON-HYPOTHESIZED
GENERAL QUESTIONS

QUESTIONS

STATISTICAL HYPOTHESES (as needed)

*Questions to be Answered*

Questions to be answered by the study are:

1. What were the problems of financial support confronted by the university during the period of time covered by the study?

2. Who were the persons that contributed significantly to the founding and continuing success of the university during the period of time covered by the study?

3. What were the roles of the persons who contributed significantly to the cause of the university and made its founding and continuing success a reality?

4. What was the "who, how, when, where, and why" of the growth and development of the student body, campus organizations, the faculty, the alumni, and the physical plant of the university?

5. How did the university, as a center of learning, influence the local metropolitan area, the state, the nation, and possible international interests of American higher education?

*Statistical Hypotheses*

There were no statistical hypotheses employed in the study.

(Comment: *Statistical hypotheses are employed in historical research where a probability model is used to draw an inference about an event. For example, suppose that the research hypothesis of an historical study is: Shakespeare was the pen name of Bacon who actually wrote all of the so-called Shakespearian plays. In the process of attempting to "prove" this hypothesis, among other approaches, the researcher hopes to show that a particular writing idiosyncrasy of Bacon's appears with a "better than chance" frequency in each Shakespearian work. In order to test this hypothesis, the researcher decides to employ statistical inference. Under these circumstances, statistical hypotheses would be submitted to test.*

*Assumptions underlying the study are: (1) By tracing the development of one American municipal university, a contribution will be made to knowledge in the field of education; and (2) It is possible to produce a valid, reliable, comprehensive history of Wayne University in terms of its influence on, and contribution to, the intellectual, cultural, and complex industrial life of the metropolitan area, the state, and ultimately the nation.*)

UNIVERSE

DESCRIPTION
FINITE
INFINITE

The main sources of data for the study formed what could be considered an infinite universe, composed of official documents and written accounts, located in:

1. Various libraries both within and without the City of Detroit:
   (a) Reference Library—Wayne University
   (b) Education Library—Wayne University
   (c) Detroit Public Library—Burton Historical Collection and Social Science Departments
   (d) Reference Library—Administrative Offices, Detroit Board of Education
   (e) Library of the *Detroit News* (a local newspaper)
   (f) Library of the University of Detroit
   (g) The University of Michigan Library, Ann Arbor, Michigan
2. The files of many of the faculty and administrative officers of the university.

3. The correspondence files, albums, and other forms of storage for documents and written accounts of educators and certain civic-minded citizens in the metropolitan Detroit area.

All official documents, first-hand accounts (both written and oral), and written records of pertinent events were employed as primary sources of data. Second-hand reports, such as interviews with persons who had been informed about, but were not actually present, at a pertinent event; news-paper stories that were not the result of "on the spot" reporting; and other similar materials found in books, monographs, magazines, and other forms of literary works were employed as secondary sources of data.

Many of the primary sources of data were in the form of memoranda, letters, personal memoirs, and official publications of the university and the Detroit Board of Education. The majority of the secondary sources of data were personal interviews with many persons who were indirectly con-nected with events considered to be pertinent to the founding and continuing success of the uni-versity.

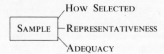

SAMPLE — How Selected / Representativeness / Adequacy

*How Sample of Study was Selected*

The sample employed in the study (and for that matter in every study classified under "historical research") was a judgment-purposive type (see page 43). This type of sample must be employed in historical research because the items selected from the universe of data are those, in the researcher's *judgment*, that best satisfy the *purposes* of the study.

Guide lines for selecting the items to be included in the sample are provided by the "general questions to be answered," or in certain cases (not in the present study), the "operational hypo-theses." It should be noted at this point that the person who attempts to do historical research should have the proper "educational background for the interpretation of historical facts." The proper educational background is a fundamental aspect of judgment-purposive sampling procedures associated with studies qualifying for classification as historical research efforts.

*Representativeness*

The representativeness of samples associated with historical studies is determined, basically, by the amount of data included from "primary sources" of the population. In the present study, at least 95 per cent of the data included in the sample were drawn from primary sources. Thus, the sample of the study was considered "highly" representative of the universe of data from which it was drawn.

*Adequacy*

The adequacy of the sample of the study was insured by the researcher covering the "pro" and "con," and the "who, how, what, when, where, and why," of each aspect covered by the "general questions" of the study.

(Comment: *It is possible to compute values of an "adequate" sample size for various phases of an historical study. It should be pointed out, however, that such computations are rarely employed in actual practice.*)

DATA COLLECTION — Conditions / Methods

*Conditions of Data Collection*

The conditions of data collection associated with the study were:

1. All persons and agencies involved in the study were willing participants.
2. The researcher was able to visit personally all of the agencies and persons that composed the sources of data for the study.

3. All documents and records requested by the researcher were made available to him.

4. Memoranda, personal memoirs, letters, and personal notes were readily made available when requested by the researcher.

5. Personnel employed by a local newspaper, the Wayne Library, the Detroit Public Library, and the other libraries and agencies involved, were provided by these organizations *to help* procure the data sought by the researcher.

*Methods of Data Collection*

The instrumentalities and procedures composing the methods of data collection employed in the study were as follows:

*Instrumentalities.* Locally constructed "library research outlines" and interview schedules were the instrumentalities employed in the study. In order to insure complete coverage of events and topics considered important to the historical development of the university, a skeletal outline covering the subjects of "pro" and "con," and asking the questions of "who?", "what?", "when?", "where?", "why?", and "how?", was employed as a means of recording data taken from records, documents, letters, memoranda, personal letters, and other primary sources of data. The "outlines" were also used in the library research efforts of the study. The interview schedules were "informal" outlines employed as vehicles for note-taking during discussions with persons who were associated with events that contributed significantly to the founding and growth of the university, or with persons who had been witnesses of events of interest to the study. The interview schedules, although informal, were designed to cover the same topics and questions that were covered by the "library research outlines."

*Procedures.* The procedures of the collection of the data associated with the study effort were those involving the location, examination, and analysis of both published and unpublished materials located in libraries, offices, and in the memories of those persons who were interviewed. Whenever a possible source of data was discovered, it was evaluated for its validity, accuracy, and importance to the study effort. If the source was deemed to be "authentic," the information it could provide was analyzed in terms of its relationship to one, or more, of the following categories:

1. The growth and development of the student body, the campus organizations, the alumni, the faculty, and the physical plant.

2. The problem of financial support of the university during the period of time under investigation by the researcher.

3. The roles of the persons who contributed significantly to the cause of the university and made its founding and continuing success a reality.

4. The influence of the university, as a center of learning, on the local metropolitan area, the state, the nation, and the international interests of American higher education.

After the relationship between the information and one or more of the four categories had been determined, the topics of: "pro" and "con," and the questions of: "who?" "what?" "when?" "where?" "why?" and "how?" were covered in the process of completing the "library research outlines" provided for the analysis of the materials under consideration. The information procured by these procedures was then classified and filed appropriately for future reference and, ultimately, for inclusion in the study report.

(Comment: *The concepts of the validity and reliability of the data-gathering instrumentalities in historical research are moot questions. These factors must be considered, but under the conditions of this type of research, are not of as much concern as they are in the other basic types.*)

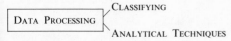

DATA PROCESSING
CLASSIFYING
ANALYTICAL TECHNIQUES

*Classification of the Data*

The data produced by the study were mainly in statement form, or in those cases where enumeration was involved, in the nominal scale of measurement. As the data of the study were collected they were classified under one or more of the four categories previously described. After the initial categorical classification of information was completed, the material was analyzed for inter-relatedness and prepared for the narrative and descriptive form the report of the study was to take. The main guide line for this approach to classification was the chronological dimension in which the report was to be presented. The decisions as to which facts were more important than others to the presentation, and therefore should be classified as such, were derived as the result of the analytical techniques employed in the study.

*Analytic Techniques Employed*

There were two main types of analytic techniques employed in the study: (1) content analysis, and (2) historical criticism. Although they were not employed in the study, statistical techniques such as chi-square or the Kolmogorov–Smirnov test, see nonparametric statistics, Chapters 24 and 25, could have been employed in the analysis of the limited amount of "nominal" data resulting from certain content analyses conducted in the study. The main part of the analysis of data associated with the study was covered by the method of "historical criticism."

(Comment: *It should be noted that, if the statistical techniques mentioned above had been employed to analyze the "enumerative" data realized from certain content analyses employed in the study, it would have been necessary to describe the statistical hypotheses associated with these techniques under the "general questions" element of the model.*)

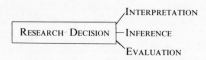

*Interpretation of Data*

In historical research, interpretations of data and inferences are inextricably entwined. Under these circumstances, these facets of the research decision element must be treated in "combination."

*Inferences*

The combined inferences and interpretations drawn from the data were derived in terms of the framework of the chronological narrative form of the study report. The report exposition was concerned with the presentation of facts concerning the establishment and development of the university starting with the seven existing schools and colleges operated by the Detroit Board of Education in August, 1933, and terminating with the structure of Wayne University as it existed in September, 1950. The report was presented in appropriate form in terms of "pro" and "con," and the "who, how, what, when, where, and why" of the following five areas: (see "questions to be answered").

1. The problems of financial support confronted by the university during the period of time covered by the study.

2. The persons who contributed significantly to the founding and continuing success of the university during the period of time covered by the study.

3. The roles of the persons who contributed significantly to the cause of the university and made its founding and continuing success a reality.

4. The growth and development of the student body, campus organizations, the faculty, the alumni, and the physical plant of the university.

5. The influence of the university, as a center of learning, on the local metropolitan area, the state, the nation, and the international interests of American higher education.

The report was terminated with a section dealing with the topic of "prognosis of the future." In essence, the prognosis based upon trends evident in the historical study, envisioned the future of Wayne University as highly inter-related with the future of the local, state, national and international communities which its educational programs and services had been designed to serve. It was concluded that: "As the university expands its programs of community service, primarily upon the local and state levels, it will continue to prosper and grow in importance as an institution of higher learning."

*Evaluation*

The evaluation of the study is left as an exercise for the reader. The evaluation should be conducted in terms of the procedures stated on pages 80-88, with the additional standards of "historical criticism" being included as well, see pages 127–128.

(Comment: *It should be noted that evaluation of the research effort is a continually on-going process associated with historical studies. The researcher involved in this type of study must continually analyze and evaluate sources of data, information of all types, procedures by which the data are obtained, how the interpretations of the data are being made, whether certain sources are being sampled too heavily and thus are presenting only one side of the picture, so to speak, and, finally, whether the data can withstand the tests of internal and external historical criticism.*

*In view of these circumstances, the reader who chooses to evaluate the actual study presented here, will find it to be a thorough and relatively precise effort to cover a most difficult area of concern. The reader can gain some insight into the problems associated with institutional historical research by considering only that aspect of the study which calls for identifying persons who "contributed significantly to the cause of the university." The question involved in determining a "significant" contribution calls for a rigorous examination of a comprehensive area of concern, to say the least.*)

*Chapter 12—References*

See Bibliography: 1, 6, 18, 23, 24, 28, 56, 73, 74, 78, 79, 82, 83, 94, 102, 116, 118, 134, 137, 151, 170, 194, 195, 196; 3a, 51a, 76a, 85a, 100a.

*Chapter Thirteen*

# *Field Research*

COMPARATIVELY RECENT DEVELOPMENTS in such areas as anthropology, sociology, economics, and political science have made it necessary for research teams to "live-in" while conducting large scale inquiries in the field. Such inquiries are of a decidedly different scope and character from the other basic types of research that have been described. Gaining most of their uniqueness from the problems encountered in the field, these research efforts are broadly classified under the heading "Field Research."

Strangely enough, field research does not begin in the field. It may begin in a laboratory, an office, or even an armchair; but wheresoever it may occur, field research begins with a statement of the problem. Following this step, a hypothesis and the accompanying operational hypotheses are formulated; or, if the nature of the problem indicates such an approach, general questions to be answered are framed. The universe or population is then specified, and it is at this point that the field inquiry begins to take shape. Depending upon the universe under study, a representative and adequate sample is selected to be used in conducting the field inquiry. Since field research is primarily concerned with the collection of *first-hand* data on a large scale, the sample selected for such work may demand the "observer" or "observers" to establish residence in: (1) a school district, (2) different areas or districts of a large community, (3) a metropolitan area, or even (4) several nations. Naturally, such items as time, money, equipment, and staff play an important part in determining the scope and extent of the field research effort.

With the problem stated, the hypotheses or general questions framed, the universe defined, and a representative and adequate sample determined, the research comes to grips with the real problem. This problem is the decision concerning the conditions and the methods of data collection to be used in order to collect first-hand information in a large-scale operation.

Lundberg indicates: "There are two principal ways of gathering facts from the field: (1) In the *direct method* the investigator may observe and record data by his own direct observation; or (2) In the *indirect method* the investigator secures his data from others, perhaps from the oral or written testimony of persons having had first-hand contact with the data."[1]

The direct method can be illustrated by the research worker who sets out to determine, as a socio-economic index of different districts, the number of brick garages and swimming pools in a particular section of a large metropolitan area. Record may also be made of the number of two-car and three-car families in the section, the number of memberships in country clubs, and the number of children from a given school district attending private schools—to mention only a few of a host of possibilities. The investigator may even have access to facilities whereby a segment of a community can receive health examinations, vaccinations, and various types of tests, the results of which he may utilize in his research. Although some of the data may need interpretation by medical experts or technicians, the fact remains that the research worker is gathering the data on a first-hand basis. This latter point has been contributory to the origin of the research team approach in field research. Under this plan each member conducts the field inquiry in his own area of specialty. The results are then synthesized under the auspices of a research director, elected from the membership of the team. The team approach makes possible a more efficient and frequently a broader-scaled effort than would otherwise be possible.

Although employing the direct method of gathering data, the investigator can, if he wishes, have his objective observations checked by other observers. The check system provides a means for the establishment of the reliability and, to a certain extent, validity of the observations the researcher has made. This method is frequently employed in science laboratories. In such settings the check system is considered to be an integral part of the laboratory method for conducting research.

Where a choice is possible, the use of the direct method is preferred to the indirect method primarily because the latter approach depends upon persons other than the research worker for its data. The group of persons associated with the indirect method is composed of two sub-groups: (1) employed staff and (2) respondents. The more reliable source of data of the two sub-groups is the employed staff. This statement is true, however, only if sufficient time has been given to the training and motivation of the staff. An untrained group of workers, lacking a motivational "feel" for the project, may contribute greatly to bias and error in the findings. The respondents are considered less reliable than trained staff members because of the various social and psychological elements that may be present when answers or responses are given. In order to counteract these forces, the methods and instrumentalities for collecting data in the field must be carefully considered and developed for reliability and validity.

The usual methods, or techniques, of data collection associated with the indirect method are: (a) questionnaire responses, (b) personal inventory forms, (c) the interview method, (d) the schedule method, (e) the documentary method, and (f) the projective method.

The questionnaire method involves the use of an instrumentality which the respondent fills out. This method demands that a well-written letter accompany the questionnaire, in order to motivate and reassure the respondent and stress the importance of his response. The questionnaire should be as clearly and concisely constructed as possible, and be free of items that "pull" certain types of responses. In order to determine such factors, pilot study "runs" are made on small samples (less than thirty persons) with the instrument. Such efforts not only aid in the construction of the questionnaire, but frequently provide the basis for establishing criteria of reliability and validity of the instrument as well. Naturally, it is impossible to present here a full treatment of the topic, and in view of this fact, the reader who is interested is urged to review Chapter 6 and consult the references listed at the end of that chapter. The questionnaire method is not an easy one to carry out in any type of research, and is particularly difficult to effect in the large-scale operations of field research.

Personal inventory forms are check lists of pre-determined items. The respondent is asked to check those items which do *not* describe his "feelings." The inventory has the advantage of being an easy form for the respondent to complete, and the results are easily analyzed by the investigator. The difficulties encountered with inventories, however, are those of clarity of meaning; the motivation and truthfulness of the respondent; and "loaded" items. The open-end response found in the questionnaire is avoided in the inventory, but for the most part, the problems encountered with questionnaires are present with the use of inventory forms.

The interview method does not demand the formal structure for gaining responses that a self-administered instrument does. The training of the interviewer, however, in terms of his personality, sensitivity, motivation, and ability to elicit responses without bias are major problems associated with the interview method. In order to establish reliability and validity of data gathered by this method, a "participant observer" is utilized. The participant observer can become a part of a community or situation which is under investigation, and supply information that may serve as criteria for the reliability and validity of the data gathered by the interviewer. If the interview is to be conducted over a metropolitan area, it is possible to establish a panel of observers to supply information from the various districts of the area, by which the reliability and validity of the data can be checked. In all, a well-trained staff of interviewers can bring excellent results in field research, but such a situation is almost impossible without substantial financial backing of the research effort.

The schedule method employs the use of an instrument called the "schedule," which is a set of directions, reminders, questions, and alternatives to be employed by the observer (sometimes an interviewer) in carrying out the data collection process. A good schedule tends to standardize the observations and other forms of data gathered by observers and/or interviewers. The development of the schedule, however, is a most difficult and technical matter; a further treatment of the topic may be found in the sources listed at the end of Chapter 6.

The documentary method is a search of records, autobiographies, letters, and other literary forms for data relevant to the research problem. The case study is sometimes incorporated here and contributes greatly to a fuller description of data taken from records. This approach to field research is mainly employed where a form of historical research is necessary to the successful realization of the object of the research.

The projective method is one of the relatively recent efforts to be employed in field research, and may incorporate the questionnaire, the inventory, the interview, or the schedule technique. The respondent is asked to project himself into a particular role extant in the community under study, and answer the questions as though he were in that role. Such an approach frequently strips the respondent of certain psychological and sociological mechanisms which might otherwise affect his response. This method also has the advantage of giving the researcher a good notion of the respondent's attitudes toward the community, and the role in question, especially if the projective technique is followed by a request for the respondent to fill out the same form according to his present position or status in the community under study. To illustrate, a teacher might be asked to respond to a set of questions, considering himself to be a principal when answering. The teacher then is requested to respond to the same questions as a teacher.

The conditions and methods of collecting data, the key points of differentiation between field research and the other basic types, have been given a brief treatment here in order to show how they are important to the "field" situation. No effort has been made to describe completely the specific conditions and methods of a particular field project. Complete descriptions of these facets of field research can be found in appropriate sources listed at the end of the chapter.

Among special types of field research are: the survey, the field study, and the cross-cultural method. Although a field study and a survey are similar in many ways, there are important differences between them. The survey has greater scope while the field study has greater depth. The latter type is not primarily concerned with sampling; the *processes* under investigation have signal importance. A single community or group is studied in terms of its social structure. While the survey also deals with such inter-relations, the on-going processes are generally inferred from statistical data. On the other hand, the field study either attempts observations of social interaction or investigates perceptions and roles in a social complex. The field study approach is unique in that it provides for the observation and measurement of social processes as they occur in a natural setting.

Field studies may range from those employing an extreme type of anthropological description to those using a highly quantified approach with data collection routinized through various kinds of measurements. Many studies may, of course, use a combined methodology. Early studies, such as Schanck's study of Elm Hollow,[2] were generally restricted in scope and thoroughness. A multiperceptional orientation is found in Newcomb's[3] social-psychological field study of Bennington College, self-images as well as objective ratings being involved. The Lynd's *Middletown*[4] project is a sociological application of the anthropological process; however the Lynds went beyond the traditional method and used quantitative techniques to supplement their qualitative materials. Festinger and Katz[5] emphasize the importance of both the anthropological and the quantitative approaches in comprehensive studies.

The cross-cultural method is distinguished from the other types of field research in that it mainly employs statistical techniques to test theory, i.e., probability theory is used extensively to support or reject theories (bodies of hypotheses) pertaining to areas of anthropological and sociological study. Although this method has been in existence for some seventy years, only recently has its scope and its usefulness in inter-disciplinary research in the behavioral sciences been recognized.

In closing the discussion of field research, it should be noted that study efforts which can be classified as this type of research are difficult to conduct in an efficient manner. Apparatus, equipment, and instrumentalities frequently must meet special requirements in order to yield reliable and valid data. Field research requires an extensive amount of forethought and planning in order that as many of the necessary operations as possible be completed prior to the beginning of work in the field. The pre-planning and field situation should be so designed that a minimum number of decisions need be made in the field setting.

With this background, we shall now adapt the general model of research to a selected field research project. Although the selected study is not closely related to education, *per se*, the analogy between the field study presented and those that might be conducted in school districts, a given school, or, for that matter, a given classroom, should be obvious.

---

FIELD RESEARCH MODEL                                      CROSS-CULTURAL TYPE

## ELMTOWN'S YOUTH[6]

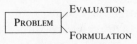

*Evaluation of the Problem*

By sociological definition, adolescence is that period of time in the life of the individual during which society ceases to regard him as a child, but still does not accord him full adult status roles. The sociological definition is in contrast to the one for which physiologists, psychologists, and educators have shown the greatest concern. The definition to which the latter group of professionals has turned its attention deals with the physical and psychological phenomena connected with adolescence, with the major emphasis being placed upon physical maturation.

The Research Planning Committee of the American Sociological Society in 1934 produced an outline for the type of research it believed would be fruitful for an understanding of adolescent behavior from a socio-cultural viewpoint. In contrast to this approach, is the one that blends evolutionary theory with physical growth, assumes that the individual in the course of his life recapitulates the evolutionary development of the human species, and thus establishes the persistent notion of the causal connection between the physical manifestations of adolescence and social behavior.

It was in this setting that the researcher felt the need for a study which concerned itself with adolescent behavior rather than physical adolescence. A need to study high school pupils in order to answer the question: Is the social behavior of the adolescent a function of physiological changes in the maturing individual, or is it a function of his experiences in society?

After preliminary investigations, it became apparent that the formulation of the question did not encompass what appeared to be the most important factors that determine the social behavior of an adolescent. The three main factors not accounted for were: (1) family background; (2) community structure; and (3) the place the family occupied in the community structure. It was at this point that the researcher decided there was a need to study the social behavior of high-school-aged youth, regardless of whether or not they attended high school, to determine if their activities were related to their family backgrounds.

*Formulation of the Problem*

The purpose of the study was to observe and measure, wherever possible, the social behavior of high-school-aged adolescents in "Elmtown, a typical Middle-western community," during the school year 1941–42, to determine if the "behavior" of adolescents is related functionally to the positions their families occupy in the social structure of the community. The study was to be conducted as a field research with a participant observer residing in the community.

(Comment: *The need and purpose of the study are clearly stated. The significance of the study is implied.*)

*Research Hypothesis*

The hypothesis of the study could be stated as follows:

The social behavior of adolescents is related functionally to the positions their families occupy in the social structure of the community

Operational Hypothesis I—The community institutions with which adolescents become affiliated are related functionally to the positions their families occupy in the social structure of the community.

Operational Hypothesis II—The circle of friends established by adolescents is related functionally to the positions their families occupy in the social structure of the community.

(Comment: *The two operational hypotheses stated above compose a small sample of all the operational hypotheses tested by the researcher.*)

*Statistical Hypotheses*

Only certain operational hypotheses were cast into appropriate statistical alternative hypotheses $(H_1)$, and their corresponding null hypotheses $(H_0)$ tested by the chi-square technique (see Chapter 24). Many of the operational hypotheses were tested by descriptive, qualitative information yielded by "statement" data.

For those operational hypotheses that were tested by means of statistical inference, the procedures for acceptance were the same as those described in Chapter 3. The level of significance ($\alpha$) employed with each test of a null hypothesis, was set at the 1 per cent level, i.e., $\alpha = .01$.

(Comment: *The hierarchy of hypotheses of the study was clearly established by the researcher. One of the major assumptions underlying the hypotheses is: the social behavior of adolescents is their adaptive complex adjustment to their status in society. A second assumption is: the adolescent's position in the social structure of his peer group is very similar to that of his family's in the social structure of the community.*)

The source of data for the study was a defined finite universe of: (1) 369 boys and 366 girls between the ages of thirteen and nineteen inclusive, who resided in the community during the school year 1941–42, and who had completed their elementary school education between 1938 and 1941; (2) the family of each adolescent included in the universe; and (3) persons outside the families who were well acquainted with them and could provide information about their (the families') positions in the social structure of the community. Although the defined universe of the study was finite in size, it was necessary for the researchers to select a series of samples from the population throughout the course of the research effort.

(Comment: *The description presented above is but a brief introduction to the description of the universe found in the study report. Our purposes, coupled with limitations of space, time and efficiency, prevent further discussion of the "universe" element of the model at this point.*)

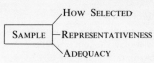

HOW SELECTED

SAMPLE — REPRESENTATIVENESS

ADEQUACY

### How Sample of Study was Selected

The stratum of the defined universe composed of 369 boys and 366 girls was used in its entirety. The parents of the adolescents were selected as subjects for a series of purposive-judgment samples employed throughout the study. In similar fashion, the "observers" of families were selected for the various samples as the need arose.

The data were gathered gradually through a series of samples disturbing the life spaces and daily activities of the town's residents as little as possible. Since the researchers were mainly interested in gaining information about what the study group of adolescents and their families did in the natural setting of the community, instead of observing their reactions to a manipulated (controlled) environment, no part of the field research provided for experimentation.

Since the adolescents were the principal source of information about their activities, topics of conversations, attitudes, friends, and social interactions, the research team spent most of the observational time with them. Good rapport was established with the youth, and members of the team became accepted and trusted members of the school and regular community. The researchers, as participant observers, came to know the families of the adolescents very well; this led to better observation of the family units than otherwise would have been possible.

### Representativeness

Meticulous planning in the definition of the population and its strata, coupled with carefully prepared sampling procedures, provided many representative samples of the universe throughout the course of the study. A procedure involving the use of "observer-raters" not only classified the families in the social structure of the community, but provided a check on the representativeness of the samples employed. This result was accomplished by comparing the families "ratings" with a "controlled," empirically established, check-list of social qualities extant in the structure of the community.

### Adequacy

Although statistical formulas for establishing the adequacy of the sizes of samples employed in the study were not used, the fact that all of the adolescents, at least one parent from each adolescent's family, and two "outside observers" were included in every sample of the effort, indicates that the sample size was probably adequate in each case. Among the types of samples that could have been employed in the study, as well as the judgment samples that were employed, are: sequential samples, simple random samples, stratified random samples, cluster samples, multi-stage samples, and allocations of samples to strata of the population.

(Comment: *In general, the sampling design of the study is considered a very good one for field research. This type of research places a heavy demand on the sampling procedures employed, and frequently, as a result of participant observation by the researcher who resides in the community, informal samples of data are produced that cannot account for the biased error that might be introduced.*)

CONDITIONS

DATA COLLECTION

METHODS

### Conditions of Data Collection

In addition to the conditions of data collection described concurrently with the "sample" element of the model some of the other conditions were:

1. The researchers established residence in the community, and performed the roles of participant observers in the study effort.

2. Each adolescent's family was treated as a separate case, even if two or more youth involved in the study came from the same family.

3. The original high school schedule for adolescents was filled out in semi-private interviews in one corner of the high school principal's office. This arrangement was not wholly satisfactory, but was the best available under the circumstances.

4. Schedules employed with adolescents later in the study were completed whenever and wherever the informant could be seen privately.

5. Schedules for adolescents not in school were completed whenever and wherever an interview could be arranged with the potential respondent. Some of these interviews were conducted on street corners, in automobiles, or in favorite assembling places of these youth.

6. The family schedule was completed during interviews held in connection with home visits in the presence of one or more members of the family.

(Comment: *The six conditions described here are only samples of the many other conditions described in detail in the study report.*)

*Methods of Data Collection*

The instrumentalities and some of the procedures of which the methods of data collection of the study were composed are as follows:

*Instrumentalities.* The instruments used to collect data in the study were: (1) interview schedules; (2) participant observer recordings; (3) tests; and (4) inventories. In addition, other records found in the city hall, churches, and hospitals served as instrumentalities of data collection also. It should be noted that mailed questionnaires were not employed in the study. The type of information usually procured by questionnaires was obtained solely by means of the interview schedule in this study.

The inventories employed in the study were: Mooney's *Problem Check List,* Bavelas' *Ideas on Moral Values* and his *Interest Index.* The tests and interview schedules employed were locally constructed instruments prepared as the need for them arose. The autobiographies were written by the Freshman class and the Senior class only. Thus, the youth who were in the Sophomore and Junior classes, plus those who were not attending high school, were not represented, *per se,* in this form of data collection.

(Comment: *The reliability, validity, objectivity, and discriminatory factors of the locally constructed instrumentalities could have been checked by means of procedures described in Chapter 6. The study report does not deal specifically with this problem. It can be assumed, however, that as a group of trained researchers, the team provided for these matters. The standardized instruments employed in the study provided quantitative descriptions of the four factors in their accompanying "manuals.")*

*Procedures.* The main procedures of data collection employed in the study were:

1. The researcher established residency in the community, and proceeded to gather data through informal conversations with certain citizens of the town in order to orient the study.

2. Visits were paid to the local newspaper, the elementary school, the high school, and the offices of municipal government to hold informal conversations with officials responsible for the operations of these agencies. The conversation-interviews provided data for constructing later approaches to data collection.

3. Participant observer field notes were employed to gain descriptive data pertaining to the customs, mores, and traditions of the community.

4. The testing and inventory programs were instituted in the high school along with the writing of autobiographies by the Freshman and Senior classes.

5. Two types of interviews were conducted with the adolescents: (a) the undirected, or "concealed" interview; and (b) the directed, open-end interview. Many of these interviews were conducted in informal settings.

6. Families of the adolescents were interviewed by means of both the "undirected" and "directed" approaches.

7. "Raters" of the families were interviewed, for "initial" assessments.

8. Tests and inventories completed by the adolescents were "scored." The autobiographies of the freshmen and seniors were processed through procedures of content analysis.

9. Data were collected from school records and the documents and records of other public agencies about the adolescents and their families.

10. Ratings were procured for the families involved in the study.

(Comment: *See "conditions" of data collection, and descriptions under the "sample" element of the model for further details pertaining to the data collection element of the model. Many "procedures" other than those listed above are described in the report of the study.*)

DATA PROCESSING — CLASSIFYING / ANALYTICAL TECHNIQUES

### Classification of the Data

The data yielded by the study were those of: (1) the descriptive, qualitative type (statements); (2) the nominal scale of measurement; (3) the ordinal scale of measurement; and (4) the interval scale of measurement. Data of primary importance to the study were those of the descriptive-qualitative type. Those of secondary importance were the "ratings" of the families of the adolescents, which were distributed over data of the nominal, ordinal, and interval scales of measurement. Included in the class of data categorized as "secondary" in importance were those data produced by the tests, inventories, and autobiographies of the adolescents. These too were distributed over the nominal, ordinal, and interval scales of measurement.

Each rating received by a family was weighted and then recorded on a Hollerith card. The families involved were class-types, ranked according to their weighted scores' locations on the scale of social classification employed in the study.

Data procured from the "structured" and "unstructured" interviews were used to "qualify" descriptively the hypotheses of the study. In those cases where statistical hypotheses were advanced for testing, the data of the nominal scale of measurement, and those of the ordinal and interval scales that were categorized, were employed to reject or not reject the "null."

### Analytic Techniques Employed

The hypothesis stated, in effect, that the behaviors of the adolescents were conditioned by the positions of their families in the social structure of the community. This condition implied that "family position" was the independent variable and the "adolescent's behavior" was the dependent variable. Employing this fact as the basis of the "logical" analysis of the descriptive-qualitative (statement) data, the procedure was to analyze the data concerning various segments of the adolescents' behaviors as they "seemed" to relate to the fixed variable of family position.

(Comment: *A correlational analysis could have been employed here instead of the process of mediating qualitative data.*)

Where statistical hypotheses, and thus statistical inferences, were involved, the chi-square technique was employed in the analysis of the "nominal" data. The chi-square analysis was applied to tests of single classification and tests of independence involving the social behavior of the adolescent: in terms of school, church, job, recreation, and other activities, and the position of the family in the social structure of the community.

(Comment: *Other nonparametric techniques could have been employed along with, or instead of, the chi-square approach.*)

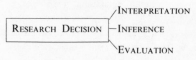

RESEARCH DECISION — INTERPRETATION / INFERENCE / EVALUATION

### Interpretation of the Data

Some of the data of the study were interpreted in terms of providing guide lines for other phases of the research effort. Much of the statistical information produced by the study was used as descriptive evidence in the interpreting processes. Statistical data employed in the process of statistical inference are reported under the "inference" section.

The data of the "structured" and "unstructured" interviews with the adolescents and their families were interpreted in terms of "answers" to the "question areas" covered by certain operational hypotheses. Some of the data produced by the "unstructured" interviews extended beyond the areas of concern covered by the operational hypotheses. These "extension" data were interpreted as background information and "depth dimensions" for inferences and "conclusions" drawn by the research team.

*Inferences*

No effort has been made to cover the multitude of inferences and conclusions about the operational and research hypotheses of the study. Some of the inferences drawn by the researchers are:

1. It was found that an adolescent's behavior, in terms of the factors employed (e.g., church and school), was related to the position of the adolescent's family, as "rated" by the "observers," in a highly significant ($\alpha = .01$ level) fashion.
2. Adolescent behavior (measured as "social behavior") is a product of conditioning by the family's mores, customs, and social beliefs.
3. The effects of differential learning in the home and neighborhood (in a city like Elmtown) are basic conditioning factors of the social behaviors of adolescents.
4. There are significantly different behaviors between adolescents whose families are considered to be in significantly different positions of the social structure of the community.
5. Adolescents reared by a family in a given position of the social structure of the community will exhibit behavior characteristics peculiar to the social class represented by the family's "position."
6. Wide differences prevail in the social behaviors of adolescents in Elmtown.
7. Wide differences prevail between the "studied" families' positions in the social structure of the community.
8. Wide differences in adolescents' behaviors can be attributed to the wide differences in social "positions" of the families involved.
9. The behaviors of adolescents in school are highly significantly related to family position in the social structure of the community.
10. The behaviors of adolescents in church activities are significantly related to family position.
11. The behaviors of adolescents in positions of employment are significantly related to family position.
12. The behaviors of adolescents in recreational activities are significantly related to family position.

(Comment: *The twelve inferences stated above form a small sample of the many inferences presented in the study report. It should be noted that statistical inference was employed quite frequently throughout the course of the study.*)

*Evaluation*

The evaluation of the study is left as an exercise for the reader. Procedures found on pages 80-88 provide the means for evaluating the effort.

(Comment: *For a number of years the "Elmtown" study has been considered a foundation stone in the structure of field research. Its high involvement in school activities and settings illustrates how field work can be conducted by an "outsider" coming into the school as a participant observer.*)

### Chapter 13—References

See Bibliography: 5, 6, 10, 15, 20, 28, 33, 35, 47, 50, 56, 63, 73, 74, 78, 82, 83, 88, 94, 96, 100, 102, 116, 117, 120, 132, 134, 137, 149, 150, 152, 170, 171, 174, 196, 197; 3a, 22a, 35a, 50a, 61a, 90a, 98a, 101a, 115a.

# PART IV

## Statistical Techniques and Models

EARLIER DISCUSSIONS of a general model and its adaptation to problems of educational research have shown that basically the research decision is most affected by the nature of the problem and the characteristics of the model of inquiry being employed. The solution of the problem is derived by procedures prescribed by the elements of the research model, and the model's structure. These procedures, we recall, are broadly classified as analytical and numerical types. The analytical procedures are deductive in nature, and the numerical procedures are basically inductive in character. These two types of procedures are not mutually exclusive in a model of inquiry. At best, either one type or the other is predominant in the elements and the basic structure of the "adapted" form of the model.

Analytical procedures are predominant in most of the elements composing the models adapted to problems of educational research in historical, action, and field efforts. The element of data processing, however, because of extensive use of various models of statistical tests, mainly employs numerical procedures. The numerical procedures usually employed in most of the models of educational research are mainly statistical in character, and contribute greatly to the derivation of the research decision. Because of its very important function in the adapted forms of the general model of educational research, it is necessary to discuss, in some detail, certain aspects of statistical inquiry. The discussion will deal with: (a) certain basic concepts, (b) numerical aspects of sampling, (c) particular techniques of estimation, and (d) testing statistical hypotheses by means of selected models of statistical distributions.

In a broad categorical sense, statistics concerns itself with two types of problems. The first type of problem is that of *description*, the second is that of *statistical inference.*

*Descriptive Statistics.* Descriptive statistics deals with the collection of large amounts of quantitative information from which there are abstracted certain representative values. Such figures as the average number of children per American family, or the average annual income of the American factory worker, are examples of descriptive statistics. The main purpose of descriptive statistics is to organize and condense a large number of observations that might be conceptually unwieldly into a more understandable and convenient form.

*Statistical Inference.* Statistical inference deals mainly with two types of problems: (a) estimation, and (b) the testing of statistical hypotheses. The word "inference" is used here to mean the conclusions derived from, and the process used to arrive at, the conclusions.

### ESTIMATION (SINGLE VARIATE)

Single variate estimation deals with making statements about such *population parameters* as the mean ($\mu$), the standard deviation ($\sigma$), or other population characteristics, based upon the values of their counterpart "statistics" (e.g., mean, $\overline{X}$, and a standard deviation, $S$) computed from the observations ($X$) of a random sample drawn from the population, and used as a point of reference in the appropriate sampling distribution. For example, if we have a random sample of limited size, drawn from a population of values ($X$), we could compute the mean value ($\overline{X}$) of the quantities composing the random sample, and derive with a prescribed amount of confidence, two values of $\overline{X}$ in the sampling distribution of the mean for sample size $n$ between which the value of the mean of the population ($\mu$) is estimated to lie.

### ESTIMATION (RELATED VARIATES)

When a population is composed of *related variates*, i.e., when it is a *bivariate population*, it is more helpful to make estimates *not* on the basis of the values of $X$ alone, but to involve in the estimation process the additional set of values $Y$ that is related to $X$. In this type of situation it is frequently possible to estimate the value of $X$ from a given value of $Y$. The method of estimation employed with a bivariate population is that of regression and correlation. These topics will be discussed in detail later.

Whether a single variate or related variates population is involved, the central problem of estimation remains the same, that of estimating the value of a population parameter from a sample of values selected from the universe (population) involved.

### TESTING STATISTICAL HYPOTHESES (INFERENCE)

The process of testing statistical hypotheses involves a rigorous logical basis for advancing a statistical hypothesis of magnitude, relationship, or difference; randomly sampling a population of appropriate values; and applying the theory of probability in deriving the decision to reject, or not reject, the hypothesis under consideration. The approach is composed of the following seven steps:

1. State the statistical hypothesis which is known as the "null hypothesis" ($H_0$) (a hypothesis of "no difference," supposed to be true, but stated with the hope that the data will reject it).

2. Choose a statistical test for testing the null hypothesis ($H_0$). The statistical test chosen must incorporate the following features:

   (a) Its level of measurement requirement (see "Data Processing" Chapter 7) must be satisfied by the data employed in the research.

   (b) It must be applicable under the assumptions of the nature of the population. For example, a normal distribution statistical test should not be employed if the population is distributed according to a Poisson distribution (found in many statistical quality control situations in industry).

(c) It should be the most powerful one available under the same size $n$ and level of significance $\alpha$ being employed. Put in another way, the power of the statistical test employed is based upon the probability of the test rejecting the null hypothesis $H_0$ when it is false and should be rejected; the test selected should be the one that best accomplishes this purpose under the conditions of the sample size $n$ and the level of significance $\alpha$ being employed.

3. Specify the level of significance $\alpha$ and a sample size $n$.

4. Determine the appropriate form of the sampling distribution of the statistical test being employed under the supposition that the null hypothesis $(H_0)$ is true.

5. On the basis of steps 2, 3, and 4, determine the critical region, i.e., the region of the distribution that includes the values of the "statistic" that indicate the rejection of the null hypothesis.

6. From the data of the sample, compute the value of the "statistic" necessary to determine the value of the statistical test.

7. If the value of the statistic, or the value of the test, whichever is employed, is in the critical region, i.e., the region of rejection, reject the null hypothesis $(H_0)$, and accept the statistical alternative hypothesis $(H_1)$.* If the value is not in the region of rejection, the null hypothesis cannot be rejected at the particular level of $\alpha$ being employed, and we are not permitted to accept $H_1$.

It is with this latter phase of statistical inference—testing statistical hypotheses—that we will be most concerned in this section.

In order to present a better picture of the process of statistical inference, it will be necessary to explain certain statistical concepts that are basic to the approach and others that play important roles in the process. Obviously, statistical inference covers a multitude of ideas, some simple and some complex. We propose to approach this vast field by beginning with a discussion of certain basic concepts of histograms, frequency distributions and their characteristics, the relationship between probability and frequency distributions, populations and samples, and a treatment of the fundamental properties of the normal distribution.

---

* See Chapter 3.

*Chapter Fourteen*

# Basic Concepts

THE HISTOGRAM. A frequently used graphical presentation of grouped data is the histogram. The histogram is a block diagram in which the widths of the blocks indicate the length of the class interval, and the heights of the blocks equal the frequency of occurrence of the respective intervals. The class intervals are of equal length, but the frequencies naturally may vary. The histogram is a particularly useful device when a large number of measurements are involved. To illustrate, suppose that in the Model of Field Research, page 138, it were desirable to measure to the nearest inch the heights of 300 male students involved in the study.

The distribution of the fictitious data is presented in Table III. The first two columns of the table form a frequency table, a widely used method for reporting data of this type. To draw a histogram of these data the heights, expressed to the nearest inch, are laid off along a horizontal line or scale. The frequency of occurrence of each height is represented by adding an equal unit of area

Table III
Height to Nearest Inch of 300 Male Students Involved in Study Associated
with the Model of Field Research
(*Fictitious Data*)

| Inches of Height | Frequency | Relative Frequency | Cumulative Relative Frequency (Proportion) |
|---|---|---|---|
| 60 | 1 | .0033 | .0033 |
| 61 | 2 | .0067 | .0100 |
| 62 | 4 | .0133 | .0233 |
| 63 | 7 | .0233 | .0466 |
| 64 | 8 | .0267 | .0733 |
| 65 | 12 | .0400 | .1133 |
| 66 | 29 | .0967 | .2100 |
| 67 | 41 | .1367 | .3467 |
| 68 | 60 | .2000 | .5467 |
| 69 | 42 | .1400 | .6867 |
| 70 | 36 | .1200 | .8067 |
| 71 | 13 | .0433 | .8500 |
| 72 | 12 | .0400 | .8900 |
| 73 | 9 | .0300 | .9200 |
| 74 | 10 | .0333 | .9533 |
| 75 | 7 | .0233 | .9766 |
| 76 | 3 | .0100 | .9866 |
| 77 | 2 | .0067 | .9933 |
| 78 | 1 | .0033 | .9966 |
| 79 | 1 | .0034 | 1.0000 |
| Total | 300 | 1.0000 | |

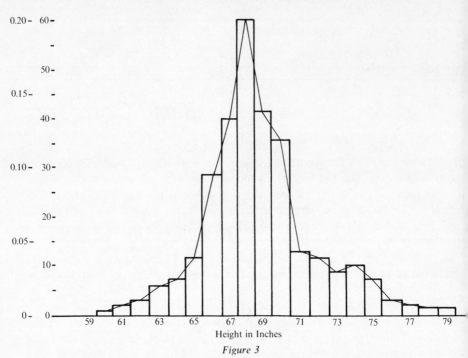

*Figure 3*

Histogram of 300 Male Student Heights to Nearest Inch in the Model of Field Research
(*Fictitious Data*)

above the particular value of height in question thus forming a block of that interval (see Figure 3).

The histogram as drawn here assumes that height is a discrete variable, that is, it could only be 60, or 61, or 62, or 63, etc. inches. This condition does not mean that the description of how to construct a histogram will apply only to discrete measurements as they occur. The procedures described will also apply to continuous measurements, if they are grouped by categories. For example, if the measurements of heights discussed above were made with greater precision they could be represented by the above histogram on the basis that all measurements between, say, 64.5 and 65.5 inches, would be combined into the group at 65 inches, all measurements between 67.5 and 68.5 inches into the group at 68 inches, and so on. In these cases, the lengths of the respective intervals are reported in terms of one inch units. It should be noted, however, that the measurements can be grouped into any length of interval desired. Suppose that the precision of measurement was to the nearest half inch, and thus the length of interval for the measurements had been expressed in one-half inch units. For example, all measurements between 66.25 and 66.75 would be represented by 66.5, those between 66.75 and 67.25 by 67.0 inches, etc. This condition shows that a histogram of similar appearance to the one

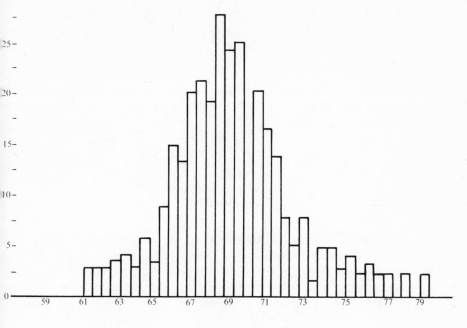

*Figure 4*

*Histogram of 300 Male Student Heights to Nearest Half-Inch*
*(Fictitious Data)*

in Figure 3 would occur, except for the fact that the data would be "intervalized" into approximately twice as many groups (see Figure 4). This alteration of interval size will call for making each rectangular block half as wide, in order to indicate that the readings are now to the nearest half inch, but at the same time increasing the height of each of them, in order to hold the area constant for each observation. It should be noted that the total area always must contain 300 units of area to represent 300 observations, regardless of the size of the units of area.

In order to give a clear picture of the data, it is important to take account of the precision of measurement and allow enough intervals to discern the shape of the distribution. At the same time, it is important not to have so many intervals that too much detail interferes with picturing the general structural form of the distribution. As a general rule of thumb, eight to twenty groups (intervals) are considered the minimum and maximum number of categories (groups), respectively, which will provide an adequate picture of the general structure of the distribution associated with most studies.

Obviously, if more and more observations were made with increasingly more precise measurement, and the histogram were constructed by grouping the measurements into intervals of less and less width, it is possible that the histogram would approach a smooth curve which would represent the distribution of continuous measurements (see Figure 5).

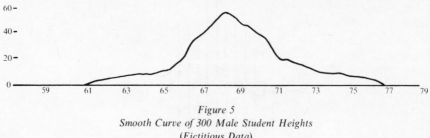

*Figure 5*
*Smooth Curve of 300 Male Student Heights*
*(Fictitious Data)*

In many cases, in order to have comparable pictures for different total numbers of observations, proportions are indicated in place of the frequencies. This change leaves the shapes of the distributions the same, and changes only the frequency scales on the left of the diagrams. If this alteration were incorporated in Table III, we would see in the column labeled "Relative Frequency" that, for example, the height of 60 inches occurred 1/300 = .0033 of the total number of observations, that of 61 inches 2/300 = .0066 of the total, and that of 62 inches 4/300 = .0133 of the total. This is an important concept in connection with *frequency polygons* which we are now prepared to discuss.

*Frequency Polygon.* Another form of graphical presentation of the *frequency* with which each observation occurs is that of the *frequency polygon.* The construction of the frequency polygon is effected by drawing line segments between the mid-points at the top of each column in the histogram. A frequency polygon is shown in Figure 3.

*Frequency Distributions.* When the *relative frequency* (proportion) scale is used in connection with the histograms, or frequency polygons, instead of actual frequencies, the figures are called *frequency distributions* of the measurements involved. If the proportion column is used in Figure 3, we have a *frequency distribution* of the (*fictitious data*) heights of the 300 male students involved in the study associated with the Model of Field Research, page 138. It is important to notice that in a frequency distribution the total area under the bounding curve of the distribution is always equal to 1.0 square unit. (See total of "Relative Frequency" column in Table III, and last entry of "Cumulative Relative Frequency" column.)

If we wish to know the per cent of the 300 male students that are shorter than a particular height, we start at the left of Figure 3, and progressing toward the right along the horizontal line showing height, we see, from the vertical "proportion" scale, that when we reach the value 60.5 inches, one student or .33 per cent is below the value; at value 61.5 inches a total of three students, or 1.0 per cent is below that value; at 62.5 inches, a total of seven students, or 2.33 per cent is below that value; and at 63.5 inches, a total of 14 students or

4.66 per cent is below that value. By consulting the column headed "Cumulative Relative Frequency (Proportion)," and multiplying the figures by 100, the cumulative per cent of the 300 students less than any particular height may be read. It should be noted that each interval accounts for a one inch unit. For example, the interval represented by 64 covers values from 63.5 to 64.5 inches, hence the cumulative per cent of the 300 students below 64 inches must be computed from 64.5, the upper limit of the interval represented by "64." This approach leads to the possibility of constructing a *cumulative-distribution polygon* (ogive) which we shall now investigate for the purpose of determining "percentiles."

*Percentiles.* A percentile is defined as $\frac{1}{100}$ of a distribution. The first percentile, $P_1$ is that point of a distribution above which 99 per cent of the observations in the distribution lie. To illustrate, the 85th percentile, $P_{85}$, is that value (in our example, 71.5 inches) above which 15 per cent of the distribution of values will fall. This value, or the value for any other percentile, can be obtained by reference to the cumulative-distribution polygon in Figure 6. The cumulative-distribution polygon (ogive) may be used in two ways. If we wish to know the score that goes approximately with the 20 per cent point on the left-hand scale, we draw a horizontal line to the ogive, and then draw a line downward from that point to the horizontal axis. At that point we would read a value slightly less than 66, but since we know the heights are reported to the nearest inch, we could assume that 66 inches was approximately the value that about 20 per cent of the students' heights were less than. If a more exact answer was demanded the height $P_{20}$ could be estimated in tenths as: $P_{20} =$ 65.9. In similar fashion, we note that $P_{50} = 68$ inches approximately.

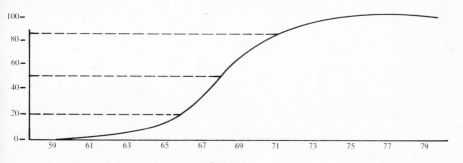

*Figure 6*
*Height in Inches of 300 Male Students Involved in Study Associated With the Model of Field Research*
*(Fictitious Data)*

The *percentile rank* for any particular height, that is, the per cent of students who are shorter than some particular height, may be found by using the ogive. For example, any student who is 71 inches tall is in the 85th percentile rank of the group. That is, only 15 per cent of the students in the group are taller than he is. This figure is obtained by drawing a vertical line from the point marked 71 inches on the horizontal axis to the ogive, then a horizontal line is drawn from that point to the scale on the left where 85 per cent may be read as an approximation.

### CHARACTERISTICS OF A FREQUENCY DISTRIBUTION

In the last section various forms of the frequency distribution were described. In this section we present certain characteristics of a frequency distribution and the types of computation necessary to obtain specific measures of the characteristics. The four major characteristics are:

1. The *area* of the distribution.
2. *Measures of central tendency*, e.g., the arithmetic mean, median and the mode.
3. *The dispersion measures*, e.g., the range, the variance, and the standard deviation.
4. *The skewness*, or lack of symmetry of the distribution.

Before further presentation of these points, it is necessary to acquaint the reader with certain symbols and mathematical manipulations employed in the discussion of these concepts.

*Symbols.* Frequently it will be necessary to add several numbers. When the Greek letter capital sigma ($\sum$) is used, it means "the sum of," and indicates the addition of certain expressions. For example, if there are six observations $X_1, X_2, X_3, X_4, X_5, X_6$, and we wish to indicate their addition we may write: $\sum_{i=1}^{6} X_i = X_1 + X_2 + X_3 + X_4 + X_5 + X_6$. If we wish to indicate the sum of 35 observations $X_1, X_2, \ldots X_{34}, X_{35}$; we may write $\sum_{i=1}^{35} X_i$ which is read as "the sum of 35 observations $X_1$ up through $X_{35}$." The subscript $i$ refers to the $i$-th observation, and $X_i$ is the value of the $i$-th observation. The symbol $\sum_{i=1}^{35}$ indicates that $i = 1, i = 2, i = 3, \ldots, i = 35$ in the expression immediately following the $\sum$, and the $\sum$ indicates that the 35 numbers involved are to be added. After a certain amount of familiarity with the symbolization is attained, the symbol may be reduced to $\sum X_i$ or $\sum X$, with the understanding that the 35 observations $X_1, X_2, X_3, \ldots, X_{34}, X_{35}$ are to be added.

The following formulas, and their equivalent statements, are examples that occur quite frequently in the computational phases of statistical practice:

1. The sum of the 6 "squared" observations:

$$\sum_{i=1}^{6} X_i^2 = X_1^2 + X_2^2 + X_3^2 + X_4^2 + X_5^2 + X_6^2$$

2. The sum of the products formed by multiplying each of the observations by a constant $a$:

$$\sum_{i=1}^{6} aX_i = aX_1 + aX_2 + aX_3 + aX_4 + aX_5 + aX_6$$

$$= a(X_1 + X_2 + X_3 + X_4 + X_5 + X_6) = a \sum_{i=1} X_i$$

Thus, if $a$ is a constant, then:

$$\sum_{i=1}^{N} aX_i = a \sum_{i=1}^{N} X_i$$

3. The sum of the products of pairs of values:

$$\sum_{i=1}^{6} X_i Y_i = X_1 Y_1 + X_2 Y_2 + X_3 Y_3 + X_4 Y_4 + X_5 Y_5 + X_6 Y_6;$$

also

$$\sum_{i=1}^{6} f_i X_i = f_1 X_1 + f_2 X_2 + f_3 X_3 + f_4 X_4 + f_5 X_5 + f_6 X_6$$

where $f$ designates "frequency of occurrence" of the $i$-th observation.

4. The sum of a constant $a$ taken $N$ times:

$$\sum_{i=1}^{N} a = a + a + a + \ldots + a + a = Na$$

Specific example:

$$\sum_{i=1}^{4} 4 = 4 + 4 + 4 + 4 = 16$$

5. The sum of deviations of $N$ observations from the number $a$ is equal to the sum of the $N$ observations minus $N$ times $a$:

$$\sum_{i=1}^{N} (X_i - a) = \sum_{i=1}^{N} X_i - \sum_{i=1}^{N} a = \sum_{i=1}^{N} X_i - Na$$

Specific example;

$$\sum_{i=1}^{4} (X_i - 5) = \sum_{i=1}^{5} X_i - \sum_{i=1}^{5} 5 = \sum_{i=1}^{5} X_i - (5)(5)$$

The factorial symbol (!) designates a special type of product. For example:

$$7! = 7 \cdot 6 \cdot 5 \cdot 4 \cdot 3 \cdot 2 \cdot 1$$
$$10! = 10 \cdot 9 \cdot 8 \cdot 7 \cdot 6 \cdot 5 \cdot 4 \cdot 3 \cdot 2 \cdot 1$$

By definition $1! = 1$ and $0! = 1$.

When we discuss the topic of probability it will be convenient to have counting formulas. The two most important symbols that will be used in these discussions are $_NP_r$, and $C_r^N$:

1. The number of different arrangements of $N$ different things taken $r$ at a time, $_NP_r$ is defined as:

$$_NP_r = \frac{N!}{(n-r)!}$$

Specific example:

$$_7P_3 = \frac{7!}{(7-3)!} = \frac{7!}{4!} = \frac{7 \cdot 6 \cdot 5 \cdot 4 \cdot 3 \cdot 2 \cdot 1}{4 \cdot 3 \cdot 2 \cdot 1} = 210$$

2. The number of different combinations of $N$ different things taken $r$ at a time; $C_r^N$ is defined as:

$$C_r^N = \frac{N!}{r!(N-r)!}$$

Specific example:

$$C_3^7 = \frac{7!}{3!(7-3)!} = \frac{7!}{3!4!} = \frac{7 \cdot 6 \cdot 5 \cdot 4 \cdot 3 \cdot 2 \cdot 1}{(3 \cdot 2 \cdot 1)(4 \cdot 3 \cdot 2 \cdot 1)} = 35$$

With this symbolization, we can now discuss the four major characteristics of a frequency distribution and the relationship between the concept of probability and the frequency distribution.

*Four Major Characteristics of a Frequency Distribution*

1. *The Area of the Distribution.* We have already touched upon the discussion of the area of a distribution under our treatment of "cumulative distributions" earlier. We saw that when a frequency distribution is converted into a "relative frequency" (proportions) distribution, then the area under the bounding curve of the distribution is unity (1.0 square units), regardless of whether the distribution is associated with a population or a sample.

Generally speaking, we find two types of questions answered by the area under a distribution:

(a) What proportion (or per cent) of the distribution (area) lies between two given values of the variate $X$, say $X_1$ and $X_2$?

(b) What value of the variate $X$ corresponds to a specified proportion (or per cent) of the distribution?

We may illustrate how the area of a distribution is employed to answer these questions by considering the fictitious data in Table III. Suppose that we are asked to find the proportion of all heights in the group of 300 male students that occur between 5 and 6 feet (that is, from 60.5 inches up to 71.5 inches). Note that since the question stated "between" the respective values, we take the upper limit (60.5) of the lower bounding value (5 feet), and the lower limit

(71.5) of the upper bounding value, to define the interval in which we are interested. This problem is an example of question (a) above.

The proportion of the sample falling between 5 feet and 6 feet, that is, between 60.5 and 71.5 inches, is found on the assumption that the frequency for a given value is uniformly distributed over the particular class interval in question. This assumption allows us to consider that the frequency for the value 61 is uniformly distributed over the interval from 60.5 to 61.5. Therefore, if we begin with the frequency of this class interval symbolized by "61" and add the frequencies of all the values up to and including that of interval designated by 71 (70.5 to 71.5), we should have the total in which we are interested. Adding these frequencies we find that a total of 254, or 84.67 per cent of the sample of 300, lies *between* the heights of 5 feet and 6 feet.

To illustrate the second, or (b), type of question, suppose we wanted to know below what height 25 per cent of the group fell. To answer such a question we turn to Figure 6, and finding the point on the vertical scale corresponding to 25 per cent, draw a line horizontally across to the ogive. Then from this point we draw a vertical line to the horizontal axis and read the value found at that point (66.8).

If we did not have this diagram, we could proceed on the assumption (as did the diagram) that the frequencies associated with the respective values are uniformly distributed over the class intervals. We know that the values involved constitute 25 per cent of the sample of 300 values. If we were to accumulate 75 (25 per cent of 300) frequency counts beginning with the class interval designated by "60," and we were able to compute the height value which we should find at that point of accumulation, we would have the answer to the question. In order to calculate the value which is found at the point of accumulation of 75 frequencies, we must employ the following formula:

$$X_P = X_L + \frac{i(f_P - f_L)}{f_i}$$

where $X_P$ is the value sought; $X_L$ is the value of the lower limit of the class interval in which the total of the cumulating frequencies, taken from the lower end of the distribution, occurs; $i$ is the length of the class interval; $f_P$ is the total of the cumulating frequencies associated with the desired, or sought, value; $f_L$ is the frequency to the lower limit of the class interval in which the value sought lies; $f_i$ is the frequency associated with the interval in which the sought value lies.

Employing the formula in our example, we have from Table III:

$$f_P = 75; \qquad f_L = 1 + 2 + 4 + 7 + 8 + 12 + 29 = 63; \qquad X_L = 66.5;$$

$$i = 1; \qquad f_i = 41$$

Substituting in the formula, we have:

$$X_P = 66.5 + (1)\frac{(75 - 63)}{41} = 66.5 + \frac{12}{41} = 66.5 + .3 = 66.8$$

Thus, the height below which 25 per cent of the sample of 300 heights occurs is 66.8 inches, assuming a uniform distribution of frequencies over a continuous (every height possible) variable.

The method employed above is the one by which *percentiles* are calculated. The values of $X$ which divide the distribution in 100 equal parts are called percentiles. If we choose the values of $X$ which divide the distribution into 10 equal parts (e.g., the 10th, 20th, 30th, and 40th, percentiles), we find the *deciles* of the distribution. Similarly those values which divide the distribution into four equal parts are called *quartiles*. All of these values may be calculated by the general formula described and illustrated above.

2. *Measure of Central Tendency.* A measure of central tendency is one that refers to the location of the center of the distribution along the scale (horizontal

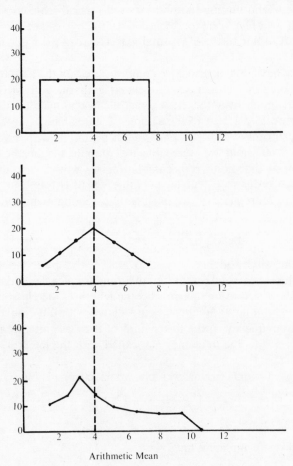

Arithmetic Mean

*Figure 7*
*Three Frequency Distributions with Same Mean ($\overline{X} = 4.0$)*

line) of the variate. One such measure is that of the "average." This measure may lie anywhere between the two extremes of the distribution, although rarely is it found very close to either end of the distribution. Figure 7 illustrates that the same *central value* ($\overline{X} = 4.0$) can be obtained from frequency distributions of different shapes. The top distribution is called a "rectangular" distribution. Each value from 1 to 7 appears with equal frequency, and thus all values of this distribution are considered to be equally "typical." The distribution in the middle of the figure is single peaked (unimodal), similar to a normal distribution, and its values are grouped reasonably near to the central value. In such cases, the "average" is frequently used as representative of the group. The distribution at the bottom of the figure shows relatively little concentration, and hence the central value should not be used as representative of the group.

The important fact about *central value*, or "average," is that it is a point which is used as a reference from which to measure deviations of the several values of the variate, thus providing a measure of *variability* of the distribution. Other uses of "average" are those associated with estimation and the testing of statistical hypotheses referred to earlier in our discussion.

(a) *The Arithmetic Mean.* Probably the most important "average" used in statistics is the *arithmetic mean*. It is defined as the sum of a series of values of the variate (variable) divided by the number of values which accounted for the sum. Using symbols described earlier, the arithmetic mean of a sample is computed by the following formula:

$$\overline{X} = \frac{\sum\limits_{i=1}^{n} X_i}{n} \tag{1}$$

where $\overline{X}$ symbolizes the "mean" of the sample; $\sum\limits_{i=1}^{n} X_i$ is the sum of all the individual values of the variate *in the sample* from 1 to $n$; and $n$ is the number of observations in the *sample*. Thus, equation (1) is an expression for the arithmetic mean of a *sample*.

The arithmetic mean of a population is expressed as follows:

$$\mu = \frac{\sum\limits_{i=1}^{N} X_i}{N} \tag{2}$$

where $\mu$ (mu) is the arithmetic mean of the population; $\sum\limits_{i=1}^{N} X_i$ is the sum of all the individual values of the variate in the *population* from 1 to $N$; and $N$ is the number of elements in the *population*. Thus, equation (2), similar in form to equation (1), represents the value of the *population mean*.

When there are many $X_i$ values, they may be grouped into intervals. Table III is an illustration of this point, where the class interval is: $i = 1$.

When the data are grouped into intervals, it is inconvenient to use the type of formula which is symbolized by formulas (1) and (2). In this situation it is better to employ the following formulas:

$$\text{(sample) } \overline{X} = \frac{\sum_{1}^{K} f_j X_j}{\sum_{1}^{K} f_j} = \frac{\sum_{1}^{K} f_j X_j}{n} \tag{3}$$

$$\text{(population) } \mu = \frac{\sum_{1}^{K} f_j X_j}{\sum_{1}^{K} f_j} = \frac{\sum_{1}^{K} f_j X_j}{N} \tag{4}$$

where $X_j$ is the midpoint of any interval, $f_j$ is the number of measurements in an interval, and $K$ is the number of groups. Formulas (3) and (4) differ only to the extent that one designates the mean of a sample, and the other the mean of the population. To illustrate how these formulas may be used, assume that we had a sample of 500 persons' heights measured to the nearest inch, and the data were grouped, or intervalized, as follows:

| Group Number $K$ | Interval of Height (Inches) | Midpoint of Interval $X_j$ | Number $f_j$ | Product $f_j X_j$ |
|---|---|---|---|---|
| 1 | 59.5–62.5 | 61 | 50 | 3,050 |
| 2 | 62.5–65.5 | 64 | 100 | 6,400 |
| 3 | 65.5–68.5 | 67 | 200 | 13,400 |
| 4 | 68.5–71.5 | 70 | 100 | 7,000 |
| 5 | 71.5–74.5 | 73 | 50 | 3650 |
| Sum | | $\sum_{1}^{K} f_j = n = 500$ | $\sum_{1}^{K} f_j X_j =$ | 33,500 |

It should be noted that the class interval boundaries, 59.5, 62.5, 65.5, 68.5, 71.5, and 74.5 are values that could not occur in the observations, since all measurements are to the nearest inch. This condition permits the measurements to fall unambiguously within one of the defined intervals. Naturally, all heights between 60 and 62 *inclusive* are tallied in the first interval, those between 63 and 65 inclusive are tallied in the second interval, and so on. Reading the appropriate values, we substitute in formula (3), and calculate the sample mean, $\overline{X}$, to be:

$$\overline{X} = \frac{\sum_{1}^{K} f_j X_j}{\sum_{1}^{K} f_j} = \frac{33,500}{500} = 67 \text{ inches} \qquad \text{(sample)}$$

It should be pointed out that there well may be a difference between this result and that which might have been obtained if the data had not been grouped. Any such difference would be termed "*the error due to grouping.*" Usually this error is small, and is usually considered negligible. With the ready availability of desk calculators and electronic computers, the trend is away from grouping data. If the need arises, Shepherd's correction can be applied for adjusting error due to grouping.[1]

*Characteristics of Arithmetic Mean.* There are two important characteristics of the arithmetic mean: (1) the algebraic sum of the deviations of the individual values about their arithmetic mean is zero; and (2) the sum of the squares of the deviations from the arithmetic mean is a minimum. The first property can be shown to be true in a few steps. By definition, we know:

$$\overline{X} = \frac{X_1 + X_2 + X_3 + \ldots + X_n}{n}$$

Subtracting $\overline{X}$ from both sides of the equation, we obtain:

$$0 = \frac{X_1 + X_2 + X_3 + \ldots + X_n}{n} - \overline{X}$$

Multiplying both sides of the equation by $n$, we find

$$0 = X_1 + X_2 + X_3 + \ldots + X_n - n\overline{X}$$

Now, since we have $n$ means ($\overline{X}$'s), we may distribute them to the $n$ terms, and obtain:

$$0 = (X_1 - \overline{X}) + (X_2 - \overline{X}) + (X_3 - \overline{X}) + \ldots + (X_n - \overline{X})$$

which demonstrates that the sum of the deviations of the individual values about their arithmetic mean is zero.

The statement of the second property of the arithmetic mean is another way of saying that the sum of squares of deviations about any other value of the distribution will be larger than the one obtained by using the arithmetic mean as the reference point for calculating deviations. The proof of this statement is as follows: Let $a$ be any point from which deviations are measured. Form all possible deviations $(X - a)$, and sum them $\sum(X - a)$. The sum of the squares becomes $\sum(X - a)^2$. We are seeking the value of $a$ which makes this sum of squares a minimum. It can be shown by calculus that this expression becomes a minimum when $\sum(X - a) = 0$. Solving for $a$, we have:

$$\sum X - \sum a = 0$$

$$\sum X - na = 0$$

$$na = \sum X$$

$$a = \frac{\sum X}{n}$$

This value of $a$ is the definition of $\overline{X}$, the arithmetic mean.

In closing the discussion of the arithmetic mean, some of its advantages should be noted. First, it is a point of reference for measuring variability. Second, it is a convenient estimate to use in showing difference, or relationship, in a characteristic common to two or more groups. Third, under certain conditions it can be treated as a "typical" value. Fourth, and finally, it plays an important role in such statistical techniques as analysis of variance, analysis of covariance, multiple regression, and others.

(b) *The Median.* Another kind of average which is used frequently is the *median.* The median is considered to be the middle value in a series of values which have been arranged in order of magnitude.* The median is based upon order; it is not determined on the basis of absolute differences in the magnitudes of successive pairs of values. For this reason, the median is frequently termed the "positional average." To illustrate these points, the following arrays of five values have the same median, 80:

(1)  15, 50, <u>80</u>, 90, 100
(2)  1, 1, <u>80</u>, 100, 100
(3)  10, 10, <u>80</u>, 85, 90

In contrast, the arithmetic mean, which depends upon the magnitude of the total sum of the respective values, for the first array is 67, for the second is 56.4, and for the third is 55.

When the array is composed of an odd number of values, the median is always one of the values included in the set. This situation is demonstrated clearly in the three samples of five values, above. In this case the median is the $[(n + 1)/2]$ value, counting from either end, where $n$ is the number of values arranged in order of magnitude. Note that if $n = 5$, the median is the third value.

In an array consisting of an even number of values, the median is assumed to fall midway between the two middle values. Put in another way, it is the arithmetic mean of the two middle values of the array. For example, the median of the array composed of the six values: 20, 23, 27, 28, 30, and 31; is $(27 + 28)/2 = 27.5$.

In a frequency distribution, the median is the value of the variate $(X)$ corresponding to the $n/2$ observation, or the 50th percentile. Since the median is the 50th percentile of a frequency distribution, it can be computed by employing the formula for $X_p$ (page 157), with $f_p$ equal to $n/2$. Thus the formula becomes:

$$X_{md} = X_L + i\frac{(n/2 - f_L)}{f_i}$$

where all symbols are the same as in the formula for $X_p$, and $n$ is the total frequency of occurrence of the variate $X$, in the distribution. To illustrate, we use the data in Table III with $n/2 = 300/2 = 150$, $X_L = 67.5$; $i = 1$; $f_L = 104$;

---

* A series of values which have been arranged in order of magnitude is called an "array."

$f_i = 60$; and find the value of the median to be

$$X_{md} = 67.5 + \frac{(1)(150 - 104)}{160}$$

$$= 67.5 + \frac{46}{160}$$

$$= 67.5 + .29 = 67.79 \text{ or } 67.8$$

The median answers the question: What value of $X$ divides the area of the distribution into two equal parts? The arithmetic mean, on the other hand, answers the question: What value of $X$, say $X = a$, divides the quantity designating the sum of the deviations of the individual values about that point, symbolically $\sum_{1}^{K} f_j(x_j - a)$, into two equal magnitudes with opposite signs?

Put in another way, if a measure of location that halves the area under the curve of the distribution is desired, the median is calculated; if a measure that will halve the weighted deviations about a point $a$ is desired, the arithmetic mean is computed. The median and arithmetic mean values will be the same only if the distribution is symmetrical about some center value of the variate $X$.

One instance where the median can be calculated, but the arithmetic mean cannot, is the case of a distribution with open-end intervals. This situation could be demonstrated by supposing that the end intervals of the distribution of height of the 300 male students shown in Table III, were designated as "less than 60" and "79 and over," respectively. Under these conditions a midpoint value could not be assigned to the end intervals, and the arithmetic mean could not be calculated. The median, however, being based upon frequencies could be determined.

Since open-end frequency distributions limit not only the calculation of arithmetic means, but also the calculation of measures of variability, their use should be discouraged. If such distributions are used, the "estimated" arithmetic means of the open-end intervals should be provided by the researcher in case the arithmetic mean of the distribution had to be computed.

(c) *The Mode.* A third type of average is the *mode*, which is defined to be the value of the variate that appears most frequently in the distribution. There are certain difficulties associated with the calculation and use of this form of average. First, it has no meaning for a rectangular distribution. Second, it is influenced greatly by the width of the interval selected for grouping. Finally, a distribution may have more than one peak, which would mean that the distribution might have more than one mode. Such is the case with bi-modal distributions.

In a symmetrical single peaked (unimodal) distribution, such as the theoretical normal distribution, the values of the arithmetic mean, the median, and the mode are equal. In a nonsymmetrical distribution they are not equal.

To illustrate how the mode of a frequency distribution is calculated, we use the following "miniature" distribution.

| Interval of Height (Inches) | Frequency $f_j$ | |
|---|---|---|
| 74.5–77.5 | 2 | |
| 71.5–74.5 | 3 | $f_3$ |
| 68.5–71.5 | 10 | $f_2$ |
| 65.5–68.5 | 7 | $f_1$ |
| 62.5–65.5 | 5 | |
| 59.5–62.5 | 3 | |
| Sum | 30 | |

The interval with the highest frequency is designated by $f_2$. The first interval below (and adjacent to) this interval is designated by $f_1$, and the first one above the $f_2$ interval is designated by $f_3$. The mode is then computed by the following formula:

$$X_{mo} = X_L + \frac{i(f_2 - f_1)}{(f_2 - f_1) + (f_2 - f_3)} \tag{5}$$

where $X_L$ is the lower limit of the interval with the highest frequency ($f_2$); $i$ is the length of this interval; and $f_1$, $f_2$, and $f_3$ designate the frequencies of the intervals to which they were assigned, respectively.

In this example:

$$X_{mo} = \frac{(3)(10-7)}{(10-7)+(10-3)}$$
$$= 68.5 + \frac{9}{3+7}$$
$$= 68.5 + .9$$
$$= 69.4$$

In formula (5) the principle followed is that, within the modal interval, the mode is proportional to the differences between the modal-frequency and the two adjoining frequencies. Now, if the two adjoining frequencies are equal, then the mode is in the middle of the interval of highest frequency. If such is not the case, the mode is in the direction of that adjacent frequency which is the higher.

Another formula that is used frequently to compute the mode of a distribution, providing the *arithmetic mean and the median* are known, is as follows:

$$\text{Mode} = \text{Mean} - 3(\text{Mean} - \text{Median}) \tag{6}$$

The ease with which the mode can be calculated from formula (6) makes it a more popular one than formula (5).

Other measures of central tendency are the *geometric mean* and the *harmonic mean*. Since we shall have no need for these "measures" in our education research models, we do not discuss them here. The reader who is interested in these concepts will find them covered by Mode.[2]

3. *Dispersion Measures (Variability)*. Variability is an important concept in statistical inquiry. As variability is accounted for, estimates and inferences are improved. We discuss briefly here the following measures of variability: (a) the range, (b) the semi-interquartile range, (c) the mean deviation, (d) the variance, and the standard deviation, and (e) the coefficient of variation.

(a) *The Range*. The difference between the minimum value of $X$ and the maximum value of $X$, in an *actual* (not theoretical) distribution, is called the *range* of the variate $X$. The range of a set of values can supply important information. The medical doctor is usually very interested in the range of the fluctuating temperature of a patient; the stock broker in the range of the daily fluctuating value of a stock; and the climatologist in the annual range of temperature values for a particular geographical region. Similar applications can be found in certain areas of school operation, but because there are more exact and valid measures of variability available, the range is used relatively infrequently in educational research.

(b) *The Semi-interquartile Range*. From our discussion of the topics of area of the frequency distribution and percentiles, it should be obvious that 50 per cent of the total distribution is comprised of variate values lying between the first quartile, $Q_1$, (25th percentile), and the third quartile, $Q_3$ (75th percentile). Now, since the value found at the second quartile (the 50th percentile) is the median, it has been suggested that one half the interval $Q_3 - Q_1$ would be a good measure of the "average" deviation of the variates from the median, or some other intermediate value. Thus, the semi-interquartile range, or the quartile deviation, $Q$, is defined as:

$$Q = \tfrac{1}{2}(Q_3 - Q_1) \tag{9}$$

where $Q_3$ is the third quartile (75th percentile), and $Q_1$ is the first quartile (25th percentile). Formulas for the third and first quartile are adaptations of the percentile formula (see page 157), and are as follows:

$$Q_3 = X_L + \frac{i(\tfrac{3}{4}n - f_L)}{f_i} \tag{10}$$

$$Q_1 = X_L + \frac{i(n/4 - f_L)}{f_i} \tag{10'}$$

where the symbols have the same meaning as they do in the percentile formula.

A good example of the application of the semi-interquartile range can be presented in connection with the interpretation of the test results of a particular group. Suppose that 500 persons have taken a particular test. The test scores (variate $X$) range from 200 to 900. The $X$ value associated with $Q_1$ is 460, and the score associated with $Q_3$ is 624. Thus, the semi-interquartile range, or quartile deviation, of the test score is:

$$Q = \tfrac{1}{2}(Q_3 - Q_1)$$
$$= \tfrac{1}{2}(624 - 460)$$
$$= \frac{164}{2}$$
$$= 82$$

This result could be interpreted roughly to mean that 50 per cent of the test scores deviated from the median, or some other intermediate value, by less than 82 points. The other 50 percent of the scores deviated by more than 82 points.

(c) *The Mean Deviation.* Another measure of variability, which is not readily susceptible to algebraic treatment, and therefore is not an extremely important measure, is the *mean deviation*. The *mean deviation* is defined as the arithmetic mean of the *absolute deviations* of $n$ variates $X_1$, $X_2$, $X_3, \ldots, X_n$ from their arithmetic mean $\overline{X}$. Symbolically, the formula is:

$$M.D. = \frac{\sum\limits_{i=1}^{n} |X_i - \overline{X}|}{n} \tag{11}$$

where *M.D.* is the mean deviation, $\sum\limits_{i=1}^{n} |X_i - \overline{X}|$ indicates the addition *without regard to algebraic sign* of the difference between each of the $n$ values and the arithmetic mean. The algebraic signs of the deviations of the values from the arithmetic mean are ignored in order to arrive at a value for the expression. If the *absolute values* of these differences were not employed, their sum would be equal to zero, because, as we have seen in earlier discussion (page 161), the algebraic sum of the deviations of the values composing a distribution from the arithmetic mean of that distribution is always zero.

A short example should illustrate the previous discussion. Suppose that the test scores in a given subject for ten selected pupils were as follows:

$$100, 60, 72, 48, 80, 60, 65, 75, 83, 57$$

The arithmetic mean of this set of scores is found to be 70. Thus, the *absolute deviations*, $|X_i - \overline{X}|$, are:

$$30, 10, 2, 22, 10, 10, 5, 5, 13, 13$$

with a sum of 120. Thus:

$$M.D. = \tfrac{120}{10} = 12$$

This result means that the test scores deviated, on an average, 12 points from the mean score of 70.

(d) *Variance and Standard Deviation.* Dispersion measures of fundamental importance in statistical analysis are the variance and the standard deviation. In a *finite population*, the *variance* is defined as the arithmetic mean of the sum of the squares of the deviations of all the variate values about the population arithmetic mean. The *standard deviation* of the population is merely the *square root of the population variance*. In terms of population values, the formula for the variance is as follows:

$$\sigma^2 = \frac{\sum\limits_{i=1}^{N} (X_i - \mu)^2}{N} \tag{12}$$

where $\sigma^2$ (sigma squared) is the variance, $X_i$ is the variate, $\mu$ (mu) is the population arithmetic mean of the variate $X_i$, and $N$ is the number of $(X_i)$ variates in the population. Since the population standard deviation is merely the square root of the population variance, its formula becomes:

$$\sigma = \left( \frac{\sum\limits_{i=1}^{N} (X_i - \mu)^2}{N} \right)^{\frac{1}{2}} \tag{12'}$$

Since it is computationally inconvenient to find the difference of each variate from the population arithmetic mean, square each of the differences, and then sum these quantities; an equivalent form of the formula which greatly simplifies the computation procedures is now developed. Beginning with formula (12), we have:

$$\sigma^2 = \frac{\sum\limits_{i=1}^{N} (X_i - \mu)^2}{N}$$

Squaring the differences as indicated:

$$\sigma^2 = \frac{\sum\limits_{i=1}^{N} (X_i^2 - 2\mu X_i + \mu^2)}{N}$$

Summing:

$$\sigma^2 = \frac{\sum\limits_{i=1}^{N} X_i^2 - 2\mu \sum\limits_{i=1}^{N} X_i + \sum\limits_{i=1}^{N} \mu^2}{N}$$

Applying summation rules, pages 154–155, and substituting $\sum\limits_{i=1}^{N} X_i/N$ for $\mu$, we have:

$$\sigma^2 = \frac{\sum\limits_{i=1}^{N} X_i^2 - 2\left( \dfrac{\sum\limits_{i=1}^{N} X_i}{N} \right)\left( \sum\limits_{i=1}^{N} X_i \right) + N\left( \dfrac{\sum\limits_{i=1}^{N} X_i}{N} \right)^2}{N}$$

Performing indicated operations and reducing:

$$\sigma^2 = \frac{\sum\limits_{i=1}^{N} X_i^2 - 2\frac{\left(\sum\limits_{i=1}^{N} X_i\right)^2}{N} + \frac{\left(\sum\limits_{i=1}^{N} X_i\right)^2}{N}}{N}$$

$$\sigma^2 = \frac{\sum\limits_{i=1}^{N} X_i^2 - \frac{\left(\sum X_i\right)^2}{N}}{N} \tag{13}$$

Formula (13) reduces the computation of the variance to first squaring the values of the variate, summing these squares, summing the original values of the variate, squaring that sum, dividing it by $N$ as indicated, and then performing the other indicated operations of subtraction and division. By taking the square root of formula (13), we have the *computational form* of the population standard deviation:

$$\sigma = \left(\frac{\sum\limits_{i=1}^{N} X_i^2 - \left(\sum X_i\right)^2/N}{N}\right)^{\frac{1}{2}} \tag{13'}$$

To this point we have only discussed *population values* of the *variance* and *standard deviation*. In those cases where the population is infinite instead of finite, it is necessary to estimate the population variance, and/or standard deviation from a random sample of variate values. Designating the *sample variance* by $S^2$, and the sample standard deviation by $S$, the formulas are as follows:

$$S^2 = \frac{\sum\limits_{i=1}^{n} X_i^2 - \left(\sum X_i\right)^2/n}{(n-1)} \tag{14) (Variance}$$

$$S = \left(\frac{\sum\limits_{i=1}^{n} X_i^2 - \left(\sum X_i\right)^2/n}{(n-1)}\right)^{\frac{1}{2}} \tag{14'}$$

where $X$ is the variate and $n$ is the number of $X$ values in the sample. It should be pointed out that the *sample variance* and standard deviation involve division by $(n-1)$, one less than the number of elements in the sample, so that a better estimate of the *population variance*, and/or *population* standard deviation is made.*

To illustrate the foregoing formulas, suppose that we have a *population* composed of the following seven values:

---

* For algebraic development of why division by $(n-1)$ provides the "best" estimate of the population value of $\sigma^2$, see Lindquist[112].

| $X$ | $X^2$ |
|---|---|
| 5 | 25 |
| 3 | 9 |
| 9 | 81 |
| 11 | 121 |
| 4 | 16 |
| 7 | 49 |
| 2 | 4 |
| $\sum X = 41$ | $\sum X^2 = 305$ |

$$\sigma^2 = \frac{\sum X^2 - \left(\sum X\right)^2/N}{N}$$

$$= \frac{305 - (41)^2/7}{7}$$

$$\sigma^2 = \frac{305 - 1681/7}{7}$$

$$= \frac{305 - 240.143}{7}$$

$$= \frac{64.857}{7}$$

$\sigma^2 = 9.265$      (variance of population)

$\sigma = \sqrt{9.265}$   (standard deviation of population)
$\sigma = 3.04$

The values for the *population variance* ($\sigma^2$) and the *population* standard deviation ($\sigma$) are calculated as shown.

Now suppose that a *sample* composed of five elements is selected from the population of seven values. Then if the following five elements have been selected, the values of the sample variance ($S^2$) and the sample standard deviation ($S$) are as follows:

| $X$ | $X^2$ |
|---|---|
| 5 | 25 |
| 9 | 81 |
| 11 | 121 |
| 7 | 49 |
| 2 | 4 |
| $\sum X = 34$ | $\sum X^2 = 280$ |

$$S^2 = \frac{\sum X^2 - \left(\sum X\right)^2/n}{n - 1}$$

$$S^2 = \frac{280 - (34)^2/5}{4}$$

$$= \frac{280 - 1156/5}{4}$$

$$= \frac{280 - 231.20}{4}$$

$$S^2 = \frac{48.80}{4}$$

$$S^2 = 12.20 \qquad \text{(sample variance)}$$

$$S = \sqrt{12.20} \quad \text{(sample standard deviation)}$$

$$S = 3.5$$

We see that the value of the *sample* standard deviation of $S = 3.5$ is at best a rough estimate of the value of the *population standard deviation*, $\sigma = 3.05$. Thus we can derive an estimate of $\sigma^2$ and/or $\sigma$ from a random sample of values drawn from the population, and the estimates are designated as $S^2$ and $S$, respectively.

(e) *The Coefficient of Variation*. To this point, only absolute measures of variability have been discussed. In some situations, however, absolute measures are not as meaningful and as important as relative variability. The *coefficient of variation*, defined as the ratio of the standard deviation to the arithmetic mean of the variate $X$, is a measure of relative variability. The formula for the coefficient is:

$$CV = \frac{S}{\overline{X}} \tag{15}$$

where $S$ is the *sample standard deviation*, and $\overline{X}$ is the sample arithmetic mean—estimates of the values of the population standard deviation ($\sigma$) and the population arithmetic mean ($\mu$), respectively.

The standard deviation is greatly affected by the size of the magnitude of the values of the variate $X$ in the set of values under consideration. For example, a standard deviation of, say, 9 in one distribution does not necessarily mean greater *relative dispersion* than a standard deviation of 0.3 in another distribution; because the value in the first distribution may all be of an order thirty times as large as those in the second distribution. Thus, a vehicle by which variability measures can be made comparable is that of the coefficient of variation. The comparison is possible because the coefficient states variability in terms of the mean of the distribution, and the mean responds directly to the general order of size of the values of the variate $X$ involved. This latter characteristic of the coefficient of variation makes it a useful tool in the process of determining an adequate size of a sample to employ under the existing conditions of the research.

4. *The Skewness.* Skewness is a measure of symmetry of a distribution about some central value of the variate $X$. The mode, median, and mean all have the same value (are located at the same point) in a symmetrical distribution. Thus, in a symmetrical distribution, the skewness is zero. When the extended part of the distribution (the long tail) is to the right, the skewness index is positive. When the extended part (the long tail) is to the left, the skewness index is negative.

Although several measures of skewness have been proposed, the simplest and most frequently employed index is:

$$\text{Skewness} = \frac{Mean - Mode}{S} = \frac{Mean - [Mean - 3(Mean - Median)]}{S}$$

$$= \frac{3(Mean - Median)}{S}$$

$$= \frac{3(\overline{X} - X_{md})}{S} \tag{16}$$

where $\overline{X}$ is the sample arithmetic mean, $X_{md}$ is the sample median, and $S$ is the sample standard deviation. Naturally, in the case of a finite population, the formula would hold with the respective values of $\mu$, $\sigma$, and the "median" of the *population* replacing their "sample" counterparts (statistics).

Obviously the skewness index is positive when the arithmetic mean is larger than the median, and negative in sign when the median is larger than the mean. In a symmetrical distribution, since the mean is equal to the median, formula (16) shows the skewness index is equal to zero.

The skewness index is important because most distributions encountered in practice are not symmetrical, and the amount of skewness must be known in order to make allowances for it in the process of deriving estimates and inferences of values of population parameters based upon samples that should reflect approximately the skewness of the populations from which they were drawn.

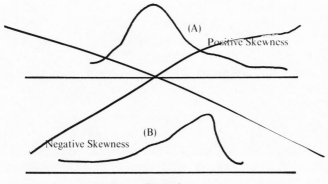

*Figure 8*
*Examples of Skewness*

In Figure 8, two fictitious distributions are shown. The first, (A), illustrates a case of positive skewness and the second, (B), shows a situation of negative skewness. Whenever the skewness index is $\geq \pm 1$ (is greater than or equal to positive or negative one), assuming $S$, the value of the sample standard deviation, remains constant, the distribution is considered to be highly skewed.

This discussion concludes the treatment of selected basic concepts of statistics and the characteristics of a frequency distribution. Full understanding of these concepts is necessary to good comprehension of the facets of statistical inquiry that are frequently associated with many models of educational research.

*Chapter 14—References*
See Bibliography: 4, 19, 27, 40, 41, 44, 45, 49, 52, 53, 55, 62, 65, 69, 71, 76, 77, 85, 87, 89, 90, 95, 97, 103, 105, 106, 112, 118, 122, 123, 126, 128, 131, 133, 136, 141, 146, 148, 153, 155, 156, 157, 159, 163, 165, 169, 180, 181, 182, 184, 185, 186, 190, 197, 198, 200; 36a, 68a, 72a, 91a, 95a, 114a, 119a.

*Chapter Fifteen*

# Probability and Frequency Distributions

MOST PEOPLE have an intuitive sense of the notion of probability, and come in contact with it through its application in the fields of insurance, industry, and certain recreations. Although each of us has had some type of experience with probability, it is difficult to construct a completely adequate definition of the term. This difficulty may be traced, in part, to the existence of at least two general aspects of probability—the empirical and the mathematical. Empirical probability concerns itself with *observed uniformities* in specified characteristics of populations. Mathematical probability is *a form of mathematical logic* which has internal consistency, and maintains external consistency by attempting to account rigorously for the observed uniformities associated with empirical probability.

## EMPIRICAL PROBABILITY

Historically, empirical probability dealt with observed uniformities in games of chance, rates of birth and death, and human error involved in the use of measuring instruments. In these areas of interest it was noted that under specified conditions, certain relative frequencies, or ratios, remained fairly constant. From these empirical ratios certain generalizations were made, and thus the concept of empirical probability was formed.

The empirical probability of the occurrence of a particular characteristic $(X)$ in a given population is simply the ratio formed by dividing the number of population elements with the characteristic by the total number of elements forming the population. Put in another way, the empirical probability of the occurrence of the characteristic in question is the relative frequency of its occurrence in the population. Symbolically, the formula is:

$$Pr(X) = \frac{N_i}{N} \qquad (1)$$

Where $Pr(X)$ is the probability of occurrence of the $X$ characteristic, $N_i$ is the number of population elements with the characteristic $X$, and $N$ is the total number of elements composing the finite population under consideration.

If it were not possible to consider the total population of elements, a random *sample* of elements could be drawn, and $Pr(X)$ could be estimated. Under these conditions, the formula would be:

$$pr(x) = \frac{n_i}{n} \tag{2}$$

Where $pr(x)$ is an *estimate* of the population probability $Pr(X)$, $n_i$ is the number of elements with the characteristic *in the sample*, and $n$ is the total number of elements in the sample. Although mathematicians consider the empirical approach to probability, at best, approximative, it is used frequently in statistical practice.

As a simple example of the foregoing, suppose we have a *loaded* die so that the events of 1, 2, 3, 4, 5, 6 no longer occur "equally likely." How can probabilities be assigned to these values? In such a situation we can define the probability of getting, say, a "6," empirically or statistically, by rolling the die a large number of times, and actually keeping a "count" of the number of times "6" appears. The probability of the "6" is defined to be the relative frequency of occurrence of the number in $n$ rolls. Symbolically the probability would be stated as: $pr(6) = n_i/n$; where $n_i$ is the frequency of occurrence of "6" in $n$ rolls of the die.

It should be noted that this definition would not be precise, because if the loaded die were rolled, say, 1000 times, we would begin to realize that the probability of the occurrence of each of the six numbers on it would not be "equally likely." Thus, we would have different values of $pr(1)$, $pr(2)$, $pr(3)$, $pr(4)$, $pr(5)$, and $pr(6)$, a situation that would not exist if the die were a "fair" one (each number would then occur approximately an equal number of times), a fact borne out by a mathematical probability analysis of a die composed of six faces.

If the die were a fair one, however, the discrepancy between the relative frequency describing the empirical probability of the occurrence of the number "6," and the mathematical probability of its occurrence would be very small. Therefore the *empirical* definition is considered, for all practical purposes, a satisfactory definition of probability in cases where the possible events are *equally likely* to occur.

## Mathematical Probability

Mathematical probability is defined in mathematical terms on an axiomatic basis in such a fashion that it is consistent with actual observation, but is not expressed in empirical or non-mathematical terms. Although not the only *way of defining* "mathematical probability," for there are many diverse approaches to this controversial subject, a typical mathematical definition of probability is as follows:

If an event $(X)$ can occur successfully in $s$ ways and fail in $f$ ways, and each of these occurrences is equally likely, the probability $Pr(X)$ of it successfully happening is $s/(s + f)$, and that of it failing $Qr(X)$ is $f/(s + f)$.

Under the conditions of this mathematical definition of probability, the event in question is certain to occur successfully or fail to occur. Hence, the sum of the chances for success and failure must represent *certainty*. If we can consider certainty to be represented by unity, we have, using $Pr(X)$ and

$Qr(X)$ as previously defined:

$$Pr(X) + Qr(X) = 1 \qquad (3)$$

For equation (3) we see that: $Pr(X) = 1 - Qr(X)$ and that $Qr(X) = 1 - Pr(X)$. It should also be noted that the probability for success $Pr(X)$, or the probability for failure $Qr(X)$, can only vary in value between 0 and 1, inclusive. Put in another way, $Pr(X)$ must be a positive proper fraction, as must $Qr(X)$.

The definition of mathematical probability may be given in a slightly different form, which expands its possibility of application, and, at the same time, renders it consistent for application to an empirical situation. The different form is developed on the supposition that there are a number of events $A, B, C, \ldots$ of which one, and only one, must occur. Now if $a, b, c, \ldots$ are the number of ways respectively in which these events can happen, and each of these ways is equally likely to occur, and if the total number of events is $n = a + b + c + \ldots$, then the probability that $A$ will occur is $a/n$, the chance that $B$ will occur is $b/n$, and so on. By the same token, the probability that $A$ will *not* occur is $1 - a/n$; that $B$ will *not* occur is $1 - b/n$; that $C$ will *not* occur is $1 - c/n$, and so on. Through this interpretation we see that many more than two probabilities might occur in a given consideration, but that their total will still be unity. We also note that this interpretation would be easily applicable to an empirical situation which fits this mathematical model of probability.

From the foregoing remarks, we can summarize that mathematical probability is a number ranging from 0 to 1, inclusive. When the number of alternatives is finite (as previously discussed), a probability of 1 means certainty; a probability of 0 means impossibility. Finally, if $Pr(X)$ is the probability for success of an event, and $Qr(X)$ is the probability of failure, then $Pr(X) + Qr(X) = 1$.

It becomes obvious that the application of mathematical probability theory requires the accurate counting of elements, events, or numbers of ways of doing things. In view of this fact, and before turning to a brief discussion of a limited number of types of probability, and ultimately the relationship between frequency distributions and probability, we now discuss combinations and permutations as a means of rapidly counting events and objects. From the frequencies derived by applying the counting formulas, the formulation of desired mathematical probabilities is realized with the formation of the proper mathematical ratios.

## PERMUTATIONS AND COMBINATIONS

A *permutation* is defined as each of the different *orders*, or *arrangements*, of a group of things. A *selection* or *group* of things, considered without reference to their order or arrangement, within the selection, is defined to be a *combination*.

To exemplify the above definitions, we consider the four letters $A, B, C, D$. The number of *permutations* which can be made by taking these letters two at a time is twelve. They may be listed as follows:

*AB, AC, AD, BC, BD, CD, BA, CA, DA, CB, DB,* and *DC*

If these letters were taken three at a time, there would be twenty-four *permutations*, namely:

$$ABC, \ ABD, \ ACD, \ BCD$$
$$BAC, \ BAD, \ CAD, \ CBD$$
$$ACB, \ ADB, \ ADC, \ BDC$$
$$BCA, \ BDA, \ CDA, \ CDB$$
$$CAB, \ DAB, \ DAC, \ DBC$$
$$CBA, \ DBA, \ DCA, \ DCB$$

The *combinations* which can be made by taking the letters $A, B, C, D$ two at a time are six in number, namely:

$$AB, \ AC, \ AD, \ BC, \ BD, \text{ and } CD$$

It should be noted that each of these listings present a different *group* of two letters. By the same token the number of *combinations* which can be made by the letters taken three at a time are four in number, namely:

$$ABC, \ ABD, \ ACD, \text{ and } BCD$$

It becomes evident that in forming *combinations* only the number of things each selection contains is important, while in forming *permutations* the order, or arrangement, of things forming the selection must be considered. If the total number of things from which the selection is to be made is small, there is relatively little difficulty in determining the number of *permutations* and/or *combinations* which might be of interest. When the total number of things is large, however, the approach which was employed above is not only cumbersome, but almost impossible to apply. It is at this point that the "counting formulas," actually the mathematical formulas for the *number of permutations*, and the number of *combinations* of $N$ different things taken $r$ at a time, becomes important.

*A fundamental theorem concerning permutations states that the number of permutations of $N$ different things taken $r$ at a time*, denoted by $_NP_r$, is given by the formula:

$$_NP_r = \frac{N!}{(N-r)!} \tag{4}$$

where $N! = N \cdot (N-1) \cdot (N-2) \cdot (N-3) \ldots (3) \cdot (2) \cdot (1)$

Applying formula (4) to our earlier example involving the letters $A, B, C, D$, we find that if we wish to know the number of permutations resulting from the selection of four different letters taken two at a time, we have:

$$_4P_2 = \frac{4!}{(4-2)!} = \frac{4 \cdot 3 \cdot 2 \cdot 1}{2 \cdot 1} = 12$$

the same number we found by actually listing the different possibilities.

To find the number of permutations if the four different letters are selected three at a time, as in one of our previous examples, we have:

$$_4P_3 = \frac{4!}{(4-3)!} = \frac{4 \cdot 3 \cdot 2 \cdot \cancel{1}}{\cancel{1}} = 24$$

the same number we found by actually listing the possibilities.

*A fundamental theorem concerning combinations states that the number of combinations of N different things taken r at a time*, denoted by $\overset{N}{\underset{r}{C}}$, is given by the formula:

$$\overset{N}{\underset{r}{C}} = \frac{N!}{r!(N-r)!} \tag{5}$$

Applying formula (5) to the previous example of determining the *number of combinations* resulting from taking the four different letters two at a time, we have:

$$\overset{4}{\underset{2}{C}} = \frac{4!}{2!(4-2)!} = \frac{4!}{2!2!} = \frac{\cancel{4} \cdot 3 \cdot 2 \cdot 1}{(\cancel{2} \cdot 1)(\cancel{2} \cdot 1)} = 6$$

the same number we found by actually listing the possibilities. By the same token, applying the formula to the case where three of the numbers were to be selected, we have:

$$\overset{4}{\underset{3}{C}} = \frac{4!}{3!(4-3)!} = \frac{4 \cdot \cancel{3} \cdot \cancel{2} \cdot \cancel{1}}{(\cancel{3} \cdot \cancel{2} \cdot \cancel{1})(1)} = 4$$

the same number we found by actually listing the possibilities.

We are now ready to discuss four different types of probability: (1) the probability of independent events, (2) the probability of mutually exclusive events, (3) conditional (dependent) probability, and (4) the probability of exactly $x$ successes among $n$ outcomes.

### 1. The Probability of Independent Events

If the occurrence of a first event ($A$) is independent and unrelated to the occurrence of a second event ($B$), then the probability of their *joint occurrence* is the product of their respective probabilities. Symbolically, if $Pr(A)$ represents the probability of the occurrence of event $A$ and is equal to $n_A/N_A$, and $Pr(B)$ represents the probability of event $B$ and is equal to $n_B/N_B$, then:

$$Pr(A \text{ and } B) = Pr(A) \cdot Pr(B) = \frac{n_A}{N_A} \cdot \frac{n_B}{N_B} = \frac{n_A n_B}{N_A N_B} \tag{6}$$

This formula may be generalized for $K$ independent events as follows:

$$Pr(A \text{ and } B \text{ and } C \text{ and} \dots K) = Pr(A) \cdot Pr(B) \cdot Pr(C) \cdot Pr(D) \cdot \dots Pr(K)$$

$$= \frac{n_A}{N_A} \cdot \frac{n_B}{N_B} \cdot \frac{n_C}{N_C} \cdot \frac{n_D}{N_D} \cdot \dots \frac{n_k}{N_k} \tag{7}$$

where the symbols employed are analogous in meaning to those employed in formula (6).

The following examples illustrate our discussion:

*Example 1.* What is the probability of getting all "tails" in a single "toss" of three pennies? Under ordinary circumstances, what happens to *one* penny when *three* are tossed, does not affect the other two. Each of them acts independently of the others. If such is not the case, the principle of "independent events" does not hold. Assuming that the principle does hold, we know that the probability of getting all tails on one toss would be the product of the probabilities of getting a tail on each one of them. The probability of getting a tail on one toss of a penny is one out of two, or $\frac{1}{2}$. Thus the probability of getting 3 tails is:

$$Pr(A \text{ and } B \text{ and } C) = \tfrac{1}{2} \times \tfrac{1}{2} \times \tfrac{1}{2} = \tfrac{1}{8}$$

*Example 2.* A particular group of students under observation is composed of 5 boys and 7 girls. The research problem calls for the selection of two samples, with replacements, of 3 students each. It is decided that boys will be represented by red chips and girls by blue chips. Two drawings, each of 3 chips, will be made from a box which will contain 5 red and 7 blue chips. Each time a chip is drawn, it will be replaced before the next drawing.* The researcher wishes to know the probability of the event in which the first drawing is composed of all boys (3 red chips), and the second of all girls (3 blue chips).

Under the conditions of the problem, the first drawing in no way affects the second drawing of chips, nor does the second affect the first. We, therefore, have an "independent events" probability situation.

The number of ways of drawing 3 chips is:

$$\underset{3}{\overset{12}{C}} = \frac{12!}{3!(12-3)!} = \frac{\overset{2}{\cancel{12}} \cdot 11 \cdot 10 \cdot \cancel{9} \cdot \cancel{8} \ldots \cancel{3} \cdot \cancel{2} \cdot \cancel{1}}{(\cancel{3} \cdot \cancel{2} \cdot \cancel{1})(\cancel{9} \cdot \cancel{8} \cdot 7 \ldots \cancel{3} \cdot \cancel{2} \cdot \cancel{1})} = 220$$

The number of ways of drawing 3 red chips is:

$$\underset{3}{\overset{5}{C}} = \frac{5!}{3!(5-3)!} = \frac{5 \cdot 4 \cdot \cancel{3} \cdot \cancel{2} \cdot \cancel{1}}{(\cancel{3} \cdot \cancel{2} \cdot \cancel{1})(\cancel{2} \cdot \cancel{1})} = 10$$

The number of ways of drawing 3 blue chips is:

$$\underset{3}{\overset{7}{C}} = \frac{7!}{3!(7-3)!} = \frac{7 \cdot \cancel{6} \cdot 5 \cdot \cancel{4} \cdot \cancel{3} \cdot \cancel{2} \cdot \cancel{1}}{(\cancel{3} \cdot \cancel{2} \cdot \cancel{1})(\cancel{4} \cdot \cancel{3} \cdot \cancel{2} \cdot \cancel{1})} = 35$$

Thus, the probability of 3 red in the first drawing is:

$$Pr(3 \text{ red}) = \frac{\underset{3}{\overset{5}{C}}}{\underset{3}{\overset{12}{C}}} = \frac{10}{220} = \frac{1}{22}$$

---

* This activity is defined to be "sampling with replacement."

and the probability of 3 blue in the second drawing is:

$$Pr(3 \text{ blue}) = \frac{C_3^7}{C_3^{12}} = \frac{35}{220} = \frac{7}{44}$$

Hence, the probability of both occurring (3 boys in first sample, *and* 3 girls in the second) is: $\frac{1}{22} \times \frac{7}{44} = \frac{7}{968}$.

It should be pointed out that all values of probabilities employed in the previous examples were calculated on the basis of *mathematical probability laws*. They are *theoretical*, or *expected* values, and would be approached in actuality only if the assumptions underlying them are true or approximated, and a large number of random samples is employed.

## 2. The Probability of Mutually Exclusive Events

Events which cannot occur simultaneously as a result of the same action, are called *mutually exclusive* events. For example, when one coin is flipped it must fall in such a fashion that it portrays a head (*H*), or a tail (*T*). It is impossible for the coin to show an *H* and a *T* simultaneously. Thus the event *H* and the event *T*, *on a given coin*, are mutually exclusive events.

*If an event can occur in two or more different ways, and those ways are mutually exclusive, the probability of occurrence of the event is the sum of the probabilities of its occurring in these different ways.* In this situation the assumption is made that any one of the mutually exclusive events is equally likely, and, hence, the sum of their individual probabilities is one.

Symbolically speaking, if:

$$Pr(A) = \frac{n_A}{N}; Pr(B) = \frac{n_B}{N}; \quad Pr(C) = \frac{n_C}{N}; \dots ; Pr(K) = \frac{n_k}{N};$$

then:

$$Pr(A \text{ or } B \text{ or } C \text{ or } D \dots \text{ or } K) = Pr(A) + Pr(B) + Pr(C) + Pr(D)$$

$$+ \dots + Pr(K)$$

$$= \frac{n_A}{N} + \frac{n_B}{N} + \frac{n_C}{N} + \frac{n_D}{N} + \dots + \frac{n_K}{N}$$

$$= \frac{n_A + n_B + n_C + n_D + \dots n_K}{N}$$

where *N* is the number of elements in the finite population, and $n_i$ ($i = A, B, C, D,\dots$) denotes the number of population elements showing the characteristic in question (e.g., *A*, or *B* or *C*), and the meaning of the word "or" is used in its inclusive, or "both," sense.

*Example 1.* In a *single flip* of a coin, what is the probability of getting a head (*H*), or a tail (*T*).

Let $Pr(A)$ be the probability of a $H: Pr(A) = \frac{1}{2}$
Let $Pr(B)$ be the probability of a $T: Pr(B) = \frac{1}{2}$

Hence, the probability of a $H$ or a $T$ becomes: $Pr(A \text{ or } B) = Pr(A) + Pr(B) = \frac{1}{2} + \frac{1}{2} = 1$. Thus, since the coin must fall heads or tails, we are certain to get either an $H$ or a $T$.

*Example 2.* What is the probability of getting a 1 or a 2 or a 3 or a 6 in a single throw of a die?

Let $Pr(A)$ be the probability of a $1: Pr(A) = \frac{1}{6}$
Let $Pr(B)$ be the probability of a $2: Pr(B) = \frac{1}{6}$
Let $Pr(C)$ be the probability of a $3: Pr(C) = \frac{1}{6}$
Let $Pr(D)$ be the probability of a $6: Pr(D) = \frac{1}{6}$

Hence,

$$Pr(A \text{ or } B \text{ or } C \text{ or } D) = Pr(A) + Pr(B) + Pr(C) + Pr(D) = \frac{1}{6} + \frac{1}{6} + \frac{1}{6} + \frac{1}{6}$$
$$= \frac{4}{6} = \frac{2}{3}$$

### 3. *Conditional (Dependent) Probability*

If the successful occurrence of a second event (*B*) is dependent upon the occurrence of a first event (*A*), then the probability of their joint *occurrence* is termed "conditional probability." Generalizing this statement to *K* dependent events, and letting $Pr(A)$ denote the probability of the first event $A$; $Pr(B/A)$ the probability of $B$ given that $A$ has already occurred; $Pr(C/B \text{ and } A)$ the probability of $C$ given that $A$ and $B$ have already occurred; ... $Pr[(K/A \text{ and } B \text{ and } C \text{ and } \ldots K - 1)]$ the probability of $K$ given that $A$ and $B$ and $C$ and $D$ through $K - 1$ have already occurred, then the probability of total success is: $Pr(A \text{ and } B \text{ and } C \text{ and } \ldots K) = Pr(A) \cdot Pr(B/A) \cdot Pr(C/B \text{ and } A) \cdot \ldots Pr(K/A \text{ and } B \text{ and } C \text{ and } \ldots K - 1)$.

*Example 1.* Suppose the same research problem and conditions of Example 2 (page 178) exist, except the group is composed of 6 boys and 9 girls, and the selection of sample elements is conducted *without replacement*. Thus, two drawings, each of 3 chips, are made from a box containing 6 red and 9 blue chips, *under the condition that the chips included in the first drawing are not replaced before the second drawing.* Find the probability that the first drawing will yield 3 blue (all girls) and the second will yield 3 red (all boys) chips.

In the first drawing, 3 chips of either color may be drawn in $\overset{15}{C}_{3}$ ways, and 3 blue chips may be drawn in $\overset{9}{C}_{3}$ ways. Thus, the chance of 3 blue chips in the first drawing =

$$\frac{\overset{9}{C}}{\underset{3}{\overset{15}{C}}} \cdot \overset{15}{\underset{3}{C}} = \frac{\overset{3}{\overbrace{9 \cdot 8 \cdot 7 \cdot 6}} \cdots 3 \cdot 2 \cdot 1}{(3 \cdot 2 \cdot 1)(6 \cdot 5 \cdot 4 \cdot 3 \cdot 2 \cdot 1)} \div \frac{\overset{5}{\overbrace{15 \cdot 14 \cdot 13}} \cdots \overset{7}{\overbrace{3 \cdot 2 \cdot 1}}}{(3 \cdot 2 \cdot 1)(12 \cdot 11 \cdot 10)}$$

$$= \frac{84}{455} = \frac{12}{65}$$

After 3 blue chips have been removed, the box will contain 6 red and 6 blue chips. Hence, in the second drawing 3 chips may be drawn in $\overset{12}{\underset{3}{C}}$ ways, and three red chips may be drawn $\overset{6}{\underset{3}{C}}$ ways. Therefore, the chance of 3 red chips in the second drawing

$$= \frac{\overset{6}{\underset{3}{C}}}{\underset{3}{\overset{12}{C}}} = \frac{6 \cdot 5 \cdot 4 \cdot 3 \cdot 2 \cdot 1}{(3 \cdot 2 \cdot 1)(3 \cdot 2 \cdot 1)} \div \frac{12 \cdot 11 \cdot 10 \cdot 9 \cdot 8 \cdots 3 \cdot 2 \cdot 1}{(3 \cdot 2 \cdot 1)(9 \cdot 8 \cdot 7 \cdots 3 \cdot 2 \cdot 1)} = \frac{20}{220} = \frac{1}{11}$$

The probability of the compound event $= (\frac{12}{65})(\frac{1}{11}) = \frac{12}{715}$.

*Example 2.* What is the chance of one particular player out of four being dealt the king and queen of a certain suit?

The number of ways in which the king and queen of a certain suit can be dealt to one of four players is equal to the number of permutations of 13 different things taken 2 at a time:

$$_{13}P_2 = \frac{13!}{(13 - 2)!} = 13 \cdot 12$$

By similar reasoning the total number of ways in which the particular king and queen can be dealt is

$$_{52}P_2 = \frac{52!}{(52 - 2)!} = 52 \cdot 51$$

Therefore the chance in question

$$= \frac{_{13}P_2}{_{52}P_2} = \frac{13 \cdot 12}{52 \cdot 51} = \frac{1}{17}$$

In practice, *conditional probability* arises, usually, when random sampling is effected, *without replacements*, from a *finite* population. If, after each sample element is drawn, *replacement* is made, a situation of *independent probability* exists.

## 4. The Probability of Exactly x Successes among n Outcomes

This type of probability is associated with a particular type of event known as a "binomial event." If we denote the probability of a "success" as $p$ and that of a "failure" as $q$, then the probability of getting exactly $x$ successes and $(n - x)$ failures, where the events are considered to be independent, is given by the successive terms of the binomial distribution:

$$(p + q)^n = \sum_x {}^n_xC \, p^x q^{n-x}$$

where $p + q = 1$, and ${}^n_xC$ is the number of different combinations of $n$ different things taken $x$ at a time.

The idea may be approached in another way by considering *independent events* of a particular type, from an *infinite population* each with probability of occurrence $p$. Then the chance of exactly $x$ of these *independent events* occurring is the product of the individual probabilities $p$ taken $x$ times, or $p^x$. By analogous reasoning, the probability of $(n - x)$ independent events failing to occur is $q^{n-x}$. Hence, the probability of getting $x$ successes and $(n - x)$ failures is the product of the two probabilities $p^x q^{n-x}$. Now there are

$$\underset{x}{\overset{n}{C}} = \frac{n!}{x!(n - x)!}$$

possible selections of $n$ events, $x$ of which are "successes" and $(n - x)$ of which are "failures." These $\underset{x}{\overset{n}{C}}$ selections are mutually exclusive, because two different such selections could not occur at the same time as a result of one set of $n$ trials. Thus, following the addition principle for mutually exclusive events, we have:

$$Pr(x \text{ successes } or \text{ less}) = \sum_{x=0}^{n} \underset{x}{\overset{n}{C}} \, p^x q^{n-x}$$

where $x = 0, 1, 2, 3, \ldots$ or, $n$

$$Pr(\text{exactly } x \text{ successes}) = \underset{x}{\overset{n}{C}} (p^x q^{n-x})$$

This type of probability has many kinds of application, some of which are demonstrated in the following examples.

*Example 1.* What is the probability of getting, 0, or 1, or 2, or 3 heads in tossing 6 pennies at once, under the assumption of random events with the probability of success being $p = \frac{1}{2}$, and that of failure, $q = \frac{1}{2}$. What is the probability of getting 3 or less heads under these conditions?

We may employ the binomial distribution to calculate the required probability.

$$(p + q)^n = \sum_{x=0}^{n} \underset{x}{\overset{n}{C}} \, p^x q^{n-x} = \underset{0}{\overset{n}{C}} \, p^0 q^n + \underset{1}{\overset{n}{C}} \, p^1 q^{n-1} + \underset{2}{\overset{n}{C}} \, p^2 q^{n-2} + \cdots + \underset{n}{\overset{n}{C}} \, p^n q^0$$

Remembering that $p^0 = q^0 = 1$, and substituting the appropriate values in the formula, $x = 0, 1, 2,$ and 3 heads, and $n = 6$, we have:

$$(\tfrac{1}{2} + \tfrac{1}{2})^6 = \overset{6}{\underset{0}{C}} (\tfrac{1}{2})^0(\tfrac{1}{2})^6 + \overset{6}{\underset{1}{C}} (\tfrac{1}{2})^1(\tfrac{1}{2})^5 + \overset{6}{\underset{2}{C}} (\tfrac{1}{2})^2(\tfrac{1}{2})^4 + \overset{6}{\underset{3}{C}} (\tfrac{1}{2})^3(\tfrac{1}{2})^3$$

$$= \frac{6!}{6!}(\tfrac{1}{2})^6 + \frac{6!}{5!}(\tfrac{1}{2})^6 + \frac{6\cdot 5\cdot 4!}{2!4!}(\tfrac{1}{2})^6 + \frac{\overset{3}{6}\cdot 5\cdot 4\cdot \overset{}{3!}}{3!3!}(\tfrac{1}{2})^6$$

For $x = 0$ heads, we see the probability is: $(\tfrac{1}{2})^6 = \tfrac{1}{64}$
For $x = 1$ heads, we see the probability is: $6(\tfrac{1}{2})^6 = \tfrac{6}{64} = \tfrac{3}{32}$
For $x = 2$ heads, we see the probability is: $15(\tfrac{1}{2})^6 = \tfrac{15}{64}$
For $x = 3$ heads, we see the probability is: $20(\tfrac{1}{2})^6 = \tfrac{20}{64} = \tfrac{5}{16}$

The probability of getting 3 or less heads is:

$$\tfrac{1}{64} + \tfrac{3}{32} + \tfrac{15}{64} + \tfrac{5}{16} = \tfrac{42}{64} = \tfrac{21}{32}$$

*Example 2.* In a poll made by the central purchasing office of a large metro-politan area school system with twenty high schools, the number of "free lunches" that were considered necessary was over-estimated in seventeen of the schools and under-estimated in three of them. If the sampling and estimation were not biased, and the sample was large enough, the number of schools over-estimated would be approximately offset by the number underestimated. Thus, the expected division would be 10 to 10. The actual division, however, was 17 to 3. If an equal division of estimates was expected, what is the chance of getting the 17 to 3 division which was observed?

This problem may be thought of as tossing 20 coins and computing the prob-ability of getting 17 or more heads (or tails) in a single toss. This probability may be obtained by summing the terms of the binomial expansion beginning with the term $\overset{20}{\underset{17}{C}} (\tfrac{1}{2})^{20}$ and ending with $\overset{20}{\underset{20}{C}} (\tfrac{1}{2})^{20}$. The sum is as follows:

$$\overset{20}{\underset{17}{C}} (\tfrac{1}{2})^{20} + \overset{20}{\underset{18}{C}} (\tfrac{1}{2})^{20} + \overset{20}{\underset{19}{C}} (\tfrac{1}{2})^{20} + \overset{20}{\underset{20}{C}} (\tfrac{1}{2})^{20} = \frac{20\cdot 19\cdot \overset{3}{18}}{3\cdot 2\cdot 1} (\tfrac{1}{2})^{20} + \frac{\overset{10}{20}\cdot 19}{2\cdot 1} (\tfrac{1}{2})^{20}$$

$$+ 20(\tfrac{1}{2})^{20} + (\tfrac{1}{2})^{20}$$

$$(1140 + 190 + 20 + 1)(\tfrac{1}{2})^{20} = \frac{1351}{2^{20}} = .001288 + \approx .0013$$

Thus, we see that the probability of getting 17 or more schools "overestimated," if a 10 to 10 division was expected, is approximately 13 in 10,000. Since the prob-ability of these results occurring by chance under these conditions is so small, there is a good probability that a bias is present in the methods employed.

We recall at this point that a "frequency distribution" is a distribution which shows the occurrence of values under consideration in a "relative frequency," or "ratio" form. From this fact, we can note the relationship of probability and frequency distributions. We know from formula (1) (page 173) that the probability of the occurrence of a particular characteristic $X$ is: $Pr(X) = N_i/N$. In essence $Pr(X)$ is a *"relative frequency"* of occurrence of $N_i$ out of $N$ elements. We also know that the frequency distribution is merely the accumulation of the many such possible *"relative frequencies,"* for the various values of the characteristic $X$. Hence, the frequency distribution is closely related to "probability," and can be used as a probability distribution. Before this latter condition can be assumed, however, we must be certain that the frequency distribution shows stability.

*Stability of Frequency Distributions*

Before probability statements can be made from a frequency distribution, we must be sure that: (1) the frequency distribution of the population characteristic in question actually exists; (2) the distribution is fairly fixed, or stable, or, if not, its basic pattern of change is known; (3) the distribution's shape is defined over the range of values of the variate under study; and (4) any distribution which is obtained is based upon a random sample drawn from the defined population.

The four criteria for the stability of a frequency distribution can only be met by taking large, repeated random samples from the population periodically. This approach will account for the shape of the population distribution, its skewness, and at the same time, ascertain any pattern of shifts which might exist within it.

The above four steps relate "empirical" probability with frequency distributions, in good fashion, but how is "mathematical" probability related? An easy way to develop this relationship is to show how certain observations and certain probability concepts parallel each other.

We have seen that mathematical probability includes certain basic rules, such as: (a) the probability of independent events, (b) the probability of mutually exclusive events, (c) the probability of dependent (conditional) events, and (d) the probability of exactly $x$ successes out of $n$ possible events (binomial events). Considering these four basic rules, we see that:

1. Within a frequency distribution the relative frequency of occurrence of events may be accumulated (added) over the distribution. The addition factor also exists in the determination of the probability of mutually exclusive events.

2. A frequency distribution based upon the existence of conditional relative frequencies has its counterpart in the concept of conditional probability.

3. The binomial distribution (a frequency distribution) has a clearly established relationship with the concept of the probability of exactly $x$ successes out of $n$ possible outcomes. This fact is so clearly established that frequently such a probability event is termed a "binomial event."

4. Finally, the probability of independent events, computed on a multiplication basis, can be found from the area under an appropriate frequency distribution curve of clearly defined shape, range, and central tendency.

With the relationship between probability and frequency distributions established, we now define statistics to be: *the science which applies the theory of probability to the processes of estimation and inference concerning the characteristics of a population of quantified objects.*

There has been frequent reference to the word "sample" throughout our discussion of probability and frequency distributions. The concept of "sampling" is fundamental to the understanding of statistical inquiry. For this reason we now turn our basic concepts discussion to the topic of "universe and sample."

UNIVERSE AND SAMPLE

The concepts of "universe" and "sample" have been accorded a complete discussion in Chapter 4. These concepts, however, are of such basic importance to the understanding of the statistical inquiry phase of the suggested general model of educational research, that it becomes necessary to treat them, at least briefly, once again.

We have defined a *population* (or universe) to be any set, or totality, of objects under consideration. A *sample* of a population is any subset of that population. In connection with the concept of population, we may have a *real* or a *hypothetical* one. A *real population* is one that actually exists. A *hypothetical* population is a theoretical one, that is, an *ideal*, or *mathematical model*, population. The distributions of real populations approach the distributions of theoretical populations as limits.

In order to avoid the construction of a mathematical curve of a population frequency distribution, we use certain calculable characteristics (parameters) to describe it. The population arithmetic mean, symbolized by the Greek $\mu$ (mu); the population variance, symbolized by $\sigma^2$ (small sigma squared); and the population standard deviation, $\sigma$, are three such characteristics. Other characteristics that might be employed are: the median, the mode, the range, and the average deviation. In practice, however, these latter parameters of the population distribution are rarely employed.

The distribution of a sample also has identifying calculable characteristics (statistics). The arithmetic mean of a sample, symbolized by $\bar{X}$, the sample variance by $S^2$, and the standard deviation by $S$, are some of the more frequently employed statistics of the sample. The values of these statistics *are estimates* of their population counterparts $\mu$, $\sigma^2$, and $\sigma$, when the latter are associated with populations which are, or are considered to be, infinite. It is important to notice that in the latter case the values of $\bar{X}$, $S^2$, and $S$ may vary from sample to sample, while those of $\mu$, $\sigma^2$, and $\sigma$ remain constant, that is, the parameters have particular values for the particular universe under consideration.

To this point we have confined our remarks to population and sample distributions. There is a third type of distribution, however, of great importance in statistical work, the distribution which is called, in general terms, the "sampling distribution." This distribution is of such paramount importance that we shall accord it special treatment.

*Sampling Distributions*

A sampling distribution is one which is composed of a number of values of a particular statistic computed or compiled from each of *all possible samples of a given size n* which could be drawn, with replacement, from the population (or universe) under consideration. To exemplify, suppose that by sampling *with replacement* we took *all possible samples of twenty-five people from a given group of persons* (finite population), and computed the arithmetic mean, the variance, the standard deviation, the median, and the mode of the weights of the "sample" persons, *for each sample*. Now, if we constructed a distribution composed of all the "means" that could be computed from all the possible different samples of size 25, that could be drawn from the population, and another composed of all the "variances" that could be computed, and still another of all standard deviations, another of all the medians, and one composed of all such modes, we would have constructed *a sampling distribution of the mean for sample size 25, a sampling distribution of the variance for sample size 25, a sampling distribution of the standard deviation for sample size 25, and a sampling distribution of the mode for sample size 25, respectively.* It should be noted that each *statistic* has a particular sampling distribution for the sample size 25.

From the previous example we may now generalize that a sampling distribution exists for every *statistic* (e.g. $\overline{X}$, $S^2$, and $S$) which can be calculated from each of all possible samples of size $n$, selected *with replacement* from the population under consideration. The sampling distributions most frequently employed in educational research are those of $\overline{X}$ and $S^2$. This statement brings us to how the sampling distribution is employed in statistical practice.

The mean value of the sampling distribution of the mean for sample size $n$ ($\mu_{\overline{X}}$) is a good estimate of the value of the population mean, $\mu$. The mean value of the sampling distribution of the variance ($\mu_{S^2}$) is a good estimate of the value of the population variance, $\sigma^2$. The mean value of the sampling distribution of the standard deviation ($\mu_S$) is a good estimate of the value of the population standard deviation, $\sigma$. This pattern holds for the sampling distribution of any particular statistic for sample size $n$.

Since the sampling distribution of the mean for sample size $n$ is the one most frequently employed by statisticians, we shall now discuss the following very important characteristic of it:

*If the population distribution is approximately normal and has a finite variance, the sampling distribution of the mean for sample size n will be approximately normally distributed, providing the sample size n is sufficiently large.* This fact allows the statistician to assume the theoretical normal distribution when working with the sampling distribution of the mean, which in turn provides the method by which the construction of an *actual* sampling distribution of the mean, a most tedious task, can be avoided.

The mean of the sampling distribution of a statistic provides an estimate of the value of the population parameter to which the statistic is a counterpart. It also provides information about how frequently the statistic involved will fall in any interval which might be of interest. *Thus, sampling distributions are employed to make estimates and inferences about the values of the particular population parameters under consideration.*

The following relationship exists between the variance of the sampling distribution of the mean and the population variance:

$$\sigma_{\bar{X}}^2 = \frac{\sigma^2}{n} \tag{1}$$

from which we have:

$$\sigma_{\bar{X}} = \frac{\sigma}{\sqrt{n}} \tag{2}$$

where $\sigma_{\bar{X}}$ symbolizes the "standard error of the mean," $\sigma$ is the population standard deviation, and $n$ is the size of the samples taken in order to compute the values of the mean, $\bar{X}$, which form the sampling distribution of the mean. From this relationship we see that the "standard error of the mean," $\sigma_{\bar{X}}$, is equal to the population standard deviation ($\sigma$) divided by the square root of the sample size, $\sqrt{n}$.

The sampling distribution of the mean for sample size $n$ is particularly useful if we have an infinite population with a mean, $\mu$, of unknown value; and a population standard deviation, $\sigma$, of unknown value; and we wish to get an estimate of the value of $\mu$.

Since estimates vary in precision, it is necessary that an estimate be accompanied by a statement which describes "how near" the estimate may be to the quantity which it is supposed to approximate. *Confidence intervals* provide a means for showing or stating the precision of an estimate. The following example shows the procedures associated with finding a confidence interval:

Take a comparatively large sample of, say, $n = 100$. Compute the value of the mean $\bar{X}$. Let us suppose $\bar{X} = 75$. We also compute the standard deviation of the sample, $S$, and find it to be $S = 5$. Now, since the population mean, $\mu$, is approximated by the mean of the $\bar{X}$'s ($\mu_{\bar{X}}$), for a sample size $n$, and is also approximated by the mean of the sample, $\bar{X}$, of adequate size, we see that the value of the mean of the sample could serve as an estimate of the value of $\mu_{\bar{X}}$ of a sampling distribution of the mean for sample size $n$. Thus, in this case, *although we should technically employ the t-distribution,* we could set up a theoretical normal distribution with $\mu_{\bar{X}} = 75$. The standard deviation of this sampling distribution of the mean for sample size $n = 100$, would then be approximately

$$\sigma_{\bar{X}} = \frac{5}{\sqrt{100}} = \frac{5}{10} = \frac{1}{2}$$

In the latter formula, the value of the sample standard deviation, $S = 5$, is substituted for $\sigma$ in the formula as an estimate (*therefore we should technically use the t-distribution*) of the population standard deviation.

In a *theoretical* normal distribution, the central 95 per cent of the values are bounded by the values ($\mu - 1.96\sigma$) and ($\mu + 1.96\sigma$). Hence, if we wished to make an estimate of the value of the population mean, $\mu$, by introducing such an "interval," we would have, working off the sampling distribution of the mean for sample size $n = 100$, the following "95 per cent confidence interval" established:

$$75 - 1.96\left(\tfrac{1}{2}\right) < \mu < 75 + 1.96\left(\tfrac{1}{2}\right)$$

$$74.02 < \mu < 76.98$$

Put in another way, we could say that 95 per cent of the intervals obtained in this manner will include the value of $\mu$; in this case the interval is from $\overline{X} = 74.02$ to $\overline{X} = 76.98$. This range of values is called a "95 per cent confidence interval." The values "bounding" this interval are called *confidence limits*. It should be recalled at this point that the population mean, $\mu$, has a certain value, but it is unknown to us. What we have constructed is an interval, based on the value of the sample mean, $\overline{X} = 75$, and this interval has a 95 per cent chance of containing the value of the population mean, $\mu$. It should be pointed out that when an "interval" is determined, we cannot be absolutely certain that the value of the population mean is actually included in that interval. We only know that if we repeatedly estimate $\mu$ in this way, we shall include the value of $\mu$ in these intervals 95 per cent of the time.

*In order to clarify certain previous "esoteric" references to the t-distribution, it should be pointed out that it is actually necessary to know the population standard deviation,* $\sigma$, *to estimate* $\mu$ *as just demonstrated* (i.e., by the normal distribution). Since $S$ is only an estimate of $\sigma$, we should arrive at values for the *confidence limits*, by employing the *t*-distribution. We should point out that the sampling distribution of $(\overline{X} - \mu_{\bar{x}})/(S/\sqrt{n})$ (the $t$) differs from the sampling distribution of: $z = (\overline{X} - \mu_{\bar{x}})/\sigma/\sqrt{n}$ (the normal), and that our employment of 1.96 does not *absolutely insure* 95 per cent confidence limits on the *t*-distribution. We can only correctly form a 95 per cent confidence interval with a normal distribution if we know the value of $\sigma$. If we estimate the value of $\sigma$ by employing the value of $S$, we should use the *t*-distribution, in which case we would not necessarily employ the value of "1.96" in the formula in order to determine the values of the confidence limits.

The normal distribution plays a most important role in the estimation of certain parameters. Further investigation would show an amazing pervasiveness of the normal distribution throughout the realm of probability and chance operations. Some statisticians have referred to the normal distribution as the "most important probability distribution in statistics." In view of its importance in statistical practice and inquiry we shall now conclude our discussion of basic concepts with a treatment of the normal distribution.

*Chapter 15—References*

See Bibliography: 4, 26, 27, 40, 41, 45, 49, 52, 53, 60, 65, 69, 71, 85, 95, 104, 105, 106, 107, 112, 123, 126, 128, 133, 141, 147, 148, 155, 156, 159, 180, 181, 182, 183, 184, 185, 190, 197, 198; 7a, 12a, 21a, 66a, 75a, 84a, 104a, 117a.

*Chapter Sixteen*

# The Normal Distribution

THE NORMAL DISTRIBUTION, or normal probability curve, is a theoretical frequency distribution which has important theoretical and practical applications. Many populations, containing a large number of elements, have distributions which approximate "normality." For example, if the heights of all men in the Armed Services during World War II were recorded according to frequency of occurrence, a population which was approximately normally distributed would result. The distribution of IQ's of all school children at a particular grade level, in a given school system, should approach the normal curve. The probability distribution of the occurrence of a particular event in a game of chance will approach a normal distribution, providing a sufficiently large sample of trials is involved. If we made our measures of any of these cases extremely precise, we would provide a multitude of possible values for the event under consideration. If we were now to construct a histogram for the situation it would be composed of an almost infinite number of rectangular blocks, one for each of the possible values. We could then construct a frequency polygon by connecting the midpoints of the tops of the almost infinite number of rectangles forming the histogram. Under these conditions a smooth curve would result. This curve would approximate the shape of a normal curve (see Figure 9)

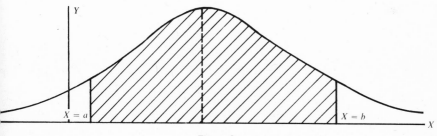

*Figure 9*
*The Normal Probability Curve*

It should be emphasized at this point that the normal curve is a theoretical one, an idealized model of an actual distribution that occurs quite frequently in practice. Employment of the idealized model instead of the actual distribution simplifies computations, and frequently provides a better opportunity to study significant characteristics of the universe, which in turn might provide a better understanding of the problem under investigation.

In Chapter 7, pages 71–78, we discussed levels of measurement of data, and pointed out the difference between continuous and discrete measures. Discrete data are those characterized by an all-or-none type attribute. These data can be counted or enumerated only, but cannot be measured. Characteristics producing this type of data are called "attributes." Data that, at least theoretically, can continue to take on more precise numerical values with increased refinements of the measuring instruments, are considered to be continuous. Characteristics producing the types of data that are always capable of some form of measurement are called "variates." The normal distribution, or normal probability curve, is what mathematicians term a "continuous curve." It is constructed on the assumption that the data that it represents are of variate nature. These data are in contrast to the attribute, or discrete, type of data. These facts mean that the probabilities for normal variates are functions of, or represented by, areas under parts of the normal probability curve. In the case of discrete distributions, such as those formed on the basis of a binomial event (an item discussed in connection with examples found on pages 197–202), the probability may be computed directly from the "terms" of the distribution without involving the use of area. However, in those cases where the sample size is so large that the calculation of probabilities directly from the binomial distribution proves to be unwieldly, the tabled values of the area under given sections of the normal probability curve can be used as good approximations to the events of interest. This utilization of the normal distribution is especially helpful and convenient in finding answers to questions related to the occurrence of mutually exclusive events involving a large number of trials.

The mathematical equation for the normal probability curve is:

$$Y = \frac{1}{\sigma\sqrt{2\pi}} e^{-\frac{1}{2}[(X-\mu)/\sigma]^2}$$

where $X$ is the distributed variate, $\mu$ is the arithmetic mean of the population of values, $\sigma$ is the standard deviation of the population of $X$ values, $Y$ is the probability density of any particular $X$ value, and $e$ and $\pi$ are two constants, the approximate values of which are: $e = 2.71828$ and $\pi = 3.1416$.

If we wished to know the probability of $X$ having a value which occurs between the points $X = a$ and $X = b$, we would obtain our answer by determining how much area was under the curve between the respective points. The cross-hatched sector in Figure 9 shows the area in which we would be interested. The amount of area under the curve between $X = a$ and $X = b$ is found by means of the calculus. This need not be our concern, however, since tables of such area sectors have been constructed in such a fashion that with a modicum of arithmetical work the magnitude of any particular sector can readily be determined. Although we have not included a table of values of the normal distribution, we shall show the more frequently used segments of such tables, and explain how to use them. Before proceeding to this discussion, however, we shall consider some of the characteristics of the normal probability curve.

## Characteristics of the Normal Probability Curve

1. Since the normal probability curve is a continuous curve, and is constructed on the basis of the values of a variate (continuous measurement), it is impossible to distinguish between the amount of area accumulated from $X = -\infty$ (negative infinity) to a point $X < b$, and the amount of area accumulated from $X = -\infty$ to a point $X \leq b$ ($X$ equal to or less than $b$). Put in another way, since area designates probability, we cannot differentiate between the probability or occurrence of values of $X < b$, $Pr[X < b]$ and the probability of occurrence of values of $X \leq b$, $Pr[X \leq b]$. Although it would at first appear that the difference between $Pr[X < b]$ and $Pr[X \leq b]$ is $Pr[X = b]$, *technically* the area under the normal curve at the point $X = b$ is zero. Thus we must conclude that the difference between $Pr[X < b]$ and $Pr[X \leq b]$ is zero. Obviously, this condition need not hold for an attribute (discrete measurement), $X$. Under the latter condition of discontinuous measures ($X$), which might be approximately normally distributed, it is possible to find the difference between $Pr[X < b]$ and $Pr[X \leq b]$. Thus, $Pr[X < b]$ and $Pr[X \leq b]$ need not be equal for an *attribute* $X$ (discrete), but are equal for the *variate* $X$ (continuous). By the same token, $Pr[X > b]$ and $Pr[X \geq b]$; and $Pr[a < X < b]$ and $Pr[a \leq X \leq b]$ are equal, or different, depending upon whether $X$ is an approximately normally distributed *variate* (continuous measure), or an *attribute* (discrete measure), respectively.

2. The normal probability curve is symmetrical with respect to a line perpendicular (vertical) to the point $X = \mu$ located on the horizontal scale (line) of the distribution.

3. By means of calculus it can be determined that the normal probability curve has a maximum value at the point ($X = \mu$, $Y = .399/\sigma$).

4. The total area under the curve from $X = -\infty$ to $X = +\infty$ is equal to unity, i.e., one square unit of area.

5. Since the normal curve is symmetric with a vertical line constructed at the point $X = \mu$, the area accumulated from $X = -\infty$ to $X = \mu$ is 0.5 (50 per cent) of the total area (one square unit) under the curve. Thus, we may make the following probability statement:

$$Pr[X < \mu] = Pr[X > \mu] = 0.5 = 50 \text{ per cent}$$

6. There are basically three types of normal distribution: (a) leptokurtic (high peakedness), (b) mesokurtic (middle peakedness), (c) platykurtic (low peakedness). Figure 10 shows the respective curves. The leptokurtic curve has a smaller standard deviation than either the mesokurtic or the platykurtic curve. As the kurtosis (peakedness) of the curve diminishes, the value of the standard deviation increases.

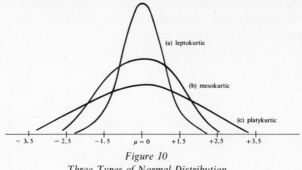

*Figure 10*
*Three Types of Normal Distribution*

It should be noted that almost all of the normal distribution lies within three standard deviations ($\sigma$'s) of the mean. Approximately .003 of the area under the curve lies outside of that range.

*The Standard Normal Curve*

The standard normal curve is a basic normal curve employed frequently in statistical practice, because other normal curves are easily reduced to it by employing the following expression:

$$z = \frac{X - \mu}{\sigma} \quad \text{(Population)} \tag{1}$$

where $z$, the normal deviate, designates the variate in standard deviation units, $X$ is the original value, $(X - \mu)$ is the deviation of $X$ from the population mean $\mu$, and $\sigma$ is the population standard deviation.

The standard normal curve has $z = 0$ (equivalent to $\mu = 0$) and $z = 1$ (equivalent to $\sigma = 1$) i.e., a unit standard deviation. Equation (1) is the expression for the normal deviate in terms of population values. Since this form of variate (normal deviate) is independent of the actual unit of measurement of the original data, it is used as the basis of the tables of areas and ordinates of the normal probability curve. Examples demonstrating how the normal deviate is independent of the unit of measurement, and may be employed in connection with other forms of data, are shown by equations (1) and (2)

$$z = \frac{X - \mu}{\sigma} \quad \text{(Population)} \tag{1}$$

$$z = \frac{\overline{X} - \mu_{\bar{x}}}{\sigma_{\bar{x}}} \quad \begin{array}{l}\text{(Sampling distribution of} \\ \text{mean for sample size } n)\end{array} \tag{2}$$

In equations (1) and (2), $z$ is the normal deviate, $X$ is the original value, $\overline{X}$ is the mean of the sample of size $n$, $\sigma$ is the standard deviation of the population, $\mu_{\bar{x}}$ is the mean of the sampling distribution of the mean for sample size $n$, $\sigma_{\bar{x}}$ is the standard deviation of the sampling distribution of the mean for the sample size $n$, called the "standard error of the mean."

Equation (1) has extensive application, because it converts any normally distributed variate into the *normal deviate* variate, with a zero mean and a standard deviation of unity. The development of a normally distributed variate $z$ is for the purpose of providing a means of translating all normal probability questions into one table of areas under the normal curve. This action allows us to use one probability table while we deal with an unlimited number of different normally distributed variates of different means and different standard deviations.

Summarized below are some of the more important values of the cumulative area under the normal curve from: $z = -\infty$ to the particular point indicated in the $z$ column.

| $z$ | Cumulative Area | $z$ | Cumulative Area |
|---|---|---|---|
| −3.09 | .0010 | +1.00 | .8413 |
| −3.00 | .0013 | +1.282 | .9000 |
| −2.576 | .0050 | +1.645 | .9500 |
| −5.50 | .0062 | +1.96 | .9750 |
| −2.326 | .0100 | +2.00 | .9772 |
| −2.00 | .0228 | +2.336 | .9990 |
| −1.96 | .0250 | +2.50 | .9938 |
| −1.645 | .0500 | +2.576 | .9950 |
| −1.282 | .1000 | +3.00 | .9987 |
| −1.00 | .1587 | +3.09 | .9990 |
| 0.00 | .5000 | | |

Pictorially, the area under the normal curve from $z = -\infty$ to the point $z = -1.00$, would be the shaded area in Figure 11.

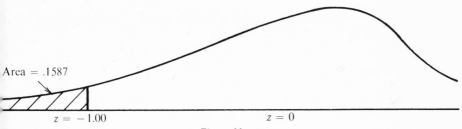

Area = .1587

$z = -1.00$          $z = 0$

*Figure 11*
*Area from $z = -\infty$ to $z = -1.00$*

If we wished to know the probability of occurrence of a $z$-value of $+1.00$, or less, we would be interested in the shaded area of Figure 12.

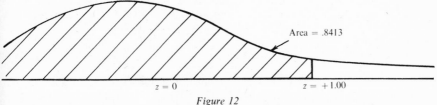

Area = .8413

$z = 0$          $z = +1.00$

*Figure 12*
*Area from $z = 0$ to $z = +1.00$*

Similarly the probability of occurrence of $z$-values between $z_1 = -1.96$ and $z_2 = +1.645$ is $\text{Area}_{z_2} - \text{Area}_{z_1} = .9500 - .0250 = .9250$, shown as the shaded area in Figure 13.

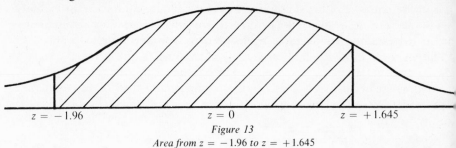

$z = -1.96$ 　　　　　　　$z = 0$ 　　　　　　　$z = +1.645$

*Figure 13*
*Area from $z = -1.96$ to $z = +1.645$*

With a normal probability table, we are able to find probabilities associated with normally distributed variates, $X$'s. Two examples are presented here to illustrate the point.

1. Given a population of reading scores ($X$) which is normally distributed with $\mu = 70$, and $\sigma = 10$, find the following probabilities:

(a) $Pr[X < 50]$
(b) $Pr[X < 80]$
(c) $Pr[50 < X < 80]$
(d) $Pr[X > 60]$
(e) $Pr[45 < X < 95]$
(f) Find the number $r$, such that $Pr[r < X < 90] = .4772$.

(a) In order to evaluate $Pr[X < 50]$, we employ the normal deviate expression:

$$z = \frac{X - \mu}{\sigma}$$

Hence,

$$z = \frac{50 - 70}{10} = \frac{-20}{10} = -2.0$$

Employing the "summary" table of the cumulative areas under the normal curve, we find that the cumulative area under the curve and to the left of the point $z = -2.0$ is .0228. Thus, we can say that $Pr[X < 50] = .0228$, or the probability that we shall find a value of $X$ (a score) less than 50 is approximately two chances out of one hundred.

(b) Employing the normal deviate expression: $z = (X - \mu)/\sigma$, we have:

$$z = \frac{80 - 70}{10} = \frac{10}{10} = +1.00$$

From the table we find that the cumulative area to $z = +1.00$ is .8413.

Thus, $Pr[X < 80] = .8413$, or the probability that a score less than 80 will occur is approximately 84 chances out of 100.

(c) In order to find the probability of a value of $X$ occurring between 50 and 80, we take $Pr[X < 80]$ and subtract from it $Pr[X < 50]$. Thus, $Pr[50 < X < 80] = .8413 - .0228 = .8185$, or the probability that a score between 50 and 80 will occur is approximately 82 chances out of 100.

(d) In order to compute the value for $Pr[X > 60]$, we must first find $Pr[X < 60]$. Thus,

$$z = \frac{60 - 70}{10} = \frac{-10}{10} = -1.00$$

The cumulative area under the normal curve from $z = -\infty$ to $z = -1.00$ is: .1587. Thus, $Pr[X < 60] = .1587$. If $Pr[X < 60] = .1587$, then $Pr[X > 60] = 1.0000 - Pr[X < 60] = 1.0000 - .1587 = .8413$, or the probability that a score greater than 60 will occur is approximately 84 chances out of 100.

(e) To evaluate $Pr[45 < X < 95]$, the probability that an $X$ value will occur between $X = 45$ and $X = 95$, we find first $Pr[X < 45]$:

$$z = \frac{45 - 70}{10} = \frac{-25}{10} = -2.5$$

The cumulative area to $z = -2.5$ is: .0062. Next we find $Pr[X < 95]$:

$$z = \frac{95 - 70}{10} = \frac{25}{10} = +2.5$$

The cumulative area to $z = +2.5$ is: .9938. Since,

$$Pr[45 < X < 95] = Pr[X < 95] - Pr[X < 45]$$

We know $Pr[45 < X < 95] = .9938 - .0062 = .9876$.

(f) In order to find the value of $r$ in the expression $Pr[r < X < 90]$, we proceed as follows: From the table we read that $Pr[X < 90] = .9772$, because

$$z = \frac{90 - 70}{10} = \frac{20}{10} = +2.00$$

We were given the fact that $Pr[r < X < 90] = .4772$, and since $Pr[r < X < 90] = Pr[X < 90] - Pr[X < r]$ we have by substituting the appropriate values:

$$Pr[X < 90] - Pr[X < r] = .4772$$

or

$$.9772 - Pr[X < r] = .4772$$

and by algebraic methods:

$$.9772 - .4772 = Pr[X < r]$$

and

$$Pr[X < r] = .5000$$

Now, the cumulative area of .5000 yields a $z$-value of $z = 0$. We may now substitute in the expression $z = (X - \mu)/\sigma$, and find: $0 = (r - 70)/10$ from which we find that: $0 = r - 70$ and thus: $r = 70$.

2. From a normally distributed population of $X$ values with $\mu = 50$, and $\sigma = 15$, we randomly select a sample of 25 items.

(a)  What is the chance that this sample has a mean less than 53?
(b)  Find two points such that the chance of the mean of the sample of 25 lying between them is the central 90 per cent of all the area under the normal curve.
(c)  Same as (b), but 95 per cent instead of 90 per cent.
(a)  In order to find the chance that a sample of 25 values taken from this population has a mean less than 53, we employ the normal deviate expression associated with the sampling distribution of the mean for sample size $n$, which we know is normally distributed. Thus, we employ equation (2), page 192.

$$z = \frac{\overline{X} - \mu_{\bar{x}}}{\sigma_{\bar{x}}} \tag{2}$$

We know $\sigma_{\bar{x}} = \sigma/\sqrt{n}$. Hence, for this case:

$$\sigma_{\bar{x}} = \frac{15}{\sqrt{25}} = \frac{15}{5} = 3$$

Substituting the respective values in (2), we have:

$$z = \frac{53 - 50}{3} = \frac{3}{3} = +1.00$$

The cumulative area from $z = -\infty$ to the point $z = +1.00$ is: .8413. Thus, the chance that this sample has a mean less than 53 is: .8413, or approximately 84 chances out of 100.

(b)  The central 90 per cent of all the area under the normal curve lies between the points $z = -1.645$ and $z = +1.645$. Hence:

$$-1.645 = \frac{\overline{X} - 50}{3} \quad \text{and} \quad +1.645 = \frac{\overline{X} - 50}{3}$$

$$-4.935 = \overline{X} - 50 \qquad\qquad 4.935 = \overline{X} - 50$$

and the points are:

$$\overline{X}_{\text{Lo}} = 45.065 \qquad \overline{X}_{\text{Up}} = 54.935$$

(c) The central 95 per cent of the area under the normal curve lies between the points $z = \pm 1.96$. Hence:

$$\pm 1.96 = \frac{\overline{X} - 50}{3} \qquad \pm 5.88 = \overline{X} - 50$$

and the desired points are:

$$\overline{X}_{\text{Lo}} = 44.12 \text{ and } \overline{X}_{\text{Up}} = 55.88$$

*Normal Approximation of Binomial Probabilities.*

We recall from earlier discussion that a probability of exactly $X$ successes occurring out of $n$ possible events was termed a "binomial event." Frequently populations can be formed that represent two parts (presence or absence) of a particular characteristic. These types of populations are called "dichotomous." Such divisions as male and female; "yes" and "no" votes; Republicans and Democrats; defectives and non-defectives, result in dichotomous populations. These populations can be analyzed by assigning the number 1 to each of the elements exhibiting the characteristic $X$ under study. The value of 0 is assigned to each of the elements in the population not exhibiting the characteristic $(X)$. Thus, the dichotomous population is quantified by the values: $X = 1$, and $X = 0$.

If we let $P$ represent the *proportion* of the *population* elements with the characteristic that has been assigned the number 1, $(X = 1)$, and $Q$ represent the *proportion* of the *population* elements not exhibiting the characteristic, $(X = 0)$, then we know that: $P + Q = 1$. If $N$, the size of the finite population, is sufficiently large, it can be shown that the binomial distribution of the population can be written as:

$$(P + Q)^N = \sum_{X=0}^{N} {}^{N}_{X}C \, P^X Q^{(N-X)} \qquad \text{Population} \quad (3)$$

If a sample of size $n$ is drawn from the dichotomous population, it can be shown that the binomial distribution of the *sample* can be expressed as:

$$(p + q)^n = \sum_{X=0}^{n} {}^{n}_{X}C \, p^X q^{(n-X)} \qquad \text{Sample} \quad (4)$$

where $p$ denotes the *proportion* of elements in the *sample* exhibiting the characteristic, $q$ denotes the *proportion* of elements in the *sample not* exhibiting the characteristic; and $p + q = 1$.

Formula (4) not only gives the probability of exactly $X$ successes, where $n$ is the number of trials (sample) involved, but provides a very good approximation to the *population* distribution, which if $N$, the size of the population, is sufficiently large, approximates a normal distribution with mean: $\mu = P$; and standard deviation: $\sigma = \sqrt{PQ}$. The *sample* itself will approximate normality if $n$, the sample size, is sufficiently large, and the product $np$ is greater than 5 $(np > 5)$. Under these circumstances, the mean of the *sample* can be written as: $\overline{X} = p$; and the standard deviation as: $S = \sqrt{pq}$.

The sampling distribution of the sample proportion $p$ for sample size $n$, derived from a population with finite variance, will be approximately normally distributed if the sample size $n$ is sufficiently large. The mean of the sampling distribution of sample proportions ($p$'s) for sample size $n$ approximates in value the mean of the dichotomous population, $P$. Expressed symbolically, the statement becomes:

$$\mu_p \approx \mu = P$$

Similarly, the standard deviation of the sampling distribution of the sample proportions ($p$'s) for sample size $n$ is expressed as:

$$\sigma_p = \frac{\sigma}{\sqrt{n}} = \sqrt{\frac{PQ}{n}} \tag{5}$$

If the population values of $P$ and $Q$ are unknown, they can be approximated by $p$ and $q$ of the sample, respectively. Thus, the "standard error of the sample proportion $p$" expressed by formula (5), can be approximated by formula (5'):

$$\sigma_p \approx \sqrt{\frac{pq}{n}} \tag{5'}$$

The continuous normal distribution can be used as an approximation of the discrete binomial distribution if: (1) the data are adjusted by adding or subtracting .5 to or from the values involved in order to effect a better transition of the attribute (discrete binomial) data to the variate (continuous normal) data (see examples below); and (2) the value of the product $np$ is greater than 5; i.e., if $np > 5$.

The form of the normal deviate equation associated with the sampling distribution of the sample proportion ($p$) for sample size $n$ is:

$$z = \frac{p - \mu_p}{\sigma_p} \qquad \text{(Sampling Distribution of } p \text{ for sample size } n.) \tag{6}$$

Examples are now presented to illustrate certain points of the previous discussion.

1. If 64 fair coins are tossed, find the probability that the number of "heads" will be between 29 and 35. Use the normal distribution approximation method, if the conditions for its use are satisfied.

Solution: Since, $np = 64(\frac{1}{2}) = 32 > 5$, we can use the normal probability approximation.

From a *population* of *fair* coins we would expect the proportion of occurrence of heads to be: $\mu = P = .5$; and $\sigma = \sqrt{PQ} = \sqrt{(.5)(.5)} = .5$. Based upon the *appropriate adjustment of the attribute data* from the dichotomous population, the probability sought is: $Pr(29.5 < p < 34.5)$

$$Pr(29.5 < p < 34.5) = Pr(p < 34.5) - Pr(p < 29.5)$$

Transforming 29.5 heads to a proportion $p$ of the sample of 64 elements (heads and tails resulting from the tossing of 64 coins); we have:

$$p = \frac{29.5}{64} = .461$$

Similarly, in the form of a proportion $p$ of the sample of 64 elements, 34.5 heads becomes

$$p = \frac{34.5}{64} = .539$$

Applying formula (6), we have:

$$z = \frac{p - \mu_p}{\sigma_p} = \frac{p - \mu_p}{\sigma/\sqrt{n}}$$

$$z = \frac{.539 - .5}{.5/\sqrt{64}} = \frac{(.039)(8)}{.5} = \frac{.312}{.5} = +.624$$

Then:

$$Pr(p < 34.5) = \underset{z = +.624}{\text{Area}} = .7337 \quad \text{(Read from area column of a Normal Probability table with } z = +.624).$$

Similarly, to find $Pr(p < 29.5)$, we have:

$$z = \frac{p - \mu_p}{\sigma_p} = \frac{.461 - .5}{.5/8} = \frac{(-.039)(8)}{.5} = -.624$$

Therefore,

$$Pr(p < 29.5) = \underset{z = -.624}{\text{Area}} = .2663 \quad \text{(Read from area column of a Normal Probability table with } z = -.624).$$

Thus, $Pr(29.5 < p < 34.5) = .7337 - .2663 = .4674$; i.e., if 64 fair coins are tossed, approximately 47 per cent of the time we shall expect to find between 29 and 35 heads.

2. A multiple-choice examination is composed of 150 questions. Each question contains five "choices," one of which is the correct answer for that question. A student decides that he will select a "choice" for each question, without reading the question. If $X$ denotes the number of correct answers selected by the student, answer the following questions:
  (a) What is the exact probability distribution of $X$?
  (b) Could we consider $X$ to be approximately normally distributed? If so, what is the mean and standard deviation of the sampling distribution?
  (c) If a passing score is 75 or more correct answers, what is the approximate probability that this student passes the examination by guessing exactly 75 correct answers?

(d) What is the approximate probability that he will get between 45 to 60 *inclusive* correct answers, by selecting choices without reading the question?

(a) The exact probability distribution of $X$ is the binomial distribution:

$\sum_{X=0}^{n} {}_{X}^{n}C\, p^X q^{n-X}$, where $n$ is the number of possible trials $= 150$, $X$ is the number of correct answers, $p$ is the probability of success for selecting (by chance) the correct choice (in a given question) $= \frac{1}{5}$, and $q$ is the probability of failure to select the correct choice (by chance, in a given question) $= \frac{4}{5}$. Thus, the specific distribution becomes:

$$\sum_{X=0}^{150} {}_{X}^{150}C\, p^X q^{150-X} = \sum_{X=0}^{150} {}_{X}^{150}C\, (\tfrac{1}{5})^X (\tfrac{4}{5})^{150-X}$$

(b) Since, $np = (150)(\frac{1}{5}) = 30$; i.e., $np > 5$, we can assume that $X$ is approximately normally distributed, and apply the normal probability curve values as close approximations to the exact binomial probabilities that are in question. Under these conditions the mean of the sample becomes:

$$\bar{X} = p = \tfrac{1}{5} = .2; \quad \text{therefore:} \quad q = .8$$

and the standard deviation of the sampling distribution $(\sigma_p)$ of the proportions for sample size $n = 150$, is *approximated* to be:

$$\sigma_p = \sqrt{\frac{pq}{n}} = \sqrt{\frac{(.2)(.8)}{150}} = \frac{.4}{\sqrt{150}} = \frac{.4}{12.25} = .033$$

(c) The *approximate* probability of the student guessing exactly 75 correct answers can be found by evaluating: $Pr(74.5 < X < 75.5)$; by means of the normal probability distribution. Thus, since:

$$Pr(74.5 < X < 75.5) = Pr(X < 75.5) - Pr(X < 74.5)$$

we must translate $X = 74.5$ and $X = 75.5$ into appropriate proportions ($p$'s) of the sample of 150 questions composing the text. Thus:

(1) $p = \dfrac{74.5}{150} = .497;$　　and　　(2) $p = \dfrac{75.5}{150} = .503$

Then, employing formula (6): $z = (p - \mu_p)/\sigma_p$; we find:

(1') $z = \dfrac{.497 - .2}{.033} = \dfrac{.297}{.033} = +9.00;$

and

(2') $z = \dfrac{.503 - .2}{.033} = \dfrac{.303}{.033} = +9.18$

Thus, the $Pr(X < 74.5)$ is the *area* under the normal curve from $z = -\infty$ to $z = +9.00$; which can be written as: $.9999999+$. In similar fashion, the $Pr(X < 75.5)$ is the area under the normal curve from $z = -\infty$ to $z = +9.18$; which for all practical purposes can be considered to be: $.9999999+$. Therefore, under these conditions, the approximate probability of the student "*guessing*" *exactly* 75 *correct answers without reading the question* is:

$$Pr(X < 75.5) - Pr(X < 74.5) = .9999999 + - .9999999 + = 0$$

It should also be pointed out that for all practical purposes the approximate probability of the student "*guessing*" 75 *or more* correct answers is also $.0000000+$, i.e., the result of evaluating the expression:

$$1 - Pr(X < 74.5) = 1 - .9999999 + = 0$$

(d) The approximate probability of the student "guessing" between 45 to 60 *inclusive* correct answers is found by evaluating the expression:

$$Pr(X < 60.5) - Pr(X < 44.5)$$

Translating 60.5 and 44.5 to appropriate proportions ($p$'s) of the sample of 150 questions composing the test, we have:

(1) $\quad p = \dfrac{44.5}{150} \approx .297 \quad$ and $\quad$ (2) $\quad p = \dfrac{60.5}{150} \approx .403$

Applying formula (6): $z = (p - \mu_p)/\sigma_p$; we find:

(1') $\quad z = \dfrac{.297 - .20}{.033} = \dfrac{.097}{.033} \approx +3.00;$

(2') $\quad z = \dfrac{.403 - .20}{.033} = \dfrac{.203}{.033} = +6.15$

Then:

$$\underset{z = +3.00}{\text{Area}} = .9987; \quad \text{and:} \quad \underset{z = +6.15}{\text{Area}} = .99999+$$

(Values of areas read from appropriate column of Normal Probability table, with $z = +3.00$; and $z = +6.15$, respectively.) Therefore: $Pr(X < 60.5) - Pr(X < 44.5) = .99999 + - .9987 \approx .0013 \approx .13$ per cent— the probability of the student "guessing" between 45 to 60 (inclusive) correct answers.

If the figures of Example 2 are compared with the "probabilities" of students "guessing" (not reading the question before selecting a response) answers to True–False questions, it becomes apparent that tests composed of multiple-choice questions, each of which involves five "choices," provide far less opportunity for the student to "pass by guessing," than does the True–False type of examination.

We have now covered the basic concepts of statistical inquiry necessary for a better understanding of certain elements of the suggested general model of education research. Before proceeding to a discussion of the topics of "estimation" and "inference," we must consider a subject of great importance to these two processes—the *numerical aspects of sampling.*

*Chapter 16—References*

See Bibliography: 4, 27, 40, 41, 45, 49, 52, 53, 69, 71, 89, 93, 95, 105, 106, 112, 123, 126, 127, 128, 133, 141, 148, 155, 156, 159, 180, 181, 182, 183, 184, 185, 190, 197, 198, 200; 7a, 12a, 43a, 75a, 84a, 104a, 107a, 108a, 116a, 117a.

# Numerical Aspects of Sampling

ONE OF THE MOST IMPORTANT PARTS of statistical inquiry is that of selecting sample elements from a population. This aspect of statistical procedure is called *sampling*.

The topic of sampling has received a great deal of attention from statisticians and has almost become a field of study in and of itself. Because of this extensive development, it is almost impossible for the researcher to become an expert in sampling, and at the same time be of sufficient expertise in other areas of statistics to carry out the normal demands of the inquiry. For obvious reasons, the purpose of this discussion is not to produce experts in sampling, but to provide a basic understanding of certain numerical aspects of the process, so that it may be properly integrated with other numerical procedures of the suggested general model of educational research.

Regardless of the type of sample, there are three basic criteria by which a sample may be evaluated:

1. How the sample is selected.
2. The representativeness of the sample.
3. The adequacy of the size of the sample for making estimates and inferences about the values of certain population parameters.

These criteria are not mutually exclusive. They are interrelated. How the sample is selected, in great part, determines the type of sample being employed. The representativeness of it depends not only upon how it is selected, but the number of sample elements composing it.

It is our primary purpose here to discuss (1) how to derive certain estimates from different types of samples, and (2) how to find the size of sample necessary to provide *adequate* estimates of the population parameters involved in the research inquiry. Since the nine different types of samples to be included in this presentation have already been discussed, they will not be reiterated here. Readers who are interested in this background material are referred to Chapter 4.

In the process of employing the nine types of samples under consideration in the "adapted" models of educational research, the specific formula for a given estimate, and the one employed for adequacy of sample size, depends not only on the situation, but upon whether errors of estimation based upon repeated sampling fall within specified limits that are consistent with the relative sampling error the researcher is willing to accept. Thus, the acceptable relative sampling error is a limiting condition around which the statistical inquiry must be designed.

With this brief background, we are now prepared to begin discussion of certain numerical aspects of sampling associated with the "adapted" models of educational research.

### 1. *Simple Random Sample*

Probably the most elementary problem connected with the simple random sample is determining an adequate size sample, $n$, for estimating a proportion ($P$) of a dichotomous population showing a given characteristic. This problem may be exemplified by a situation where it is necessary to determine the size of the sample needed from a finite population in order to obtain an estimate of a characteristic found in, say, approximately 20 per cent of the population. The problem may be approached by treating it as a binomial event (see "Binomial Event Probability" pages 197–202). Since an estimate of a characteristic is desired, we are actually attempting to determine what the probability is that a simple random sample of some size will be selected *without having that characteristic present. If this probability can be kept to a minimum the problem will be solved.*

The following dialectic is employed in solving the problem. In the population where $P = .20$, 80 per cent of the elements *do not have* the characteristic. Thus, the probability that a random sample of size $n$ will come from this group alone is $(.80)^n$ (see topic "Probability of Exactly $x$ Successes," page 181). By the method of trial and error, we can determine the size of $n$ that will be adequate for the purposes of the problem. We begin by setting $n = 10$, and find: $(.80)^{10} \approx .1074$. This result would mean that we could expect approximately 11 per cent of repeated simple random samples of size $n = 10$, not to show an element with the characteristic under consideration. If we try $n = 50$, we have:

$$(.80)^{50} \approx .0000143$$

This shows that we would expect only fourteen samples in 1,000,000 repeated simple random samples of size $n = 50$, not to show an element with the "desired" characteristic. Under these conditions, a sample size of $n = 50$ should be an adequate one to estimate the proportion of the population elements ($P = .20$) showing the characteristic in question.

Analysis of the equation for the *standard error of the mean* (see "Sampling Distribution," page 41), for sample size $n$ drawn from an infinite population, namely:

$$\sigma_{\bar{X}} = \frac{\sigma}{\sqrt{n}} \tag{1}$$

demonstrates how simple random samples taken from highly variable distributions, although mathematically accurate, can lead to results which are most inadequate for actual operations. This situation occurs because of the direct variation between the standard error of the mean ($\sigma_{\bar{X}}$) and the population standard deviation ($\sigma$). In those cases where the value of $\sigma$ is extremely large, and hence $\sigma_{\bar{x}}$ is very large, the size of the sample $n$ which would be adequate to reduce $\sigma_{\bar{x}}$ to a usable value might be so large as to be impractical. This situation, in effect, means that simple random samples cannot be employed efficiently in cases where the variability of the variate $X$ is relatively large. These types of cases are frequently encountered in skewed distributions (see "Skewness," page 171), and certain modifications of simple random sampling, stratification for example, are required so that adequate estimates and inferences about the value of the population mean ($\mu$) might be made.

The expression in formula (1) provides us with a vehicle for determining the minimum sample size required to give a specified relative sampling error for the *arithmetic mean*. Now, if the sampling distribution of the mean for sample size $n$ is normally distributed we can use multiples of $\sigma_{\bar{x}}$ to enclose different proportions of the normal distribution. Letting $z$ represent the normal deviate, we would modify (1) as follows:

$$\sigma_{\bar{X}} = \frac{z\sigma}{\sqrt{n}} \tag{2}$$

If we solve (2) for $n$, and square both terms of the new equation, we have (3) as follows:

$$n = \frac{z^2\sigma^2}{\sigma_{\bar{X}}^2} \tag{3}$$

Now, if we divide both numerator and denominator by $\bar{X}^2$, which is an estimate of $\mu^2$, we have (4):

$$n = \frac{z^2\left(\dfrac{\sigma}{\bar{X}}\right)^2}{\left(\dfrac{\sigma_{\bar{X}}}{\bar{X}}\right)^2} = \frac{z^2(CV)^2}{P_s^2} \tag{4}$$

where $\sigma/\bar{X} = CV$ is the coefficient of variation of $X$, and $\sigma_{\bar{X}}/\bar{X} = P_s$ is the relative sampling error with respect to the mean. *Equation (4) determines an adequate simple random sample size $n$ without regard to cost, where $n$ is to be selected from an infinite population.*

For sampling a finite population, we modify (2) as follows:

Let:

$$\sigma_{\bar{X}}^2 = \left(\frac{z^2\sigma^2}{n}\right)\left(\frac{N-n}{N}\right)$$

or

$$\sigma_{\bar{X}}^2 = \frac{z^2\sigma^2}{n} - \frac{z^2\sigma^2}{N} \tag{5}$$

Where $N =$ the size of the finite population, and all other symbols are defined as they were in equations (1) and (2). Solving equation (5) for *n*, we have:

$$n = \frac{z^2\sigma^2}{\sigma_{\bar{X}}^2 + z^2\sigma^2/N} \tag{6}$$

dividing both numerator and denominator of (6) by $\bar{X}^2$, and letting $\sigma/\bar{X} = CV$ and $\sigma_{\bar{x}}/\bar{X} = P_s$, we have (7):

$$n = \frac{z^2 C^2}{P_s^2 + z^2(CV)^2/N} \tag{7}$$

If $z^2(CV)^2/N$ is small in value, it may be neglected, and under this circumstance we have equation (4).

The coefficient of variation $(CV)$ is usually derived on the basis of pilot study data, or previous knowledge of the population mean and standard deviation. The relative sampling error with respect to the mean $(P_s)$, is determined on the basis of the amount of error the researcher is willing to accept in making the estimate. The normal deviate $(z)$ determines the acceptable confidence interval to be associated with the estimate, and is an interval that the researcher considers satisfactory under the conditions imposed, and thus is chosen in view of these conditions. Probably the most significant factor involved in the choice of the relative sampling error of the mean $(P_s)$, and the normal deviate $(z)$, is the amount and frequency of sampling error which the researcher feels that the operation can withstand, and still provide reliable and valid results. With these considerations, we shall now illustrate the employment of formula (4).

Suppose that a pilot study of a characteristic forming an infinite population has been run, and the sample of thirty-six items employed shows a mean of $\bar{X} = 60$, and a standard deviation of $S = 15$. Suppose further that a simple random sample was to be employed in the actual research study, and the question of an adequate sample size *n* for estimating the population mean from this simple random sample has been raised. How could the researcher determine *n*—the adequate sample size?

From the pilot study data the researcher can establish the value of the coefficient of variation as $CV = \frac{15}{60} = \frac{1}{4}$. The value of $\frac{1}{4}$ is but an estimate of $CV$, because it cannot be derived on the basis of the (unknown) population values of $\sigma$ and $\mu$, but for all practical purposes the "estimate" is adequate for the job at hand. With the establishment of the approximate value of $CV$, the researcher must now determine the value of $z$, the normal deviate, which he wishes to employ. If a 95 per cent confidence interval is desired for the estimated value of $\mu$, the value of $z = +1.96$ (see table, page 193) will be necessary. If 99 per cent confidence limits are to be employed, $z = +2.576$, or $+2.58$ will be used. Other values of $z$ may be employed, depending upon the research and the desired confidence interval. The usual practice, however, is to employ the value of $z = +1.96$, or $z = +2.58$, depending upon the amount of reliability the researcher feels the operation demands from the sample. Let us suppose for this example that the value of $z = 1.96$ will be sufficiently "reliable." The derivation of the values of $CV$ and $z$ leaves only the selection of a value for the relative sampling error $(P_s)$.

In the selection of a value for $P_s$, the pilot study data are assumed to be reliable, and an estimated value of $\sigma_{\bar{x}}$ is found to be: $\sigma_{\bar{x}} = 15/\sqrt{36} = \frac{15}{6} = 2.5$. Rounding this value to: $\sigma_{\bar{x}} = 3$; we find an estimate of the value of the relative sampling error to be: $Ps = \sigma_{\bar{x}}/\overline{X} = \frac{3}{60} = \frac{1}{20} = .05 = 5$ per cent.

Under the conditions of $CV = \frac{1}{4}$, $z = +1.96$, and $P_s = .05$, formula (4) would show the adequate size $n$ of a simple random sample selected from an infinite population, to be:

$$n = \frac{(1.96)^2(\frac{1}{4})^2}{(.05)^2} = 96\frac{1}{25} \approx 97$$

The value of $96\frac{1}{25}$ is rounded to 97, the next highest value, in order to preserve the "adequacy" of the sample size $n$ under the conditions imposed on the operation. Generally speaking, in order to insure adequacy, for the conditions imposed, it is wise to round to the next higher number any time a fractional value, regardless of its magnitude, occurs.

If the sample were to be drawn from a population of finite size $N$, we would have employed formula (7) in the example above:

$$n = \frac{z^2(CV)^2}{P_s^2 + z^2(CV)^2/N} \tag{7}$$

Of course, if $N$ is of such magnitude that $z^2(CV)^2/N$ becomes so small in value that it can be neglected, we would continue to use equation (4) with the knowledge that since its derivation was based upon an *infinite* population, it would most certainly provide an adequate $n$ for a *finite* population situation.

It should be noted that unless the coefficient of variation ($CV$) is reasonably small, something less than $\frac{1}{4}$, a relatively large sample size is required to estimate the population mean under such specifications as 95 per cent confidence limits ($z = 1.96$), and a relative sampling error of $P_s = .05$. If the coefficient of variation is large, certain mathematical transformations may be employed to reduce it. For example, if two variates—say $X$ and $Y$—have large variances, the adequate sample size to satisfy each condition may be so large that the advantages of sampling may be lost. Under such conditions a new variate of the form $X/Y$ may be formed, and have a much smaller variation relative to its mean. Through such a transformation a smaller $n$ would be required for adequacy, and a better sampling design would result.

Although transformations may improve the design and lower the size of a simple random sample for adequacy, they are rarely used. Other methods, such as stratified random sampling, have been found to be more practical, and in the long run more reliable, than the mathematical transformation approach. We shall now discuss "adequacy" formulas related to stratified random samples.

## 2. *Stratified Random Samples*

We have discussed the simple random sample, and pointed out that, unless it is very large, it might easily fail to provide adequate estimates if it is selected from a highly variable population. It was also pointed out that mathematical transformations of the variables may be employed to reduce the coefficient of variation. More frequently, the method employed to reduce the variability of estimates, under the condition of the sample being selected from a highly variable population, is that of *stratifying* the population. Stratification of a population is accomplished by dividing the universe into a number of groups (called "strata") on the basis of factors related to the variate $(X)$. The selection of a sample of elements from each stratum provides a "total" sample of $n$ elements from which more precise estimates of values of population parameters under consideration can be calculated than otherwise would be possible. Stratification may be applied to finite and infinite populations alike by "grouping" the variate $(X)$ on the basis of treatment, time, place, order, condition, method, or other factors.

There are four main problems associated with designing and using a stratified random sample: (1) the number of strata to employ, (2) a sample of adequate size, (3) the proper weighting of values from the different strata, and (4) the time validity of the sample design.

1. The problem of the *number of strata* is a complicated one, and depends upon various factors. Four of the more important factors are: (a) the variability of the variate $(X)$, (b) the number of bases employed for stratification, (c) "natural" strata of the variate, and (d) the cost associated with sampling each stratum. These problem factors are not mutually exclusive, nor have they been listed in order of precedence. We shall see that these factors are highly interrelated and of almost equal importance in all cases where stratifying seems desirable.

(a) In regard to the factor of the *variability of the variate X*, we know that the purpose of stratification is to reduce the variability. The researcher must be alert to the possibility of reducing variability at the expense of some other factor. It is entirely possible that the reduction of variability may lead to a situation of such increased cost that stratification to that degree is not feasible. This condition would call for modification of the original plan, and possible further investigation for a more effective approach.

(b) *Stratifying on the basis of multiple-criteria* must be approached with great care, because of the rapid increase in the number of strata with each additional base that is employed. This condition results because the total number of strata is the product resulting from multiplying the number of classes in each base together. To illustrate, if a particular school has 8 grade levels and 6 arithmetic classes, and stratification is being carried out on such criteria, there will be $8 \times 6 = 48$ strata. As another example, if we had 25 different *classes* of some criterion $A$, and 10 *types* of $B$ criterion within each of the classes, and 5 *divisions* of criterion $C$ within each type, and we were stratifying on the basis of these criteria, we would have $25 \times 10 \times 5 = 1250$ strata.

(c) Although there may be a great temptation to *stratify on the basis of "natural" classifications*, such as administrative structure, natural association grouping, and clusters of units in a particular geographic location, stratification on these bases must be carefully examined to insure that such "natural" strata are the ones that reduce the variability of $X$ most effectively. The effectiveness of stratification must be determined by actual tests, that is, by comparing sample variances of the respective strata with population estimates (from pilot studies, experience, or other forms of "previous information").

(d) The *cost of sampling strata* must constantly be kept in mind by the researcher. The cost of sampling each element within a stratum, based upon the cost of data collection and processing per each sample element, provides the best method for analyzing the effectiveness of stratification in this dimension. To illustrate, if it costs $1.00 to collect the data yielded by one sample element in each stratum, and we have $6 \times 4 = 24$ strata, and 10 sample elements per stratum, we know the cost of sampling under these conditions will be $24 \times 10 \times 1 = $240$. This will be the cost of merely collecting the data. The cost of processing and treating the data will be in addition to the cost of data collection. It is obvious that the factor of cost of sampling strata is most important, especially if it becomes necessary to employ a large sample.

In summary, note that the *number of strata* most satisfactory for a given project cannot be determined by means of some mathematical formula. The best method for determining the number of strata to be employed is to find the point of diminishing return in terms of value received versus cost, time, and energy input. At the same time, the researcher must beware of taking the "easy" road of natural grouping or clustering, and the pitfalls that may accompany it. By the same token, under conditions where cost might not be a factor, the researcher may become almost "too precise" by employing multiple-criteria that lead to extensive time and energy inputs in the matter of collecting and processing the data from an excessively large number of strata.

(2) The problem of *determining a sample size that is adequate for a stratified random sample approach* is composed mainly of two general considerations: (a) the acceptable amount of error at a chosen level of risk, and (b) the capability, financial and otherwise, of procuring an adequate sample.

In some cases there is a need for making estimates of a number of variates, instead of the usual one. *The design of a sample, however, must be based upon one variate. Thus, the most important variate is selected as the basis for determining an adequate size of sample. In those cases where there are variates of equal importance, the most variable one is chosen as the basis for determining the size of an adequate sample.*

After the most important variate has been selected, the maximum amount of acceptable error must be determined, and the level of risk at which the error can be accepted must be established. These two factors are probably the most basic parts of determining the design and size of the sample.

When the acceptable error and level of risk have been determined, the researcher must consider the amount of money and personnel available for conducting the sampling operation. From this information the cost of the design can be determined. Deciding whether the cost of the operation is too high depends upon the importance of the estimate that is to be made from the sample, and whether the cost can be decreased by changing the size of the acceptable error, providing the research can allow such change.

(3) *The weighting of a stratified random sample* is important to the extent that the money saved in data collection, due to this type of sample design, may be expended along with additional amounts for computation associated with determining the proper weights for the various strata. Methods of proportional allocation and optimum allocation will be discussed, later in connection with the subject of determining a "best" method for simplifying the problem of weighting.

(4) *The design of an effective sample* depends upon whether the sample is to be taken from a static or a dynamic population. An effective sample, selected from a static population, remains effective. When the population is dynamic, the sample may not remain effective. In such cases, the problem of designing an effective sample takes on the added dimension of the need for determining whether the sample design remains effective over a period of time. It is in this connection that we become concerned with the *time validity of the sample design.*

The problem of *time validity* demands the following types of consideration: (a) Basing stratification upon the more important population characteristics that have a high degree of time-correlation. That is, basing the design upon characteristics that maintain a certain level of value over the course of time. For example, the height variate of a population of college seniors would tend to be relatively stable over a period of time. If height were a characteristic upon which stratification could be based, and a research effort dealing with, say, the weight of college seniors was being conducted, the time-correlation of the factor of height would be such that the stratification would continue to account for a considerable portion of variance in weight (taller people should be heavier, shorter ones lighter) of this particular population over a period of time. Of course, with the great variability in the height characteristic of elementary school children, grades $K - 6$, this factor (height) could not serve the same function in a study concerned with such a population.

(b) Adjusting for changes in the number of elements of a finite population. The adjustment may be accomplished by serial selection, the process of selecting every $i$-th element in the population. Through such an approach, if the number of population elements between two given time periods increases, the sample size automatically increases. If the population decreases, the sample size also decreases.

(c) Adjusting the sample size, stratification, and weightings periodically on the basis of new data that have been collected at regular intervals. This approach may be made through a complete census of the finite population at regular intervals wherein consideration is given to elements that have vanished and new elements that have appeared.

With this background information we are now ready to consider certain formulas associated with stratified random samples—some that are basic to "adequacy" formulas discussed later, and others that will prove useful in dealing with stratified random samples in educational research models.

1. *Estimate of Population Mean Derived from Stratified Random Sample of K Strata*

$$\bar{X} = \sum_{1}^{K} \frac{N_j \bar{X}_j}{N} = \frac{N_1 \bar{X}_1}{N} + \frac{N_2 \bar{X}_2}{N} + \frac{N_3 \bar{X}_3}{N} + \cdots + \frac{N_k \bar{X}_k}{N} \tag{8}$$

$$= \frac{N_1 \bar{X}_1 + N_2 \bar{X}_2 + N_3 \bar{X}_3 + \cdots + N_k \bar{X}_k}{N}$$

where $\bar{X}$ denotes the estimate of the value of $\mu$, $N_j$ = the number of population elements in the "$j$-th" stratum, $\bar{X}_j$ = estimated arithmetic mean of the "$j$-th" stratum, $N$ = total number of elements in the finite population.

2. *Standard Error of the Mean* $(\sigma_{\bar{x}})$ *from a Simple Random Sample of Size n taken from a Finite Population of N Elements*

Although we let : $\sigma_{\bar{X}}^2 = (z^2 \sigma^2/n)(N - n/N)$ in formula (5) (page 205), for convenience in computing an adequate size $n$ for a simple random sample *in normal deviate form*, the *actual* formula is:

$$\sigma_{\bar{X}}^2 = \left(\frac{\sigma^2}{n}\right)\left(\frac{N - n}{N - 1}\right) \tag{9}$$

hence, the standard error of the mean for a simple random sample of size $n$ from a finite population of $N$ elements is:

$$\sigma_{\bar{x}} = \sigma \sqrt{\frac{(N - n)}{n(N - 1)}} \tag{9'}$$

where $\sigma_{\bar{x}}$ = standard error of the mean for sample size $n$, $\sigma$ = population standard deviation, and $N$ = number of elements in the finite population.

3. *Standard Error of the Mean* $(\sigma_{\bar{x}})$, *for a Stratified Random Sample of K Strata Taken from a Finite Population of N Elements*

Starting with the variance, we have:

$$\sigma_{\bar{X}}^2 = \frac{1}{N^2} \sum_{1}^{K} \frac{N_j^2 S_j^2}{n_j}\left(\frac{N_j - n_j}{N_j - 1}\right) \tag{10}$$

hence, the standard error of the mean becomes:

$$\sigma_{\bar{x}} = \frac{1}{N} \sqrt{\sum_{1}^{K} \frac{N_j^2 S_j^2}{n_j}\left(\frac{N_j - n_j}{N_j - 1}\right)} \tag{10'}$$

where $\sigma_{\bar{x}}$ = standard error of the mean, $N$ = number of elements in the finite population, $N_j$ = number of population elements in the $j$-th stratum, $n_j$ = sample size for $j$-th stratum, and $S_j^2$ is the known or estimated variance of elements composing the $j$-th stratum.

*Examples*

In order to further clarify the three foregoing stratified random sample formulas, we shall now present examples that involve their application.

*Example 1.* Suppose we have divided a population into four strata, each stratum composed of 50, 70, 36, and 104 population elements, respectively. We know the sum of the $X_1$ *values* forming the first stratum is: $\sum X_1 = 200$. The sum of the $X_2$ values in the second stratum: $\sum X_2 = 420$. The sum of the $X_3$ values: $\sum X_3 = 108$; and $\sum X_4 = 728$. Estimate the value of the population mean $\mu$, on the basis of the stratified random sample data.

In order to solve this problem, we would apply formula (8), page 211:

$$\overline{X} = \sum_{1}^{K} \frac{N_j \overline{X}_j}{N} = \sum_{1}^{4} \frac{N_j \overline{X}_j}{N}$$

Thus, we have:

$$\overline{X} = \frac{N_1 \overline{X}_1}{N} + \frac{N_2 \overline{X}_2}{N} + \frac{N_3 \overline{X}_3}{N} + \frac{N_4 \overline{X}_4}{N}$$

We know:

$$\overline{X}_1 = \frac{\sum X_1}{N_1} = \frac{200}{50} = 4; \overline{X}_2 = \frac{\sum X_2}{N_2} = \frac{420}{70} = 6; \overline{X}_3 = \frac{\sum X_3}{N_3} = \frac{108}{36} = 3;$$

and

$$\overline{X}_4 = \frac{\sum X_4}{N_4} = \frac{728}{104} = 7$$

We also know that:

$$N = 50 + 70 + 36 + 104 = 260$$

Substituting, we have:

$$\overline{X} = \frac{(50)(4)}{260} + \frac{(70)(6)}{260} + \frac{(36)(3)}{260} + \frac{(104)(7)}{260}$$

$$= \frac{200 + 420 + 108 + 728}{260} = \frac{1456}{260} \approx 5.9$$

Hence our estimate of $\mu$, under these conditions is $\overline{X} \approx 5.9$, where the symbol $\approx$ means "approximately equal to."

*Example 2.* Suppose that we are asked to calculate a value for the standard error of the mean based upon the data of the stratified random sample of Example 1. Let us also assume that the strata variances ($S_j^2$) are known to be: $S_1^2 = 1.0; S_2^2 = 2.25; S_3^2 = 0.25;$ and $S_4^2 = 4.0;$ and that the number of sample elements to be taken from the first stratum is: $n_1 = 10$; from the second stratum is: $n_2 = 14$; from the third is: $n_3 = 9$; and from the fourth is: $n_4 = 20$.

Applying formula (10′):

$$\sigma_{\bar{X}} = \frac{1}{N}\sqrt{\sum_1^K \frac{N_j^2 S_j^2}{n_j}\left(\frac{N_j - n_j}{N_j - 1}\right)}$$

We would have:

$$\sigma_{\bar{X}} = \frac{1}{260}\left[\frac{(50)^2(1)^2}{10}\left(\frac{50 - 10}{49}\right) + \frac{(70)^2(1.5)^2}{14}\left(\frac{70 - 14}{69}\right) + \frac{(36)^2(.5)^2}{9}\left(\frac{36 - 9}{35}\right)\right.$$

$$\left. + \frac{(104)^2(2)^2}{20}\left(\frac{104 - 20}{103}\right)\right]^{\frac{1}{2}}$$

thus,

$$\sigma_{\bar{X}} = \frac{1}{260}\left[\frac{(250)(1)(40)}{49} + \frac{(350)(2.25)(56)}{69} + \frac{(144)(.25)(27)}{35}\right.$$

$$\left. + \frac{(26)(104)(4)(84)}{(5)(103)}\right]^{\frac{1}{2}}$$

$$= \frac{1}{260}\left(\frac{10,000}{49} + \frac{44,100}{69} + \frac{972}{35} + 1764.84\right)^{\frac{1}{2}}$$

$$= \frac{1}{260}[204.08 + 639.13 + 27.77 + 1764.84]^{\frac{1}{2}}$$

hence,

$$\sigma_{\bar{X}} = \frac{1}{260}(2635.82)^{\frac{1}{2}} = \frac{51.34}{260} \approx .197$$

*Example 3.* An artificial population is stratified as shown in the table below. Compare the standard error of the mean based upon a random sample of three elements with that obtained from a random selection of one element from each of the three strata.

| Stratum | $X_j$ | $N_j$ | $N_j X_j$ | $N_j X_j^2$ | $(X_j - \mu)$ | $(X_j - \mu)^2$ | $N_j(X_j - \mu)^2$ |
|---|---|---|---|---|---|---|---|
| | 0 | 5 | 0 | 0 | -6 | 36 | 0 |
| A | 1 | 10 | 10 | 10 | -5 | 25 | 250 |
| | 2 | 20 | 40 | 80 | -4 | 16 | 320 |
| | 5 | 30 | 150 | 750 | -1 | 1 | 30 |
| B | 6 | 40 | 240 | 1440 | 0 | 0 | 0 |
| | 7 | 30 | 210 | 1470 | 1 | 1 | 30 |
| | 10 | 20 | 200 | 2000 | 4 | 16 | 320 |
| C | 11 | 10 | 110 | 1210 | 5 | 25 | 250 |
| | 12 | 5 | 60 | 720 | 6 | 36 | 180 |
| Total | | 170 | 1020 | | | | 1380 |

For this finite population $\mu = \frac{1020}{170} = 6$; $\sigma^2 = \frac{1380}{170} \approx 8.12$, and $\sigma \approx 2.85$. The standard error of the mean for sample size $n = 3$, estimated from a random sample drawn from the entire population is:

$$\sigma_X = \frac{\sigma}{\sqrt{n}} = \frac{2.85}{\sqrt{3}} \approx 1.645$$

In order to find $\sigma_j^2$ we use the proper data from the columns $N_j X_j^2$, $N_j X_j$, and $N_j$, as follows:

$$\sigma_A^2 = \frac{\sum N_A X_A^2 - \left(\sum N_A X_A\right)^2 / N_A}{N_A} = \frac{90 - (50)^2/35}{35} = \frac{26}{49} \approx .531$$

$$\sigma_B^2 = \frac{\sum N_B X_B^2 - \left(\sum N_B X_B\right)^2 / N_B}{N_B} = \frac{3660 - (600)^2/100}{100} = \frac{60}{100} \approx .6$$

$$\sigma_C^2 = \frac{\sum N_C X_C^2 - \left(\sum N_C X_C\right)^2 / N_C}{N_C} = \frac{3930 - (370)^2/35}{35} = \frac{18.57}{35} \approx .531$$

Since we are taking one element from each stratum, $n_j = 1$, the expression $(N_j - n_j)$ becomes $(N_j - 1)$ in formula (10). Thus, the formula under these conditions becomes:

$$\sigma_{\bar{X}} = \frac{1}{N} \sqrt{\sum_1^K N_j^2 S_j^2}$$

hence

$$\sigma_{\bar{X}} = \frac{1}{N} (N_A^2 \sigma_A^2 + N_B^2 \sigma_B^2 + N_C \sigma_C^2)^{\frac{1}{2}}$$

$$= \frac{1}{170}[(35)^2(.531) + (100)^2(.6) + (35)^2(.531)]^{\frac{1}{2}}$$

$$= \frac{1}{170}(650.475 + 6000 + 650.475)^{\frac{1}{2}} = \frac{1}{170}(7300.95)^{\frac{1}{2}}$$

$$\sigma_{\bar{X}} \approx \frac{85.45}{170} \approx .503$$

Through the process of stratification, the standard error of the mean for sample size $n = 3$, was reduced approximately 70 per cent, that is, $1.645 - .503 = 1.142$ is the amount of the reduction, and $1.142/1.645 \approx .70$ reduction. This reduction would indicate that a reasonably large part of the population variance is associated with the variation between the three strata. By stratifying the population, the variation in the mean associated with the "between groups" source is eliminated.

Another way of appraising stratified random samples is by calculating the size $n$ of the simple random sample which would yield the same sampling variance as that of the stratified random sample. In our example, $\sigma^2 \approx 8.12$, while $\sigma_{\bar{X}}^2 = (.503)^2 = .253$, *from the stratified random sample.* Hence, from the relationship:

$$\sigma_{\bar{X}}^2 = \frac{\sigma^2}{n}$$

we have:

$$.253 = \frac{8.12}{n}$$

and:

$$n \approx 32$$

or a sample almost eleven times as large as that of the stratified case ($n = 3$). This ratio which measures the *efficiency* of stratification can be found directly by comparing the value of the sampling variance for the simple random sample with that of the stratified sample, or:

$$\text{Efficiency of Stratified Random Sample} = \frac{\sigma_{\bar{X}}^2 \text{ (random)}}{\sigma_{\bar{X}}^2 \text{ (stratified)}}$$

In our particular example:

$$\text{Efficiency} = \frac{(1.645)^2}{(.503)^2} = \frac{2.71}{.253} \approx 10.7 \approx 11$$

*Example 4.* By means of a pilot study, values of standard deviations ($S_A$, $S_B$, $S_C$, $S_D$) were computed for each stratum, ($A, B, C, D$) respectively, as estimates of $\sigma_A$, $\sigma_B$, $\sigma_C$, $\sigma_D$ (stratum population standard deviations). Stratum size ($N_j$) of $A$, $B$, $C$, and $D$ was estimated, and the following table was constructed to optimally allocate the pre-determined (adequate) *sample size n = 300* to the four strata.

| Stratum | $N_j$ | $\sigma_j$ | $N_j\sigma_j$ | $\dfrac{N_j\sigma_j}{\sum N_j\sigma_j}$ | $n_j$ |
|---|---|---|---|---|---|
| A | 600 | 8 | 4800 | .17 | (.17) (300) = 51 |
| B | 900 | 10 | 9000 | .32 | (.32) (300) = 96 |
| C | 1200 | 9 | 10800 | .38 | (.38) (300) = 114 |
| D | 300 | 12 | 3600 | .13 | (.13) (300) = 39 |
| Total | 3000 | | 28200 | | $n = 300$ |

The column headed $N_j\sigma_j/\sum N_j\sigma_j$ indicates that according to the principle of optimum allocation for a fixed sample size $n$, 17 per cent of $n = 300$ must be allocated to stratum $A$, because $\frac{4800}{28200} = .17$; 32 per cent of $n = 300$ to stratum $B$ (9000 ÷ 28,200 = .32); 38 per cent (10,800 ÷ 28,200) to Stratum $C$, and 13 per cent (3600 ÷ 28,200) to Stratum $D$.

Analysis of the principle of optimum allocation shows:

1. If $N_j\sigma_j$ for the strata are approximately equal, the per cent of the fixed sample to be allocated to each stratum will be approximately the same for all strata, and the total sample will be allocated accordingly.

2. If the standard deviations ($\sigma_j$) for the strata are approximately equal, then the allocation of *n* to each of the strata is merely proportional to $N_j$, the stratum population size.

3. If the standard deviation of the stratum ($\sigma_j$) is approximately equal to the stratum mean ($\mu_j$), then the stratum aggregate ($N_j\mu_j$) can be employed for allocation instead of $N_j\sigma_j$.

4. If conditions are such that $n_j$, the number of elements allocated to a given stratum from the fixed sample size *n*, is greater than, or equal to, the stratum size $N_j$; then all of that stratum ($N_j$) must be employed in the sample. For example, suppose that $N_j = 65$ for a particular stratum, and that $(N_j\sigma_j/\sum N_j\sigma_j)(n) = 90$. The total 65 elements of the stratum would be employed in the sample of that stratum, and the remainder of the fixed sample size ($n = 90$) would be allocated to the remaining strata according to the value of the product $(N_j\sigma_j/\sum N_j\sigma_j)(n)$ for each of them.

*Optimum Allocation for Undetermined Total Sample Size n*

If the total sample size *n* cannot be pre-determined on the basis of pilot study data, prior knowledge of the researcher, or sampling limitations enforced by factors of time, administration, or the research setting, another approach of optimum allocation termed "undetermined total sample size *n*" may be employed. This approach makes no effort to pre-determine the total sample size, but stipulates a specified precision in the estimate to be made from the sample. By incorporating this precision in the determination of the number of elements to be allocated to each stratum ($n_j$), a total sample size *n*, equal to the sum of the various $n_j$'s, will result. This type of optimum allocation accomplishes "adequacy" of sample size *n* and its allocation at the same time:

1. Let *h* become the factor to be determined, and

$$hn_j = N_j\sigma_j$$

or

$$n_j = \frac{N_j\sigma_j}{h}$$

2. Starting with the fact that the population sampling variance of an aggregate, based upon all possible random samples taken from a stratified population of *K* strata, *for which finite population correction is not necessary*, is:

$$\sigma_{N\bar{X}}^2 = \sum_1^K \frac{N_j^2\sigma_j^2}{n_j}$$

Then, by substituting the value $n_j = N_j\sigma_j/h$, we have:

$$\sigma_{N\bar{X}}^2 = \sum_1^K \frac{N_j^2\sigma_j^2}{N_j\sigma_j/h} = h\sum_1^K N_j\sigma_j$$

3. If the required precision ($p$) (for adequacy) is determined by the expression:

$$p = \frac{\sigma_{N\bar{X}}}{N\bar{X}}$$

Where $N\bar{X}$ is the estimated aggregate, and $\sigma_{N\bar{X}}$ is the standard error of the aggregate, which can be estimated by $S_{N\bar{X}}$.

4. Squaring the expression for $p$, we have:

$$p^2 = \frac{\sigma_{N\bar{X}}^2}{(N\bar{X})^2}$$

Substituting for $\sigma_{N\bar{X}}^2$,

$$p^2 = \frac{h \sum_{1}^{k} N_j S_j}{(N\bar{X})^2}$$

Solving for $h$;

$$h = \frac{p^2(N\bar{X})^2}{\sum N_j S_j}$$

In this expression for $h$, the value of $p$ may be chosen by the researcher, and $N\bar{X}$, $N_j$ and $S_j$ may be determined by pilot study data, or prior knowledge of the situation.

5. After $h$ has been determined, $n_j$ may be determined by the expression:

$$n_j = \frac{N_j \sigma_j}{h}$$

Then $\sum_{1}^{K} n_j = n$, the total sample size necessary and adequate to meet the specified precision $p$ and satisfy the factor $h$.

This method of optimum allocation may be illustrated by the following example and tabular arrangement:

Suppose that a pilot study has been conducted, and from these data an estimate of the population aggregate is determined as:

$$N\bar{X} = 20,000$$

The researcher decides that the error in this estimate must be held at $p_s = .05$ (5%), and that no correction for sampling from a finite population need be made.* A tabular arrangement of the data is made, and the total of the $N_j \sigma_j$

---

* If correction for sampling from a finite population is necessary, we proceed as follows to determine $h$:

The sampling variance of an aggregate taken from a stratified finite population is:

$$\sigma_{N\bar{X}}^2 = \sum \frac{N_j^2 \sigma_j^2 (N_j - n_j)}{n_j(N_j - 1)}$$

Let $n_j = N_j \sigma_j / h$, and replace $(N_j - 1)$ by $N_j$. Hence, $\sigma_{N\bar{X}}^2 = h \sum N_j \sigma_j - \sum N_j \sigma_j^2$. But we let $p_s^2 =$

column is found to be: $\sum N_j \sigma_j = 4000$. With this value and the previous estimates, $N\bar{X}$ and $p$, we find:

$$h = \frac{p^2(N\bar{X})^2}{\sum N_j \sigma_j} = \frac{(.05)^2(20,000)^2}{4000} = (.0025)(100,000) = 250$$

| Stratum | $N_j$ | $\sigma_j$ | $N_j\sigma_j$ | $\dfrac{N_j\sigma_j}{\sum N_j\sigma_j}$ | Uncorrected $\dfrac{N_j\sigma_j}{h} = \dfrac{N_j\sigma_j}{250} = n_j$ | Corrected[1] $n_j = \dfrac{N_j\sigma_j}{254.5}$ |
|---------|-------|-----------|--------------|------------------------|--------------------------|-------------------------|
| A | 200 | 4 | 800 | .20 | 4 (approx.) | 4 (approx.) |
| B | 300 | 2 | 600 | .15 | 3 (approx.) | 3 (approx.) |
| C | 100 | 6 | 600 | .15 | 3 (approx.) | 3 (approx.) |
| D | 400 | 5 | 2000 | .50 | 8 (approx.) | 8 (approx.) |
| Total | 1000 | | 4000 | 1.00 | $n = 18$ | $n = 18$ |

From the "Total" row above we see that the total sample size $n = \sum n_j = 18$, for either the *corrected* or the *uncorrected* finite population. Usually the sample for a corrected finite population is less than that for an uncorrected one.

If conditions are such that $n_j$ for a particular stratum is greater than $N_j$ the population size of that stratum, then the total $N_j$ is used as the sample size of that stratum. When a finite population is treated as though it were an infinite one, that is, "without correction," the resulting $\sum n_j = n$ provides a slightly greater precision than $p_s$. Although this fact is not obvious from our example, the actual values computed for $n_j$ under the respective "no correction" (infinite population) and "correction" columns, show, for the same value of $p_s = .05$, a value for $\sum n_j = n$ under the "no correction" column that is larger than the one computed for the "correction" column. Since, theoretically at least, the larger sample provides greater precision than the smaller one, and the smaller one is adequate for maintaining a precision of $p_s = .05$, the larger (uncorrected) sample must provide a slightly greater precision than $p_s$. Thus, in connection with adequacy of sample, the uncorrected population approach is a form of assurance that the sample size will be more than large enough to provide any selected precision $p_s$. For this reason, the "uncorrected approach" is most frequently employed in practice, *where the cost of sampling per unit is not prohibitive.*

When the situation is such that the cost factor must be considered in connection with optimum allocation, the following formula may be employed:

$$n_j = \frac{\gamma N_j \sigma_j}{C_j}$$

Where $n_j$ is the number of sampling elements allocated to the $j$-th stratum; $\gamma$ is a

---

$\sigma^2_{N\bar{X}}/(N\bar{X})^2$, and thus $\sigma^2_{N\bar{X}} = p_s^2(N\bar{X})^2$. Hence: $p_s^2(N\bar{X})^2 = h\sum N_j\sigma_j - \sum N_j\sigma_j^2$; and

$$h = \frac{p_s^2(N\bar{X})^2 + \sum N_j\sigma_j^2}{\sum N_j\sigma_j}$$

For the example in tabular form:

$$h = \frac{(.05)^2(20,000)^2 + 18,000}{4000} = 250 + 4.5 = 254.5$$

proportionality factor, $N_j$ is the population size of the $j$-th stratum, and $\sigma_j$ its standard deviation; and $C_j$ is the cost per sampling element within the $j$-th stratum. Although we shall not discuss this formula further, it should be noted that this concept of $C_j$ provides for varying costs associated with sampling the various strata of the population.[1]

With this background in stratified sampling, we shall now move to a discussion of sequential sampling, sometimes referred to as "sequential analysis."

*Chapter 17—References*

See Bibliography: 4, 15, 37, 41, 45, 48, 49, 52, 53, 54, 65, 66, 91, 93, 100, 101, 113, 116, 137, 140, 141, 148, 151, 158, 159, 161, 175, 178, 182, 183, 194, 195, 196; 3a, 12a, 21a, 22a, 24a, 28a, 54a, 57a, 58a, 63a, 70a, 71a, 76a, 84a, 86a, 87a, 88a, 94a, 101a, 104a, 107a, 108a, 115a; 2b.

*Chapter Eighteen*

# Numerical Aspects of Sampling

(*Sequential Sampling*)

THE APPROACH of sequential sampling *does not involve a predetermined sample size.* Sample elements are selected until a decision concerning the alternative hypotheses under test is reached. Although the main application of sequential sampling is found in the inspection phase of industrial statistical quality control, it also has application in certain educational research situations.

The method of sequential sampling is based upon procedures of simple random sampling of an infinite population. It is applicable to both discrete (attributes) and continuous (variates) measurements, and its main purpose is to test one hypothesis against an alternative, while providing a rapid correct decision based upon a small amount of information.

## BASIC PROCEDURES

The basic procedures of sequential sampling are as follows:

1. Elements (or groups of elements) are selected from the population one at a time. After every selection a decision must be made concerning three possible courses of actions: (1) to accept the hypothesis $H_1$; or (2) to accept an alternative hypothesis $H_2$; or (3) to continue the sampling process. If neither $H_1$ nor $H_2$ can be accepted after a particular selection, the sampling process is continued until one of them can be accepted. *It should be noted that neither $H_1$ nor $H_2$ is a null hypothesis. The method is designed to test a single hypothesis ($H_1$) against an alternative ($H_2$), instead of testing the null hypothesis ($H_0$) against its statistical alternative hypothesis ($H_a$).*\*

2. Certain limits, $A$ and $B$, must be determined so that whenever the value of the statistic falls *within* the interval $A$ to $B$, the sampling process continues. When the value of the statistic falls outside the interval, either hypothesis $H_1$ or $H_2$ is accepted, depending upon whether the statistic falls "below $A$" or "above B." To be more specific, if $H_1$ were defined to be related to the region "below $A$," and thus $H_2$ were related to the region "above $B$," and if the value of the test statistic fell "*below A*," $H_1$ would be accepted. Similarly, if the value of the test statistic fell "*above B*," $H_2$ would be accepted. If the test statistic value fell *within* the interval $A$ to $B$, the researcher could not commit himself to a decision, and the sampling process would be continued.

---

\* See Chapter 3, for discussion of testing the "null vs. the statistical alternative hypothesis."

3. In order to determine the limits $A$ and $B$, it is necessary to know $\alpha$ and $\beta$. The symbol $\alpha$ indicates the risk, expressed in per cent, of rejecting the hypothesis $H_1$, *when $H_1$ is actually true*. The symbol $\beta$ denotes the risk, expressed in per cent, of *accepting $H_1$, when $H_2$ is actually true*. The limits $A$ and $B$ are approximately given by the equations:

$$A = \frac{\beta}{1 - \alpha} \qquad B = \frac{1 - \beta}{\alpha}$$

4. It is necessary to determine the critical region for each sample size in order to decide which of the three possible actions to take. This activity requires the computation of $Pr_1$, the probability that $k$ elements, collected up through any point of the sequential sampling process, would occur *if alternative hypothesis $H_1$ were true*; and the computation of $Pr_2$, the probability that these $k$ elements would occur *if alternative hypothesis $H_2$ were true*. The computation of $Pr_1$ and $Pr_2$ differ slightly between sequential tests for proportions, means, and variances. Formulas for $Pr_1$ and $Pr_2$ will be discussed under only the first of these three situations. For information concerning tests pertaining to the other situations (means and variances) the reader is referred to sources indicated at the end of the chapter.

5. A likelihood ratio $(L)$ is established as:

$$L = \frac{Pr_2}{Pr_1}$$

in order to determine the proper course of action to pursue. When $Pr_1$ is much larger than $Pr_2$, the alternative hypothesis $H_1$ is accepted. The alternative $H_2$ is accepted if $Pr_2$ is much larger than $Pr_1$. If there is relatively little difference between $Pr_1$ and $Pr_2$, another selection of sample element(s) is indicated. Where $\alpha$ and $\beta$ have the same definition as in paragraph 3, it can be shown that:

(a) if $Pr_2/Pr_1 \leq \dfrac{\beta}{1 - \alpha}$ the alternative hypothesis $H_1$, is accepted;*

(b) if $Pr_2/Pr_1 \geq \dfrac{1 - \beta}{\alpha}$ the alternative hypothesis $H_2$ is accepted;

(c) if $\dfrac{\beta}{1 - \alpha} < Pr_2/Pr_1 < \dfrac{1 - \beta}{\alpha}$ sampling is continued.

The sampling process continues until condition (a) or condition (b) occurs.

6. Sequential sampling can be applied in tests for proportions (binomial populations), in tests for means (normal populations), and in tests for variances (normal populations). In each case, sequential sampling requires the calculation of the ratio $L$ after each selection of sample element(s), then by comparing

---

* The formulas (a), (b), and (c) can be expressed in terms of the limits A and B, by substituting: $A = \dfrac{\beta}{1 - \alpha}$; in (a) and (c); and $B = \dfrac{1 - \beta}{\alpha}$; in (b) and (c).

the value of *L* with appropriate tables or charts of boundary values, a decision is made relative to which of the three courses of action to pursue. Either a graphic or tabular procedure may be employed to determine when the sampling selection should end.

*Sequential sampling cannot be employed in all research situations.* Two conditions are necessary: (1) random sampling for any sample size (individual items, or subgroups) must be possible; and (2) it must be possible to increase the sample size indefinitely at any stage of the sequential procedure.

Condition (1) fails to exist where a small sample cannot approximately represent the universe under study. To illustrate, if we wish to examine the voting preference of a particular community, we would want to be certain that our sample included persons from: several levels of income, several professions, several ethnic groups, and other such stratifications. Under these circumstances a small random sample would not adequately represent the universe being studied, i.e., the "preference" pattern of the community, and a sequential sampling approach should not be employed. *In general, sequential sampling should not be employed where stratified or multistage sampling is indicated.*

Condition (2) fails to exist when it is not possible to include additional selections in a sample after the research has begun. This condition prevails frequently in educational research where a particular classroom of students is being employed as an experimental (or control) group, and in social surveys where it is difficult (or expensive) to increase the number of sample elements during the course of the survey.

In order to apply sequential sampling, the following general conditions should prevail.

1. It should be possible to select sample elements one at a time (or in groups) without too much time elapsing between selections.

2. Sample elements should be located in a relatively small area and be easily accessible.

3. Sample elements should be uniquely defined and easily identified, thus preventing ambiguity in the selection of an element.

4. Sample elements should be capable of easy and efficient manipulation, thus allowing for adjustment in sample size at any time during the procedure.

5. The populations (or universes) under study should tend to be small and concentrated.

### Sequential Sampling—Proportions (Binomial Population)

The binomial distribution is a theoretical one which has application to a dichotomous population where *P* is the true or postulated probability of occurrence of a specific characteristic in a single trial, and $Q = (1 - P)$, is the probability of the characteristic not occurring. The successive terms of the expansion of $(P + Q)^n$ give the probabilities that, in a random sample of size *n*, the characteristic will occur exactly 0, 1, 2, 3, 4, ..., $(n - 2)$, $(n - 1)$, or *n* times. The *general term* of a binomial distribution (population) may be symbolized as:

$$\overset{N}{\underset{x}{C}} P^x Q^{(N-x)} = \frac{N!}{x!(N-x)!} P^x Q^{(N-x)} = \frac{N!}{x!(N-x)!} P^x (1-P)^{(N-x)}$$

where *N* is the number of elements in the finite population, *x* is the exact number of times the characteristic occurs, $(N-x)$ is the exact number of times the characteristic fails to occur in the population, and *P* and *Q* are as previously defined.*

Sequential sampling may be applied to the problem of testing a proportion in a binomial population providing the five general conditions listed on page 222 prevail. For example, sequential sampling has been applied successfully in acceptance inspection of large lots of items, each of which are to be determined good or bad. We shall now illustrate the use of sequential sampling in educational research.

A research project designed to investigate the general worth of a therapy program for emotionally disturbed children, conducted in a public school special classroom setting, had proceeded to the point where 260 children with the same syndrome of symptoms had been selected as participants. Visiting teachers had collected a large amount of family background data, and psychiatrists had compiled various neuro-physical instrument test results, behavior pattern data, and other related materials, on each participating child. This information composed an extensive file for each child.

Early in the experiment a modification of the established therapy program was proposed, because of the possibility of the existence of a particular complex of certain family backgrounds and types of emotional traits, in a sizable proportion of the group of children participating in the project. In order to determine the existence of this complex, it would be necessary to investigate thoroughly all information in a child's file. There was a slight difference of opinion between members of the research team as to the importance of providing for the complex in the therapy program, if, in fact, it existed in a sufficient number of cases to make it worth consideration. It was decided that if the proportion of the group of children in the project who possessed the complex was 30 per cent or less ($P \leq .30$), the therapy program *would not be modified* to accommodate it. If the proportion of these children was 40 per cent or more ($P \geq .40$), the program would be modified accordingly. Since the five general conditions of sequential sampling prevailed, and because of the time demand and cost involved in a thorough examination of each child's file, it was agreed that a sequential analysis (sample) of the finite population of files should be conducted (drawn).

---

* The formula for the general term of a binomial distribution (sample) may be written by replacing *P* with *p*; *Q* with *q*, and *N* with *n* (sample size). The expression then becomes:

$$\overset{n}{\underset{x}{C}} p^x q^{(n-x)} = \frac{n!}{x!(n-x)!} p^x q^{(n-x)} = \frac{n!}{x!(n-x)!} p^x (1-p)^{n-x}$$

The sequential test was conducted under the following conditions:

$$H_1 : P_1 = .30 \qquad H_2 : P_2 = .40$$

$$\alpha = .05$$

$$\beta = .10$$

In statement form:

1. Reject the hypothesis ($H_1 : P_1 = .30$) of the *existence of the complex* only 5 per cent ($\alpha = .05$) of the time if the proportion of children having it is $P = .30$, and *do not* modify the therapy program.
2. Accept the hypothesis ($H_1 : P_1 = .30$) of the *existence of the complex* only 10 per cent of the time if the proportion of children having it is actually $H_2 : P_2 = .40$. (If the actual proportion of children showing the complex is $P = .40$, the therapy program *is to be modified*.)

These conditions imply that if the proportion of children with the complex were less than 30 per cent ($P < .30$) the risk of rejecting $H_1$ *when actually it was true*, would occur even less frequently than 5 per cent of the time. By the same token, if the proportion were greater than 40 per cent ($P > .40$), the risk of accepting $H_1$ *when $H_2$ was actually true* would occur less frequently than 10 per cent of the time.

If it was assumed that the proportion of the population of 260 children possessing the complex was: $P_2 = .40$, the probability that, say, $s_k$ "complex present" cases and $f_k$ "complex absent" cases would occur in some particular order among the first $k$ selections of sample elements (files), would be:

$$Pr_2 = P_2^{s_k}(1 - P_2)^{f_k}; \quad \text{where} \quad (s_k + f_k = k)$$

or in numerical values:

$$Pr_2 = (.40)^{s_k}(1 - .40)^{f_k} = (.40)^{s_k}(.60)^{f_k}$$

Similarly, if it was assumed that the proportion of the population possessing the complex was: $P_1 = .30$, the probability of getting $s_k$ "complex present" cases and $f_k$ "complex absent" cases among the first $k$ selections of sample elements (files) would be:

$$Pr_1 = P_1^{s_k}(1 - P_1)^{f_k}; \quad \text{where} \quad (s_k + f_k = k)$$

or, numerically:

$$Pr_1 = (.30)^{s_k}(1 - .30)^{f_k} = (.30)^{s_k}(.70)^{f_k}$$

From these values the likelihood ratio ($L$), would be:

$$L = \frac{Pr_2}{Pr_1} = \frac{P_2^{s_k}(1 - P_2)^{f_k}}{P_1^{s_k}(1 - P_1)^{f_k}} = \frac{(.40)^{s_k}(.60)^{f_k}}{(.30)^{s_k}(.70)^{f_k}}$$

With these values established the random selection of elements (students' files) was begun.

In order to illustrate more clearly how the sequential process operates, suppose the first file *drawn at random showed* "complex present." Then $Pr_1$ and $Pr_2$, *after the first draw*, become:

$$Pr_1 = (.30)^1(.70)^0 = (.30)(1) = .30 \qquad \left(\begin{array}{c} s_k + f_k = k \\ 1 + 0 = 1 \end{array}\right)$$

$$Pr_2 = (.40)^1(.60)^0 = (.40)(1) = .40$$

The likelihood ratio ($L$) is:

$$L = \frac{Pr_2}{Pr_1} = \frac{.40}{.30} = 1.33$$

Since $Pr_2/Pr_1 = 1.33$; the condition of:

$$\frac{\beta}{1 - \alpha} < \frac{Pr_2}{Pr_1} < \frac{1 - \beta}{\alpha}$$

(see 5c page 221) prevails. Numerically:

$$\frac{.10}{1 - .05} < \frac{4}{3} < \frac{.90}{.05}$$

$$\frac{2}{19} < \frac{4}{3} < 18$$

The existence of this condition means that sampling must continue. Another sample element is randomly selected. Suppose the second element (file) shows "complex absent." Conditions $Pr_1$ and $Pr_2$ become:

$$Pr_1 = (.30)^1(.70)^1 = .21 \qquad \left(\begin{array}{c} s_k + f_k = k \\ 1 + 1 = 2 \end{array}\right)$$

$$Pr_2 = (.40)^1(.60)^1 = .24$$

The likelihood ratio, *after the second element (file) has been drawn randomly*, becomes:

$$L = \frac{Pr_2}{Pr_1} = \frac{.24}{.21} = \frac{8}{7}$$

Since, $\frac{2}{19} < \frac{8}{7} < 18$, the sampling must continue.

Suppose that continued random selection of sample elements showed a succession of "complex absent" cases. After, say, the eighth element is drawn, the maximum likelihood ratio would be:

$$L = \frac{Pr_2}{Pr_1} = \frac{(.40)^1(.60)^7}{(.30)^1(.70)^7} \approx \frac{4}{9} \qquad \left(\begin{array}{c} s_k + f_k = k \\ 1 + 7 = 8 \end{array}\right)$$

Since, $\frac{2}{19} < \frac{4}{9} < 18$, the sampling would be continued. If the *succession of* "complex absent" *cases continued to appear* in the sequential process, we would find after the random selection of the sixteenth file, that the maximum likelihood would become:

$$L = \frac{(.40)^1(.60)^{15}}{(.30)^1(.70)^{15}} \approx .1008 \qquad \left(\begin{array}{c} s_k + f_k = k \\ 1 + 15 = 16 \end{array}\right)$$

Since $.1008 < \frac{2}{19}$, sampling would be discontinued (see formula 5a, page 221) and the hypothesis, $H_1 : P_1 = .30$, would be accepted. This finding would mean acceptance of the plan *to not modify the therapy program.*

## Operating—Characteristic Function (*OC*)

A more general picture of the design is presented by the operating-characteristic curve function (*OC*). The operating-characteristic curve represents the function which shows the probability of accepting the plan to "not modify" the therapy program when $P$ is the actual, or true, proportion of occurrence of "complex present" cases in the total group. To establish the *OC* we employ the four known values: $\alpha$, $\beta$, $P_1$, $P_2$, and that of a value $P'$, located between $P_1$ and $P_2$, given by the formula:

$$P' = \frac{\log \dfrac{1 - P_2}{1 - P_1}}{\log \dfrac{1 - P_2}{1 - P_1} - \log \dfrac{P_2}{P_1}}$$

where the logarithms employed are *common logarithms* to the base 10. In our illustration, the value of $P'$ becomes:

$$P' = \frac{\log \dfrac{1 - .40}{1 - .30}}{\log \dfrac{1 - .40}{1 - .30} - \log \dfrac{.40}{.30}} = \frac{\log \dfrac{.60}{.70}}{\log \dfrac{.60}{.70} - \log \dfrac{.40}{.30}}$$

$$= \frac{\log \frac{6}{7}}{\log \frac{6}{7} - \log \frac{4}{3}} = \frac{\log 6 - \log 7}{\log 6 - \log 7 - \log 4 + \log 3}$$

$$= \frac{.77815 - .84510}{.77815 - .84510 - .60206 + .47712} = \frac{-.06695}{-.19189}$$

$$= .3489$$

Figure 14 shows the *operating characteristic curve* for the design of our particular illustration. The curve shows that when the proportion of "complex present" is zero, the probability of accepting the "do not modify program" plan is 1; while if the proportion of "complex present" is 1 (all cases show "complex present"), then the probability of accepting the "do not modify" plan is zero. If the *true proportion of "complex present" is less than .30*, the "do not modify program" plan will be accepted more than 95 per cent of the time, and at the same time those sequences that show a .40 proportion of "complex present," *under the true condition of $P = .30$*, will lead to acceptance of a "modification of program" plan less than 10 per cent of the time. It should be noted that $P_1$ cannot be equal to $P_2$ if this system of analysis is applied to such research situations (i.e., sequential sampling applied to situations involving the determination of *probable values* of a population proportion, $P$).

The values of $P$ and $OC$ function, by which the curve was roughly sketched, are presented in the schedule below:

| $P$ | (Prob. of Acceptance), or $OC$ Function |
|---|---|
| 0 | 1 |
| $P_1 = .30$ | $1 - \alpha = .95$ |
| $P' = .3489$ | .5622 |
| $P_2 = .40$ | $\beta = .10$ |
| 1 | 0 |

where the value (height) of the $OC$ function corresponding to the value of $P' = .3489$ is computed by the formula:

$$\frac{\log \dfrac{1 - \beta}{\alpha}}{\log \dfrac{1 - \beta}{\alpha} - \log \dfrac{\beta}{1 - \alpha}} = \frac{\log \dfrac{1 - .10}{.05}}{\log \dfrac{1 - .10}{.05} - \log \dfrac{.10}{1 - .05}} = \frac{\log \dfrac{.90}{.05}}{\log \dfrac{.90}{.05} - \log \dfrac{.10}{.95}}$$

$$= \frac{\log 18}{\log 18 - \log 1 + \log 9.5} = \frac{1.25527}{1.25527 - 0 + .97742} = \frac{1.25527}{2.23269} = .5622$$

*Sampling Chart*

A mathematical graph could have been constructed and employed in conducting this sequential analysis, if such an approach were desired. If the

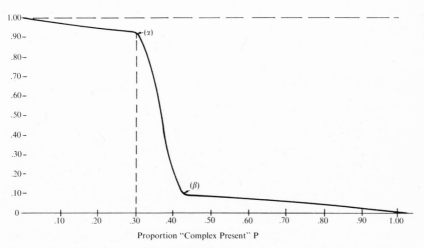

*Figure 14*
*Operating Characteristic Curve*

graphing approach had been employed, it would have been necessary to determine certain critical values for the construction of the graph. Equations 5(a) and 5(b) on page 221, would be employed to determine these values as follows:

$$\frac{Pr_2}{Pr_1} = \frac{P_2^{s_k}(1 - P_2)^{f_k}}{P_1^{s_k}(1 - P_1)^{f_k}} = \left(\frac{P_2}{P_1}\right)^{s_k}\left(\frac{1 - P_2}{1 - P_1}\right)^{f_k} = \frac{\beta}{1 - \alpha} \qquad (s_k + f_k = k) \quad (5a)$$

Taking common logarithms of both sides of the equation, we have:

$$s_k \log \frac{P_2}{P_1} + f_k \log \frac{1 - P_2}{1 - P_1} = \log \frac{\beta}{1 - \alpha} \tag{5a'}$$

Similarly equation (5b) becomes:

$$s_k \log \frac{P_2}{P_1} + f_k \log \frac{1 - P_2}{1 - P_1} = \log \frac{1 - \beta}{\alpha} \tag{5b'}$$

In our illustration, equations (5a') and (5b') become:

$$s_k \log \frac{.40}{.30} + f_k \log \frac{1 - .40}{1 - .30} = \log \frac{.10}{1 - .05} \tag{5a'}$$

$$s_k \log \frac{.40}{.30} + f_k \log \frac{1 - .40}{1 - .30} = \log \frac{1 - .10}{.05} \tag{5b'}$$

or

$$s_k \log \frac{4}{3} + f_k \log \frac{6}{7} = \log \frac{1}{9.5} \tag{5a''}$$

and

$$s_k \log \frac{4}{3} + f_k \log \frac{6}{7} = \log 18 \tag{5b''}$$

Substituting proper values for the logarithms found in a table of common logarithms, we have:

$$.12494 \, s_k - .06695 \, f_k = -.97772 \tag{5a'''}$$

$$.12494 \, s_k - .06695 \, f_k = 1.25527 \tag{5b'''}$$

These equations are represented by lines on the graph (see Figure 15). Although two points determine a line, four points are found on each of the respective lines, with the third and fourth points being used as check points for construction. The following schedules show the values of $s_k$ (complex present) and $f_k$ (complex absent) which determine and check the positions of the respective lines:

$$.12494 \, s_k - .06695 \, f_k = -.97772; \tag{5a'''}$$

$$.12494 \, s_k - .06695 \, f_k = 1.25527 \tag{5b'''}$$

| $s_k$ | $f_k$ | | $s_k$ | $f_k$ |
|---|---|---|---|---|
| 0 | 14.60 | $(s_k + f_k = k$ Sample Elements) | 0 | −18.75 |
| 10 | 33.27 | | 10 | −.09 |
| 20 | 51.93 | | 20 | 18.57 |
| −7.82 | 0 | | 10.05 | 0 |

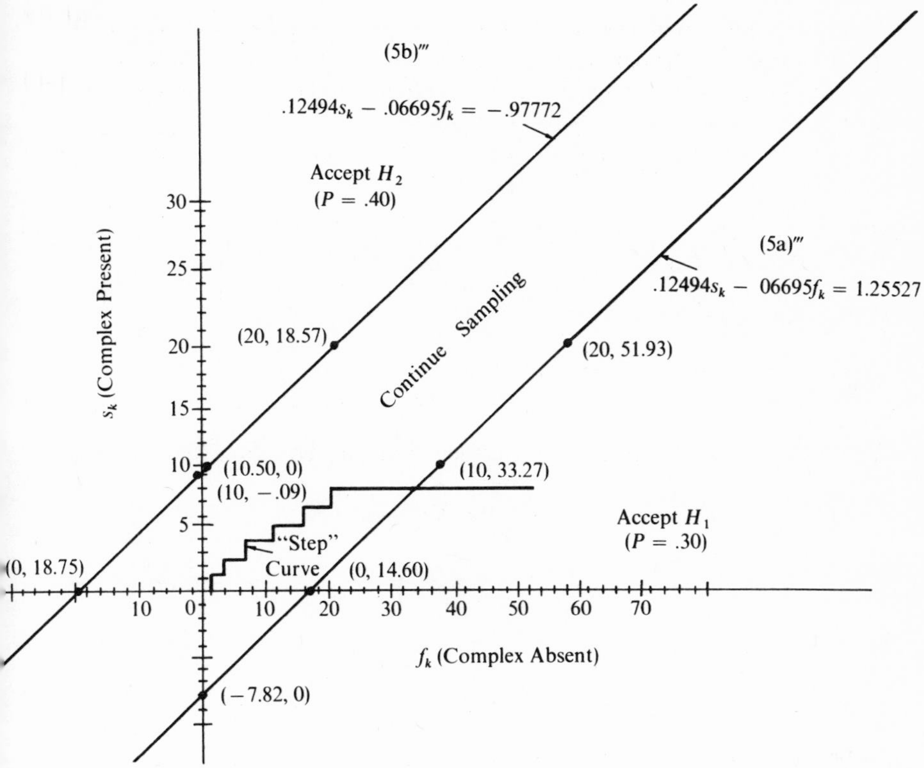

*Figure 15*
*Sequential Analysis Graph of Proportions Example*

The graphs of the respective lines, shown in Figure 15, should be constructed before the sequential sampling procedure is begun, so that the result of "complex present" ($s_k$), or that of "complex absent" ($f_k$), may be recorded after each sample selection by merely drawing a line one unit up if $s_k$ occurs, or one unit to the right if $f_k$ occurs. The "step" shaped curve in the area of "continue sampling" of the graph illustrates a sequential sampling process, wherein $s_k$ and $f_k$ had the following order of occurrence:

*fsfsfffsfffffsffffffsfffsffffffff*

The "step" curve intersects the (5a''') line after the selection of the thirty-second element (file) in this example, and thus the sampling is terminated at that point, and the hypothesis, $H_1 : P_1 = .30$, is accepted, which in turn means that the plan to not modify the therapy program is adopted.

Where the graph of line (5a‴) intersects the $f_k$-axis ($s_k = 0$, and $f_k \approx 15$), we read the number of elements (15) required for decision if *each of all the files selected from the beginning of the sequential procedure had shown* "complex absent" ($f_k$). Similarly, where line (5b‴) intersects the $s_k$ – axis ($s_k = 10.05$, or 11, and $f_k = 0$), we read the number of elements (11) required for decision, *if each of all files obtained from the beginning of the sequential sample had shown* "*complex present*" ($s_k$). These results may be obtained mathematically as follows:

From formula (5b), page 221, if all selections are "complex present" ($s_k$), we have:

$$\left(\frac{P_2}{P_1}\right)^{s_k}\left(\frac{1 - P_2}{1 - P_1}\right)^0 = \frac{1 - \beta}{\alpha} \tag{5b}$$

since:

$$\left(\frac{1 - P_2}{1 - P_1}\right)^0 = \frac{1}{1} = 1; \qquad \text{because} \left(\frac{x}{y}\right)^0 = \frac{x^0}{y^0} = \frac{1}{1} = 1$$

we have:

$$\left(\frac{P_2}{P_1}\right)^{s_k} = \frac{1 - \beta}{\alpha}$$

Taking common logarithms of both sides of the last equation, we find:

$$s_k \log \frac{P_2}{P_1} = \log \frac{1 - \beta}{\alpha}$$

or:

$$s_k = \frac{\log \dfrac{1 - \beta}{\alpha}}{\log \dfrac{P_2}{P_1}}$$

Substituting values from our example, we find:

$$s_k = \frac{\log \dfrac{1 - .10}{.05}}{\log \dfrac{.40}{.30}} = \frac{\log 18}{\log \dfrac{4}{3}} = \frac{1.25527}{.12494} = 10.05, \quad \text{or} \quad 11*$$

for intersection of "step curve" and line (5b‴).

From formula (5a), page 221, if all selections are "complex absent" ($f_k$), we have:

$$\left(\frac{P_2}{P_1}\right)^0\left(\frac{1 - P_2}{1 - P_1}\right)^{f_k} = \frac{\beta}{1 - \alpha} \tag{5a}$$

---

\* Since it would be impossible to select "10.05 files," and we must be sure that an adequate number of files be involved to "sample" the situation, i.e., $n > 10.05$, the next largest integral value (11) is employed.

since:

$$\left(\frac{P_2}{P_1}\right)^0 = \frac{1}{1} = 1$$

we have

$$\left(\frac{1 - P_2}{1 - P_1}\right)^{f_k} = \frac{\beta}{1 - \alpha}$$

Taking common logarithms of both sides of this equation, we find:

$$f_k \log \frac{1 - P_2}{1 - P_1} = \log \frac{\beta}{1 - \alpha}$$

$$f_k = \frac{\log \dfrac{\beta}{1 - \alpha}}{\log \dfrac{1 - P_2}{1 - P_1}}$$

Substituting values from our example, we find:

$$f_k = \frac{\log \dfrac{.10}{1 - .05}}{\log \dfrac{1 - .40}{1 - .30}} = \frac{\log \dfrac{.10}{.95}}{\log \dfrac{.60}{.70}} = \frac{-.97772}{-.06695} = 14.60, \quad \text{or} \quad 15$$

for intersection of "step curve" and line (5a‴).

If the *true* population proportion of "complex present" cases is $P_1$, the *average size of the sample* ($\overline{K}$) required to reach a decision is given by the formula:

$$\overline{K} = \frac{(1 - \alpha) \log \dfrac{\beta}{1 - \alpha} + \log \dfrac{1 - \beta}{\alpha}}{P_1 \log \dfrac{P_2}{P_1} + (1 - P_1) \log \dfrac{1 - P_2}{1 - P_1}}$$

In our example:

$$\overline{K} = \frac{(1 - .05) \log \dfrac{.10}{1 - .05} + (.05) \log \dfrac{1 - .10}{.05}}{.30 \log \dfrac{.40}{.30} + (1 - .30) \log \dfrac{.60}{.70}} = \frac{(.95) \log \dfrac{1}{9.5} + (.05) \log 18}{(.30) \log \dfrac{4}{3} + (.70) \log \dfrac{6}{7}}$$

$$= \frac{-(.95)(.97772) + (.05)(1.25527)}{(.30)(.12494) - (.70)(.06695)} = \frac{-.9288340 + .0627635}{.0374820 - .0468650}$$

$$= \frac{-.8660705}{-.0093830} = 92.3 \quad \text{or} \quad 93$$

If the *true* proportion of "complex present" cases is $P_2$, the *average sample number* $(\bar{K})$ required to reach a decision is given by the formula:

$$K = \frac{\beta \log \dfrac{\beta}{1 - \alpha} + (1 - \beta) \log \dfrac{1 - \beta}{\alpha}}{P_2 \log \dfrac{P_2}{P_1} + (1 - P_2) \log \dfrac{1 - P_2}{1 - P_1}} \tag{2}$$

In our example:

$$\bar{K} = \frac{.10 \log \dfrac{.10}{1 - .05} + (1 - .10) \log \dfrac{1 - .10}{.05}}{.40 \log \dfrac{.40}{.30} + (.60) \log \dfrac{.60}{.70}} = \frac{(.10) \log \dfrac{1}{9.5} + (.90) \log 18}{(.40) \log \dfrac{4}{3} + (.60) \log \dfrac{6}{7}}$$

$$= \frac{-(.10)(.97772) + (.90)(1.25527)}{(.40)(.12494) - (.60)(06695)} = \frac{-.0977720 + 1.1297430}{.0499760 - .0401700}$$

$$= \frac{1.0319710}{.0098060} = 105.2, \quad \text{or} \quad 106.$$

The average sample number $(\bar{K})$ required to reach a decision, if the true proportion is $P'$, the value found between $P_1$ and $P_2$, is given by the formula:

$$\bar{K} = \frac{\log \dfrac{\beta}{1 - \alpha} \log \dfrac{1 - \beta}{\alpha}}{\log \dfrac{P_2}{P_1} \log \dfrac{1 - P_2}{1 - P_1}} \tag{3}$$

In our example where $P' = .3489$

$$\bar{K} = \frac{\log \dfrac{.10}{.95} \log \dfrac{1 - .10}{.05}}{\log \dfrac{.40}{.30} \log \dfrac{1 - .40}{1 - .30}} = \frac{\log \dfrac{1}{9.5} \log 18}{\log \dfrac{4}{3} \log \dfrac{6}{7}}$$

$$= \frac{-(.97772)(1.25527)}{-(.12494)(.06695)} = \frac{1.227302}{.008365} = 146.7, \quad \text{or} \quad 147$$

Expressions (1), (2), and (3) are very useful in actual practice because they provide a beforehand estimate of the average size sample required to reach a decision under the condition imposed by the values of $P_1$, $P_2$, $P'$, $\alpha$, and $\beta$. By adjusting these latter values an excessive amount of sampling may be avoided. It should be noted that the *maximum value for the average sample number* occurs at a point very near the value of $P'$. Our example computations demonstrate this point with a value of $\bar{K} = 147$ for the point $P'$, as compared to $\bar{K} = 106$ for $P_2 = .40$, and $\bar{K} = 93$ for $P_1 = .30$.

*Sample Selections in Groups*

Under certain conditions, say those of cost, it might be less expensive to take sample values in groups, instead of selecting one element at a time. If group selection is employed, results are recorded in group terms instead of single selection values, and the only effect on the sequential procedure is an increase in all values throughout by an amount equal to the number of items included in each group. For example, if we select *groups of ten items* at a time, the values that prevailed throughout the *single selection procedure* after, say, the selection of the tenth, twentieth, and thirtieth items are found to exist after the first, second, and third drawings of groups of ten, respectively. The main difference is that under single element selection, values are computed for 0, 1, 2, 3, 4, ... $n$; while under group selection with, say, ten per group, values are computed for 0, 10, 20, 30, 40, ... $n$. The values for acceptance of $H_1$, or acceptance of $H_2$, are the same in both *group* and *single* selection sequences for sample size 10, 20, 30, 40, and so on, i.e., for any multiple of ten sample size that occurs in both sets. To illustrate, if selection was carried out in *groups of ten* we *might* have for $L$, after the first selection:

$$L = \frac{P_2}{P_1} = \left(\frac{P_2}{P_1}\right)^6 \left(\frac{1 - P_2}{1 - P_1}\right)^4 \qquad \left(\begin{matrix} s_k + f_k = k \\ 6 + 4 = 10 \end{matrix}\right)$$

after the second selection of a group of ten $L$ *might* become:

$$L = \frac{P_2}{P_1} = \left(\frac{P_2}{P_1}\right)^{14} \left(\frac{1 - P_2}{1 - P_1}\right)^6 \qquad \left(\begin{matrix} s_k + f_k = k \\ 14 + 6 = 20 \end{matrix}\right)$$

after the third selection, ten items to a group, $L$ *might* be:

$$L = \frac{P_2}{P_1} = \left(\frac{P_2}{P_1}\right)^{20} \left(\frac{1 - P_2}{1 - P_1}\right)^{10} \qquad \left(\begin{matrix} s_k + f_k = k \\ 20 + 10 = 30 \end{matrix}\right)$$

These illustrative values might also occur in the single element selection process after the drawing of the tenth, twentieth, and thirtieth items, respectively. In both processes $L$ would have the same values at these points of the sequential process. If ten items at a time are examined, the *average sample number* would be increased by not more than ten.

*Sequential Sampling—Methods or Processes (Dichotomous Population—Success or Failure)*

Another application of sequential sampling is found in situations where it becomes necessary to decide whether method $A$ (or process) is better than method $B$ (process), based upon two different outcomes, one classified "success," the other "failure."

The procedure employs paired values obtained by applying first one method, then the other. The discriminating paired values are those in which one method produces a "success" and the other process (method) produces a "failure." The pairs of values in which both methods produce "success," or those in which both methods produce "failure," are ignored. This latter condition means that a test chart can be constructed in terms of $Y$, the number of pairs of observations favorable to, say, method $A$, as a function of the total number of pairs favorable to either method $A$ or method $B$, that is, those favorable to $A$ plus those favorable to $B$.

If the test is to be used to compare an *experimental* method $A$ to a standard method $B$, it should be constructed in such fashion that method $A$ will have to demonstrate decided superiority over method $B$ in order to be accepted. The rationale of this approach is that a method currently in operation should not be abandoned in favor of a new method, if the new method is only slightly better than the existing method. Thus, the design of the sequential analysis in this case is such that unless the difference between the experimental method and the currently operating one is greater than a certain pre-determined criterion value, the sequential sample will tend to favor the acceptance of the existing method $B$.

The difference between two methods is measured in sequential sampling by a so-called odds ratio ($U$) defined as:

$$U = \frac{P_a/(1 - P_a)}{P_b/(1 - P_b)} = \frac{P_a(1 - P_b)}{P_b(1 - P_a)}$$

where $P_a$ is the proportion of successes yielded by method $A$, and $P_b$ the proportion of successes obtained by method $B$. The ratio $U$ is employed instead of the simple difference ($P_a - P_b$) because the difference between methods depends not only upon the absolute magnitude of the difference ($P_a - P_b$), but on the order of magnitude, of $P_a$ and $P_b$, as well.

Four quantities must be stipulated for a sequential analysis (sample) design of this type:

1. $U_1$, the value of the odds ratio below which method, or process, $B$ (the standard method) is superior.
2. $U_2$, the value of the odds ratio above which method, or process, $A$ (the experimental method) is superior.
3. $\alpha$, the risk of rejecting method $B$ (the standard) when it actually is superior.
4. $\beta$, the risk of accepting method $A$ (the experimental) when method $B$ (the standard) is actually superior.

Since the designation of method $A$ as the experimental method, and $B$ as the standard method, is arbitrary, their identifications with odds ratios $U_2$ and $U_1$, respectively, is by definition only. The relationships may be interchanged by re-definition if so desired. To establish a systematic approach for our procedure here, $U_2$ will always be identified with the so-called experimental phase of the analysis, and $U_1$ with the "standard" process. Hence, by our definition, $U_2$ *will always be of greater magnitude than* $U_1$. Under these circumstances either method $A$ or method $B$ can be designated "experimental," but the method so designated must then be identified with odds ratio $U_2$. Naturally, it follows that the method designated as "standard" must then be associated with odds ratio $U_1$.

When the value of the odds ratio $U$ is 1, the proportions of successes for the two methods are equal. Since the experimental method is not to be selected as superior to the standard method unless it can be demonstrated that it is substantially better than the one (standard) currently being employed, the magnitude of $U_2$ will ordinarily be a chosen value greater than 1. Frequently, $U_1$ is chosen to be slightly greater than 1, on the basis that if the experimental method can demonstrate a superiority under the circumstance of $U_1 > 1$, it certainly will be superior under the condition of $U_1 = 1$.

The equations of the boundary lines defining the limits of the three zones in the test chart ((1) experimental method superior, (2) continue sampling, and (3) standard method superior) are:

$$Y_1 = \frac{-\log \dfrac{1-\alpha}{\beta}}{\log \dfrac{U_2}{U_1}} + \left(\frac{\log \dfrac{U_2+1}{U_1+1}}{\log \dfrac{U_2}{U_1}}\right)(n) \tag{6a}$$

$$Y_2 = \frac{\log \dfrac{1-\beta}{\alpha}}{\log \dfrac{U_2}{U_1}} + \left(\frac{\log \dfrac{U_2+1}{U_1+1}}{\log \dfrac{U_2}{U_1}}\right)(n) \tag{6b}$$

where $Y_1$ and $Y_2$ indicate the number of pairs of observations favorable to the experimental method, $n$ is the sum, or combination of the number of observations favorable to the standard method *and* the number favorable to the experimental method; and $\alpha$, $\beta$, $U_1$, and $U_2$ are as previously defined. All of the logarithms employed in the formulas are to base 10.

The process will be demonstrated by the following example:

A standard screening and admission procedure (method $B$), designed to deal with the admission of "probationary" students to a particular university, is to be compared with an experimental admission procedure (method $A$) devised to process the same type of student cases. The comparison is to be made on the basis of the number of students *successfully identified as potential "successes" or "failures,"* where "success" is defined as the student becoming fully admitted after one semester of academic work taken under specified conditions.

Each student of the probationary type is screened by both methods. If one, or both, of the methods indicates a success potential for the student, he is to be admitted for one semester's prescribed academic work under specified conditions. If both methods indicate fail potential, the student is not admitted. At the end of the "trial" semester the probationary students, on the basis of their academic records are either admitted as fully matriculated students, or are asked to leave the university.

*A success for a method* is declared if its original prediction is fulfilled. For example, if method $A$ indicates the student would be successful, and method $B$ predicts failure, the student is admitted. If at the end of the trial semester the student's academic standing is such that it permits his admission as a fully matriculated student, method $A$ is rated a success, and method $B$ a failure. If the student had failed to gain matriculated admission, method $A$ would be rated a fail, and $B$ a success. In those cases where both methods indicate success potential, they are both rated a success, or a fail, as the student gains, or does not gain, a matriculated admission. Since these latter types of cases are ignored in this system of analysis, they in no way affect the decision about the comparative superiority of the respective methods, and will not be treated further here.

An odds ratio of $U_2 = 2.8$ or more was selected arbitrarily as the criterion of superiority for method $A$ (experimental), and one of $U_1 = 1.0$ or less as the criterion of superiority for method $B$ (standard). The Type $I$ error was set as: $\alpha = .02$, and Type II as: $\beta = .04$. With these values established, the investigation of student files to determine "successful" predictions was begun.

The fictitious data from the experiment are presented as follows:

| (1)<br>Number of "Trial"<br>Students. | (2)<br>Cumulative Number of<br>Pairs Favorable to Method<br>A (Exp) $(Y)$ | (3)<br>Cumulative Number of<br>Pairs Favorable to Method<br>B (Stand.) | (4)<br>Total Cumulative Number<br>of Pairs Favorable to Either<br>$A$ or $B$ |
|---|---|---|---|
| 19 | 0 | 1 | 1 |
| 26 | 1 | 1 | 2 |
| 31 | 1 | 2 | 3 |
| 33 | 1 | 3 | 4 |
| 34 | 1 | 4 | 5 |
| 37 | 2 | 4 | 6 |
| 40 | 3 | 4 | 7 |
| 46 | 3 | 5 | 8 |
| 49 | 4 | 5 | 9 |
| 51 | 4 | 6 | 10 |
| 52 | 4 | 7 | 11 |
| 58 | 4 | 8 | 12 |
| | | | Accept standard Method<br>$B$ as Superior. |

Basic calculations for determining the equations of the two boundary lines, defining the regions of "Accept $A$," "continue sampling," and "Accept $B$," respectively, are as follows:

$$\alpha = .02 \qquad \log \frac{1 - \alpha}{\beta} = \log \frac{1 - .02}{.04} = \log \frac{98}{4} = \log 24.5;$$

$$\beta = .04 \qquad \log \frac{1 - \beta}{\alpha} = \log \frac{1 - .04}{.02} = \log \frac{96}{2} = \log 48.0;$$

$$\begin{aligned} U_1 &= 1.0 \\ U_2 &= 2.8 \end{aligned} \qquad \log \frac{U_2}{U_1} = \log \frac{2.8}{1.0} = \log 2.8;$$

$$\log \frac{U_2 + 1}{U_1 + 1} = \log \frac{3.8}{2.0} = \log 1.9$$

Hence:

$$Y_1 = \frac{-\log \dfrac{1 - \alpha}{\beta}}{\log \dfrac{U_2}{U_1}} + \left( \frac{\log \dfrac{U_2 + 1}{U_1 + 1}}{\log \dfrac{U_2}{U_1}} \right)(n) \tag{6a}$$

$$Y_1 = \frac{-\log 24.5}{\log 2.8} + \left( \frac{\log 1.9}{\log 2.8} \right)(n) \tag{6a$'$}$$

$$Y_1 = -3.11 + .623\,(n) \tag{6a$''$}$$

$$Y_2 = \frac{\log \dfrac{1 - \beta}{\alpha}}{\log \dfrac{U_2}{U_1}} + \left( \frac{\log \dfrac{U_2 + 1}{U_1 + 1}}{\log \dfrac{U_2}{U_1}} \right)(n) \tag{6b}$$

$$Y_2 = \frac{\log 48}{\log 2.8} + \left( \frac{\log 1.9}{\log 2.8} \right)(n) \tag{6b$'$}$$

$$Y_2 = 3.76 + .623\,(n) \tag{6b$''$}$$

The test chart which accompanies this example is composed of a vertical axis ($Y$) which designates the cumulative number of pairs favorable to the experimental method $A$ (column (2) of the table); a horizontal axis ($n$) which accounts for the total cumulative number of pairs favorable to either method $A$ or method $B$ (column (4) of the table); the two boundary lines (6a$''$) and (6b$''$); the three regions of "Accept $A$," "continue sampling," and "Accept $B$"; and, finally, the "Step" curve of the experimental data. The chart is shown in Figure 16. The boundary lines were plotted and checked by the following points:

| (6a$''$) | $Y_1$ | $n$ | (6b$''$) | $Y_2$ | $n$ |
|---|---|---|---|---|---|
| | $-3.11$ | 0 | | 3.76 | 0 |
| | 0 | 4.99 | | 0 | $-6.04$ |
| | 3.12 | 10 | | 9.99 | 10 |
| | 9.35 | 20 | | 16.22 | 20 |

Accept Experimental Method $A$:     $Y_2 = 3.76 + .623n$
Accept Standard Method $B$:     $Y_1 = -3.11 + .623n$

After examining fifty-eight student files (Column 1), it is found that the "step" curve intersects the lower boundary line between 11 and 12 cumulative number of pairs favorable to either $A$ or $B$, and the sample point is located in the region of "Accept Standard Method $B$." Thus, the decision is made to continue using the standard method $B$.

It might be interesting to note that if the sequential sample were to show alternately the experimental method and the standard method as favorable, the sample points will describe a straight line with the equation of $Y = n/2$. In other

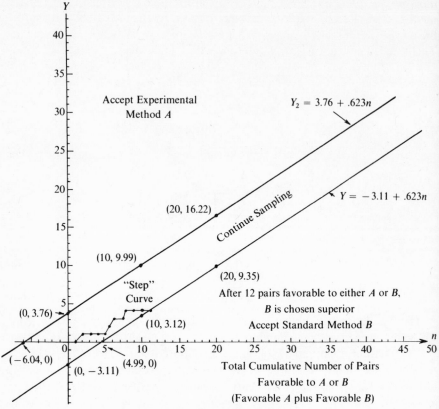

*Figure 16*
*Sequential Analysis Graph of Methods Example*

words, out of every two items found to be favorable to either $A$ or $B$, one is favorable $A$. Thus $Y$, the number of items favorable to $A$, must be half of $n$, the total cumulative number of items favorable to either $A$ or $B$. If this situation existed, that is, where the methods are equally good, we would find that the line $(Y = n/2)$ intersects $(Y_1 = -3.11 + .623\,n)$ where $n = 25.28$, as follows:

$$
\begin{array}{lr}
Y = -3.11 + .623n & (6a'') \\
-Y = \phantom{-3.11}\;0\;\; - .500n & (1) \\
\hline
0 = -3.11 + .123n & \\
\end{array}
$$

$$3.11 = .123n$$
$$25.28 = n$$

This solution indicates that the experimental method would be rejected after $n$ had attained a value of 26.

In closing the discussion of this application of sequential sampling it should be pointed out that a most fundamental part of this approach is the determination of the odds ratios $U_1$ and $U_2$, respectively. The values chosen for these ratios must be adequate and consistent with the limiting conditions of the experimental, or research, situation. This circumstance frequently demands much in the way of preliminary investigation and planning on the part of the researcher. The decision concerning the magnitude of the values to be assigned to $U_1$ and $U_2$, respectively, is a difficult one to make, and can only be reached by a thorough consideration of all statistical and non-statistical factors involved in the problem situation.

*Chapter 18—References*

See Bibliography 2, 3, 15, 36, 37, 48, 49, 91, 93, 129, 137, 161, 178, 179, 194, 195, 196; 22a, 76a, 108a.

*Chapter Nineteen*

# *Estimation*

THE NUMERICAL ASPECTS of the phases of the "adapted" models of educational research dealing with *data processing* and the *research decision* are basically concerned with two types of problems associated with statistical inquiry. The first problem is that of *estimation*, the second is that of *inference*. We are concerned here with the discussion of the problem of *estimation*.

Earlier in our discussions we covered such basic concepts of statistical inquiry as frequency distributions, probability, and sampling. These concepts will prove to be useful in the discussion of the numerical aspects of the educational research models that are involved with the problems associated with statistical estimation.

As one of the illustrations of the application of the normal distribution, we presented an example of how the sampling distribution of the mean for sample size $n$ could be employed to establish a *confidence interval* for an *estimate* $(\overline{X})$ (derived from a sample) of the value of the population mean ($\mu$). The mean of a sample ($\overline{X}$) is but one of many types of *estimates* which can be *derived from individual values* ($X$) *composing a sample* drawn from the population. Other magnitudes *frequently employed* as *estimates* are proportions, aggregates, variances, and standard deviations. The general process of obtaining *estimates*, along with accompanying *errors of estimate* and *confidence intervals*, is called *estimation*.

When a study of the total population is impossible, or unnecessary, to make, knowledge of certain population characteristics (parameters) can be derived by examining their counterpart *estimates* (statistics) computed from values composing a random sample of size $n$. The *estimate* calculated from the sample is used as a substitute for the true but unknown population value (parameter), and theoretically approaches more and more closely the true value of the parameter with increasing sample size. Although it might appear that such estimates are inadequate for the rigorous demands of research, such is not the case if these estimates are kept within permissible operating limits. One of the major jobs of the researcher is to determine the range of variation that is allowable for estimates, and to design the research inquiry so that values of these estimates will occur within the specified limitations with a given probability of occurrence.

The permissible range of error allowable for a given estimate varies with the research problem. The basic criterion is how much random error the research can withstand. In some problems of educational research a 20 per cent error may be condoned, in others a margin of 10 per cent may be tolerated, while in others the permissible deviation from the population value might be 1 per cent or even less. As a general rule, an optimum degree of approximation is the aim of estimation. This objective implies that the estimate should be neither unnecessarily precise—taking into account such factors as, say, cost, level of measurement of the data, and the reliability and validity of the data—nor should it be allowed to occur in such great error that its use would be risky in deriving the research decision.

The error associated with an estimate derived from a random sample can be considered to be made up of two parts. One part is composed of the biased error, while the other is composed of the unbiased error involved. The main source of unbiased error is random sampling. This part of the total error can be controlled by means of a proper sampling design. Biased error arises from different sources, but is constant in direction and is usually associated with the individual observations involved in the research effort. This part of the total error can be controlled by carefully designing and accounting for the methods, instrumentalities, and procedures employed in the phases of data collection and data processing of the model of research. Any other amount of biased error that might occur because of the type of estimate, or the method of estimation being employed, can be eliminated by using a more appropriate method. Neither the biased nor the unbiased error should be ignored. Each type should be reduced in magnitude as much as possible, or at least to the point where the resulting total error falls within limits that can be tolerated by the research.

Under the section dealing with certain numerical aspects of sampling, formulas for computing values of certain estimates, under conditions of the sampling method being discussed, where presented. In each case, estimates were derived from the sample on the basis of some variate, say, $Y$. Under certain circumstances, it is better to avoid making estimates on the basis of $Y$ values alone. If the set of $Y$ values is related to a set of values of $X$, and the relationship is a comparatively good one, then it is possible to estimate the value of $Y$, given a value of $X$. If the case is such that $X$ is a variate that can be estimated with a relatively small error, then good estimates of $Y$ might be made through an equation defined by the pattern of paired points occurring in a stable sample. This method of estimation is accomplished by means of *regression*, a topic we shall discuss later.

It should be noted that whether a single variate, or correlated variates are employed in making estimates, the basic problem is the same—the estimation of a value of a population parameter by means of an estimate derived from values composing a sample. To this point we have emphasized how estimates of population parameters can be made from samples involving values of a single variate. We now turn our attention to the task of making estimates from two or more related variates.

### LINEAR REGRESSION AND CORRELATION

Estimation, whether based upon a random sample of $Y$ values or upon the relation between a set of $X$ values and a set of $Y$ values, is concerned with approximating an unknown population value for some purpose of the research. The derived estimate will be a satisfactory measure of reality only to the extent that the pattern of past data, upon which the estimate was derived, remains approximately stable in the future; or to the extent which the pattern shift, if such occurs, can be anticipated. These conditions compose any rationale for lógical estimation and/or prediction. Prediction in the "exact" sciences is usually highly successful because of the high degree of stability in basic characteristics and their relationships.

It should be pointed out that although $Y$ might be related to $X$, it does not necessarily follow that $X$ is the cause of $Y$, nor that $Y$ is the cause of $X$, although the existence of causality is possible. The relation might be based upon certain common elements or processes, or some third variable (possibly time), or a complex set of elements, variables, and conditions. Even though there is no logical basis for the relationship between $X$ and $Y$, a spurious one may exist because of the time factor. For example, there might well be a correlation between the number of drownings $(X)$ at a particular bathing beach and the amount of the sales of ice cream cones $(Y)$ at the beach's refreshment stand over the course of a given summer. Recognizing these facts, we shall now discuss the nature of correlation and regression.

Correlation indicates the extent to which two series vary concomantly. A coefficient of correlation can be computed when, and only when, scores in two related series are *paired*. For example, the coefficient of correlation between history scores and reading scores can be determined if each student of the class has a score in history and a score in reading. As another example, the scores of a group of boys may be correlated with those of a group of girls if both groups have taken the same test, and we are attempting to determine how closely the two sexes are related on the basis of the proportion of boys and the proportion of girls answering correctly the several items composing the test. In this case, each item of the test would have a pair of scores, the proportion of the boy's group getting the correct answer paired with the proportion of the girl's group getting the correct answer·to the particular question. If it is not possible to bind two series of values by some form of *pairing*, it is not possible to apply methods of correlation in the technical sense of the technique.

Regression techniques are employed to *estimate* (or predict) the values of one variable when the values of the correlated variable are known. Correlation, on the other hand, indicates the degree to which the two variables are related. Regression and correlation techniques are highly related, and differ only in terms of their goals and end results. The process of regression analysis results in an empirically determined *regression equation*, which serves the purpose of a *prediction* "formula." Correlational analysis results in the determination of a *correlation coefficient*, r, the magnitude and algebraic sign of which indicates how the two variables, say, X and Y, are related.

The simplest form of regression analysis deals with the notion of a *positive linear* relationship between the two variables X and Y. To illustrate, suppose we have the following *paired observations* for each of twelve individuals.

| X | Y | X | Y |
|---|---|---|---|
| 9 | 27 | 6 | 18 |
| 10 | 30 | 4 | 12 |
| 7 | 21 | 8 | 24 |
| 1 | 3 | 8 | 24 |
| 5 | 15 | 2 | 6 |
| 4 | 12 | 3 | 9 |

If we consider (X, Y) the paired observations on the *first* individual, we note that the value of Y (27) is three times that of X (9). Similarly, the value of Y (30) is three times that of X (10) in the second case, as well. Examination of the remaining paired values in the table shows that Y is equal to 3X in each case. If this pattern (relationship) were to hold throughout the total group from which these twelve cases were selected, we could determine a given individual's Y-value as soon as we knew his X-value. Thus, because X determines the value of Y in the equation defining the relationship: $Y = 3X$; X is termed the *independent* variable, and Y the *dependent* variable. The general form of this *linear equation* is:

$$Y = bX \qquad (1)$$

where b is a constant (3 in our example) which indicates the slope of the line, and is called the "regression coefficient." Linear equation (1) is one form of a *simple regression equation*.

The graphic representation of the twelve paired observations is a straight line which increases positively, that is, extends upward toward the right. Such an orientation indicates a positive relationship between the variables, and because the graph is one of a straight line, we say that such a graph indicates a *positive linear* relationship.

We have stated that b is the "slope" of the line as well as the regression co-efficient. In analytical geometry, the slope of a line may be found by the formula:

$$b = \text{slope} = \frac{Y_2 - Y_1}{X_2 - X_1}$$

where $(X_2, Y_2)$ and $(X_1, Y_1)$ are the *coordinates* of any two points on the line. To exemplify, suppose we chose the point (8,24) as $(X_2, Y_2)$ and the point (3,9) as $(X_1, Y_1)$. We would find that (see figure);

$$b = \text{slope} = \frac{24 - 9}{8 - 3} = 3$$

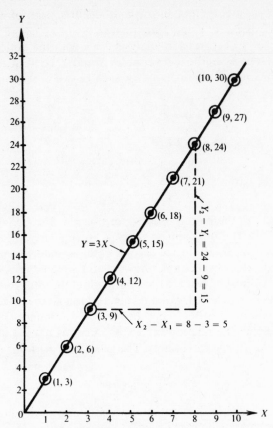

The previous example illustrated the "simplest" form of the regression equation ($Y = bX$), a line which passes through the origin $(0,0)$ of the $X$- and $Y$-axes. We now consider the case where the line has a $Y$-intercept different from $(0,0)$, that is, the line intersects the $Y$-axis at any point other than $(0,0)$. The $Y$-intercept is denoted by the letter $a$ and modifies equation (1) into the form:

$$Y = a + bX \tag{2}$$

The relationship indicated by (2) is still a linear one, but now includes *two* constants: $b$ the regression coefficient slope; and $a$ the $Y$-intercept of the line. To illustrate, we present another set of paired observations of twelve individuals.

| X | Y | X | Y |
|---|---|---|---|
| 9 | 21 | 6 | 15 |
| 10 | 23 | 4 | 11 |
| 7 | 17 | 8 | 19 |
| 1 | 5 | 8 | 19 |
| 5 | 13 | 2 | 7 |
| 4 | 11 | 3 | 9 |

The relationship between $X$ and $Y$ is still a positive linear one, but its mathematical pattern may not be as evident as that of the first example. The relationship this time is:

$$Y = 2X + 3$$

If we examine $(X_1, Y_1)$, we see that:

$$Y = 2(9) + 3 = 21$$

and in similar fashion we could find each of the respective values of $Y$ in the table. Graphically, the equation $Y = 2X + 3$ appears as shown below:

$$b = \frac{19 - 9}{8 - 3} = 2$$

$$a = 3$$

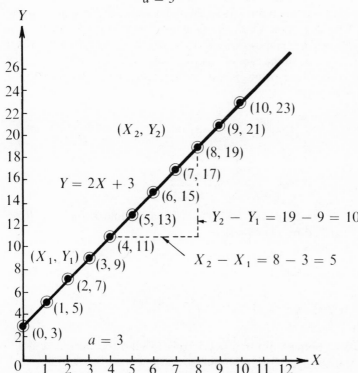

In summary, we note that the general equation of a positive linear relationship is:

$$Y = a + bX; \quad \text{or} \quad Y = bX + a$$

where $a$ is a constant and indicates the point where the regression line intersects the $Y$-axis; $b$ is a constant which indicates the ratio of "rise" to "run," or slope, of the curve, and is called the "regression coefficient." We can find a value for

$Y$ by multiplying its corresponding value of $X$ by $b$ and adding the value of the constant $a$. In the particular case where the regression line passes through the origin of both axes, the point $(0, 0)$, the value of the constant $a$ in equation (2) becomes 0, and the resulting equation of the regression line becomes equation (1):

$$Y = bX$$

### Negative Linear Relationships

To this point we have discussed only positive linear relationships between the two variables $X$ and $Y$. Linear relationships between $X$ and $Y$, however, are frequently not positive, hence it is necessary to know something about *negative linear relationships*. Once the basic idea of positive linear relationship is mastered, that of the negative relationship is easily understood. A negative linear relationship exists when the regression coefficient (slope) of the line, $b$, is negative and the line representing the regression decreases positively, that is, with an increasing value of $X$, the value of $Y$ decreases. A line depicting the negative relationship slopes downward from left to right rather than upward from left to right, as in the case of positive relationship. To illustrate, we present a table of paired observations for five individuals, and an accompanying graph of the regression line.

| $X$ | $Y$ |
|---|---|
| 3 | 3 |
| 2 | 4 |
| 5 | 1 |
| 4 | 2 |
| 6 | 0 |

The relationship between $X$ and $Y$ is a negative linear one, and follows the pattern prescribed by the equation:

$$Y = -X + 6$$

$$b = \text{slope} = \frac{3 - 1}{3 - 5} = \frac{2}{-2} = -1$$

$$a = 6$$

It should be pointed out that not all relationships between $X$ and $Y$ in a bivariate population are linear. Nonlinear patterns relating $X$ and $Y$ may occur relatively frequently. When such cases do occur, the regression equation is not that of a straight line. Some of the nonlinear forms which have been employed are: the parabola $(Y = bX^2)$; the hyperbola $[(Y = 1/(a + bX)$; and $Y = X/(a + bX)]$; power functions $(Y = aX^3)$; and exponentials $(Y = ce^{aX})$; and $(Y = ab^X)$. All of these nonlinear forms can be transformed into the linear form $(Y = a + bX)$. Since nonlinear forms have rather limited occurrence in educational research, we shall deal only with the linear equation form at this point of our discussion. Later we discuss briefly certain factors of nonlinear

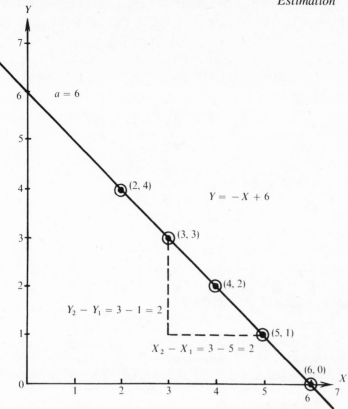

regression and correlation. For those who may be interested in a more detailed discussion of nonlinear forms than those presented here, Rosander[1] has accorded the topics an excellent treatment through a discussion of the "least square principle applied to nonlinear patterns," and "estimates from correlated variates—nonlinear regression and correlation."

### The Principle of Least Squares

In our previous examples the paired observations "fit" the linear pattern perfectly and were located exactly on the straight line of the equation form ($Y = a + bX$). Under such conditions the values of $a$ and $b$ were easily determined, and the specific linear regression equation was derived. Perfect prediction conditions rarely exist in research situations. The condition which does occur quite frequently, however, is the one in which the paired observations $(X, Y)$ show a general tendency to fall along (but not necessarily upon) a particular straight line. The problem associated with such a condition is that of finding the equation of the regression line that *best fits* the paired observations. In order to obtain an equation for the unique straight line that best fits a set of paired observations $X$ and $Y$, some criterion must be established whereby a *best* value of $a$ and of $b$ in the equation ($Y = a + bX$) may be computed from the jointly observed values of $X$ and $Y$. The *principle of least squares* provides such a criterion *by minimizing the total sum of squares of the deviations of the paired observations (points) from the "trend" line to be fitted to the data.*

To help clarify the explanation of the application of the *least squares method* we use the *paired observations* for each of eight individuals shown in the table and graph below.

| $X$ | $X^2$ | $Y$ | $Y^2$ | $XY$ |
|---|---|---|---|---|
| 9 | 81 | 17 | 289 | 153 |
| 7 | 49 | 19 | 361 | 133 |
| 1 | 1 | 7 | 49 | 7 |
| 5 | 25 | 9 | 81 | 45 |
| 4 | 16 | 10 | 100 | 40 |
| 3 | 9 | 8 | 64 | 24 |
| 8 | 64 | 14 | 196 | 112 |
| 2 | 4 | 3 | 9 | 6 |
| 39 | 249 | 87 | 1149 | 520 |

The expression for each *vertical deviation* of a point from the straight line for a given value $X$; is $Y_i - (a + bX_i)$. Thus, the mathematical expression to be minimized by means of the calculus is:

$$\sum (Y_i - a - bX_i)^2$$

To obtain the values of the two "unknowns" $a$ and $b$, the normal equations* resulting from minimizing,† with respect to $a$ and $b$, the expression $\sum (Y_i - a - bX_i)^2$ are employed and solved simultaneously. The two equations are:

$$\sum Y_i = na + b\sum X_i$$
$$\sum X_i Y_i = a\sum X_i + b\sum X_i^2 \tag{3}$$

From equations (3), we derive the following expressions for $a$ and $b$:

$$a = \frac{\sum Y_i \sum X_i^2 - \sum X_i \sum X_i Y_i}{n\sum X_i^2 - (\sum X_i)^2}$$
$$b = \frac{n\sum X_i Y_i - \sum X_i \sum Y_i}{n\sum X_i^2 - (\sum X_i)^2} \tag{4}$$

For our example, the values of $a$ and $b$ become:

$$a = \frac{(87)(249) - (39)(520)}{(8)(249) - (39)^2} = \frac{21,663 - 20,280}{1992 - 1521} = \frac{1383}{471} \approx 2.93$$

$$b = \frac{(8)(520) - (39)(87)}{(8)(249) - (39)^2} = \frac{4160 - 3393}{1992 - 1521} = \frac{767}{471} \approx 1.63$$

and the equation of the regression line is: $Y = 2.93 + 1.63X$.

---

* *Sets* of equations like those shown in (3) are often called "normal equations."

† "Minimizing" is an operation associated with the topics of "maxima" and "minima" found in differential calculus. In this case "minimizing" specifically refers to the partial differentiation of $\sum (Y_i - a - bX_i)^2$ with respect to the parameters $a$ and $b$, respectively. For further explanation of the process see the sections of any calculus book dealing with the topics of "maxima" and "minima."

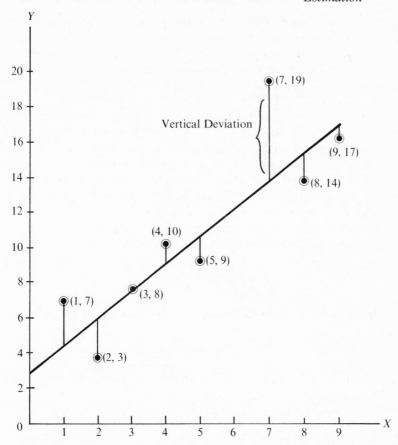

When the sum of squares of the *horizontal deviations* are employed instead of the vertical deviations, a different equation, and hence a different straight line, is found, except in the unique case in which there is a perfect one-to-one relation between $X$ and $Y$ (i.e., $X = Y$). If the sum of the squares of the *vertical deviations approach* is employed, we find the form of the equation $Y = a + bX$ to be the line of best fit. If the *horizontal deviations approach* is used, we would find the form of the equation to be: $X = a + bY$. The latter equation is found by *minimizing* the *horizontal deviations* between the points and the line being *fit*, applying the appropriate calculus differentiation to the quantity $\sum (X_i - a - bY_i)^2$, where $b$ is once again the slope of the trend line, this time $a$ is the $X$-intercept of the line, and $X$ and $Y$ are as previously defined in connection with the *vertical deviations* approach.

Each of the lines, $Y = a + bX$, and $X = a + bY$ can be rewritten in the following forms:

$$Y - \bar{Y} = b_{YX}(X - \bar{X}) \tag{5}$$

$$X - \bar{X} = b_{XY}(Y - \bar{Y}) \tag{6}$$

where in (5) $b_{YX}$ is the slope of the line, $\overline{X}$ and $\overline{Y}$ are the arithmetic means of the respective sets of $X$ and $Y$ values, and the subscript $YX$ attached to $b$ shows that $b$ is the *slope* of the regression of $Y$ on $X$ line, since $Y$ is being estimated for a fixed value of $X$. The line defined by equation (6) is called the "regression of $X$ on $Y$," since $X$ is being estimated for a fixed $Y$. This situation accounts for the subscript $XY$ being affixed to $b$ in the equation. The values $b_{YX}$ and $b_{XY}$ are, in general, not the same (only in the unique case of $Y = X$). *Ordinarily the vertical deviations form of the regression line is employed*, hence the subscript of $b$ is usually not attached. Usually the *horizontal deviations* regression line is not calculated, because it is known at the outset of most estimating problems which variate is to be estimated, and which is to be assigned fixed values. With this knowledge the estimated (dependent) variate is usually designated by $Y$ and the assigned values (independent) variate is denoted by $X$.

If we had chosen to write the regression equation of our example in the form of (5), that is, the *score form of the equation*, we would have:

$$Y - \overline{Y} = b(X - \overline{X})$$

$$Y - 10.875 = 1.63(X - 4.875)$$

If we perform indicated operations and solve for $Y$, we would find our original equation:

$$Y = 1.63X + 2.93$$

We note from the foregoing discussion that the principle of least squares is basically the notion that a *line best fits its data when the sum of the squares of the* "*misses*" (*errors*) *is a minimum*. The principle can be employed in connection with *vertical deviations* (misses), or in terms of *horizontal deviations* (misses). Although either the *vertical* or *horizontal deviation* approach may be employed, and with the exception of one case ($Y = X$), will result in different regression equations, the vertical approach is the one which is applied most frequently. With these points clearly in mind we shall now discuss *the standard error of estimate*.

## The Standard Error of Estimate

When the value of $Y$ is predicted from equation (5) on the basis of some assigned (or given) value of $X$, it could be considered the *most probable value* of $Y$ for that particular value of $X$ under the empirical conditions described by the equation. If the process of estimating one variable based upon its relationship to the other variable is to be a useful device in the research process, it is necessary to know just how probable such estimates are. Probably the best device for determining the accuracy with which a variable can be estimated (predicted) from the regression equation is that of the *standard error of estimate*.

The error in the prediction (estimation) of the value of $Y$ depends upon the extent to which the quantity $(Y - a - bX)^2$ *is capable of being minimized* by the least squares method. We have already seen that if the relationship between $Y$ and $X$ is perfect, that is, all of the points fall on the regression line, the value of the quantity $(Y - a - bX)^2$, becomes zero, the perfect minimum. As the value of the quantity $(Y - a - bX)^2$, called the "*residual sum of squares*," becomes larger, the prediction of values of $Y$ for assigned values of $X$ becomes progressively poorer. Put in another way, as the points *scatter* on the graph of the line, and thus the deviations between the points and the straight line of best fit increase, the predictions (estimations) of $Y$ become worse.

If we divide the *residual sum of squares* by $n - 2$, we have the formula for the *error variance*:

$$S^2_{(\text{est } Y)} = \frac{(Y - a - bX)^2}{n - 2} \tag{7}$$

where $S^2_{(\text{est } Y)}$ indicates the error variance (sometimes referred to as *residual variance*), $Y, a, b,$ and $X$ are as defined in the regression equation of $Y$ on $X$, $n - 2$ indicates the number of paired observations in the sample less 2, and is employed as a correction for bias in the estimation of the *population value* of the error variance.

If we take the square root of (5) we have one form of the formula for the *standard error of estimate*:

$$S_{(\text{est } Y)} = \sqrt{\frac{\sum(Y - a - bX)^2}{n - 2}} \tag{8}$$

Although this quantity is derived from a bivariate distribution $(X, Y)$, it corresponds to the standard deviation of a univariate distribution. The standard error of estimate given by (8) indicates the dispersion (vertical deviations) of the *observed values* of $Y$ around the estimated regression line of $Y$ on $X$. If the distribution of the observed $Y$ values about the regression line is normal, then approximately 68 per cent of them are within one plus or minus (vertical deviation) $S_{(\text{est } Y)}$ of the line.

In summary, we have seen that $S_{(\text{est } Y)}$ will be zero if the relationship between $X$ and $Y$ is a perfect one. In this case all observed values of $Y$ will be on the regression line of $Y$ on $X$, there will be no error in the prediction (estimation) of $Y$ values, and no extra residual variance after $Y$ is estimated from $X$. In the case of the "perfect fit," $X$ *accounts for all the variance in Y.* When the observed values began to *scatter*, the relationship is no longer perfect, and $X$ *does not account for all the variance in Y.* This condition indicates that some other source of variation such as measurement error, sampling error, or even that of another unaccounted-for variable, or a combination of these factors, is at work. The larger the magnitude of the error variance, the greater the unaccounted-for variance. This fact is merely pointed out at this time, but will have great significance for topics which we shall discuss later.

A computational formula for finding the error variance $(S^2_{(\text{est } Y)})$, and the standard error of estimate $(S_{(\text{est } Y)})$, *which avoids the laborious task* of summing the squared vertical deviations of the observed points from the regression line and then dividing by $n - 2$, is as follows:

$$S^2_{(\text{est } Y)} = \frac{[\sum Y^2 - (\sum Y)^2/n] - b[\sum XY - (\sum X)(\sum Y)/n]}{n - 2} \tag{9}$$

For the example that we have been employing as an illustration, the "error" variance, and the standard error of estimate, are:

$$S^2_{(est\ Y)} = \frac{[1149 - (87)^2/8] - 1.63\,[520 - (39)(87)/8]}{8 - 2}$$

$$= \frac{(1149 - 946.125) - 1.63(520 - 424.125)}{6}$$

$$= \frac{46.599}{6} = 7.7665$$

and the standard error of estimate becomes:

$$S_{(est\ Y)} = \sqrt{7.7665} \approx 2.79$$

The computational formula (9) provides a technical description of the error variance. The error variance consists of the *total variance of the Y*'s less that part of the total variance which is accounted for by the relation of the $Y$'s to $X$. The closer the relationship between $Y$ and $X$, the greater the amount of variance accounted for by $X$. From this fact it follows that as $X$ accounts for more and more of the variance, then less of it is left over for residual variance, hence the error variance becomes smaller.

### CORRELATION

In regression analysis, $Y$ may be assumed to be dependent upon $X$, or $X$ dependent upon $Y$, and the problem involved is that of finding the equation of the regression line which will give us a predicted, or estimated, value of the one variable (dependent variable) when we know the value of the other (independent variable). The error variance of the regression line of $Y$ on $X$ indicates how much of the variance in $Y$ is explained by $X$ alone, and suggests, therefore, the amount of relationship existing between $X$ and $Y$. It should be noted, however, that the error variance of the regression line of $Y$ on $X$ is not usually the same as the error variance for the regression line of $X$ on $Y$. We have only discussed and given formulas for the error variance of the line $Y$ on $X$.

If for some reason we wished to avoid designating which variate, $X$ or $Y$, was the *dependent* one, we would be forced to take into account both error variances, $Y$ on $X$, and $X$ on $Y$. In order to distinguish the two error variances, we employ the symbol $(S^2_{(est\ Y)})$ for $Y$ on $X$, and the symbol $(S^2_{(est\ X)})$ for $X$ on $Y$. Problems associated with educational research frequently call for investigating the *association* of two variates without designating the dependency (or independency) of the respective variates. In most situations of this type a measure of the degree of *mutual relationship* between the two variates is sought. The *coefficient of correlation* is computed as the desired measure of mutual relationship.

If the data are of *interval level of measurement* (see pages 71–77) the value of the *product-moment correlation coefficient*, symbolized by $r$, is calculated to indicate the mutual relationship between $X$ and $Y$. The value of $r$ ranges between

+ 1.00 and − 1.00 inclusive. When $r = -1.00$, there exists a condition of *perfect negative correlation* between $X$ and $Y$. This type of relationship indicates that when $X$ increases, $Y$ decreases. When $r = 0$, there is a condition of *no correlation* existing between $X$ and $Y$. When $r = +1.00$, there is a condition of *perfect positive correlation* existing, which means that when $X$ increases, $Y$ increases.

The computation of a correlation coefficient, as in the case of regression, demands that paired observations $(X, Y)$ for the same individual be present in the bivariate distribution. The product-moment correlation coefficient may be thought of as a ratio which indicates the extent to which changes in one variable are accompanied by changes in a second variable. This ratio will not be a stable measure of relationship if it varies in value with different units of measurement employed in connection with the variates $X$ and $Y$. In order to avoid this difficulty of differences in units, each value of the variate ($X$ or $Y$) is expressed in terms of its deviation from the mean of its distribution, that is,

$$x = (X - \overline{X}); \tag{10}$$

and

$$y = (Y - \overline{Y})$$

The deviation values $x$, and $y$, for each original value of $X$ and $Y$, respectively, are then converted into standard measures (i.e., "unit free" measures), by dividing each $x$ and each $y$ by its own standard deviation, ($s_x$) and ($s_y$), respectively. The standard measures, in formula form, become:

$$Z_x = \frac{x}{s_x}; \quad \text{and} \quad Z_y = \frac{y}{s_y}$$

The sum of the *products* of the standard measures for each *pair of observations*, divided by $n$, the number of paired observations present, will yield a ratio which *is a stable expression of relationship*. This ratio is the product-moment coefficient of correlation, and is a measure of relationship which remains constant no matter in what units $X$ and $Y$ are expressed. Symbolically, the coefficient appears as follows:

$$r = \frac{\sum (Z_x Z_y)}{n}$$

substituting for $Z_x$ and $Z_y$, we find:

$$r = \frac{\sum (x/s_x \cdot y/s_y)}{n}$$

performing indicated algebraic operations, we find:

$$r = \frac{\sum xy}{n s_x s_y} \tag{11}$$

Since: $s_x = \sqrt{\sum x^2/n}$; and $s_y = \sqrt{\sum y^2/n}$; we have by substituting in (11), and performing indicated operations:

$$r = \frac{\sum xy}{\sqrt{\sum x^2 \sum y^2}} \qquad (12)$$

a commonly employed expression for $r$, where $x$ and $y$ are defined as in (10), and $\sum x^2$ is the sum of the squares of the deviations of the $X$ distribution; and $\sum y^2$ is the sum of the squares of the deviations of the $Y$ distribution.

We note that although formula (12) is expressed in terms of deviations from the mean ($x$ and $y$ instead of $X$ and $Y$), it still involves the sum of products and the sum of squares of the $X$ and $Y$ distributions. This expression shows that the formula has still taken into account the *joint variability* of $X$ and $Y$, and their *independent variability*, as it should.

*Suggested Procedure and Formula for Computing r—Ungrouped Data*

In order to demonstrate a *suggested procedure and computation formula* for determining the value of $r$, we employ the same paired observations for each of eight individuals that were used to demonstrate the method of least squares. It should be noted at this point, however, that in actual practice at least twenty-five cases are considered necessary to compute a reasonably *reliable value of the product-moment correlation coefficient.* We use only eight cases in our example so that the elements of correlation to be explained can be more easily emphasized, and will not be lost in the details of the computational formula and procedures.

| $X$ | $X^2$ | $Y$ | $Y^2$ | $XY$ |
|-----|-------|-----|-------|------|
| 9 | 81 | 17 | 289 | 153 |
| 7 | 49 | 19 | 361 | 133 |
| 1 | 1 | 7 | 49 | 7 |
| 5 | 25 | 9 | 81 | 45 |
| 4 | 16 | 10 | 100 | 40 |
| 3 | 9 | 8 | 64 | 24 |
| 8 | 64 | 14 | 196 | 112 |
| 2 | 4 | 3 | 9 | 6 |
| 39 | 249 | 87 | 1149 | 520 |

The suggested computational formula for $r$ for ungrouped data is the "raw score" form, and is as follows:

$$r = \frac{n\sum XY - (\sum X)(\sum Y)}{\sqrt{[n\sum X^2 - (\sum X)^2][n\sum Y^2 - (\sum Y)^2]}} \qquad (13)$$

The numerator of the formula represents a modification of the covariance, which measures the amount of variance of $X$ and $Y$ together. The denominator of the formula represents modifications of the sums of squares of the $X$ and $Y$ distributions, respectively. These terms measure the amount each observation varies from the mean of its distribution. This expression shows that the computational formula preserves the notion that the correlation coefficient is a ratio of covariation to independent variation.

The value of the correlation coefficient for the data in the example is:

$$r = \frac{(8)(520) - (39)(87)}{\sqrt{[(8)(249) - (39)^2][(8)(1149) - (87)^2]}} = \frac{767}{\sqrt{(471)(1623)}} = \frac{767}{874.5}$$

$$= .877$$

With this background, the relationship between the correlation coefficient $r$ and the regression coefficient $b$ (slope) of the regression line can be discussed in more meaningful fashion than heretofore possible. Equations (14) and (15) show the relationships:

$$b_{YX} = r \frac{s_Y}{s_X} \tag{14}$$

$$b_{XY} = r \frac{s_X}{s_Y} \tag{15}$$

where $r$ is the Pearson product-moment correlation coefficient computed from the sample of paired observations $(X, Y)$, and $s_X$ and $s_Y$ are standard deviation estimates computed from the respective series of $X$ and $Y$ values composing the sample of paired observations. It is interesting to note that it is necessary to differentiate between the *regression coefficients*, $b_{YX}$ and $b_{XY}$, but that the correlation coefficient $r$ is the same value for both situations and therefore appears unchanged in both (14) and (15). This situation provides further evidence of the point that in a *correlation problem* a population is sampled, *observing two measurements on each individual in the sample*; while in a problem dealing purely with regression, the sample of paired observations is chosen with *preassigned values* of, say, the $X$ variate. Put in another way, the regression problem considers the frequency distribution of one variable when another is held fixed (is assigned values) at each of several levels. The correlation problem considers the *joint variation of two* measurements, neither of which is restricted by the researcher.

*The Interpretation of the Pearson Product-Moment Correlation Coefficient r*

There are three basic principles for interpreting the value of a correlation coefficient, $r$. The *first principle* is concerned with the fact that although $r$ measures association, it in no way gives any information about cause and effect. Since causality depends upon some type of time ordering of variables, and correlation ignores this factor, $r$ cannot indicate cause and effect. It should be remembered that the process of computing a value of the correlation coefficient only quantifies a relationship that previously existed. Of particular importance is the fact that a relationship of a certain type may exist only within certain limits, and must be examined to ascertain whether it might be linear or non-linear. The data must also be analyzed to determine if some intervening variable may be causing the association. In general, the pattern of association must be analyzed logically if any statement pertaining to significant factors, variables, or other elements of causality is to be made. The correlation coefficient, in and of itself, does not provide such information.

The *second principle* deals with the role of $r$ in determining the amount of variation in $X$ and $Y$ that is accounted for by their mutual relationship. This information is obtained by "squaring" $r$. Thus, the value of $r^2$, called the *coefficient of determination*, shows the proportion of variation which is based upon the relationship of $X$ and $Y$. To illustrate, if $r = .80$, then only $(.80)^2 = 64$ per cent of the total variation in $X$ and $Y$ is based upon their mutual relationship.

The correlation coefficient $r$ represents an *average* of paired standard scores $(Z_x, Z_y)$. As a generalized measure, $r$ can be useful for predicting (estimating) group performance. The prediction (estimation) of *individual* performance based upon one of a pair of correlated variates is rarely satisfactory. The *Index of Forecasting Efficiency* is a means of computing the probable accuracy of prediction for any value of $r$. The formula is:

$$E = 100 \left(1 - \sqrt{1 - r^2}\right)$$

where $\sqrt{1 - r^2}$ is *the coefficient of alienation*, and may be thought of as measuring the *absence* of relationship between the paired observations $(X, Y)$ in the same sense that $r^2$ measures the *presence* of relationship.

The Index of Forecasting Efficiency indicates the percent of improvement in the predictive ability of $r$ over a pure chance "guess." To examine a few values of $r$, we find:

| $r$ | $E(\%)$ | |
|---|---|---|
| .10 | .5 | |
| .30 | 4.6 | |
| .50 | 13.4 | |
| .70 | 28.6 | |
| .80 | 40.5 | |
| (.867) | (50.0) | Note: $r = .867$ provides only 50 per cent improvement over pure "guess." |
| .90 | 56.4 | |
| .95 | 68.8 | |
| 1.00 | 100.0 | |

From this array we note that unless $r = \pm 1.00$, the estimate of *individual* performance based upon $Y$ is not accurate enough to be useful. The higher values of $r$, however, might be useful in predicting *group* performance.

The term "guess" as used here does not mean that the estimation is based upon no information whatsoever. It should be remembered that when $r = 0.00$, the most probable $Y$-value estimated for every value in the $X$-distribution is $\overline{Y}$ within the limits of $(S_Y)$. In this sense, $Y$-estimates are "guesses" to the extent that they *may* fall anywhere within the given $Y$-distribution. In general, the significance of the magnitude of the value of the correlation coefficient depends upon: (1) the nature of the related factors, (2) the number of paired values involved, (3) the range of the values of the data, and (4) the purpose underlying the employment of the measure.

The *third basic principle* in the interpretation of the correlation coefficient $r$ lies in the fact that it measures only the linear relationship between two variates $(X, Y)$. If $r$ is used to measure a non-linear relationship, it will underestimate the degree of relationship, and will give other forms of misleading information. The correlation coefficient $r$ gives *only* the amount of *straight line* relationship between $X$ and $Y$. Other types of measures are employed in cases where the relationship is curvilinear. The case of curvilinear (nonlinear) correlation and regression will be discussed briefly later.

Distantly related to the three basic principles of the interpretation of $r$ is the *test for independence.*

## Test for Independence

A hypothesis frequently tested in regression and correlation analysis is that the variate $Y$ is independent of the variate $X$, and if such a condition is true, then $r$, which is an estimate of $\rho$, the population correlation coefficient, is close to (or equal to) zero. If the two variables are independent, the regression lines, $Y$ on $X$, and $X$ on $Y$, will be vertical and horizontal straight lines, respectively. This condition would indicate that the value of the population correlation coefficient, $\rho$, and its estimate $r$, would be equal to zero.

The test for independence becomes important to the extent that an estimate $Y$, in order to be made from a correlated variate $X$, should be sufficiently related to $X$ so that the standard error of estimate associated with $Y$ defines limits for values of $Y$ that occur well within the limits tolerated by the research. Put in another way, if $r$, which estimates $\rho$, is close to zero, the hypothesis of the independence of $Y$ and $X$ *would not be rejected*, while if $r$ is of such magnitude that it is considered "statistically significantly different" from zero, the hypothesis of the independence *would be rejected*, and it could be assumed that $Y$ and $X$ are dependent (related). In the first case, we would conclude that $Y$ estimates *could not be made from X values*; in the latter case, however, $Y$ *estimates could be made from X values.*

The actual method of deciding whether to reject, or not reject, the hypothesis of the independence of $Y$ and $X$ (or the hypothesis that the correlation coefficient of the population is zero), will be covered later under the topic of inference. For the present it suffices to know that in order to estimate $Y$ from $X$, it is necessary that the relationship between the variables be of such magnitude that estimated values of $Y$ and their accompanying standard errors of estimate fall within limits tolerated by the research.

With this background in the related subjects of correlation and regression, we are now prepared to discuss certain features and methods of these topics which will have particular utility in the application of the suggested general model to certain types of problems in educational research.

*Chapter  19—References*
See Bibliography: 4, 7, 8, 18, 19, 23, 27, 40, 41, 42, 43, 49, 52, 53, 54, 62, 69, 71, 76, 77, 87, 89, 90, 93, 94, 97, 108, 109, 112, 118, 122, 123, 126, 128, 131, 133, 136, 141, 146, 148, 153, 155, 156, 157, 159, 163, 165, 169, 170, 174, 175, 180, 181, 182, 183, 184, 185, 190, 197, 198, 199, 200; 7a, 11a, 30a, 68a, 76a, 84a, 91a, 95a, 100a, 110a, 116a.

# *Further Methods of Correlation and Regression*

To This Point, we have been concerned with the linear, or product-moment correlation method, and its accompanying regression equations from which values of one variable could be estimated (predicted) on the basis of the value of the other. The product moment correlation coefficient is useful in education, primarily as a measure of the relationship between test scores and other measures of performance. We know that test scores can be treated as *interval data*, a series of determinations of a continuous variate measured along a precisely defined numerical scale. Situations arise in educational research, however, where the data are of *categorical* and/or *ordinal* level of measurement. In such cases, a continuous variate, say, Y, which requires that data be of the *interval level of measurement*, cannot be employed. Other measures of correlation are needed in such situations. At the same time, there are those problems in educational research in which the relationship between the paired observations is *non-linear*, and hence cannot be described by a linear measure, say, *r*. In these types of problems, other methods of determining correlation must be employed. The purpose of this discussion is to present some of the correlational techniques that are employed when the data are of the nominal and/or ordinal scale of measurement; and are to be analyzed for relationship.

## The Rank Correlation Coefficient $(\rho_s)$

A simple type of analysis, appropriate when a *relatively small number* (fewer than thirty pairs) *of observations* (e.g. scores, or ranks) *are investigated for relationship*, is that of the *method of rank differences*. The variates are expressed in terms of rank orders, rather than in their original levels of measurement. The formula is:

$$\rho_s = 1 - \frac{6\sum D^2}{n(n^2 - 1)} \tag{1}$$

To compute the rank correlation coefficient, we begin by making a list of the *n* subjects (see figures below). Next to the observation for each subject, enter his rank for the X variable and his rank for the Y variable. Determine the value D for each subject, found by taking the difference between his X-rank and Y-rank values. For example, the difference for subject A is: $D_a = 9 - 8 = 1$; for B: $D_b = 5 - 7 = -2$, and so on, for each subject. Each value of D is

| Subject | (X) Socio-Economic Rank | (Y) Reading Ability Rank | $D^2$ |
|---------|--------------------------|---------------------------|-------|
| A | 9 | 8 | 1 |
| B | 5 | 7 | 4 |
| C | 6 | 9 | 9 |
| D | 10 | 10 | 0 |
| E | 2 | 4 | 4 |
| F | 3 | 2 | 1 |
| G | 4 | 3 | 1 |
| H | 8 | 6 | 4 |
| I | 7 | 5 | 4 |
| J | 1 | 1 | 0 |

$$\sum D^2 = 28$$

"squared" and the sum of the $D^2$ values (i.e., $\sum D^2$) is obtained. After this value is determined, it is substituted, along with the value of $n$, into the appropriate point of formula (1), to obtain a value for $\rho_s$. For our example:

$$\rho_s = 1 - \frac{6(28)}{10(100 - 1)}$$

$$\rho_s = 1 - .17 = .83$$

The method of rank differences permits a pictorial representation that is illustrative of the general meaning of correlation. In the first case presented below, each subject received the *same* rank in the $Y$ variate as he did in the $X$ variate, a situation which produces a *perfect positive correlation* (i.e., $\rho_s = +1.00$).

| Subject | Rank in X Variate | Rank in Y Variate | $D^2$ |
|---------|-------------------|-------------------|-------|
| A | 1 ⟷ 1 | | 0 |
| B | 2 ⟷ 2 | | 0 |
| C | 3 ⟷ 3 | | 0 |
| D | 4 ⟷ 4 | | 0 |
| E | 5 ⟷ 5 | | 0 |
| F | 6 ⟷ 6 | | 0 |
| G | 7 ⟷ 7 | | 0 |

$$\sum D^2 = 0$$

Suppose, now, that the subject who ranked highest in the $X$-variate ranked lowest in the $Y$-variate. The subject who ranked second highest in $X$ was next to the lowest rank in the *Y* variate, and so on throughout the list of subjects. This situation produces a representation of a *perfect negative correlation* ($\rho_s = -1.00$), as follows:

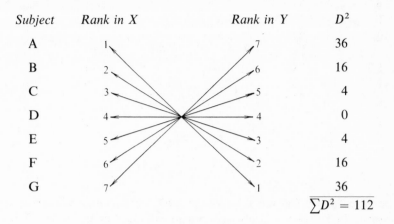

| Subject | Rank in X | Rank in Y | $D^2$ |
|---------|-----------|-----------|-------|
| A | 1 | 7 | 36 |
| B | 2 | 6 | 16 |
| C | 3 | 5 | 4 |
| D | 4 | 4 | 0 |
| E | 5 | 3 | 4 |
| F | 6 | 2 | 16 |
| G | 7 | 1 | 36 |
| | | | $\sum D^2 = 112$ |

In the third case, the rank of a subject in the *X*-variate has very little relationship to his rank in the *Y*-variate. In this situation, the value of the correlation coefficient is low, and the value of $\rho_s$ is near zero (in our example, $\rho_s = .00$).

| Subject | Rank in X | Rank in Y | $D^2$ |
|---------|-----------|-----------|-------|
| A | 1 | 4 | 9 |
| B | 2 | 3 | 1 |
| C | 3 | 6 | 9 |
| D | 4 | 2 | 4 |
| E | 5 | 7 | 4 |
| F | 6 | 1 | 25 |
| G | 7 | 5 | 4 |
| | | | $\sum D^2 = 56$ |

It should be noted that $\rho_s$, the *rank correlation coefficient*, is a measure of association which requires that the paired observations be measured in at least an ordinal scale of measurement so that the objects, or subjects, under study may be ranked in two ordered series. If two or more subjects have the same values (e.g., tie scores) in the original set of scores, each individual is assigned the mean rank position of the tie score.

To illustrate how "tied scores" are treated:

| Subject | Original X Score | Rank | Original Y Score | Rank | $D^2$ |
|---------|------------------|------|------------------|------|-------|
| A | 93 | 1 | 76 | 1.5 | .25 |
| B | 87 | 2.5 | 76 | 1.5 | 1 |
| C | 87 | 2.5 | 72 | 4 | 2.25 |
| D | 71 | 4 | 72 | 4 | 0 |
| E | 70 | 5.5 | 72 | 4 | 2.25 |
| F | 70 | 5.5 | 68 | 6 | .25 |
| G | 65 | 7 | 67 | 7 | 0 |

$$\sum D^2 = 6$$

$$\rho_s = 1 - \frac{(6)(6)}{7(48)} = .893$$

It should be noted that the value of the rank correlation coefficient $\rho_s$ will be spuriously high when a sizable proportion of each of the series of original scores are tied, thus necessitating the assignment of a considerable number of tied ranks. In our example, the $X$-series included four tied scores, i.e., two pairs of two tied scores, of the original seven scores, that necessitated the assignment of appropriate tied ranks to each of the "pairs." The $Y$-series included five tied scores, or two sub-sets, one of three tied scores the other of two tied scores, that required appropriate tied ranks to be assigned to each of the sub-sets. When the tied scores involve more than 30 per cent of their respective series ($X$ or $Y$), or distribution, the magnitude of the value of $\rho_s$ should be interpreted cautiously.

When the value of a rank correlation coefficient is calculated from less than thirty "paired" cases, the results should be generalized with reservation. On any occasion when the sample upon which the value of the rank correlation coefficient is based is not very large, interpretive statements should only be made after careful, logical analysis of the total situation or pattern.

The difference between the values of the rank correlation coefficient $\rho_s$ and its equivalent product moment correlation coefficient $r$ is so small, that for *most* purposes, the value of a given $\rho_s$ may be assumed to be equal to that of the "corresponding" $r$. The formula for translating values of $\rho_s$ into values of $r$ is trigonometric, and is as follows:

$$r = 2 \sin\left(\frac{\pi}{6}\rho_s\right) \tag{2}$$

where "sin" denotes the sine function of the angle $[(\pi/6)\rho_s]$; $\pi$ is expressed, as is $\rho_s$, in radian measure, and is equivalent to $180°$; and $r$ and $\rho_s$ are as previously defined. To illustrate how the formula may be employed, suppose that we wish to find the value of $r$ which is equivalent to that of $\rho_s = -.50$.

Substituting values in the appropriate places of formula (2), we would find:

$$r = 2 \sin\left[\frac{180°}{6}(.5)\right] = 2 \sin[(30°)(.5)] = 2 \sin 15° = 2(.25882)$$

$$r = -.51764$$

where the value for "sin 15°" is read from a table of values for "natural" trigonometric functions, and the algebraic sign $(-)$ is prefixed to the value of $r$ because $\rho_s$ was negative $(-)$ in sign. If the algebraic sign of $\rho$ had been positive $(+)$, the value of $r$ would have had a positive sign $(+)$ prefixed to it. The reason that the algebraic sign can be prefixed in the final step of the formula or, put in another way, the reason that the algebraic sign of $\rho_s$ can be ignored until the final step of the process lies in the fact that: $\sin(-\theta) = -\sin \theta$; i.e., the sine function of a negative angle (an angle that is "generated" by a clockwise sweep of the radius vector when fixed at the center of a circle and rotated from the positive end of the $X$-axis) is equal to the negative sine function of a positive angle (an angle "generated" by a counter-clockwise rotation).

Formula (2) produces values of $r$ that usually approximate closely, but are not *precisely* the same as, those computed directly from the same data. The discrepancy between the values produced by formula (2) and those produced by direct computation results from the fact that formula (2) is based upon an assumption of the shape of the distribution of scores ($X$ or $Y$) that is rarely fulfilled. For the two series of ranks assigned to the $X$ and $Y$ scores, respectively, $\rho_s$ is the same as $r$, but since the interval score data ($X$ and $Y$) rarely have the same rectangular distribution that their ranks display, $\rho_s$ for the "ranks" data and $r$ for the "interval measurement" score data must differ slightly.

## THE PHI COEFFICIENT

The phi coefficient is employed to measure the degree of relationship between two attributes (discrete measures) that are discontinuous and true dichotomies. It should be noted, however, that in practice the phi coefficient ($\phi$) is frequently calculated between two cross-classified variables that have been dichotomized, that is, two variables that are not *true* dichotomies.

The $\phi$ coefficient theoretically assumes a range of values from $-1.00$ to $+1.00$. The algebraic sign of the coefficient implies some order underlying the characteristics being correlated. In practice, occasionally, $\phi$ is used in cases where no assumption of order is permissible. In those cases, the algebraic sign of the coefficient is ignored. If the cross-classified characteristics have a meaningful order, the algebraic sign is important. The sign, under such conditions, shows *which* cells and hence in what order the frequencies are concentrated. The employment of the algebraic sign includes those cases where the cross-classification of two dichotomous attributes have positively defined frequencies (e.g., "Yes" on one item of a questionnaire and a classification of "plus" on the cross-classified item). In such cases, the sign indicates whether "yes" is associated consistently with "plus," or whether it is more consistently associated with "minus."

When a sign is considered appropriate to the $\phi$ coefficient, the conventional approach to the cross-classification is indicated in the diagram below:

|   | + | − |   |
|---|---|---|---|
| **+** | $a$ | $b$ | $a + b$ |
| **−** | $c$ | $d$ | $c + d$ |
|   | $a + c$ | $b + d$ |   |

When the numerator of the formula is of the form $ad - bc$, the algebraic sign result (sign) will automatically conform to the convention of the $(+, -)$ array of the table. Thus, the formula for the phi coefficient $(\phi)$ is:

$$\phi = \frac{ad - bc}{\sqrt{(a + c)(b + d)(c + d)(a + b)}} \tag{7}$$

To illustrate the computation of a phi coefficient, suppose we wished to determine the discriminating power of a given question on a certain test. The group of students who took the test are divided into an upper half and lower half on the basis of the total test score. We arrange the two attributes of "group" and "right-wrong" answers in a $2 \times 2$ table format, and then tabulate the number of students in each group who answered the question "right" and "wrong." The cells and marginal values have been lettered to further the understanding of the formula and computational procedures.

RESPONSES OF UPPER HALF AND LOWER
HALF GROUPS ON A GIVEN TEST QUESTION

Responses

|   | Right | Wrong | Total |
|---|---|---|---|
| Upper Half | $a$  35 | $b$  10 | $a + b$  45 |
| Lower Half | $c$  15 | $d$  30 | $c + d$  45 |
| Total | $a + c$  50 | $b + d$  40 | $n$  90 |

$$\phi = \frac{ad - bc}{\sqrt{(a + c)(b + d)(c + d)(a + b)}} = \frac{(35)(30) - (15)(10)}{\sqrt{(50)(40)(45)(45)}} = \frac{1050 - 150}{900\sqrt{5}}$$

$$\therefore \phi = \frac{900}{900(2.24)} = \frac{1}{2.24} \approx .45$$

The phi coefficient ($\phi$) is related to chi square ($\chi^2$)* by the following expression:

$$\chi^2 = n\phi^2 \tag{8}$$

This relationship permits testing for the significance of $\phi$ by referring the value of ($n\phi^2$) to the chi square table under the condition of one degree of freedom.† To illustrate the test for significance of $\phi$, we use the values of our previous example. Substituting in (8), we have:

$$\chi^2 = 90\,(.45)^2$$

$$\chi^2 = 90\,(.2025)$$

$$\chi^2 = 18.225$$

If we were to refer to a $\chi^2$ probability table, and employ $(r - 1)(c - 1) = (2 - 1)(2 - 1) = 1$ degree of freedom (where $r$ = number of rows, and $c$ the number of columns in our original contingency table—a "2 × 2"), we would find that a value of ($\chi^2 = 18.225$) would occur in less than one out of 100 samples due to chance factors alone. If the null hypothesis $H_0: \phi = 0$ is supposedly true; we would, on the basis of the "finding" ($\chi^2 = 18.225$) reject the null ($H_0$), and infer that the value of $\phi = .45$ represents a significant degree of relationship between the respective attributes of "group" and "response." On the basis of this finding, we could conclude that the "given test question" satisfactorily discriminates between the "upper half" group and the "lower half" group.

Another measure that may be employed quite satisfactorily in connection with the problem of measuring the degree of association between two attributes forming a four-fold contingency table (2 × 2), is that of Yule's $Q$. This topic is not covered here, but a good treatment of the subject may be found in Chapter 7 of Zelditch.[1] The $\phi$ coefficient is employed more frequently in educational research than Yule's $Q$, and for this reason has been discussed here in preference to a treatment of $Q$. Cases that restrict the use of $\phi$ and $Q$ are those where the variables involved are not both dichotomous. Although this restriction would seem to establish a highly limited realm of application for the measures, such is not the case. It should be noted here that it is permissible to dichotomize a continuous variable by selecting some point of division in the range of values of the variable, and then employ such measures as a point—bi-serial correlation or a tetrachoric correlation coefficient (for description of these "measures" see the sources listed at the end of the chapter). It should be pointed out, however, that *all contingency table measures are sensitive to the numbers of rows and columns included in the table, or, put in another way, are sensitive to the points of division within the range of permissible values of the variable.* Although this problem has been minimized in four-fold

---

* The chi-square test evaluates the probability of obtaining a set of *observed* frequencies from a population having certain *theoretical*, or *expected*, frequencies. See Chapter 24, pages 301–10.

† The rationale of the test for significance of $\phi$ closely parallels that of the *test for independence*. It is suggested that the reader return to the "significance of $\phi$" topic after a study of chi-square, Chapter 24, pages 300–10.

(2 × 2) tables, the fact still remains *that the values of φ and Q will be sensitive (seriously) to the point of division that is chosen for dichotomizing the continuous variable.* In view of this fact, *careful analysis and logic should be employed when a continuous variable is to be transformed into a dichotomous attribute for purposes of finding the degree of association (relationship) it might have (in its dichotomous form) with another such attribute.*

Chapter 20—*References*

See Bibliography: 8, 9, 35, 38, 41, 54, 66, 77, 89, 90, 104, 108, 109, 113, 123, 140, 141, 148, 150, 155, 159, 163, 165, 172, 183, 186, 200; 7a, 11a, 23a, 30a, 67a, 68a, 76a, 84a, 95a, 100a, 114a, 116a.

# Nonlinear Regression and Correlation

To THIS POINT we have discussed linear or straight-line patterns of relationships between two variates. In research, cases do occur where the relationship between $X$ and $Y$ is of a curvilinear or nonlinear pattern.

In linear regression there is only one form of the regression line—that of the straight line. In nonlinear (curvilinear) regression there is a wide variety of mathematical equations that could satisfy the form of the regression line which might be required to describe a large number of possible patterns. Therefore, while a linear regression has an uniqueness about it, a nonlinear regression is subject to ambiguity, since it is possible that more than one curve might be fitted to the same data. One of the problems associated with nonlinear regression, then, is that of choosing the best of several possible curves that might fit the pattern of relationship.

A nonlinear regression curve may be adequate over the range of the known data, but yield very poor results when extended (extrapolated) beyond this range. This condition results from the fact that it is usually very difficult to anticipate the pattern of data beyond their observed range. Where a linear regression can only be extrapolated along the straight line representing the linear pattern of relationship, a nonlinear may be extended, theoretically speaking, in an infinity of directions unless a theoretical curve has been assumed to fit the pattern under consideration. These are some of the more important reasons why it is difficult to make estimates, or predictions, from nonlinear regression patterns of relationship.

In practice, linear regression may be used as a reasonably close approximation to nonlinear regression, especially when the deviation from a straight line is not very pronounced. A linear regression pattern is usually a very adequate substitute over a short range of the nonlinear relationship pattern. Since in most problems with which educational research is concerned, the nonlinear regression pattern does not deviate pronouncedly from a straight line, and a comparatively short range of the data pattern is under consideration, the linear regression pattern is found to be a most adequate substitute. In view of this fact, we shall accord the topic of nonlinear correlation and regression only brief discussion here.

Certain causal systems contribute to the existence of nonlinear regression patterns. One large class of this type of regression is the *growth curve*. In a growth curve, $Y$, the variable to be predicted, is either directly or indirectly a function of time. Another type of nonlinear regression is usually associated with situations of *diminishing return or utility*. In this type of relationship the independent variate $X$ brings about a proportionally slower increase in $Y$, and results in a curved pattern of relationship. *Natural or artificial* limits that occur due to the inherent nature of the object under study account for many examples of nonlinear relationships. An example of this type of regression is the relationship between the mileage obtained from an engine as a function of the speed with which it is driven. The pattern is curvilinear and inverse.

Several nonlinear mathematical equations are used to fit the various curvilinear patterns of relationship. Some of them are: (a) *the general power series*: $Y = a + bX + cX^2 + dX^3 + \cdots$ ; (b) a special case of the power series, *the parabola*: $Y = a + bX + cX^2$ ; (c) *the square root parabola*: $Y = a + bX + cX^{\frac{1}{2}}$, (d) *the special power* form: $Y = aX^b$; (e) *the exponential*: $Y = ab^x$, a special form of which is: $Y = ae^x$, where $e = 2.71828\ldots$, the base of the natural logarithm system; (f) the hyperbola: $Y = (c + dX/a + bX)$; (g) *the Gompertz curve*: $Y = ab^{c^x}$, or in logarithm form: $\log Y = \log a + (c^x)(\log b)$; (h) the logarithmic curve: $Y = \ln X$ (natural logarithm) or $Y = \log X$ (common logarithm); (i) *the logistic curve*: $Y = c/(1 + e^{a+bX})$; and (j) the exponential: $Y = ke^{c/(a+x)^2}$. For the reader who might be interested, descriptions of these curves, and methods for fitting them are presented by Rosander.[1]

We conclude our brief discussion of nonlinear regression by presenting a limited example of fictitious data, and the accompanying scatter diagram. Suppose we have the following series of paired observations $(X, Y)$:

| $X$ | $Y$ | $X^2$ | $Y^2$ | $XY$ |
|---|---|---|---|---|
| 0 | 1 | 0 | 1 | 0 |
| 1 | 2 | 1 | 4 | 2 |
| 2 | 4 | 4 | 16 | 8 |
| 3 | 8 | 9 | 64 | 24 |
| 4 | 16 | 16 | 256 | 64 |
| 5 | 32 | 25 | 1024 | 160 |
| 15 | 63 | 55 | 1365 | 258 |

If we were to find the product-moment correlation coefficient $r$, which assumes a linear regression pattern, we would have:

$$r = \frac{n\sum XY - (\sum X)(\sum Y)}{\sqrt{[n\sum X^2 - (\sum X)^2][n\sum Y^2 - (\sum Y)^2]}}$$

$$= \frac{(6)(258) - (15)(63)}{\sqrt{[6(55) - (15)^2][6(1365) - (63)^2]}}$$

$$r = \frac{1548 - 945}{\sqrt{(330 - 225)(8190 - 3969)}} = \frac{603}{\sqrt{(105)(4221)}} = \frac{603}{665.7} \approx .906$$

Still assuming a linear regression pattern, the equation of the line that "best" fits the data is found from the following formula: $Y = a + bX$

where

$$a = \frac{\sum Y \sum X^2 - \sum X \sum XY}{n\sum X^2 - (\sum X)^2}$$

and

$$b = \frac{n\sum XY - \sum X \sum Y}{n\sum X^2 - (\sum X)^2}$$

In this example:

$$a = \frac{(63)(55) - (15)(258)}{105} = \frac{-405}{105} \approx -3.86$$

$$b = \frac{(6)(258) - (15)(63)}{105} = \frac{603}{105} \approx 5.74$$

hence, the equation of the line that "best" fits the data is:

$$Y = -3.86 + 5.74X$$

Here we note a rather odd occurrence, the paired values of $(X, Y)$ show the smallest value of $X$ with the smallest value of $Y$, the next to smallest value of $X$ with that of the next to smallest value of $Y$, and so on, until we have the largest value of $X$ with the largest value of $Y$; hence, if *the linear pattern of relationship were true, the value of r*, the product-moment correlation coefficient, should be $+1.00$. Instead $r \approx .906$. If the linear relationship existed, certain paired values from the $X$ and $Y$ arrays shown in the table would fall on the regression line, but only one of these points does $(1, 2)$. Obviously a linear relationship does not exist, but a nonlinear one does.

We note that, with the exception of the first value ($Y = 1$), all of the $Y$ magnitudes in the table are "even" numbers. Closer examination of the series will reveal that the even number values actually are powers of 2. Based upon the results of our brief analytical examination of the $Y$ observations, we decide that the nonlinear regression pattern might be described by an exponential function of the general form: $Y = ab^X$. For our specific example, we note that the values: $a = 1$, and $b = 2$, produce the function that best fits the regression pattern. Hence, our regression equation becomes: $Y = 2^X$. Figure 17 below shows the incorrect regression *line* and the correct regression *curve*. We note from the figure that our paired observations fall exactly on the curve $Y = 2^X$. Thus, the scatter or spread of the points $(X, Y)$, the paired observations, is greater about the line $y = -3.86 + 5.74X$ than it is about the curve $Y = 2^X$. In fact, since the curve $Y = 2^X$ is a perfect description (fit) of the regression pattern, the scatter of the points "about" it is zero (all points fall on the curve). From Figure 17 we should note that if a truly *nonlinear* relationship pattern is represented by a *straight line*, then we cause the pattern of the scatter of points to be greater than it would have been had we "fit" a *curve* that more suitably

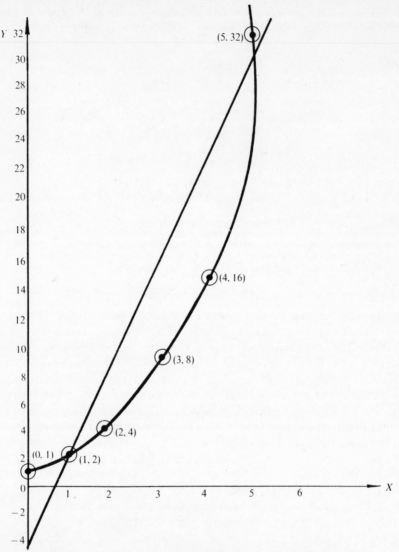

*Figure 17*
*Graph of "Incorrect" Regression Line and "Correct" Regression Curve*

described the curvilinear relationship. Therefore, the *smaller* the spread (scatter) of the paired observations about the regression *line* or the regression *curve* which is being fit to establish the *best functional description of the relationship of X and Y* (or *Y and X*), the more improved, or higher, the relationship between the two variables. It is for this reason that the product-moment correlation coefficient *r*, which is only associated with *linear* regression, always indicates a value which is *less than* the true degree of relationship, if the relationship under consideration is actually nonlinear. Since the pattern of relationship in our example was actually curvilinear, and, in the illustrative case, a linear relationship was forced upon the data, the product-moment correlation coefficient $r = +.903$ associated with that case was less than $+1.00$, the value which indicates a perfect *linear* relationship. The correlation-ratio, or coefficient of nonlinear relationship $\eta$, is the measure that provides a precise indication of relationship under conditions of nonlinear regression patterns.

*Eta* $(\eta)$ indicates the degree of concentration of paired observations $(X, Y)$ about a *regression curve*, just as $r$ measures the concentration of paired values $(X, Y)$ about a *regression line*. Eta is a more general measure than $r$, and can be applied to linear as well as nonlinear relationship patterns. When the regression pattern is linear, $\eta$ will be equal to $r$. If the regression pattern is nonlinear, however, $\eta$ will be greater than $r$. Thus, we find that $r$ is, in effect, a limiting value of the more general coefficient $\eta$, just as a straight-line relationship is a limiting case of nonlinear relationship. There are *two etas* for every correlation situation. The first correlation-ratio $(\eta_{YX})$ indicates the case of the regression of $Y$ on $X$ ($Y$ dependent). The second correlation-ratio $(\eta_{XY})$ measures the regression of $X$ on $Y$ ($X$ dependent).

Because of the mathematical quantities involved in its computation, the value of $\eta$ is always found to be *positive in algebraic sign*, and lying between .00 and 1.00. The direction of the actual relationship, be it positive or negative, must therefore be determined by a logical analysis of the relationship pattern.

Since there are many different types of curvilinear regression that can be applied to the same set of data, it is necessary to define $\eta$ independently of the particular curve that might be fitted to the relationship pattern of the data. This condition is satisfied by using the column arithmetic means as points of reference to measure variances (scatter) rather than those of the fitted line.

The formulas for $\eta_{YX}^2$ and $\eta_{XY}^2$ are as follows:

$$\eta_{YX}^2 = \frac{s_Y^2 - s_C^2}{s_Y^2} \tag{1}$$

and

$$\eta_{XY}^2 = \frac{s_X^2 - s_R^2}{s_X^2} \tag{2}$$

where $\eta_{YX}^2$ is the nonlinear correlation coefficient based upon *column means* of the correlation table; $\eta_{XY}^2$ is the coefficient based upon *row means*; $(s_C^2)$ is the variance of the deviations of the $Y$ values from their *column means* $\overline{Y}_j$; $s_R^2$ is the variance of the *deviations* of the $X$ values from their *row means* $\overline{X}_j$; $s_Y^2$ is the *total variance* of the $Y$ values about the grand mean $\overline{Y}$ (for all $Y$ values in the table), and $s_X^2$ is the *total variance* of the $X$ values about their grand mean $\overline{X}$. The variance of $Y$ about the several column means may be found by the following formula:

$$s_C^2 = \frac{\sum\limits_{1}^{k} n_j(Y_j - \overline{Y}_j)^2}{n}$$

where $n_j$ is the number of cases in each column, and $n = \sum_1^k n_j$, where the summation is over $k$ columns of $Y$ values. It is a measure of the variation of $Y$ within columns. Put in another way, $s_C^2$ is the pooled sum of squares of deviations from each column mean, weighted by the number of cases in each column, and averaged by dividing by $n$, the total size of the sample. Similarly $s_R^2$ may be found by the formula:

$$s_R^2 = \frac{\sum_1^k n_j(X_j - \bar{X}_j)^2}{n}$$

where $n_j$ is the number of cases in each row, and $n = \sum_1^k n_j$, where the summation is over $k$ *rows* of the $X$ values. It is a measure of the variation of $X$ within rows. The *total variance of $Y$ values* about the grand mean $\bar{Y}$, may be found by the formula:

$$s_Y^2 = \frac{\sum Y^2 - (\sum Y)^2/n}{n}$$

where $\sum Y^2$ is the sum of *all $Y^2$ values in the table*, $\sum Y$ is the sum of *all $Y$ values in the table*, and $n$ is the *total number of $Y$ values in the table*. Similarly, the *total variance of $X$ values* about the grand mean $\bar{X}$, may be found by the formula:

$$s_X^2 = \frac{\sum X^2 - (\sum X)^2/n}{n}$$

where $\sum X^2$ is the sum of *all $X^2$ values in the table*, $\sum X$ is the sum of *all $X$ values in the table*, and $n$ is the *total number of $X$ values in the table*.

The following example illustrates how $\eta_{YX}$ and $\eta_{XY}$ are calculated. Since a comparison of the two calculated $\eta$'s with the $r$ obtained from the same data is helpful in determining whether the regression pattern is, or is not, significantly nonlinear, the calculation of $r$ is included in the process of calculating the *etas* ($\eta$). The data presented are fictititous and simplified in order to illustrate the computations; the values of $X$ and the values of $Y$ are assumed to be discrete:

| Y | Work-Study Skills Rating—X | | | | | $n_j$ | $n_jY$ | $n_jY^2$ | $s^2_{jX}$ * | $\sum n_j(X - \bar{X}_j)^2$ |
|---|---|---|---|---|---|---|---|---|---|---|
| | 1 | 2 | 3 | 4 | 5 | | | | | |
| 8 | | | 1 | 1 | | 2 | 16 | 128 | .25 | .50 |
| 7 | | | 6 | 3 | 1 | 10 | 70 | 490 | .45 | 4.50 |
| 6 | | 4 | 15 | 8 | 3 | 30 | 180 | 1080 | .69 | 20.70 |
| 5 | | 8 | 15 | 6 | 1 | 30 | 150 | 750 | .60 | 18.00 |
| 4 | | 6 | 7 | 2 | | 15 | 60 | 240 | .46 | 8.90 |
| 3 | 2 | 1 | 3 | | | 6 | 18 | 54 | .81 | 4.86 |
| 2 | 3 | 1 | | | | 4 | 8 | 16 | .19 | .76 |
| 1 | 2 | | | | | 2 | 2 | 2 | 0 | 0 |
| (Kindergarten) 0 | 1 | | | | | 1 | 0 | 0 | 0 | 0 |
| $n_j$ | 8 | 20 | 47 | 20 | 5 | 100 | 504 | 2760 | | 58.22 |
| $n_jX$ | 8 | 40 | 141 | 80 | 25 | 294 | | | | |
| $n_jX^2$ | 8 | 80 | 423 | 320 | 125 | 956 | | | $\bar{X} = \dfrac{294}{100} = 2.94$ | |
| $s^2_{jY}$ † | .94 | 1.03 | 1.29 | .99 | .40 | | | | $\bar{Y} = \dfrac{504}{100} = 5.04$ | |
| $\sum n_j(Y - \bar{Y}_j)^2$ | 7.52 | 2.06 | 60.63 | 19.80 | 2.00 | 92.01 | | | | |

(The "Grade Level" label appears vertically alongside the Y column.)

$$s^2_C = \frac{92.01}{100} = .92; \qquad s^2_R = \frac{58.22}{100} \approx .58;$$

$$s^2_X = \frac{956 - (294)^2/100}{100} = .9164; \qquad s^2_Y = \frac{2760 - (504)^2/100}{100} = 2.1984$$

\* To find values for entries in this column, the following procedures are employed: (1) Apply formula:

$$s^2_{jX} = \frac{\sum X^2_j - (\sum X_j)^2/n_j}{n_j};$$

(2) for *row* 1 Entry (where value of $Y$ is 8); we have:

$$s^2_{1X} = \frac{(3^2 + 4^2) - (7)^2/2}{2} = \frac{25 - (49/2)}{2} = .25;$$

(3) for row 2 Entry (where value of $Y$ is 7); we have:

$$s^2_{2X} = \frac{6(3)^2 + 3(4)^2 + (5)^2 - (35)^2/10}{10} = .45;$$

(4) find values for rows 3–9 in similar fashion.

† To find values for entries in this row: (1) Apply formula:

$$s^2_{jY} = \frac{\sum Y^2_j - (\sum Y_j)^2/n_j}{n_j};$$

(2) for *column* 1 Entry (where value of $X$ is 1):

$$s^2_{1Y} = \frac{2(3)^2 + 3(2)^2 + 2(1)^2 + 1(0)^2 - (14)^2/8}{8} = \frac{7.5}{8} = .94;$$

(3) for *column* 2 Entry (where value of $X$ is 2):

$$s^2_{2Y} = \frac{4(6)^2 + 8(5)^2 + 6(4)^2 + 1(3)^2 + 1(2)^2 - (93)^2/20}{20} = 1.03$$

(4) find values for columns 3–5 in similar fashion.

Substituting in formula (1), we find $\eta^2_{YX}$ to be:

$$\eta^2_{YX} = \frac{s^2_Y - s^2_C}{s^2_Y} = \frac{2.1984 - .92}{2.1984} \approx .5815$$

$$\therefore \quad \eta_{YX} = \sqrt{.5815} \approx .762$$

Substituting in formula (2), we find $(\eta_{XY}^2)$ to be:

$$\eta_{XY}^2 = \frac{s_X^2 - s_R^2}{s_X^2} = \frac{.9164 - .58}{.9164} \approx .3671$$

$$\therefore \quad \eta_{XY} = \sqrt{.3671} \approx .606$$

The value of "$r$" for this array of data is found by the formula:

$$r = \frac{n\sum XY - (\sum X)(\sum Y)}{\sqrt{[n\sum X^2 - (\sum X)^2][n\sum Y^2 - (\sum Y)^2]}}$$

$$= \frac{100(1566) - (294)(504)}{\sqrt{[100(956) - (294)^2][100(2760) - (504)^2]}}$$

$$\therefore \quad r = \frac{8424}{\sqrt{(9164)(21,984)}} = \frac{8424}{14,196.759} \approx .593$$

We note that in our example $\eta_{YX}$ is .762, and $\eta_{XY}$ is .606, while $r$ is .593, indicating that a curvilinear pattern of relationship exists between $X$ and $Y$. The method of testing whether regression is significantly nonlinear (by statistically comparing the $\eta$'s and $r$) is presented by Garrett.[2]

The probable error of a correlation-ratio (eta) is found by the formula:

$$PE_\eta = \frac{.6745(1 - \eta^2)}{\sqrt{n}}$$

where $n$ indicates the number of paired observations. In our example, with $n = 100$, the $PE$ for $\eta_{YX} = .762$ is .028, and for $\eta_{XY} = .606$ is .043. Since both $\eta_{YX}$ and $\eta_{XY}$ are more than four times their Probable Errors they are considered to be significantly different from .00.

In closing our discussion of nonlinear regression and correlation it should be pointed out that $\eta$ is affected by the number of items in the several classes, and by the number of classes into which the population is divided. At the same time, $\zeta$ tends to have a slight positive bias, and is affected by categories, or classifications, of the independent variable that are too fine or too broad. These points, and how to correct for them, are presented in detail by Peters and VanVoorhis.[3] The reader who is interested in a further detailed presentation of many aspects of the correlation-ratio ($\eta$) should consult that source.

*Chapter 21—References*

See Bibliography: 4, 38, 41, 49, 54, 58, 60, 62, 77, 89, 104, 108, 113, 123, 141, 148, 155, 159, 163, 172, 183, 184, 186, 200; 11a, 30a, 67a, 68a, 84a, 95a, 109a, 111a.

### Chapter Twenty-two

# Multiple Correlation and Regression

PARTIAL AND MULTIPLE CORRELATION and regression are the same in principle (and parallel in approach) as simple correlation and regression. With this fact in mind, probably the best way to approach the topic is through an illustration.

Suppose we attempt or plan to predict a student's honor point average at the end of his freshman year in college based upon certain factors taken from his high school file and record. Selected factors upon which to base the prediction might be his honor point averages in: (1) high school English courses, high school mathematics courses, physical and biological science courses; (2) intelligence rating; (3) work-study skills rating; (4) average amount of time spent in study per week; and, finally, (5) a motivation score based upon interest in the curriculum being pursued in college. Since each of these factors is of differing significance, or importance, to the predicted variable (usually called "the criterion"), equal consideration cannot be given to each one of them when deriving an estimate of the criterion. This condition is accounted for by multiplying the scores on each factor by a coefficient which is determined on the basis of the relative importance of the factor to the criterion, or variable being predicted. The problem which must be solved then is that of ascertaining the relative degrees of importance with which the several components (factors) enter into the determination of the criterion, or in other words, finding the proper values for the several regression coefficients.

Another approach to the problem is that of determining the relative weights of the factors on the basis of their relative importance to the predicted variable (criterion). In our illustration we may wish to know: to what extent do the honor point averages in high school English courses, mathematics courses, and science courses, along with the intelligence rating of the individual, contribute to the prediction of the student's honor point average for his freshman year in college in a given curriculum? These relative weights are found by essentially the same procedures employed for determining the value of simple regression coefficients.

If coefficients of correlation are more familiar measures to the researcher than regression coefficients, the problem can be treated by a correlation approach. If this were the case, it would be necessary to find the extent of correlation between each of the factors and the criterion when the influence of the other factors is eliminated, or ruled out. The correlations that express the expected relation between one of the battery of factors and the criterion, *when the influence of the other factors of the battery is held constant*, are termed, *"coefficients of partial correlation.*" The statistical method of partial correlation is very useful in connection with models of experimental research wherein there is particular difficulty in attempting to control a factor, or factors, experimentally. To illustrate, suppose in our example we wished to determine the correlation between intelligence and the criterion (h.p.a. for the freshman year in college), uninfluenced by the other factors involved. The partial correlation coefficient, calculated by "partialling out" the effects of all the other factors in the battery, would indicate the degree of net relationship between the criterion and intelligence as though the other factors had been held constant, or in effect had been controlled.

The statistical method of partial correlation provides a means of "building up" a regression equation involving three or more variables from which a criterion score may be predicted when scores made by an individual on the correlated factors are known. The accuracy of the regression equation in estimating values of the criterion score is determined by the *coefficient of multiple correlation.* Thus, the *multiple correlation coefficient* indicates the correlation between a single variable and a battery of variables. If the variables involved were test scores, the multiple correlation coefficient would indicate the degree of relationship to be expected between *scores on the criterion test actually obtained* by individuals, and the *criterion test scores* predicted for the individuals by the partial regression equation.

The partial regression equation for $K$ variables may take one of three forms: (a) the deviation form, (b) the score form, and (c) the standard score form. The deviation form is:

$$\tilde{x}_0 = b_{01.234...K}x_1 + b_{02.134...K}x_2 + b_{03.124...K}x_3 + \cdots + b_{0K,1234...(K-1)}x_K \quad (1)$$

Where $\tilde{x}_0$ (tilde $x_0$) indicates *the deviation of an individual's score on the criterion test from the mean of the criterion test* scores; $x_1, x_2, x_3 \ldots x_K$ indicate the *same individual's deviation scores* on each of the $K$ tests composing the battery, and the b's are the *regression coefficients* by which we must multiply the respective *deviation score forms of the variables to lend them their appropriate weights in the battery.* The deviation form of an individual's score on test $j$ $(x_j)$ is related to his "raw" score on test $j$ $(X_j)$ by the expression:

$$x_j = X_j - \bar{X}_j$$

Substituting in equation (1), we have:

$$(\tilde{X}_0 - \bar{X}_0) = b_{01.234...K}(X_1 - \bar{X}_1) + b_{02.134...K}(X_2 - \bar{X}_2)$$
$$+ b_{03.124...K}(X_3 - \bar{X}_3) + \cdots + b_{0K.1234...(K-1)}(X_K - \bar{X}_K)$$
$$\tilde{X}_0 = b_{01.234...K}X_1 + b_{02.134...K}X_2 + b_{03.124...K}X_3 + \cdots$$
$$+ b_{0K.1234...(K-1)}X_K + \bar{X}_0 - b_{01.234...K}\bar{X}_1 - b_{02.134...K}$$
$$\bar{X}_2 - \cdots - b_{0K.123...(K-1)}\bar{X}_K$$
$$\tilde{X}_0 = b_{01.234...K}X_1 + b_{02.134...K}X_2 + b_{03.124...K}X_3 + \cdots$$
$$+ b_{0K.1234...(K-1)}X_K + K_0 \quad (2)$$

Equation (2) is the *score form of the partial regression equation for K variables*.

In equation (1) the variables, $x$'s, in the "difference" series are probably measured in terms of different test units, and thus are of unlike meaning. Similarly, the variables, $X$'s, in the "difference" series in equation (2) are probably measured in terms of different test units, and are of unlike meaning. Difficulty in the interpretation of the relationships of the variables expressed in different units of measurement throughout equation (1) and equation (2), respectively, can be avoided by developing a *standard score form* of the partial regression equation for $K$ variables. If "standard measures" are employed throughout the general equation, the variables, unit-wise, will have the same meaning, and can be interpreted accordingly. Since the standard score form of the equation can be derived from equation (1) or (2), it is a simple matter to obtain "ordinary" score results by translating from the "standard" form to equation (1) or (2) whenever the need arises. To obtain the standard score form of the general equation most easily, we merely divide each deviation score in equation (1) by the standard deviation of the array to which it belongs. Letting "$z$" symbolize the score in standard measures, we have:

$$z_0 = \frac{x_0}{s_0}; \qquad z_1 = \frac{x_1}{s_1}; \qquad z_2 = \frac{x_2}{s_2}; \cdots ; \qquad z_k = \frac{x_k}{s_k}$$

The general regression equation for $K$ variables, in *standard score form*, becomes:

$$\tilde{z}_0 = \beta_{01.234...K}z_1 + \beta_{02.134...K}z_2 + \beta_{03.124...K}z_3 + \cdots + \beta_{0K.1234...(K-1)}z_K \quad (3)$$

where the symbol $\beta$ is used to distinguish the *partial regression coefficients in terms of standard scores* from the partial regression coefficients ($b$'s) in terms of deviation and for "raw" scores of the respective variables. Regression co-efficients in terms of $\beta$ are usually called "beta weights," as opposed to the "score weights" ($b$'s) in the "ordinary" regression equations ("deviation" and "score" forms). The beta weights give the contributions of the various independent variables in the regression equation to the criterion (dependent variable). Such weights are very useful in analyzing the *comparative* contribution made by each variable of the battery to the resulting criterion variable.

The $\beta$ coefficients are related to the $b$ coefficients by the following expressions:

$$\beta_{01.234...K} = b_{01.234...K} \; \frac{s_1}{s_0}$$

$$\beta_{02.134...K} = b_{02.134...K} \; \frac{s_2}{s_0} \qquad\qquad (4)$$

$$\vdots \qquad\qquad \vdots \qquad\qquad \vdots$$

$$\beta_{0K.123...(K-1)} = b_{0K.123...(K-1)} \; \frac{s_k}{s_0}$$

The partial regression coefficients $b_{01.234...K}$; $b_{02.134...K}$; $b_{03.124...K}$, and so on, give the weight of each independent variable when $\tilde{x}_0$ or $\tilde{X}_0$ (the criterion) is to be estimated from the battery composing equation (1) or equation (2), respectively. These regression coefficients also indicate the weight which each variable has in determining $\tilde{x}_0$ or $\tilde{X}_0$, when the influence of the other variables is eliminated. Hence, the $b$'s in the regression equations (1) and (2) indicate what role each of the variables plays in determining the value of the dependent variable (criterion).

The partial regression coefficients $b$'s may be computed from the following expression:

$$b_{01.239...K} = r_{01.234...K}\frac{S_{0.123...K}}{S_{1.023...K}} \tag{5}$$

Where $r_{01.234...K}$ is a general form of the *partial correlation* coefficient, and $S_{0.1234...K}$ and $S_{1.0234...K}$ are general forms of standard errors of estimate for $K$ variables. Expression (5) will be illustrated in an example later.

The general formula for a partial correlation coefficient of the $n$-th order is:

$$r_{01.234...K} = \frac{r_{01.234...K} - r_{0K.123...(K-1)}r_{1K.0234...(K-1)}}{\sqrt{1 - r^2_{0K.1234...(K-1)}}\sqrt{1 - r^2_{1K.0234...(K-1)}}} \tag{6}$$

Where in every partial correlation coefficient, e.g., $r_{01.23}$, the *subscripts* to the *left* of the point (0 and 1), are *primary* subscripts and denote the two variables whose *net correlation* is being sought; the subscripts to the *right* of the point (2 and 3), are *secondary* subscripts denoting the variables eliminated or held constant, and the *order* of the partial $r$ is determined by the *number* of secondary subscripts (e.g., $r_{01.2}$ is first order; $r_{01.23}$ is *second* order, etc.). Although formula (6) will be employed and demonstrated in an example later, certain properties of partial $r$'s should be pointed out now. First, the order in which the *secondary* subscripts are written is immaterial. Hence, $r_{01.23} = r_{01.32}$. Secondly, the order of the *primary* subscripts is important, however, because it indicates which of the variables is considered to be *dependent*. Thus, $r_{01}$ means that $x_0$ is the dependent variable to be predicted from the independent variable $X_1$; while $r_{10}$ indicates that $X_1$ is the dependent variable predicted from $X_0$. Thirdly, *the numerical values of $r_{01}$ and $r_{10}$, however, are the same*, i.e., $r_{01} = r_{10}$ in value. Finally, if we were attempting to compute the value of a *third order partial correlation coefficient*, say, $r_{01.234}$, applying formula (6), we would be expressing the *third order coefficient* in *terms* of partial $r$'s of the *second order*. These *second order* partial $r$'s would be calculated from formula (6) in terms of *first order* partials, the values of which would have been found from formula (6) involving zero order coefficients. In other words, in order to find partial $r$'s of a given (higher) order; in every case, these $r$'s must first be expressed in terms of partial $r$'s of the next lowest order; these lower order $r$'s, in turn, must be expressed in terms of $r$'s of the next lower order, and so on until $r$'s of zero order have been employed. Thus, it is necessary to "build up" from zero order $r$'s, whenever higher order $r$'s are to be computed. Obviously, with the addition of each new variable to the battery, the calculation procedure of partial $r$'s is greatly increased, and unless the procedure is carefully planned, the arithmetic is laborious, and an arithmetic error in calculating a lower order $r$, if not discovered almost immediately, can result in a tremendous task of correction.

In order to find the value of a partial regression coefficient in (5) we must not only know how to compute partial $r$'s, but be able to find values of appropriate partial $s$'s as well. The variability ($s$) of any set of scores can be found when the influence of 1, 2, 3, ... $K$ factors is held constant. The general formula for *partial s's of any order for K variables* is:

$$s_{0.1234...K} = s_0\sqrt{1 - r_{01}^2}\sqrt{1 - r_{02.1}^2}\sqrt{1 - r_{03.12}^2}\cdots\sqrt{1 - r_{0K.123...(K-1)}^2} \quad (7)$$

where the order of a partial $s$, like the order of a partial $r$, is *determined by the number of secondary subscripts*. Formula (7) may be used to compute the *net s's* in correlation problems that involve any number of variables. To make the formula more meaningful, consider the symbol $s_{0.12}$. This partial $s$ indicates the variability of the factor $X_0$ freed of the influence exerted by the two factors $X_1$ and $X_2$.

By a simple rearrangement of the secondary subscripts, any higher order $s$ may be written in more than one way. For example, our second order partial $s_{0.12}$ may be written in two ways:

$$s_{0.12} = s_0\sqrt{1 - r_{01}^2}\sqrt{1 - r_{02.1}^2}$$

may also be written as:

$$s_{0.12} = s_0\sqrt{1 - r_{02}^2}\sqrt{1 - r_{01.2}}$$

The alternate forms of a partial $s$ are useful as a "check" on arithmetic calculations, and serve the purpose of rendering unnecessary the calculation of otherwise unused and superfluous partial $r$'s. The use of partial $s$'s for the purpose described in the latter part of the previous sentence will be illustrated later in an example.

All values of the criterion variable, $\tilde{X}_0$, estimated from a partial regression equation have a *standard error of estimate* which indicates the error made in estimating values from the regression equation instead of the actual values (e.g., those scores actually earned on the criterion test). The standard error of estimate is found by the formula:

$$s_{(est X_0)} = s_{0.1234...K} \quad (8)$$

and the *probable error* of estimate is found by the formula:

$$PE_{(est X_0)} = .6745\, s_{(est X_0)} \quad (9)$$

Since the value of $s_{0.123...K}$ must be determined in order to find the value of the partial regression coefficients, $b$'s, $s_{(est X_0)}$ is always calculated in carrying out the procedures for solving the problem. The standard error of estimate, $s_{(est X_0)}$, indicates the effect upon the variability of the criterion factor, $X_0$, when the influence of factors 1, 2, 3, 4 ... $K$ is held constant. The greater the degree to which the correlated variables $(1, 2, 3, 4, \ldots K)$ are able to account for the variability of the criterion factor the smaller $s_{(\text{est } X_0)}$ will be and the more accurate the prediction of $\tilde{X}_0$ values from the partial regression equation.

With this background we are now prepared to consider general formulas for $R$, *the coefficient of multiple correlation.* The correlation, *expressed in terms of partials $s$'s*, between a single dependent variable (criterion), $X_0$, and $K - 1$ independent variables related by means of a partial regression equation is given by formula (10):

$$R_{0(123...K)} = \sqrt{1 - \frac{s_{0.123...K}^2}{s_0^2}} \tag{10}$$

Where $R_{0(123...K)}$ is the coefficient of multiple correlation, $s_o^2$ is the variance of the criterion (dependent) series of values $(X_0)$ and $s_{o.123...K}^2$ gives the variance remaining in the criterion variable $X_0$ when factors $1, 2, 3, \ldots, K$ are held constant through the method of partial correlation.

If we replace $s_{0.123...K}$ in formula (1) by its equivalent form in terms of the entire and partial $r$'s given by formula (7), we have the *general formula for R in terms of partial coefficients of correlation for K variables* given by formula (11):

$$R_{0(123...K)} = \sqrt{1 - [(1 - r_{01}^2)(1 - r_{02.1}^2)(1 - r_{03.12}^2)\ldots(1 - r_{0K.123...(K-1)}^2)]} \tag{11}$$

Since a higher order $s$ may be written in a number of ways, the number depending upon the order of $s$, there are also several alternate forms for $R$. The forms serve as valuable means for checking arithmetic computations.

The multiple correlation coefficient, $R$, is valuable for indicating how accurately a given combination of variables equal to $X_0$ represents the actual values of $X_0$ (the criterion) when these factors are combined in a "best" *linear* partial regression equation. *The algebraic sign of R is always taken to be positive.* This attitude of $R$ means that sampling errors do not neutralize each other but become cumulative instead. As a result, the Probable Error of $R$, which is found from the formula for the *PE* of any product-moment $r$:

$$PE_r = \frac{.6745(1 - r^2)}{\sqrt{n}}$$

*is not an entirely adequate measure of R's reliability. The reliability of an obtained R is tested by comparing it with the value of that R which would be obtained from the same number of cases and the same number of variables if the variables were uncorrelated.* The formula for the $R$ which would arise from fluctuations of sampling alone is:

$$R_c = \sqrt{\frac{K - 1}{n}} \tag{12}$$

where $K$ is the number of variables and $n$ is the number of cases in the sample. The application of formula (12) will be illustrated in an example later in the discussion.

The square of the multiple correlation coefficient, $R^2$, gives the per cent of the variance of $X_0$ (i.e., $s_0^2$) which is attributable to the influence of the dependent variables $X_1, X_2, X_3, \ldots, X_k$. The value of the expression $1 - R^2$ is the per cent of the variance of $X_0$ which must be attributed to factors not accounted for in the combination, or battery, included in the partial regression equation.

A major problem associated with multiple correlation analysis is that of carrying out the many computations with a minimum expenditure of time and energy. The best approach to the situation is to first write down the formula for the regression equation, and decide which partial $r$'s and higher order $s$'s are needed to determine the values of the partial regression coefficients ($b$'s). Find the $r$'s and $s$'s and calculate the values of the regression coefficients ($b$'s). Find the standard error of estimate and the probable error of estimate. Calculate the multiple correlation coefficient $R$, and compare it with the value calculated for the "chance $R$" in order to test the reliability of the "obtained $R$." In order to illustrate the foregoing discussion we now present an outline of formulas needed for approaching situations of the application of multiple correlation involving three variables.*

### ILLUSTRATION OF CORRELATION ANALYSIS—THREE VARIABLES

Suppose that in the process of conducting a normative survey study, it becomes necessary for the researcher to determine if the variables of honor point average in high school English courses, and intelligence ratings of students taken during the senior year of high school, can be used as predictors of college capable students, where capability is determined on the basis of at least a 2.0 cumulative honor point average ($4.0 = A$; $3.0 = B$; $2.0 = C$, etc.) at the end of the freshman year in college. A sample of 200 students is selected at random, and the necessary data for each individual in the sample are compiled. The primary data, composed of such statistics as means, standard deviations, and appropriate zero order correlation coefficients, are as follows:

1. *Primary Data*

| $X_0$—H.P.A. College Freshman Year ($4.0 = A$; $3.0 = B$; etc.) | $X_1$—H.P.A. High School English Courses ($4.0 = A$; $3.0 = B$; etc.) | $X_2$—Intelligence Rating |
|---|---|---|
| $\bar{X}_0 = 2.1$ | $\bar{X}_1 = 2.5$ | $\bar{X}_2 = 110$ |
| $s_0 = .2$ | $s_1 = .3$ | $s_2 = 5$ |
| $r_{01} = .05$ | $r_{12} = .50$ | $r_{02} = .60$ |

* For outlines of formulas employed in correlational analyses involving four and five variables, respectively, and for *special* methods of solving correlation problems involving $k$ variables, see (77) Garrett, p. 480; (141) Peters and VanVoorhis, Chapter VIII; and (180) Helen Walker, *Elementary Statistical Methods*, 1st ed. (New York: Henry Holt & Co., 1943), Chapter XII.

2. *Score Form of Regression Equation and Partial Regression Coefficients*

(a)

$$\bar{X}_0 = b_{01.2}X_1 + b_{02.1}X_2 + K$$

(b) where

$$K = \bar{X}_0 - b_{01.2}\bar{X}_1 - b_{02.1}\bar{X}_2$$

(c) and:

$$b_{01.2} = r_{01.2}\frac{s_{0.12}}{s_{1.02}}$$

$$b_{02.1} = r_{02.1}\frac{s_{0.12}}{s_{2.01}}$$

(d) Substituting values found for respective $r$'s and $s$'s, we have:

$$b_{01.2} = .29\frac{.153}{.250} = (.29)(.612) \approx .177$$

$$b_{02.1} = .47\frac{.153}{3.08} \approx (.47)(.05) \approx .024$$

(e) Substituting values found for the $b$'s, we have

$$K = 2.1 - (.177)(2.5) - (.024)(110) \approx -.98$$

3. *The Partial $r$'s*

$$r_{01.2} = \frac{r_{01} - r_{02}r_{12}}{\sqrt{1 - r_{02}^2}\sqrt{1 - r_{12}^2}}; \qquad r_{02.1} = \frac{r_{02} - r_{01}r_{12}}{\sqrt{1 - r_{01}^2}\sqrt{1 - r_{12}^2}}$$

$$r_{01.2} = \frac{.50 - (.60)(.50)}{\sqrt{1 - (.60)^2}\sqrt{1 - (.50)^2}}; \qquad r_{02.1} = \frac{.60 - (.50)(.50)}{\sqrt{1 - (.50)^2}\sqrt{1 - (.50)^2}}$$

$$r_{01.2} = \frac{.20}{.69} \approx .29 \qquad\qquad r_{02.1} = \frac{.35}{.75} \approx .47$$

4. *The Partial $s$'s*

$$s_{0.12} = s_0\sqrt{1 - r_{01}^2}\sqrt{1 - r_{02.1}^2} = (.2)\sqrt{1 - (.50)^2}\sqrt{1 - (.47)^2} \approx .153$$

$$s_{1.02} = s_1\sqrt{1 - r_{12}^2}\sqrt{1 - r_{01.2}^2} = (.3)\sqrt{1 - (.50)^2}\sqrt{1 - (.29)^2} \approx .250$$

$$s_{2.01} = s_2\sqrt{1 - r_{12}^2}\sqrt{1 - r_{02.1}^2} = (5)\sqrt{1 - (.50)^2}\sqrt{1 - (.47)^2} \approx 3.8$$

5. *The Standard Error of Estimate*

$$s_{(\text{est } X_0)} = s_{0.12} \approx .153$$

and the Probable Error of Estimate becomes:

$$PE_{(est\ X_0)} = .6745 s_{(est\ X_0)} = (.6745)(.153) \approx .103$$

### 6. *The Coefficient of Multiple Correlation, R*

$$R_{0(12)} = \sqrt{1 - \frac{s_{0.12}^2}{s_0^2}} = \sqrt{1 - \frac{(.153)^2}{(.2)^2}} = \sqrt{1 - \frac{.024}{.04}} = \sqrt{.4} = .632$$

or

$$R_{0(12)} = \sqrt{1 - (1 - r_{01}^2)(1 - r_{02.1}^2)} = \sqrt{1 - .6} = \sqrt{.4} = .632$$

### 7. *The Reliability of $R_c$*

With three variables and a sample size of $n = 200$, we find the value of the "chance $R$" to be:

$$R_c = \sqrt{\frac{K - 1}{n}} = \sqrt{\frac{2}{200}} = .10$$

Comparing $R_{0(12)}$ with "chance $R$," we find $R_{0(12)} = .632$ to be more than six times as great as $R_c = .10$, we therefore may conclude that $R_{0(12)}$ is of a satisfactory degree of reliability.

### 8. *Other Calculations and Interpretations*

The beta coefficients ($\beta$'s) may be computed from formula (4) as follows:

$$\beta_{01.2} = b_{01.2} \frac{s_1}{s_0} = (.177)\frac{.3}{.2} = .2655$$

$$\beta_{02.1} = b_{02.1} \frac{s_2}{s_0} = (.024)\frac{5}{.2} = .60$$

These "beta weights" indicate the contributions of the independent variables (h.p.a. in high school English courses, and intelligence rating) in the regression equation (standard form, see below) to the dependent variable, the criterion (h.p.a.—college freshman year). They demonstrate the comparative worth of the independent variables as they bear upon the determination of the criterion. The standard form of the regression equation for our example, becomes:

$$z_0 = .2655 z_1 + .60 z_2$$

and shows the respective contributions of variables involved. It should be noted that although $\beta_2$ is greater than $\beta_1$ in magnitude, the difference in the units of measurement of the respective variables ($z_1$ and $z_2$) tend to force this condition upon the equation. A comparison of the means, $\overline{X}_1 = 2.5$ and $\overline{X}_2 = 110$, demonstrates clearly the difference in the magnitude of the respective variables. We note that it takes more "weighting" of the intelligence rating ($\beta_2 = .60$) than it does for that of the h.p.a. in English courses ($\beta_1 = .2655$), in order to determine the criterion variable (h.p.a. in college freshman year).

The square of the multiple correlation coefficient, $R^2 = .40$, shows that only 40 per cent of what contributes to the h.p.a.'s of students at the end of the freshman year in college may be attributed to differences in intelligence ratings and differences in h.p.a.'s in high school English courses. The remaining 60 per cent must be due to other factors that have not been considered.

## LIMITATIONS OF PARTIAL AND MULTIPLE CORRELATION

To conclude our discussion of partial and multiple correlation, we point out certain limitations to the use of the method. First, partial correlation coefficients are *not* valid measures of relationship *unless all zero order coefficients, from which the partials are derived, are computed from data that form a linear regression pattern.* Second, the number of elements in the sample should be large, especially if there are four or more variables involved. If the values of the coefficients are calculated on the basis of samples composed of relatively few elements, they will have little reliability and significance. Third, the *interpretation of a partial r* suffers when we attempt to "partial out" such pervasive factors as "general intelligence," "memory," "background experience," and other similar types of variables in the many problems found in educational research. For example, it would be fallacious to interpret the partial correlation between reading comprehension and history, as the net relationship between these two variables with, say, the factor of "intelligence" partialled out. The main use and interpretation of partial *r*'s is in connection with multiple regression equations, where the purpose is to determine the relative weights to be assigned to the variables involved. Interpretations which lead to the imputing of psychological meaning to the partial *r*'s should be avoided. Finally, the main limitation of the multiple correlation coefficient *R* is that it is always positive, and variable errors of sampling tend to accumulate and make the value of the coefficient too large. This limitation can be nullified significantly by employing a large sample size, the elements of the sample being selected randomly.

In leaving the topic of multiple correlation, it should be pointed out that we have not touched upon the subject of *multivariate attributes.* Situations involving multivariate attributes arise when, after the relationship between two cross-classified attributes has been determined, a third attribute is introduced to further clarify the original relationship. This approach is termed the *"elaboration"* of the relationship, and adds a third dimension to the contingency table. Since this topic is given a lucid and fairly detailed presentation by *Zelditch,*[1] and since its inclusion here is not of great importance, we omit any further discussion of the subject, and refer the interested reader to this source.

## APPLICATIONS OF CORRELATIONAL ANALYSIS TO INSTRUMENTALITIES OF DATA COLLECTION

The discussion of correlational methods in connection with the process of estimation has provided us with the means of statistically considering the four fundamental aspects of instrumentalities of data collection: (1) validity,

(2) reliability, (3) objectivity, and (4) discrimination. It will be recalled that the objectivity of a data collecting instrument is high if two or more scorers, or evaluators, arrive at approximately the same score, or results, after evaluating the responses, or answers, to the questions composing the instrument. The discriminative quality of an instrumentality is good if it has the ability to differentiate between "good" and "poor" respondents. These two aspects (objectivity and discrimination) are not as susceptible to statistical interpretation as are those of validity and reliability. Due to this fact, and because of the fundamental importance of considering the factors of validity and reliability in the construction of any type of data gathering instrumentality, we now consider certain statistical aspects of these concepts.

## VALIDITY

There are four basic types of validity with which we are concerned: (1) *content* validity, (2) *concurrent* validity, (3) *predictive* validity, and (4) *construct* validity. *Content validity*, also termed "logical validity" and "face validity," is determined by the relevance of a test to different types of criteria, such as analyses of courses of study and jobs, analyses of textbooks, analyses of examination questions, pooled judgments of "experts," and logical analyses of mental processes and behaviors. *Concurrent validity* is determined on the basis of how well instrumentality scores correspond to already accepted standards. To exemplify, test results of a certain class in a given study, say, arithmetic, are compared to the teacher's estimates of the students' abilities in this field. If there is a high degree of relationship between the test scores and the teacher's estimates of abilities, the test is considered to have *high concurrent validity*. *Predictive validity* is determined by evaluating how well predictions made from the data gathering instrumentality are confirmed by evidence collected at a later time. Predictive validity differs from concurrent validity only to the extent that the evidence on the criterion measure is collected later instead of at the same time that the test is administered. *Construct validity* is determined by demonstrating that certain explanatory constructs account for performance on the test. This type of validity is ordinarily employed when the examiner has no definitive criterion measure and indirect measures must be used. Construct validity is used primarily when the other three types of validity are insufficient to indicate the degree to which the instrument measures what it is intended to measure.

## THE DETERMINATION OF VALIDITY THROUGH CORRELATION WITH A CRITERION

Whenever possible, the validity of an instrument should be determined directly by calculating the correlation between the test and an independent criterion. The criterion is defined to be an objective measure which forms the basis upon which the test, or instrument, is evaluated or judged. A high correlation between the test and the criterion is taken as evidence of validity providing both the test and the criterion are reliable.

To exemplify the foregoing, suppose a *test is constructed* to measure achievement in an English course. Based upon previous school marks in English, linguistic aptitude scores on a given section of a particular standardized test, and a verbal proficiency score on another section of that same test, the group of students taking the achievement test are classified as "good" or "poor" in English. A 2 × 2 table is constructed as follows:

|  | Grade | | |
|---|---|---|---|
|  | High | Low | |
| Good | $a$   20 | $b$   5 | 25 |
| Poor | $c$   2 | $d$   20 | 22 |
|  | 22 | 25 | |

$$\phi = \frac{ad - bc}{\sqrt{(a + c)(b + d)(c + d)(a + b)}}$$

$$\phi = \frac{400 - 10}{(22)(25)} = \frac{390}{550} \approx .71$$

where a "high" grade is determined as any score 5 points above the group mean score on the achievement test, and a "low" grade as any score 5 points below the mean. The $\phi$ coefficient of .71 provides an indication of the validity of the test, providing all of the tests involved in the situation were reliable, an assumption we have made in order to demonstrate this concept of validity.

### VALIDITY AND THE LENGTHENING OF A TEST

Lengthening of a test tends to increase its validity by making the test a better measure of a given criterion. The formula which shows the effect of the length of the test is:

$$r_{c(nX_0)} = \frac{nr_{cX_0}}{\sqrt{n + n(n - 1)r_{X_0X_1}}} \tag{13}$$

where:

$r_{c(nX_0)}$ = the correlation between the criterion $c$ and $n$ forms of test $X_0$, or test $X_0$ lengthened $n$ times

$r_{cX_0}$ = the correlation between the criterion $c$ and the given test $X_0$

$r_{X_0X_1}$ = the reliability coefficient of the test $X_0$

$n$ = number of parallel forms of test $X_0$, or the number of times the test is lengthened

To illustrate the application of formula (13), suppose a given test has a reliability coefficient ($r_{X_0X_1}$) of .80 and a correlation of .50 ($r_{cX_0}$) with a criterion $c$. What would be the value of the validity coefficient of the test, if the test were quadrupled in length? Substituting in formula (13), we have:

$$r_{c(4X_0)} = \frac{4(.50)}{\sqrt{4 + 4(3)(.80)}} = \frac{3}{\sqrt{13.6}} \approx \frac{2}{3.7} \approx .540$$

Thus, the effect of quadrupling the length of the test, or giving four forms of the test and averaging the four scores for each subject, increases the test's correlation with its criterion from .50 to .540.

Solving formula (13) for $n$, we have formula (14):

$$n = \frac{r_{c(nX_0)}^2(1 - r_{X_0X_1})}{r_{cX_0}^2 - r_{c(nX_0)}^2 r_{X_0X_1}} \tag{14}$$

From formula (14) we can determine how many times the test would have to be lengthened, or how many forms of a test would have to be administered, in order for a given value of the validity coefficient to be attained. To illustrate, suppose that a given test has a reliability coefficient ($r_{X_0X_1}$) of .60, and a correlation with its criterion ($r_{cX_0}$) of .40. It becomes necessary to know how many times the test would have to be lengthened in order to yield a validity coefficient of $r_{c(nX_0)} = .50$? Substituting in formula (14) we have:

$$n = \frac{(.50)^2(.40)}{(.40)^2 - (.50)^2(.60)} = \frac{.10}{.16 - .15} = 10$$

The test must be ten times its present length to produce a validity coefficient of $r_{c(nX_0)} = .50$. It should be pointed out that if the value of the validity for a given test is set too high; formula (14) will yield (impossible) negative values. The upper limit of the validity coefficient of a test is given by formula (15):

$$r_{c(\infty X_0)} = \frac{r_{cX_0}}{\sqrt{r_{X_0X_1}}} \tag{15}$$

where $r_{c(\infty X_0)}$ is the correlation between the criterion $c$ and true scores $X_\infty$ in the test $X_0$; $r_{cX_0}$ is the correlation between the test and the criterion $c$, and $r_{X_0X_1}$ is the reliability coefficient of the test $X_0$. In our previous example:

$$r_{c(\infty X_0)} = \frac{.40}{\sqrt{.60}} = \frac{.40}{.774} \approx .517$$

which shows that the given test cannot be expected to yield a validity coefficient of greater magnitude than .517 no matter how much it is lengthened.

## RELIABILITY

If a test yields consistent results, it is reliable. Reliability, therefore, is measured in terms of the consistency with which an instrument produces the same results in measuring whatever it does measure. Put in another way, a test may be invalid, but if it measures whatever it measures consistently, it is reliable.

Reliability deals with a certain *class* of test characteristics. This class is composed of the test traits of *stability, equivalence,* and *internal consistency.* Methods of estimating reliability, and a brief discussion of the three kinds of coefficients obtained in conjunction with the class of test characteristics mentioned earlier, are now presented.

The rationale underlying methods of estimating reliability is that of obtaining two or more measures with the same instrument, or with "parallel" forms of the instrument, and then determining the degree of relationship, or agreement, between them. To illustrate, if a tape measure is used meticulously to measure the width of a room, and each of six times that a measurement is made the same approach is applied as carefully and precisely as possible, the disagreement between the six measurements will indicate the unreliability of the measurement approach and the tape measure itself. If there is perfect agreement between the six measurements, we conclude that the tape measure is perfectly reliable. If the measurements of room width vary in magnitude each time one is made, the unreliability will increase with an increase in the variability of the measures. In similar fashion, the closer the agreement between the results of different administrations of a given data gathering instrument, the greater its reliability.

Four methods of estimating reliability are: (1) the test-retest method, (2) equivalent-forms method, (3) split-halves method, and (4) the Kuder-Richardson method. The *test-retest* approach to estimating reliability requires two administrations of the same instrument to the same group of students. The degree of relationship between the group's paired scores is indicated by a correlation coefficient, which, for this method, is sometimes referred to as the *coefficient of stability.* The greatest disadvantage of this method occurs in the magnitude of the time interval between administrations of the test. If the test is repeated too soon, the memory factor tends to produce coefficients that are spuriously high. On the other hand, a longer time interval between tests permits such *intervening variables* as growth and unlearning to make the self-correlation inconsistent, that is, higher or lower than it should be. The *equivalence-forms* method of measuring reliability avoids the disadvantages of time intervals between administrations of the data gathering instrument. Two equivalent forms of the instrument must be constructed. The forms should be as similar as possible, but not identical, in content, difficulty, format, number of items, and other aspects. The group being examined takes one form of the test, and then the other form. The scores of the group on the first form of the test paired with those that are appropriate on the second form of the test are "analyzed" to produce a correlation coefficient which is often referred to as the *coefficient of equivalence.* If the agreement (relationship) between the two sets of scores is high, we say that each form measures consistently, and is therefore reliable. The *split-halves method* of estimating reliability divides the items of a single test into halves. The division is usually accomplished by grouping the "odd-numbered" items and comparing them with the group of "even-numbered" items. Division into halves may also be obtained by comparing the items of the "first" half of the test to the items composing the "last" half. A division can also be accomplished by assigning half the test items to one grouping by means of a random numbers table, an action which automatically assigns the remaining half of the items to the second group. The division effected by grouping "odd-numbered" items and "even-numbered" items from a single test has the advantage of reasonably equalizing between the groups such aspects of the test and the testing situation as: practice, fatigue, content, item difficulty, distractions, and other similar factors. The degree of relationship between the set of scores of the one group with the set of scores of the other group is measured by a correlation coefficient which is also sometimes referred to as the *coefficient of equivalence.*

Since under the split-halves method the reliability holds only for half of the test, it is necessary to calculate a coefficient of reliability for the total test. The reliability of tests is, like validity, a function of the length of the test, that is, reliability increases with the number of functioning items contained in the test. Thus, the reliability of a half test is less than that of a whole test. A technique, however, is available for estimating the reliability of a whole test from that of its halves.

The Spearman–Brown prophecy formula estimates the *reliability of a lengthened test.* The formula is:

$$r_{nn} = \frac{nr}{1 + (n-1)r} \tag{16}$$

where $r$ is the original reliability coefficient, and $n$ is the number of times the test is lengthened, or the number of other similar forms of the test. When $r$, the original reliability coefficient, is computed for scores on two half tests, formula (16) becomes:

$$r_{22} = \frac{2\,(\text{reliability of half test})}{1 + (2-1)\,\text{reliability of half test}}$$

or:

$$r_{22} = \frac{2r}{1+r}$$

It has been shown experimentally that formula (16) yields *predicted* reliabilities that are in close agreement with obtained whole-test reliabilities, providing the $n$ forms of the test are as equivalent as possible in terms of mean score, dispersion (variability) of scores, and types of items.

Two other split-test methods of estimating reliability are reported by Guttman[2] and Rulon.[3] The method reported by Guttman requires only the variances of each half test and the variance of the total test, and is given by formula (17):

$$r_{22} = 2\left(1 - \frac{s_1^2 + s_2^2}{s_t^2}\right) \tag{17}$$

where $s_1^2$ denotes the variance of one half-test, $s_2^2$ denotes the variance of the other half-test, and $s_t^2$ is the variance of the total test. The method reported by Rulon, given by formula (18), requires only the variance of *differences between half-test scores* and the variance of the total test.

$$r_{22} = 1 - \frac{s_d^2}{s_t^2} \qquad (18)$$

where $s_d^2$ denotes the variance of the differences between half-test scores, and $s_t^2$ is the variance of the total test.

The Kuder–Richardson[4] methods estimate the internal consistency of a test. These methods do not require splitting the test into halves, rescoring them, and then calculating a correlation coefficient. The number of items in the test, the variance of the total test, and the arithmetic mean of the total test scores are the values required for the method given by formula (19):

$$r_{nc} = \frac{n}{n-1} \cdot \frac{s_t^2 - n\bar{p}\bar{q}}{s_t^2} \qquad (19)$$

where $n$ denotes the number of items in the test, $s_t^2$ is the variance of the total test scores, $\bar{q} = 1 - \bar{p}$, and

$$\bar{p} = \frac{M_t}{n} = \frac{\text{arithmetic mean of test scores}}{n}$$

Formula (19) underestimates the homogeneity (internal consistency) of a test when there is variation in "difficulty" among the test items. It usually yields a value lower than that obtained by the split-halves method. If the variability in item difficulty is not great, formula (19) is an adequate formula for making a quick estimate of the homogeneity of the test.

The Kuder–Richardson "20" is a formula for estimating homogeneity which yields a coefficient equal to the *mean of all the possible split-half coefficients of the test*. The formula is as follows:

$$r_{20} = \frac{n}{n-1} \cdot \frac{s_t^2 - \sum pq}{s_t^2} \qquad (20)$$

where $n$ = number of items included in the test, $s_t^2$ = variance of the total test scores, $p$ = proportion of students passing each item, and $q = 1 - p$. The value of $p$ is computed for each item on the test by counting the number of persons passing the item, and then dividing this value by the total number of persons taking the test. The product $pq$ is calculated for each item included in the test, and these products are added together to find the value of $\sum pq$.

Factors affecting reliability are: length of test, range of student talent, and the testing conditions. Other than pointing out that: (1) the reliability of a test increases with an increase in the length of the instruments; (2) the reliability of a test approaches a limiting value with increasing length of instrument; (3) the curve of increase in reliability flattens out with continued lengthening of the test;[5] (4) restriction in the range of talent lowers the reliability of a test; (5) greater variability in student talent results in a higher value of the reliability coefficient; (6) conditions of administering and scoring a test may increase or decrease its reliability coefficient; and (7) the *standard error of a score* is found by the formula:

$$SE_{(meas)} = s_t\sqrt{1 - r_{X_0 X_I}}$$

where $s_t$ = standard deviation of the total test scores, and $r_{X_0 X_I}$ = reliability coefficient of the test; we shall not attempt to discuss factors affecting reliability. Those readers who might be interested in a fairly detailed presentation of these topics are referred to (146) Remmers, Gage, and Rummel.

## THE RELATIONSHIP BETWEEN VALIDITY AND RELIABILITY

Validity and reliability are closely linked concepts. Both concepts involve test efficiency. Reliability does not go beyond the test measures themselves. Validity, however, involves external and independent criteria to establish a measure of the authenticity of the instrument. On this basis, reliability becomes a simpler measure to compute than that of validity with its necessity for establishing authentic criteria by which the test is validated.

Our discussion of validity and reliability may be summarized briefly as follows:

1. Reliability and validity are concepts that refer to different aspects of test efficiency.
2. A reliable test *cannot* be invalid, *theoretically*, but it might be judged invalid from the *practical* point of view on the basis of its correlation with available independent criteria.
3. A valid test cannot be unreliable, because the correlation of a test with a given criterion is limited by its own reliability coefficient.

With these few remarks about the reliability and validity of data gathering instruments we bring to a close our discussion of the broad area of estimation. Our discussion of estimation was for the purpose of clarifying certain numerical and analytical procedures associated with data collection, data processing, and the research decision aspects of the suggested general model of educational research. We are now prepared to consider the subject of statistical inference, a most important phase of the numerical and analytical procedures associated with the element of the model known as *the research decision*.

*Chapter 22—References*

See Bibliography: 4, 7, 8, 9, 18, 23, 38, 42, 43, 49, 53, 71, 77, 87, 89, 95, 104, 105, 108, 113, 123, 141, 146, 155, 159, 163, 182, 183, 200; 53a, 68a, 95a.

*Chapter Twenty-three*

# *Statistical Inference*

PROBABLY THE MOST IMPORTANT phase of the last two elements of the suggested general model of educational research, the elements of data processing and research decision, is that of statistical inference. Statistical inference is of a dual nature. First, it is the *process* used to derive a conclusion, and second, it is the *conclusion* derived from the research data. The *inference process*, employing numerical and analytical procedures, is put on a rigorously logical basis which involves random sampling and the theory of probability. Following this rationale the process of drawing an inference becomes one of testing the statistical hypotheses of the research problem.

In Chapter 3 it was pointed out that only three statistical hypotheses exist, those of: (a) magnitudes, (b) differences, and (c) relationships. It was also noted that from the three hypotheses four types of inference are drawn, those of: (a) magnitudes, (b) differences, (c) relationships, and (d) appraisals. Inferences of "appraisal" do not involve a "new" statistical hypothesis, because such inferences are based upon combinations of the hypotheses of difference, relationship, and magnitude.

The hypothesis of a research problem is a systematic and formal statement of a proposition. The hypothesis, as used in scientific inquiry, is an *inference* (conclusion) *to test, not a prejudice to defend*. The hypothesis serves two purposes in statistical inquiry: as an *antecedent* it gives direction and boundary to the inquiry; and when rejected or accepted it is a *consequence* of the inquiry. In order to test a *research hypothesis* by the method of statistical inference, it is necessary to first "map" the hypothesis into a series of *operational hypotheses*, and then translate the operational terms of the latter type of hypotheses into mathematical statements that serve as *statistical hypotheses*. The statistical hypotheses are then tested by the principles of statistical inference.

In statistical inquiry there are two basic types of inference: *deductive* and *inductive*. The *process of deductive inference* is employed when population characteristics and probabilities are known, and *we wish to make inferences about a sample drawn from that population*. *Inductive inference processes* are employed when *we wish to make estimates and inferences about unknown population characteristics on the basis of values of these characteristics calculated from the data included in a random sample drawn from the population*.

Most of the problems of educational research involve inductive inference because the value of the population characteristic (a parameter) under study and its probability of occurrence are unknown. For this reason the following procedure is suggested as the most suitable one for applying the process of statistical inference in the general model of education research:

1. State the *null* hypothesis $(H_0)$. The null hypothesis is a statistical hypothesis formulated with the possibility and hope of its being rejected at some defined probability value. If it is rejected, *the statistical alternative hypothesis $(H_1)$ may be accepted.* The "alternative" hypothesis $(H_1)$ is the statistical hypothesis of an operational hypothesis which has been "mapped" from the research hypothesis.

The nature of the operational hypothesis determines the form of the mathematical statement which is the statistical alternative hypothesis $(H_1)$. The form of $H_1$, in turn, determines the form of the null hypothesis $(H_0)$; see Chapter 3.

2. Select the proper statistical test. Under the supposition that the null hypothesis is true, the *sampling distribution* of the proper statistical test is chosen so that the data of the research will show either a *significant discrepancy* or deviation from the "null," or *no significant deviation* from that hypothesis. The field of statistical inquiry has developed to the point where for any given research design there are a number of alternative statistical tests that might be employed to arrive at a decision concerning the possible rejection, or non-rejection, of the null hypothesis. Since there are alternative tests, a rational basis for selecting the best or most appropriate one is needed.

The "nature of the source (population) of the research data" is examined to be certain that the conditions underlying a given research problem satisfy the requirements for application of the statistical test model in question. If it is not possible to test conditions underlying the research problem, certain conditions are *assumed to exist*, and the statistical test model is selected on the basis of this assumption. In these instances, all decisions made on the basis of the statistical test must be qualified with the statement: "providing the assumption is true." The most desirable course of action, obviously, is to avoid such an assumption whenever and wherever possible.

In the early days of statistical inquiry, many assumptions were made about the nature of the population from which the data were being drawn. These assumptions were not only about the distribution of the population, but about the *parameters* of the population as well. The statistical tests employed under such assumptions became known as *"parametric"* tests. Hence, any statistical test that involves population parameters (e.g., means, medians, modes, variances) is a *parametric statistical test*.

Many statistical tests have been developed that do not involve assumptions about the distribution and/or parameters of the population. These tests are considered to be *distribution free*, and are called *"nonparametric"* tests. Conclusions drawn on the basis of *nonparametric statistical tests* require fewer qualifications than do those drawn from parametric tests where it has been impossible to determine all conditions underlying the research problem. Parametric and nonparametric tests are discussed in detail later.

When selecting the most appropriate statistical test the researcher must know whether the observations were made independently of each other, whether they were taken from a population of a particular type of distribution, and whether there are enough observations to provide an adequate basis for conclusions about the hypothesis under test. When data are of the *nominal* and/or *ordinal* level of measurement, *only a nonparametric test can technically be employed.* When data are of the *interval* and/or *ratio-interval* level of measurement, the nonparametric test *may* be employed, *but the parametric test is more appropriate* on the basis that the power-efficiency of parametric tests is better than that of nonparametric tests under such conditions of measurement.

3. Specify a level of significance ($\alpha$) and a sample size *n*. After the null hypothesis has been stated, and the appropriate statistical test has been selected, the researcher should specify a level of significance ($\alpha$) and select an adequate sample size *n*. The most commonly chosen values of $\alpha$ are either .05 or .01. This selection of values for $\alpha$ defines the *level of significance,* and determines a set of values under a section of the probability curve of the statistical test being employed, known as the "*critical region.*" Assuming that the probability curve (statistical test distribution) meets the conditions (assumed or tested) underlying the research problem, and supposing also that the null hypothesis ($H_0$) is true under these conditions, we would expect the values of the statistic being employed) in the critical region to occur five times out of 100 ($\alpha = .05$), or once out of 100 times ($\alpha = .01$), due to chance factors alone. If then, we observe a "computed" value of the statistic (e.g., $\bar{x}$) which is included in the subset of values composing the critical region, the null hypothesis ($H_0$) is rejected, and the statistical alternative hypothesis ($H_1$) may be accepted.

If the null hypothesis ($H_0$) being employed *actually is true,* the establishment of $\alpha = .05$, or $\alpha = .01$, allows the probability of a Type I($\alpha$) error (rejecting a *true* hypothesis) to be made either five in 100 times, or once in 100 times, on the basis of chance factors alone. Thus, when the value of $\alpha$ is determined (arbitrarily) by the researcher, the probability of the Type I error is determined at the same time. The Type I error, *rejecting a true hypothesis,* is not the only error that can be made in connection with the process of statistical inference. There are two types of errors that can be made: the Type I, or $\alpha$ error, and the Type II, or $\beta$ (beta) error—*not rejecting a false hypothesis. With a given sample size n,* the choosing of $\alpha = .05$, or $\alpha = .01$, not only determines the probability of the Type I error, but determines, *in part,* the probability of making the $\beta$ error (Type II), as well. To illustrate, suppose the null hypothesis states that the population mean is 20, ($H_0 : \mu = 20$). A random sample of 25 elements is drawn, and the *sampling distribution of the mean ($\bar{X}$) for sample size n* = 25, known to be normally distributed, is selected to serve as a statistical test model for this "null" ($H_0$). With the establishment of the statistical test model and the sample size of $n = 25$, the researcher sets the level of significance at $\alpha = .05$. The null hypothesis ($H_0 : \mu = 20$) is submitted to test, and if it is known that the standard deviation of the population of data is $\sigma = 5$, we can find the values of $\bar{X}$ that define the critical region, by the formula:

$$z = \frac{\overline{X} - U_{\bar{x}}}{\sigma_{\bar{x}}} = \frac{\overline{X} - U_{\bar{x}}}{\sigma/\sqrt{n}}$$

We know from the normal probability table that the value of $z$, in a two-tailed test, for $\alpha = .05$ is $z = \pm 1.96$.* Thus, we find the critical region, which includes 5 per cent of the area under the normal curve, 2.5 per cent in each tail, to be:

$$\pm 1.96 = \frac{\overline{X} - 20}{5/\sqrt{25}}$$

$$\pm 1.96 = \frac{\overline{X} - 20}{1}$$

$$\therefore \quad \overline{X}_{\text{Up}} = 20 + 1.96 = 21.96$$

and:

$$\overline{X}_{\text{Lo}} = 20 - 1.96 = 18.04$$

hence the critical region is defined by all values of the sets $\{\overline{X} < 18.04\}$ and $\{\overline{X} > 21.96\}$. The sampling distribution is shown in Figure 18.

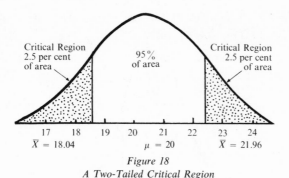

*Figure 18*
*A Two-Tailed Critical Region*

From Figure 18, we note that a computed value of $(\overline{X} < 18.04)$ or $(\overline{X} > 21.96)$, if the null $H_0$ is *actually true, can be expected to occur 5 per cent of the time due to chance factors alone, and would lead to the error of rejecting the true hypothesis that per cent of the time.*

In order to understand how the $\beta$ (beta) error is determined, *suppose* that when the null hypothesis $(H_0 : \mu = 20)$ is advanced, that the *actual*, or *true*, value of the population mean is: $\mu = 21$. Under these circumstances the null hypothesis would *actually be false*. The conditions for making the $\beta$-error (Type II) would now exist, because the $\beta$-error is that of *not rejecting $H_0$ when in actuality it is false*. The magnitude of the $\beta$-error in this case, i.e., when actually $\mu = 21$, is found as follows:

* See Chapter 16 for selected values from a normal probability table.

Employ the normal deviate formula, and substitute the *true* value of the population mean, $\mu = 21$, into the formula as follows:

$$z = \frac{\overline{X} - \mu_{\bar{x}}}{\sigma/\sqrt{\eta}} = \frac{\overline{X} - 21}{5/\sqrt{25}} = \overline{X} - 21$$

substitute in the value of the boundary of the "upper" critical region ($\overline{X}_{\text{Up}} = 21.96$), and find the value of $z$:

$$z = 21.96 - 21 = +.96$$

substitute the boundary value ($\overline{X}_{\text{Lo}}$) of the "lower" critical region, and find $z$:

$$z = 18.04 - 21 = -2.96$$

The *approximate area* accumulated under the curve from $z = -\infty$ to $z = +.96$ is $A \approx .8314$ (interpolated). The *approximate area* accumulated from $z = -\infty$ to $z = -2.96$ is $A \approx .0015$ (interpolated). Thus, the $\beta$-error *under these conditions* becomes $\beta = .8314 - .0015 = .8299$ or 83 per cent. Figure 19 shows the sampling distribution of $\overline{X}$, with the shaded area denoting the chance of *correctly rejecting* the *false* $H_0: \mu = 20$, because the value of the population mean *actually* is: $\mu = 21$; and the unshaded area denoting the chance of *making the $\beta$ (beta) error*; i.e., *of not rejecting the false* $H_0: \mu = 20$.

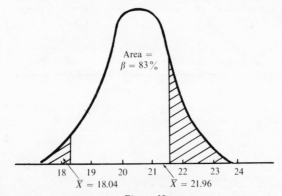

Area = $\beta = 83\%$

18    19    20    21    22    23    24
$\overline{X} = 18.04$          $\overline{X} = 21.96$

*Figure 19*
*Graphic Illustration of a Beta Error*

If the *actual* (true) *value* of the population mean had been $\mu = 22$, or $\mu = 19$, or $\mu = 20.5$, or $\mu = 18$, or $\mu = $ *to any value other than the one stated in the "null"* ($H_0: \mu = 20$), we would have found, for fixed $n = 25$, and $\alpha = .05$, a *different value* of $\beta$ for each of the *alternatives* (22, 19, 20.5, etc.). For a given research problem, such as our example, the $\beta$-error can be computed for all possible and plausible alternative values in the neighborhood of the value advanced in the null hypothesis.[1]

The *power of a test* is defined as the probability of rejecting the null hypothesis ($H_0$) when it *actually is false* and should be rejected. Expressed in formula form:

Power = 1 − probability of Type II error = 1 − $\beta$. If the sample size *n is held constant*, a decrease in $\alpha$(e.g., from $\alpha = .05$ to $\alpha = .01$) will increase $\beta$, or an increase in $\alpha$ will decrease $\beta$. The researcher should attempt to maintain an optimum balance between $\alpha$ and $\beta$ errors. The balance is most easily accomplished by *increasing* the sample size *n*, or selecting the statistical test of the highest *power-efficiency* rating for the conditions involved in the research problem. If we select $\alpha = .05$, we should make a decided effort to keep $\beta$ low in value as well. It should be pointed out, however, that in actual practice there is little effort expended to *control* $\beta$. There is a decided effort, however, to maintain some idea or notion of how large it may be under the various conditions of the research problem. As a last point of discussion of the $\alpha$ (Type I) error, and the $\beta$ (Type II) error, the effect of one-tailed tests should be mentioned.

In a one-tailed test the form of the null hypothesis would be $H_0 : \mu \geq \mu_0$ or $H_0 : \mu \leq \mu_0$. In the first case ($\mu$ *greater* than or *equal* to $\mu_0$), the critical region would be in the *lower* tail of the curve; and in the second case ($\mu$ *less* than or *equal* to $\mu_0$), the critical region would be in the *upper* tail of the curve. The effects on the $\beta$ error for changes in $\alpha$ and sample size *n*, under one-tailed tests, are investigated along lines similar to those employed in our discussion of the two-tailed tests. The relationships between $\alpha$, $\beta$, and *n* that existed under the two-tailed tests exist under the one-tailed tests as well.

The power of a statistical test is affected by whether the hypothesis calls for a one-tailed or two-tailed test. A one-tailed test is more powerful than a two-tailed test because it not only denotes *significant difference*, but *describes the direction* of the difference as well.

4. Determine the sampling distribution of the statistical test under the supposition that the null hypothesis ($H_0$) is true. The concept of *sampling distribution* has been discussed earlier (see Chapter 15) in some detail and need not be covered again. The *use* of the sampling distribution in the inference process, however, is the important point to be treated here. After the statistical test is chosen, the sampling distribution of the test statistic must be determined.

The sampling distribution of a given statistic (e.g., mean, mode) is used to determine the probabilities (under the supposition that the null hypothesis is true) that are associated with possible numerical values of the statistic being employed. The probability "associated with" the occurrence of a particular value of the statistic under the hypothesis does not mean the *exact* probability of that *particular value* of the statistic, but rather the occurrence under $H_0$ of a value *as extreme or more extreme than the particular value* of the test statistic. Thus, the sampling distribution of a given statistic is used in the inference process to make certain probability statements about the occurrence of particular numerical values of that statistic.

5. Determine the critical region. After the sampling distribution has been chosen, the possible values of the statistic that cause rejection of the null hypothesis ($H_0$) and thus form the *critical region*, or *region of rejection*, must be

determined. The critical region is so defined that the probability under the null hypothesis of the test statistic having a value in that region is α (alpha). Expressed in another way, the critical region is composed of a *set* of "extreme" values under the supposition that the null hypothesis ($H_0$) is true, and the probability of a value of the test statistic being derived from the sample falling in this region is very small (actually equal to or less than the value of α). The other important factor in determining the critical region is the "form" of the null hypothesis. If $H_0$ is stated in such a fashion that a *direction of the difference* is indicated (e.g., $H_0 : \mu \geq \mu_0$), then the *total critical region is located in one end of the sampling distribution*, and a "one-tailed test" is employed. If $H_0$ is a statement of "no difference," and therefore does not stipulate a direction (e.g., $H_0 : \mu = \mu_0$), then the critical region is divided into two equal parts, one of which is located in the "positive (upper)" end of the distribution and the other in the "negative (lower)" end of the "curve," and a "two-tailed test" is employed.

Although the *location* of the critical region varies with one-tailed and two-tailed tests, the "region" is unchanged in size. In specific terms, if α = .05, then the critical region is 5 per cent of the total area under the curve of the sampling distribution. In the case of the one-tailed test, the "5 per cent region" is located in one of the ends of the distribution, depending upon the "direction" of $H_0$. In the two-tailed test, $2\frac{1}{2}$ per cent of the total area is located in each end of the sampling distribution to form the 5 per cent critical region.

6. Compute the values of the statistic being employed in the test. The methods and mathematical procedures involved in computing the values of such statistics as, say, the mean ($\overline{X}$), the median, and the variance, have been discussed under basic statistical concepts, and will not be re-stated here. The point to be made is that the value of the statistic under consideration is calculated from the sample, and then is substituted in the appropriate places of the statistical test so that its (the test's) value may be determined.

7. Arrive at a decision to reject, or not reject, the null hypothesis ($H_0$). After completing Step 6, the statistical test yields a value. If this value falls in the critical region of the sampling distribution, the decision is to reject the null hypothesis ($H_0$), which in turn allows the statistical alternative hypothesis ($H_1$) to be accepted. If the value of the statistical test does not fall in the critical region, the decision is to *not reject* the null ($H_0$). This result does *not* mean that the null hypothesis is accepted. The null hypothesis ($H_0$) is an "empty" or "void" statement of "no difference" advanced with the hope that the data of the sample will reject it, thus permitting the statistical alternative hypothesis ($H_1$) to be accepted with a "stronger" (higher) probability than otherwise would have been possible. Thus, the "null" ($H_0$) can *never be accepted*. It can only be "rejected" or "not rejected." In those cases where the null hypothesis is *not rejected*, the statistical alternative hypothesis cannot be accepted. The reasoning involved in reaching the decision to reject, or not reject, the null hypothesis ($H_0$) is explained cogently by Siegel:

> If the probability associated with the occurrence under the null hypothesis of a particular value in the sampling distribution is very small, we may explain the actual occurrence of the value

in two ways: first, we may explain it by deciding that the null hypothesis is false, or second, we may explain it by deciding that a rare and unlikely event has occurred. In the decision process, we choose the first of these explanations. Occasionally, of course, the second may be the correct one. In fact, the probability that the second explanation is the correct one is given by $\alpha$, for rejecting $H_0$ when in fact it is true is the Type I error.... [2]

### Chapter 23—References

See Bibliography: 4, 23, 35, 38, 49, 52, 53, 66, 71, 94, 104, 113, 123, 143, 148, 150, 155, 158, 159, 170, 183; 20a, 38a, 43a, 66a, 67a, 84a.

*Chapter Twenty-four*

# Nonparametric Statistical Tests—I

THE PARAMETRIC STATISTICAL TEST MODEL is employed in those cases of research where the problem can be investigated by testing certain stipulations about selected parameters of a *defined* population from which the sample of the study is drawn. Frequently the *conditions that form the definition of the population* are only *assumed to exist* and no effort is made to test for their existence. In such cases, the reliability of the conclusions derived from the parametric test involved depends greatly upon the validity of the assumptions made about the population. At the same time, the parametric statistical test model requires that the data under analysis result from measurement at the level of at least the interval scale (see "Levels of Measurement," Chapter 7).

The nonparametric statistical test model is employed in those cases of research that do *not* involve specification of conditions about population parameters. With the exception of assuming that the observations of the sample being employed are independent, and the variable under study might be considered continuous, no other assumptions need be made. Parametric tests require that the data be of at least the interval level of measurement, and therefore technically cannot be applied to those cases where the data are of the nominal and ordinal scales of measurement. The nonparametric tests do not place a requirement on the level of measurement of the data. Technically, the nonparametric tests may be applied to data of any level of measurement: nominal, ordinal, interval, or ratio-interval. Because the parametric tests are of higher power-efficiency, when the data are of the appropriate level of measurement, they are employed more frequently than the nonparametric tests in such cases. The "nonparametrics" are mainly applied to those problems in which the data are of the nominal and ordinal levels of measurement.

Since the level of measurement of the data which permits the proper use of parametric tests is usually achieved only in those cases involving "scores" in educational research, it is important that the research worker in education have a basic understanding of nonparametric statistical test models for those cases where "categories" (enumeration statistics) and "rankings" must be analyzed correctly. The attempt here is to present a variety of nonparametric tests to help the reader develop a basic understanding of this most important area of statistics.

It will be noticed that in the application of many of the nonparametric statistical tests presented, the data are changed from scores to ranks, or scores to categories, or even to algebraic signs. This procedure usually evokes the criticism of "not using all the information available." In answer to this criticism it must be remembered that the loss of some information is preferred over the possibility of making *faulty assumptions* about the sampling distribution underlying the employment of a parametric test.

In general, the following advantages accrue in the use of nonparametric statistical test models:

1. The probability statements yielded by most nonparametric tests are *exact probabilities* regardless of the shape of the distribution of the population from which the sample is drawn.
2. Nonparametric statistical test models are particularly useful in connection with small samples: (e.g., $n = 5$).
3. Observations taken from *several different populations* may be tested by appropriate nonparametric statistical models.
4. Nonparametric statistical tests treat data in the nominal and ordinal levels (scales) of measurement.

The disadvantages of nonparametric tests are:

1. If conditions for the application of parametric tests are satisfied, the nonparametric test *forces* a waste of information.
2. Unless special assumptions are made, there is no nonparametric test suitable for the task of testing the interactions of an analysis of variance design model.

With this background we are now ready to consider certain nonparametric test models. It is the intent here to present enough tests to allow the researcher a relatively wide latitude in selecting a nonparametric technique that best fits the requirements of the model of educational research which he might be employing. For further information on nonparametric statistical tests, see Siegel.[1]

## THE CHI-SQUARE TEST

Problems in educational research frequently involve the counting of a number of persons, objects, or responses as they occur under various categories or classifications. For example, school children may be classified and counted according to their reading ability, mathematical ability, or their most frequent modes of behavior. Similarly, persons of the community may be classified according to whether they are "in favor of," "indifferent to," or "opposed to," the voting of additional millage to the school tax in a given district. In each case, the hypothesis submitted for rejection or acceptance is that the frequencies occurring in each of the categories are significantly different. The chi-square statistical test is suitable for analyzing data and problems like those mentioned. The common principle underlying the chi-square test is that the test evaluates the probability of obtaining a set of *observed* frequencies in given categories of a sample taken from a population wherein the categories have a certain set of *theoretical*, or *expected* frequencies occurring within them. The number of categories may be two or more, and the theoretical frequencies may be determined in a number of different ways, depending upon the particular problem under consideration.

There are two general classes of problems to which the chi-square statistical test model may be applied: *tests of independence*, and *goodness-of-fit tests*. In both cases, the analysis involves *enumeration* (nominal level of measurement) data only.

The technique of the goodness-of-fit type test involves the process of testing whether a significant difference exists between the *observed* frequency of occurrence of objects or items in each category, and an *expected* number derived on the basis of the null hypothesis. In order to be able to compare *observed* with *expected* frequencies, there must be some way of stating what frequencies are to be expected in each category. The null hypothesis is stated in such fashion as to provide *expected* (theoretical) frequencies for each of the categories in the population under consideration. In short, the expected, or theoretical, frequencies are deduced from the null hypothesis. The chi-square statistical test indicates whether the difference between the observed and the theoretical frequencies is of such magnitude that it has a high probability or a low probability of occurrence if the null hypothesis is considered to be true.

The formula for testing the null hypothesis is:

$$\chi^2 = \sum_{i=1}^{k} \frac{(f_0 - f_e)^2}{f_e} \qquad (5)$$

where $f_o$ denotes the observed frequency of occurrence of cases in a given category; $f_e$ denotes the expected (theoretical) frequency of occurrence of cases in the given category if the null hypothesis $(H_0)$ is considered to be true; and $\sum_{i=1}^{k}$ denotes the operation of summing the expression $(f_o - f_e)^2/f_e$ over all $k$ categories.

The chi-square test employed as a goodness-of-fit test, then, will show a small value for $\chi^2$ in formula (5) if the fit is a "good" one under the null hypothesis $(H_0)$. In such cases, the difference between the *observed frequencies* and the *theoretical frequencies* (prescribed by the null hypothesis) will be small. If the difference between the *observed* and *expected* frequencies is large, the value of $\chi^2$ will be large, and the fit will be considered to be a poor one. Thus, the greater the value of $\chi^2$ (occurring because of large differences between observed and expected frequencies) the more likely is the possibility that the observed frequencies did *not* come from the population defined by the null hypothesis $(H_0)$. In summary, then, if the value of $\chi^2$ is small, we *do not reject* the null $(H_0)$; if the value of $\chi^2$ is large, the null $(H_0)$ *is rejected*; and the statistical alternative hypothesis $(H_1)$ can be accepted.

The sampling distribution of $\chi^2$, considering $H_0$ to be true, is found from formula (5). We have seen that sampling distributions vary with the size of the sample $n$. The sampling distribution of $\chi^2$, however, varies according to the *number of categories* and *not* the *total number of observations*. This feature leads us to the concept of *degrees of freedom* (*df* ).

The number of degrees of freedom in the data depends upon how many tabular cell entries are free to vary under the restrictions imposed upon the data by the totals in the *margin* of the table. Since the *marginal totals* (constants) will vary with the organization of the data, the construction of the table is very important to the determination of the number of degrees of freedom (*df* ) involved in a given problem. For example, if 100 frequencies are classified (tabled) in two categories, we know the *marginal total* is a fixed constant, 100, and when we discover that 60 cases (frequencies) occur in the first category, we know that 40 *must* fall in the second category. Thus, only one cell entry is free to vary (*df* = 2 − 1 = 1), because once the number of cases for the first cell is determined, the entry for the second cell must be equal to *n* less the number of cases occurring in the "free" (first) cell. Suppose now that the table had been organized to cover *four* categories instead of two. The marginal total would remain 100, but now we would find that the first *three cell entries* would be "free" to vary, but the entry for the fourth cell would be *forced* to be equal to 100 less the total number of cases occurring in the first three cells. Thus, the number of degrees of freedom associated with this tabular organization of the data would be: *df* = 4 − 1 = 3. In general, when the goodness-of-fit approach is employed, and the expected frequencies ($f_e$) are fully specified by the null hypothesis ($H_0$), if there are $k$ categories in the classification, then *df* = $k − 1$.

Probability tables for the sampling distributions of chi-square can be found in almost any statistics book that contains discussions of the topic. A portion of a chi-square probability table is shown in Figure 20.

| | Probability under $H_0$ that $\chi^2 \geq$ Tabled Value | | | | | |
|---|---|---|---|---|---|---|
| *df* | .90 | .50 | .10 | .05 | .02 | .01 |
| 1 | .016 | .46 | 2.71 | 3.84 | 5.41 | 6.64 |
| 2 | .21 | 1.39 | 4.60 | 5.99 | 7.82 | 9.21 |
| 3 | .58 | 2.37 | 6.25 | 7.82 | 9.84 | 11.34 |
| 4 | 1.06 | 3.36 | 7.78 | 9.49 | 11.67 | 13.28 |
| 5 | 1.61 | 4.35 | 9.24 | 11.07 | 13.39 | 15.09 |
| 10 | 4.86 | 9.34 | 15.99 | 18.31 | 21.16 | 23.21 |
| 20 | 12.44 | 19.34 | 28.41 | 31.41 | 35.02 | 37.57 |
| 30 | 20.60 | 29.34 | 40.26 | 43.77 | 47.96 | 50.89 |

*Figure 20*
*Portion of the Probability Table of Chi-Square*

Chi-square probability tables usually are constructed with the degrees of freedom (*df* ) listed down the first column. At the top of each of the other columns are listed the *probabilities of occurrence* (two-tailed) of certain $\chi^2$ values under the null hypothesis ($H_0$). Inside the table are found the *minimum values of* $\chi^2$ that are significant at the level of probability found at the tops of the respective columns. If the value yielded by formula (5) is as great, or greater than the tabled value, the data have yielded a value of $\chi^2$ which is significant at that probability level. Although we have said that the levels of significance usually chosen are

$\alpha = .05$ and $\alpha = .01$, many researchers, when employing the chi-square statistical test, choose to state that the probability level of $\alpha = .05$ "places the 'null' $(H_0)$ in doubt"; so that the levels of $\alpha = .02$ and $\alpha = .01$ are "significant," and "highly significant," respectively; and indicate that $H_0$ should be rejected. The usual $\chi^2$ probability table shows many more columns of probability values, and many more rows of degrees of freedom values than those shown in Figure 20. The interested reader may consult any of the statistics texts footnoted prior to this point to find a complete table of chi-square.

To illustrate the use of the chi-square statistical test model under the goodness-of-fit approach, suppose that in the process of conducting a research project, it becomes necessary to know if there is a significant difference between the "yes" and "no" votes expressed by 212 respondents to a question included in a mailed questionnaire. If the general model of educational research were being employed, the researcher would proceed through the statistical inference process associated with the suggested model elements of "Data Processing" and "Research Decision" as follows:

1. *State the null hypothesis.* $H_0 : f_{no} = f_{yes}$; that is, there is no significant difference between the frequency of occurrence of "yes" and "no" votes expected in the population, and any *observed differences* are merely chance variations to be expected in a random sample of 212 responses taken from the *population of responses* under consideration. The statistical alternative hypothesis is: $H_1 : f_{no} \neq f_{yes}$; the *expected* frequencies are not equal.

2. *Select the proper statistical test.* Choose the $\chi^2$ test because the level of measurement of the data is nominal (categorical), and the null hypothesis specifies a comparison of *observed* and *expected* frequencies in discrete categories, where the categories are defined as "yes" votes and "no" votes.

3. *State the level of significance* $(\alpha)$, *and the sample size* $(n)$. The sample size of 212 is considered to be random, representative, and adequate. The level of significance is chosen as: $\alpha = .01$.

4. *Choose the proper sampling distribution of the chi-square test under the supposition that $H_0$ is true.* The proper form of the sampling distribution for $\chi^2$ is given by formula (5):

$$\chi^2 = \sum_{i=1}^{k} \frac{(f_0 - f_e)^2}{f_e} \tag{5}$$

For this particular application, formula (5) becomes:

$$\chi^2 = \sum_{i=1}^{2} \frac{(f_o - f_e)^2}{f_e}$$

5. *Determine the critical region.* In our example, the critical region will be composed of all values as *great*, or *greater than* the *critical value* of $\chi^2$ found in the $\chi^2$ probability table at the intersection of the degrees of freedom row: $df = 2 - 1 = 1$, and the probability column labeled ".01." Consulting the table in Figure 20, we find the critical value of $\chi^2$ to be: $\chi^2 = 6.64$. This entry

indicates that if the value of $\chi^2$ computed from the sample data is as large, or larger than 6.64, then the random sample of 212 responses which we have drawn departs this much from the expected equal frequencies (defined by $H_0$), only 1 per cent of the time, or less, due to chance factors alone. In other words, the null hypothesis ($H_0$) will be rejected if the observed *value* of $\chi^2$ is such that the *probability of its occurrence*, under the supposition that $H_0$ is true, for $df = 1$ is equal to or *less* than $\alpha = .01$.

6. *Compute the value of formula (5) for the data of the sample.* Suppose that 86 of the 212 responses were "no" votes, and the remaining 126 were "yes" votes. The data could be presented as shown in the chi-square table below.

Table IV
Chi-Square Table (Single Classification)

| Number of "Yes" and "No" Votes from a Sample of 212 Respondents | | | |
|---|---|---|---|
| | Yes | No | Total |
| Respondents | $f_o = 126$ $f_e = 106$ | $f_o = 86$ $f_e = 106$ | 212 |

The *observed* frequencies are denoted by $f_o$, and the *expected* frequencies by $f_e$ in the respective cells of the table. Under the null hypothesis: $[H_0 : f_{no} = f_{yes}$ (expected)] we would expect the respondents to cast 106 "no" votes and 106 "yes" votes. It should be noted that the *sum* of the *observed* frequencies must be equal to the *sum* of *expected* frequencies in the table. In our example: $\sum f_o = \sum f_e = 212$. This necessary condition may be used as a check when the values of $f_e$ for the cells of the table are determined from $H_0$. The computation of $\chi^2$ for our example is as follows:

$$\chi^2 = \sum_{i=1}^{k} \frac{(f_o - f_e)^2}{f_e} = \sum_{i=1}^{2} \frac{(f_o - f_e)^2}{f_e}$$

$$= \frac{(126 - 106)^2}{106} + \frac{(86 - 106)^2}{106}$$

$$= \frac{(20)^2}{106} + \frac{(-20)^2}{106} = \frac{400}{106} + \frac{400}{106} = \frac{800}{106}$$

$$\therefore \quad \chi^2 \approx 7.55$$

7. *The decision to reject, or not reject, the null hypothesis ($H_0$) is made.* Since the value of : $\chi^2 \approx 7.55$ is greater than $\chi^2 = 6.64$ (see Step 5) at $1 df$ for $\alpha = .01$, the decision is to *reject* the null hypothesis ($H_0 : f_{no} = f_{yes}$), which allows the acceptance of the statistical alternative hypothesis ($H_1 : f_{no} \neq f_{yes}$) for the population from which the sample was taken.

The decision to accept the statistical alternative hypothesis ($H_1$) contributes information which is necessary to the process of deriving the *research decision* concerning the problem area being analyzed.

When there are only $k = 2$ categories (1 $df$), the *expected* frequency for each cell should be at least 5, if the $\chi^2$ test is to be employed. When the number of categories is greater than $2(k > 2$; hence, $df > 1$), the $\chi^2$ test should not be used when more than 20 per cent of the *expected* frequency cell entries are less than 5, or when any particular cell shows an *expected* frequency less than 1. These conditions can be altered in some cases by combining adjacent categories. This action is only recommended if the combining of categories does not lead to a considerable loss of information about the problem under study, and naturally, only if there are more than two categories in the table that were initially under consideration.

If the original table includes but two cells (categories), and one (or both) of them shows an *expected* frequency of less than 5; or if after combining adjacent categories a table of *two cells* (categories) is formed, and the *expected* frequency of one of them is less than 5, then the *binomial* test can be employed instead of the $\chi^2$ test.

In closing our discussion of the $\chi^2$ test application *to problems of goodness-of-fit*, it should be pointed out that when there are more than two categories involved ($k > 2$, or $df > 1$), $\chi^2$ tests are insensitive to the effects of *order*, and therefore may not be the most appropriate ones to apply when the null hypothesis ($H_0$) takes order into account. The Kolmogorov–Smirnov test, which we discuss later, can be applied to goodness-of-fit problems, and usually is more appropriate to apply than $\chi^2$ tests when the data are of the ordinal level of measurement.[2]

The chi-square statistical test model may also be applied to the general class of problems including *tests of independence*. Independence is obviously the opposite of *association*, and as a result, tests of independence may be applied to hypotheses concerned with *difference* (independence) and *relationship* (association).

When the data of the research are classified under discrete categories according to frequency of occurrence, the $\chi^2$ statistical test may be employed to determine if significant differences exist among the $k$ independent groups. The null hypothesis under test is that the $k$ samples of frequencies come from the same population or identical populations, and *do not differ* among themselves. The null ($H_0$) is tested by applying formula (6):

$$\chi^2 = \sum_{i=1}^{r} \sum_{j=1}^{k} \frac{(f_{oij} - f_{eij})^2}{f_{eij}} \tag{6}$$

where $f_{oij}$ is the *observed frequency* of occurrence of the characteristic to be categorized in the $i$-th row of the $j$-th column; and $f_{eij}$ is the *expected frequency* of occurrence of the characteristic anticipated under $H_0$, and to be categorized in the $i$-th row of the $j$-th column. The expected frequency ($f_{eij}$) for each cell is found by multiplying the two marginal totals common to a particular cell, and then dividing this product by the total number of cases in the table, $n$ (see example). $\sum_{i=1}^{r} \sum_{j=1}^{k}$ indicates that the quantity $(f_{oij} - f_{eij})^2/f_{eij}$ is to be summed over all cells formed by the intersections of the $i$ rows and $j$ columns of the contingency table.

The values of $\chi^2$ found from formula (6) are distributed approximately as chi-square with degrees of freedom $(df) = (r - 1)(k - 1)$, where $r =$ the number of rows, and $k =$ the number of columns in the contingency table. Following the same procedure associated with the goodness-of-fit approach: if the value of $\chi^2$ computed from the data by formula (6) is equal to, or greater than, the critical $\chi^2$ value for a particular level of significance and a given number of degrees of freedom: $[df = (r - 1) \cdot (k - 1)]$, found in the chi-square probability table, then the null hypothesis $(H_0)$ is rejected at the level of significance $(\alpha)$.

To illustrate this particular type of application of $\chi^2$, i.e., its application to hypotheses of *difference* (independence), suppose that in the mailed-survey model of descriptive research (Chapter 10), the question was raised as to whether the reaction to the statement shown below was independent of the degree held by the respondent.

1. The program, or plan of work, I pursued while obtaining my latest degree from the college:
    (a) Was of great help to me on my present job. (G)
    (b) Was of some help to me on my present job. (S)
    (c) Was of little or no help to me on my present job. (L)

The procedure for determining whether group membership (degree held) affects the response to the statement is as follows:

1. *State the null hypothesis* $(H_0)$

$$H_0: \begin{cases} P_{BG} = P_{BS} = P_{BL} \\ P_{MG} = P_{MS} = P_{ML} \\ P_{DG} = P_{DS} = P_{DL} \end{cases}$$

or put into statement form: the proportion of graduates in the three alternative degree classifications [undergraduate (B), master's (M), and doctorate (D)] is the same in all classifications of response [great (G), some (S), little or no help (L)]. The statistical alternative $(H_1)$ is: the proportion of graduates in the three alternative degree classifications differs among the three response classifications.

2. *Select the proper statistical test.* Since the data under consideration are classified into more than two discrete categories that are considered to be independent under the null hypothesis, the $\chi^2$ test is an appropriate one.

3. *State the level of significance* $(\alpha)$, *and the sample size* $(n)$. The sample size of $n = 420$ is considered to be random, representative, and adequate. The level of significance is chosen as: $\alpha = .01$.

4. *Choose the proper sampling distribution of the chi-square test under the supposition that* $H_0$ *is true.* The proper form of the sampling distribution of $\chi^2$

for this type of application under $[df = (r - 1) \cdot (k - 1)]$ is given by formula (6):

$$\chi^2 = \sum_{i=1}^{r} \sum_{j=1}^{k} \frac{(f_{oij} - f_{eij})^2}{f_{eij}} \tag{6}$$

in this case, formula (6) under $[df = (3 - 1) \cdot (3 - 1) = 4]$, becomes:

$$\chi^2 = \sum_{i=1}^{3} \sum_{j=1}^{3} \frac{(f_{oij} - f_{eij})^2}{f_{eij}}$$

5. *Determine the critical region.* In this example, the critical region will be composed of all values as *great*, or *greater than*, the critical value of $\chi^2$ found in the $\chi^2$ probability table at the intersection of the degrees of freedom row: $[df = (3 - 1) \cdot (3 - 1) = 4]$, and the probability column labeled ".01." Consulting the table in Figure 20, we find the critical value of $\chi^2$ to be: $\chi^2 = 13.28$. This entry tells us that if the value of $\chi^2$ computed from the sample data is as large, or larger than, 13.28, the probability associated with its occurrence, under the supposition that $H_0$ is true, is equal to or less than $\alpha = .01$.

6. *Compute the value of formula (6) for the data of the sample.* Suppose that the 420 responses are arranged as shown in the contingency table below:

Table V
A Contingency Table Showing Responses of Graduates
(Fictitious Data)

| Latest Degree | Response | | | Total |
| --- | --- | --- | --- | --- |
| | Great | Some | Little or None | |
| Doctorate | $f_o = 35$ $f_e = 22.5$ | $f_o = 50$ $f_e = 46$ | $f_o = 20$ $f_e = 36.5$ | 105 |
| Master's | $f_o = 22$ $f_e = 27$ | $f_o = 60$ $f_e = 55.2$ | $f_o = 44$ $f_e = 43.8$ | 126 |
| Bachelor's | $f_o = 33$ $f_e = 40.5$ | $f_o = 74$ $f_e = 82.8$ | $f_o = 82$ $f_e = 65.7$ | 189 |
| Total | 90 | 184 | 146 | $n = 420$ |

The *observed* frequencies of the respective cells are denoted by $f_o$, and the *expected* frequencies by $f_e$. The values of the expected frequencies are found as follows: the marginal totals of the respective columns and rows are considered to be representative of the population distribution. Thus, the proportion of the population whose latest degree is the doctorate is 105/420; the proportion whose latest degree is the master's is 126/420; and the proportion whose latest degree is the bachelor's is 189/420. Considering the column of responses labeled "Great," we would expect 105/420 of the marginal total of 90 to be given by the "Doctorate" group. This supposition means that $(90)(105)/420 = 22.5$ should be the expected frequency for that cell. Similarly, we would expect 126/420 of the total of 90 responses to be made by the "Master's" group. This conclusion means that $(90)(126)/420 = 27$ should be the expected frequency for that particular cell. In similar fashion, the expected frequency for each cell of the contingency table is calculated. As a mathematical rule approach to the calculation of expected frequencies for the contingency table we may state that *the expected frequency for each cell may be found by multiplying the marginal totals common to a particular cell* [e.g., $(105) \cdot (90)$], *and then dividing this product by the total number of cases in the table*, $n$, [e.g., $[(105)(90)]/420 = 22.5$]. The value of $\chi^2$ is found as follows:

$$\chi^2 = \sum_{i=1}^{r} \sum_{j=1}^{k} \frac{(f_{oij} - f_{eij})^2}{f_{eij}}$$

$$\chi^2 = \frac{(35 - 22.5)^2}{22.5} + \frac{(50 - 46)^2}{46} + \frac{(20 - 36.5)^2}{36.5} + \frac{(22 - 27)^2}{27}$$

$$+ \frac{(60 - 55.2)^2}{55.2} + \frac{(44 - 43.8)^2}{43.8} + \frac{(35 - 40.5)^2}{40.5}$$

$$+ \frac{(74 - 82.8)^2}{82.8} + \frac{(82 - 65.7)^2}{65.7}$$

$$\chi^2 \approx 6.94 + .35 + 7.46 + .93 + .42 + .00 + 1.36 + .93 + 4.04$$

$$\therefore \quad \chi^2 \approx 22.43$$

7. *The decision to reject, or not reject, the null hypothesis* $(H_0)$ *is made.* Since the value of $\chi^2 \approx 22.43$ is greater than $\chi^2 = 13.28$ (see Step 5) at $4df$ for $\alpha = .01$, the decision is to *reject* the null hypothesis, which allows the acceptance of the statistical alternative hypothesis $(H_1)$, and we may conclude that the responses of the group are *not independent* of classification according to the latest degree held.

In the foregoing we have shown how the $\chi^2$ test can be applied to tests of independence under hypotheses of difference. We now consider how the $\chi^2$ test of independence may be applied under hypotheses of relationship (association). Before proceeding to that discussion, however, it should be noted that problems in educational research frequently require that the $\chi^2$ test be applied to contingency tables involving two rows $(r = 2)$, and 2 columns $(k = 2)$. These tables are special cases of $(r \times k)$ contingency tables, and are known as "2 $\times$ 2 tables." The $\chi^2$ test for 2 $\times$ 2 tables *under hypotheses of difference* is a straightforward application of procedures employed in the last example presented. When the hypothesis of independence (difference) is rejected, it makes possible an hypothesis of the degree of dependence (association, or relationship) existing in the situation under study. It is this latter hypothesis that we shall now discuss briefly.

In our discussion of the *phi* ($\phi$) *coefficient* in Chapter 20, we discussed briefly how the $\chi^2$ test might be employed to *test for the significance of this measure of association*. We recall that the *phi* coefficient ($\phi$) is related to $\chi^2$ by the formula: $\phi = \sqrt{\chi^2/n}$. The presence of $\chi^2$ in the expression suggests that if the test of independence is rejected for a 2 × 2 table, which is accomplished by a sufficiently large value for $\chi^2$, then the larger the discrepancy between the *expected* and *observed* frequencies of the cells of the table, the larger is the degree of possible *association* between the two variables; and hence, the higher the value of $\phi$. In this sense, if the value of $\chi^2$ is great enough, the $\phi$ coefficient can be considered significantly different from zero under $[(r - 1) \cdot (k - 1) = (2 - 1) \cdot (2 - 1) = 1 \, df]$. For example, suppose that in the expression for $\phi$, the value of $\chi^2$ is 10, and the sample size is $n = 40$. The value of $\phi$ would be $\phi = \sqrt{\frac{10}{40}} = .50$. Now the question is posed: is the value of $\phi = .50$ under these conditions significantly different from zero? Since $\phi$ is computed from a 2 × 2 table, and the value of $\chi^2 = 10$ has been computed from that same table (1 *df*), and further that the critical value of $\chi^2$ at the .01 level of significance under 1 *df* is $\chi^2 = 6.64$, we could reject the hypothesis of independence of the factors categorized in the rows and columns of the table in question and conclude that the factors are significantly related in the population. Since this conclusion is derived on the basis of a $\chi^2$ value which occurs with a probability less than $\alpha = .01$, we could conclude that $\phi = .50$ is significantly different from zero.

*Chapter 24—References*

See Bibliography: 4, 27, 49, 52, 53, 71, 76, 77, 89, 109, 123, 126, 128, 148, 155, 165, 180, 183, 200; 7a, 8a, 11a, 23a, 30a, 34a, 66a, 67a, 72a, 78a, 81a, 84a, 104a, 116a.

# Nonparametric Statistical Tests—II

*The Kolmogorov–Smirnov Statistical Test Model*

THERE ARE TWO TYPES of Kolmogorov–Smirnov statistical tests. The first type, known as the "one-sample test," is a test of goodness-of-fit. The second type, known as the "two-sample test," is a test of whether two independent samples have been drawn from the same universe, or from universes with the same distribution. Both types of tests are concerned with testing for the agreement between two cumulative distributions. The one-sample test is concerned with the amount of agreement between the *cumulative distributions* of *observed* (*sample*) *relative frequencies* and *expected* (*theoretical*) *relative frequencies*. The test determines whether the distribution of the cumulative relative frequencies of the sample compares reasonably with the distribution of the cumulative relative frequencies expected under the null hypothesis ($H_0$). The two-sample test is concerned with the degree of agreement between the two cumulative distributions of the relative frequencies *observed* in the respective samples. If the two samples have actually been drawn from the same population, or populations having the same distribution, the cumulative distributions of both samples should be reasonably close to each other over the range of values involved. If the two-sample cumulative distributions evidence too much divergence at any point, there is a given probability that the samples might come from different populations. If the deviation between the two cumulative distributions at any point is so great that it would occur, according to the appropriate Kolmogorov-Smirnov probability distribution, less than 5 per cent, or 1 per cent of the time, due to chance factors alone, the null hypothesis (no difference between the respective cumulative distributions) is rejected in favor of the statistical alternative hypothesis ($H_1$).

In the one-sample test, the cumulative distribution of the expected (theoretical) relative frequencies is determined on the basis of the null hypothesis ($H_0$). After this distribution is determined, the cumulative distribution of the observed (sample) relative frequencies is compiled. The two *cumulative* distributions are then compared point by point on the basis of the difference (deviation) between them. The point at which the *cumulative* distributions show the greatest deviation (poorest fit) is determined, and the value of the divergence at that point is referred to the appropriate Kolmogorov-Smirnov sampling distribution to determine the probability of a·deviation that large occurring by chance, if the null hypothesis ($H_0$) were true. If the maximum deviation is of such magnitude

Table VI

Selected Critical Values of $D$ for the
Kolmogorov–Smirnov One-Sample Test*

| Sample Size $n$ | Level of Significance for $D$ Max. $\|F_0(X) - S_n(X)\|$ | | |
|---|---|---|---|
| | .10 | .05 | .01 |
| 1 | .950 | .975 | .995 |
| 2 | .776 | .842 | .929 |
| 3 | .642 | .708 | .828 |
| 4 | .564 | .624 | .733 |
| 5 | .510 | .565 | .669 |
| 10 | .368 | .410 | .490 |
| 15 | .304 | .338 | .404 |
| 20 | .264 | .294 | .356 |
| 30 | .220 | .240 | .290 |
| 35 | .210 | .230 | .270 |
| Over 35 | $1.22/\sqrt{n}$ | $1.36/\sqrt{n}$ | $1.63/\sqrt{n}$ |

* Sidney Siegel, *Nonparametric Statistics*, Table E, p. 251.

that its probability of occurrence is less than that set by the level of significance ($\alpha$), the null hypothesis is rejected.

Employing the symbolization of Siegel, the specified *theoretical* cumulative distribution under $H_0$, *for the one-sample test*, is denoted by: $F_0(X)$. The value of $F_0(X)$, for any given value of $X$, is equal to the *sum* of the *expected relative frequencies* for values less than and equal to $X$.[1]

The observed cumulative distribution of a random sample of $n$ observations is denoted by: $S_n(X)$. If $X$ is any given value of the set of possible values, then $S_n(X) = k/n$, where $k$ denotes the number of observations in the sample that have values less than or equal to the given value $X$.

Under the null hypothesis ($H_0$), it is expected that for every value of $X$ the differences between $F_0(X)$ and $S_n(X)$ are small and within limits of unbiased (random) error. The Kolmogorov–Smirnov test concerns itself with the absolute value of the *maximum deviation* (difference), $D$, of the expression $F_0(X) - S_n(X)$, that is:

$$D = \text{maximum} \, |F_0(X) - S_n(X)| \qquad (1)$$

where the expression $|F_0(X) - S_n(X)|$ indicates the *absolute* value (positive value only) of the difference.

The sampling distribution of $D$ under the null hypothesis is used to determine the probability of occurrence of a value as large as that of $D$ due to chance factors alone. Selected critical values of $D$ are presented in Table VI.

To illustrate how Table VI is used, suppose that from formula (1), the value of $D$ is found to be .325 for a one-sample test involving 20 observations ($n = 20$). Entering the first column of the table, labeled as "sample size," we proceed down the column to the point where we find the number "20." Moving across that row we find in the column labeled ".10," the value .264; in the column headed ".05," the value .294; and in the ".01" column, the value .356. Thus we find that the value $D = .325$ has a *two-tailed* associated probability of occurrence, due to chance factors alone, between $p = .05$ and $.01$.*

When the sample size $n$ is greater than 35, the critical values may be computed by the formulas found in the last row of the table. For example, if $n = 49$, the critical value for $\alpha = .10$ would be:

$$\frac{1.22}{\sqrt{49}} = \frac{1.22}{7} = .174$$

for $\alpha = .05$,

$$\frac{1.36}{\sqrt{49}} = \frac{1.36}{7} = .194$$

and, finally, for $\alpha = .01$, would be

$$\frac{1.63}{\sqrt{49}} = \frac{1.63}{7} = .233$$

THE ONE-SAMPLE TEST

To illustrate the application of the Kolmogorov–Smirnov one-sample test, we employ the fictitious model of research shown below.

*A Survey Study of the Selection of "Successful" Principals*

Problem

A huge industry opens a large facility in a small rural community. An in-migration of workers follows, and the community witnesses a rapid and tremendous growth. The local board of education faces not only the problem of a vast construction program, but the concomitant one of the selection of teaching and administrative personnel on a broader and greater scale than heretofore was necessary. It is decided that probably the most important person to the successful operation of a school building is the principal. If applicants could be screened and the best of the group be employed as principals even before construction of the buildings in which they are to fill principalships begins, valuable consultative services, and probably better results in total operation, would be realized. In order to conduct the screening and selection of candidates on the basis of sound criteria, the board decides that a survey type of research should be conducted immediately to determine personality qualities, the general pattern of experience and academic background, and certain aptitudes which seem to be common among "successful" principals of public elementary, junior high, and high schools in school districts similar to the one conducting the research.

Questions to Be Answered

Since the study is to be a survey type, the research team will be seeking answers to certain general questions rather than testing research hypotheses (hunches)

---

*For one-tailed test, see references recommended by Siegel, p. 49.

about factors of personality, aptitudes, academic background, and experience of "successful" public school principals. This situation does not mean, however, that it will not be necessary, in examining broad areas covered by the general questions, to advance statistical hypotheses (in appropriate forms of the "null") occasionally to determine conditions of magnitude, difference, or relationship. Suppose the following questions appear among the many posed for the total study:

1. Studies of administrative decision-making in public school work have shown that the predominant factor in arriving at a decision depends upon the administrator's value judgment as to which one of the three areas of: (1) community relations, (2) school faculty and staff, or (3) school curriculum and program, is the most important aspect of school operation. Therefore, the public school administrator's decisions are *mainly* based upon how they might affect the *particular category* of the three which he feels to be most important to the successful operation of the school. With this background the question is posed: Do "successful" public school principals tend to favor significantly one of the three categories: (1) community relations, (2) school faculty and staff, or (3) school curriculum and program, in administrative decision-making?

2. Studies of the successful public school administrator have shown that he has a realistic self-concept; i.e., he tends to see himself in his administrative role, including his strengths and weaknesses, as his faculty and staff see him. The following question is posed in connection with this background: From the sample selected for this study, does the statement about self-concept seem to be true? If it is true, should we include a self-concept instrument, and an accompanying "cross-check" procedure in the administrator screening and selection processes employed by the system?

### Universe

In general, the universe of data for this study would include: (1) principals of public schools (all levels), meeting the criterion of *"success"* as defined by the research team; (2) previous research findings and other information pertaining to such topics as: the role of the elementary school principal, predominant personality factors found in the "successful" public school principal, the principal and the community, and the principal as a teacher; (3) all materials pertaining to the experiences and academic backgrounds of the "successful" principals found in districts similar to the one sponsoring the study.

### Sample of the Study

We shall assume that many different samples will be selected to deal with the various aspects of the survey-type study. In each case, we shall further assume that the sample is representative, selected in an appropriate manner, and adequate for the amount of precision desired in the estimates and inferences to be drawn from the data.

### Data Collection

The instrumentalities of data collection that could be employed in this type of study are: questionnaires, rating scales of various types, interviews, and personality inventories. We shall assume that the methods and procedures of data collection are sufficiently free from biased error for the purposes of the study.

## Data Processing

After the data have been sorted according to certain aspects of the survey and according to their level of measurement, they are classified on the basis of their importance relative to providing information about the main effort of the study. During this phase of the study, suppose that the following data are to be analyzed:

The data that are responses of twenty-five "successful" elementary school principals composing a judgment-quota sample (see Chapter 4). These responses are rankings of the three categories: (1) community relations, (2) school faculty and staff, and (3) school curriculum and program. The categories are "ranked" on the basis of the respondent's order of consideration of these factors in deriving a decision for each of ten school administrative problems described in separate paragraphs. To illustrate, a paragraph description is accorded the problem of whether an "up-grading" program in arithmetic should be instituted as part of an in-service teacher training program at the principal's school. The principal is asked to accord the rank of "1" to the category of the aforementioned three which he would consider first in reaching a decision of whether to institute the program, a rank of "2" to the category he would consider next in importance in reaching his decision, and a rank of "3" to the category he would consider least important to the decision. Tied rankings are not permitted, thus different rankings must be given to each category for each of the ten "problem paragraphs." Suppose that some of the data are arrayed as shown in Table VII (only rankings of "1" are shown in the table):

Table VII
Rankings of "1" for Three Categories in Connection with Ten
Administrative Problems Considered by Twenty-five
"Successful" Elementary School Principals
(Fictitious Data)

| | Categories | | |
| --- | --- | --- | --- |
| | (1) Community Relations | (2) School Faculty and Staff | (3) School Curriculum and Program |
| $f$ = number of rankings of 1 accorded category by 25 subjects for 10 problem situations | 25 | 175 | 50 |
| $F_0(X)$ = theoretical cumulative distribution of relative frequencies under the null hypothesis ($H_0$) | $\frac{1}{3}$ | $\frac{2}{3}$ | $\frac{3}{3}$ |
| $S_{250}(X)$ = Cumulative distribution of observed relative frequencies of rankings of 1 | $\frac{25}{250} = \frac{1}{10}$ | $\frac{200}{250} = \frac{8}{10}$ | $\frac{250}{250} = \frac{10}{10}$ |
| $\lvert F_0(X) - S_{250}(X)\rvert = D$ | $\frac{7}{30}$ | $\frac{4}{40}$ | 0 |

The theoretical cumulative distribution in the row denoted by $F_0(X)$ is compiled on the basis of the null hypothesis $(H_0)$, which in this case would be that each of the three categories would receive $\frac{1}{3}$ of the rankings of "1." The cumulative distribution denoted by $S_{250}(X)$ shows the rankings of "1" accorded each of the categories for the ten problems by the twenty-five "successful" principals composing the sample. The bottom row of the table denoted by $|F_0(X) - S_{250}(X)| = D$ shows the absolute deviation of each *sample* relative frequency from its paired *expected* relative frequency.

Considering the process of statistical inference associated with this particular "problem," we would have:

1. *State the null hypothesis.* $H_0 : rf_1 = rf_2 = rf_3$. In statement form, there is no difference between the relative frequencies *expected* for each of the three categories. The statistical alternative hypothesis $(H_1)$ states the relative frequencies $rf_1$, $rf_2$, and $rf_3$ are not all equal.

2. *Select an appropriate statistical test.* The Kolmogorov–Smirnov one-sample test is selected because the research team wishes to compare an observed distribution of rankings of "1" with a theoretical distribution of these rankings.

3. *Specify a level of significance $(\alpha)$, and a sample size $(n)$.* The level of significance was chosen to be : $\alpha = .05$, and the sample size of $n = 250$ rankings of "1" is assumed to be adequate for this particular aspect of the study.

4. *Determine the appropriate sampling distribution under $H_0$.* The critical values of $D$ for selected sampling distributions associated with the levels of significance $(\alpha)$ of : .10, .05, and .01 are presented in Table VI. The critical value of $D$ for the conditions of the "problem" under consideration is found to be :

$$D = \frac{1.36}{\sqrt{250}} = \frac{1.36}{15.8} \approx .086$$

5. *Determine the critical region.* The critical region consists of all values of $D$ found by formula (1) which are of such magnitude that the probability associated with their occurrence, if the null hypothesis $(H_0)$ is supposedly true, is equal to or less than $\alpha = .05$, the specified level of significance.

6. *Compute the values of the statistics being employed.* The maximum value of $D$, with which the Kolmogorov–Smirnov test is concerned, may be read from the bottom row of Table VII and is found to be : $D = \frac{7}{30} \approx .233$.

7. *Arrive at a decision to reject, or not reject, the null hypothesis $(H_0)$.* Since the critical value of $D$ for $n = 250$, under a .05 level of significance, is $D \approx .086$, and the value of $D$ yielded by the data is $D \approx .233$, which has an associated probability under $H_0$ of $Pr < .05$, the decision of the research team is to reject the null hypothesis, and conclude that there is a significant difference between categories (1), (2), and (3) in rankings of "1" for the ten "problems" rated by twenty-five "successful" public school principals. (Note that category (2) is favored more frequently than the other two).

Decision

Based upon the findings derived here, and in other aspects of the study, criteria for selection could be determined for the local board's use in the screening and employment of principals for the various levels of schools to be constructed.

## THE TWO-SAMPLE TEST

In order to apply the Kolmogorov–Smirnov two-sample test, it is necessary to compile a cumulative distribution of relative frequencies for each sample of observations, using the same points, or intervals, for both distributions. At each point, one *cumulative* function is subtracted from the other. As in the case of the one-sample test, the maximum $D$ between the respective *cumulative* distributions is determined and compared to an appropriate Kolmogorov–Smirnov sampling distribution for a *two-sample test*.

Employing the symbolization of Siegel once again, the cumulative distribution of one of the samples is denoted by: $S_{n_1}(X) = X/n_1$, where $X$ denotes the number of values equal to or less than $X$; and the cumulative distribution of the other sample is given by: $S_{n_2}(X) = X/n_2.$[2] For the two-sample test the Kolmogorov–Smirnov model is concerned with:

$$D = \text{maximum}[S_{n_1}(X) - S_{n_2}(X)] \qquad (2)$$

for a *one-tailed test*, because $[S_{n_1}(X) - S_{n_2}(X)]$ *not being absolute in value* indicates a *direction*; and for a *two-tailed test* is concerned with:

$$D = \text{maximum}|S_{n_1}(X) - S_{n_2}(X)| \qquad (2a)$$

where $|S_{n_1}(X) - S_{n_2}(X)|$ is the maximum *absolute* value of $D$, i.e., the maximum deviation always considered positive, regardless of the original algebraic sign of the difference (does not indicate a direction).

If the data are not intervalized by natural conditions, the size and number of intervals to be employed are determined arbitrarily by the researcher. If the Kolmogorov–Smirnov test is to be employed, it is wise for the researcher to use as many intervals as are feasible. When the intervals are too few over a range of possible values, the maximum vertical deviation between the respective cumulative distributions may not be observed. It is best then to use as many intervals as conditions will permit in order to avoid wasting information in the data. An insufficient number of intervals might lead to the condition of the researcher being unable to observe a value of $D$ large enough, to permit the rejection of the null hypothesis $(H_0)$, when in fact it should be rejected.

If the two samples being tested are of the same sample size; that is, $n_1 = n_2$, and if $n_1 = n_2 \leq 40$ ($n_1$ and $n_2$ are less than or equal to 40), the maximum difference $D$ may be determined on the basis of $K_D$, which is defined as the *numerator of the largest difference between the two cumulative distributions*, or in other words, *the numerator* of $D$. Certain critical values of $K_D$ are presented in the body of Table VIII. In order to read the table, it is necessary to know the *value of $K_D$* and the *value of $N$*, where $N$ is defined as: $N = n_1 = n_2$, and whether a one-tailed test, or a two-tailed test, is to be employed.

Table VIII

Selected Critical Values of $K_D$ for the

Kolmogorov–Smirnov Two-Sample Test*

| $N$ | One-tailed Test | | Two-tailed Test | |
|---|---|---|---|---|
| | $\alpha = .05$ | $\alpha = .01$ | $\alpha = .05$ | $.01$ |
| 3 | 3 | | | |
| 4 | 4 | | 4 | |
| 5 | 4 | 5 | 5 | 5 |
| 6 | 5 | 6 | 5 | 6 |
| 7 | 5 | 6 | 6 | 6 |
| 8 | 5 | 6 | 6 | 7 |
| 9 | 6 | 7 | 6 | 7 |
| 10 | 6 | 7 | 7 | 8 |
| 15 | 7 | 9 | 8 | 9 |
| 20 | 8 | 10 | 9 | 11 |
| 25 | 9 | 11 | 10 | 12 |
| 30 | 10 | 12 | 11 | 13 |
| 35 | 11 | 13 | 12 | |
| 40 | 11 | 14 | 13 | |

* For a complete table of critical values of $K_D$, see (155) Sidney Siegel, *Nonparametric Statistics*, p. 278. For a complete table of critical values for other levels of significance see Siegel, p. 279.

To illustrate, if a two-tailed test were being employed with $N = 9$, and $\alpha = .05$, and if a value of $K_D \geq 6$ was produced by the analysis of the data, the null hypothesis $(H_0)$ would be rejected. If a one-tailed test were being employed with $N = 20$, and $\alpha = .01$, a value of $K_D \geq 10$ would be needed to reject the $H_0$.

If $n_1$ and $n_2$ are both greater than 40, and if $n_1 = n_2$, or $n_1 \neq n_2$, the value of $D$ may be found by formula (2a) page 317 and a *two-tailed test* can be conducted by comparing the observed value of $D$ with the critical one which is obtained by substituting the observed values of $n_1$ and $n_2$ in the expressions:

$$1.36\sqrt{\frac{n_1 + n_2}{n_1 n_2}} \quad \text{for} \quad \alpha = .05 \tag{3}$$

$$1.48\sqrt{\frac{n_1 + n_2}{n_1 n_2}} \quad \text{for} \quad \alpha = .025 \tag{3a}$$

$$1.63\sqrt{\frac{n_1 + n_2}{n_1 n_2}} \quad \text{for} \quad \alpha = .01 \tag{3b}$$

To illustrate, suppose that $n_1 = 64, n_2 = 81$, and we wished to conduct a two-tailed test of $H_0$ at the $\alpha = .05$ level of significance by the Kolmogorov–Smirnov two-sample test. The value of $D$ found from formula (2a) necessary to reject $H_0$ under these conditions would be one that is greater than or equal to the critical value found by formula (3), that is:

$$D = 1.36\sqrt{\frac{64 + 81}{(64) \cdot (81)}} = 1.36\sqrt{\frac{145}{(64) \cdot (81)}} = (1.36)\left|\frac{12.04}{(8) \cdot (9)}\right| = \frac{2.047}{9} = .2294$$

If a *one-tailed test* were to be conducted, when $n_1$ and $n_2$ are greater than 40, and regardless of whether $n_1 = n_2$, the value of $D$ is found from formula (2) and compared to a chi-square distribution with 2 degrees of freedom, where $\chi^2$ is computed by the formula:

$$\chi^2 = 4D^2\left[\frac{(n_1)(n_2)}{n_1 + n_2}\right] \tag{4}$$

In other words, if we wish to test the null hypothesis $(H_0)$ that two samples have been drawn from the same population against the alternative $(H)$ that one sample was drawn from a population of values *greater than* the values of the population from which the second sample was drawn, we may determine the significance of an observed value of $D$ computed by formula (2), by evaluating formula (4) with the observed values of $D$, $n_1$, and $n_2$, and then referring this value to a chi-square distribution with 2 *df*.

### ILLUSTRATIONS OF THE KOLMOGOROV–SMIRNOV TWO-SAMPLE TESTS

We shall now illustrate the various two-sample Kolmogorov–Smirnov tests by applying them to appropriate phases of problems examined by the general model of educational research regarding "successful" principals, described earlier in this chapter.

Suppose that in one phase of the survey of "successful" principals, it is necessary to know if elementary school principals' decisions tend to be based more upon the "community" dimension of decision-making than are those of high school principals (thus calling for a one-tailed test). The research team decides to draw its conclusions on the basis of a statistical inference process. A sample of 20 elementary principals is selected at random $(n_1 = 20)$, and a sample of $n_2 = 20$ high school principals is randomly selected. The sum of the "forced" rankings of 1, 2, or 3 assigned to the category of "community" and taken over the 10 problem paragraphs, is used as a measure of the weight accorded that dimension in the principal's decision. Hence, a respondent's score of 10 registered for the category of "community" would indicate that he gave great weight to that dimension in considering the 10 problem paragraphs; that is, he must have assigned a ranking of "1" to the "community" category in each of the 10 cases. On the other hand, a score of 30 registered by a respondent would show that he gave relatively little weight to the "community" dimension of administrative decision-making in considering the 10 problems (assigned "community" a ranking of "3" in each of the 10 cases). Suppose the data were arrayed as shown in Table IX.

*The statistical inference process would be as follows:*

1. *Null Hypothesis.* $H_0: rf_{n_1k} \leq rf_{n_2k}$. In statement form: the expected relative frequencies of the twenty elementary school principals $(n_1)$ are *less than* or *equal to* the expected relative frequencies of twenty high school principals $(n_2)$ for the $k$ categories covering the range of possible score values. The statistical alternative hypothesis is: $H_1: rf_{n_1k} > rf_{n_2k}$; or the expected relative frequencies

Table IX
"Scores" of Twenty Elementary School Principals and Twenty High School
Principals Indicating Weight Given to the Dimension of "Community"
in Administrative Decision-Making
Illustration: Kolmogorov–Smirnov One-Tailed Test
(Fictitious Data)

| | Scores | | | | | | |
|---|---|---|---|---|---|---|---|
| | 10–12 | 13–15 | 16–18 | 19–21 | 22–24 | 25–27 | 28–30 |
| Elementary Principals $(n_1 = 20)$ | 9 | 4 | 4 | 1 | 1 | 1 | 0 |
| High School Principals $(n_2 = 20)$ | 2 | 3 | 3 | 4 | 5 | 1 | 2 |
| $S20_1(X)$ $S20_2(X)$ | 9/20 2/20 | 13/20 5/20 | 17/20 8/20 | 18/20 12/20 | 19/20 17/20 | 20/20 18/20 | 20/20 20/20 |
| $[S_{n_1}(X) - S_{n_2}(X)]$ | +7/20 | +8/20 | +9/20 | +6/20 | +2/20 | +2/20 | 0 |

of the twenty elementary school principals $(n_1)$ are *greater than* the expected relative frequencies of the twenty high school principals $(n_2)$ for $k$ categories covering the range of possible score values.

2. *Appropriate Statistical Test.* Two small independent samples of equal size $(n_1 = n_2 = 20)$ are to be compared on a categorical basis, hence the Kolmogorov–Smirnov two-sample test is an appropriate one.

3. *Level of Significance* $(\alpha)$. Because of the comparatively small sample sizes, and the resulting conclusions to be drawn if $H_0$ is rejected, the research team chooses the level of significance as: $\alpha = .01$.

4. *Appropriate Sampling Distribution.* Selected critical values of $K_D$ for $n_1 = n_2$; where $n_1$ and $n_2$ are less than 40 are presented in Table VIII.

5. *Critical Region.* Since the null hypothesis $(H_0)$ and the statistical alternative hypothesis $(H_1)$ predict the direction of the difference $D$, a one-tailed test is to be employed. The null $(H_0)$ will be rejected if the value of $K_D$ for the maximum deviation is in the proper direction (in this case, upper end of distribution, therefore, positive $(+)$ algebraic sign required) and is of such magnitude (equal to or larger than the appropriate $K_D$ in the table) that the probability associated with its occurrence, if $H_0$ is supposedly true, is equal to or less than $\alpha = .01$.

6. *Compute the Value of the Statistic.* The value of $K_D$ with which this form of the Kolmogorov–Smirnov test is concerned is the numerator of the maximum deviation $D$ which appears in the bottom row of Table IX, and is found to be: $K_D = +9$, from $D = +\frac{9}{20}$.

7. *Decision Concerning* $H_0$. Since the critical value of $K_D$ for $n_1 = n_2 = 20$, under the one-tailed test to be employed under these circumstances at the $\alpha = .01$ level of significance is: $K_D = +10$; and the value of $K_D$ yielded by the data is: $K_D = +9$, the research team cannot reject the null hypothesis $(H_0)$.

With modification of the null hypothesis, the statistical alternative hypothesis $(H_1)$, and the sample sizes $n_1$ and $n_2$, the previous example could be used to illustrate the application of the Kolmogorov–Smirnov test when both $n_1$ and $n_2$ are larger than 40 (are not necessarily equal), and a *two-tailed test* is to be conducted.

1. *Null Hypothesis.* $H_0 : rf_{n_1k} = rf_{n_2k}$. In statement form: there is no difference between the expected relative frequencies of the two groups of "successful" principals for the $k$ categories covering the range of possible score values. The statistical alternative hypothesis is $H_1 : rf_{n_1k} \neq rf_{n_2k}$; there is a difference between the expected relative frequencies of the two groups for the $k$ categories covering the range of possible score values. Suppose the first group is composed of $n_1 = 64$ elementary school principals selected at random from the population; and the second group is composed of $n_2 = 49$ secondary school principals selected at random from the population defined for the study.

2. *Statistical Test.* Two independent samples of unequal size ($n_1 = 64$, and $n_2 = 49$), but both greater than 40, are to be compared on a categorical basis, hence the Kolmogorov–Smirnov two-sample test is an appropriate one.

3. *Level of Significance* ($\alpha$). Suppose the research team chose the level of significance $\alpha = .05$.

4. *Sampling Distribution.* The appropriate sampling distribution is the one which computes the critical value of $D$ at the .05 level as:

$$D = 1.36 \sqrt{\frac{64 + 49}{(64) \cdot (49)}} = 1.36 \left( \frac{10.63}{(8)(7)} \right) \approx \frac{1.81}{7} \approx .26 \quad [\text{See formula (3)}]$$

5. *Critical Region.* Since there is no direction of the difference $D$ predicted by either the "null" ($H_0$), or the "statistical alternative" ($H_1$), a two-tailed test is to be employed. The null hypothesis will be rejected if the value of $D$ for the observed data is equal to or greater than the critical value found for $D$ by substituting 64 for $n_1$, and 49 for $n_2$, in formula (3). The critical value of $D$ found in step 4 is: $D \approx .26$.

6. *Compute the Value of the Statistic.* Suppose the data are arrayed as shown below:

| | Scores | | | | | | |
|---|---|---|---|---|---|---|---|
| | 10–12 | 13–15 | 16–18 | 19–21 | 22–24 | 25–27 | 28–30 |
| Elementary Principals ($n_1 = 64$) | 24 | 16 | 10 | 5 | 4 | 3 | 2 |
| High School Principals ($n_2 = 49$) | 5 | 7 | 9 | 11 | 12 | 2 | 3 |
| $S64_1(X)$ | 24/64 | 40/64 | 50/64 | 55/64 | 59/64 | 62/64 | 64/64 |
| $S49_2(X)$ | 5/49 | 12/49 | 21/49 | 32/49 | 44/49 | 46/49 | 49/49 |
| $\lvert S_{n_1}(X) - S_{n_2}(X) \rvert$ | 856/3136 | 1192/3136 | 1106/3136 | 647/3136 | 75/3136 | 94/3136 | 0 |

We see from the last row of the tabled data that the maximum deviation $(D)$, between the two series, is 1192/3136, or:

$$D = 1192/3136 \approx .38$$

7. *Decision Concerning* $(H_0)$. Since the observed value of $D \approx .38$ is greater than the critical value of $D = .26$ for $n_1 = 64$, $n_2 = 49$, under a two-tailed test at the .05 level of significance, the research team would reject the null hypothesis $(H_0)$ of "no difference," which would allow the acceptance of the statistical alternative hypothesis $(H_1)$; i.e., there is "a statistically significant difference" between the two groups in the comparative use of "community" as a basis for administrative decision-making in connection with the 10 problem paragraphs that were examined.

The data set forth in step 6 of the previous inference process could be used to illustrate the application of the Kolmogorov–Smirnov two-sample test when the sample sizes $n_1$ and $n_2$ (not necessarily equal) are large (both greater than 40), and a one-tailed test is to be employed. The null hypothesis $(H_0)$, and the statistical alternative hypothesis $(H_1)$ could be modified to the form presented in the small samples illustration $(n_1 = n_2 = 20)$ (see page 320). The last row of the table in step 6 would be labeled as: "$[S_{n_1}(X) - S_{n_2}(X)]$." If such modifications were made, we could substitute the value of $D$ into formula (4), and compare the resulting value of the observed $\chi^2$ with the critical value found under the appropriate level of significance (.05 for a one-tailed test in this example) of the chi-square distribution with 2 degrees of freedom. To illustrate, the *observed* value of $D$ would be: $D \approx .38$, and substituting in formula (4), we would have:

$$\chi^2 = 4(.38)^2 \frac{(64)(49)}{[64 + 49]}$$

$$= \frac{4(.1444)(3136)}{113}$$

$$= \frac{1811.35}{113}$$

$$\chi^2 = 16.03$$

as the *observed value of* $\chi^2$. Figure 20, which shows a portion of the probability table of chi-square, includes the value of $\chi^2$ for a two-tailed test under 2 *df*, at the .05 level. The critical value in question is: $\chi^2 = 5.99$. Since this value of $\chi^2$ would be the critical one at the .025 level for a one-tailed test, and the observed value of $\chi^2 = 16.03$ is much greater than that value, the null $(H_0)$ could be rejected at the .05 level of significance of the one-tailed test.

*Chapter 25—References*

See Bibliography: 49, 53, 54, 108, 109, 113, 123, 148, 155, 165, 178, 179, 183, 189, 200; 7a, 11a, 34a, 66a, 67a, 78a, 84a, 104a, 116a, 117a.

# Nonparametric Statistical Tests—III

*(Tests Employing Related Samples and k Independent Samples)*

IN CHAPTER 3, it was pointed out that there are three types of statistical hypotheses: (1) hypotheses of magnitude, (2) hypothesis of relationship, and (3) hypotheses of difference. Frequently, two-sample statistical tests are employed to test hypotheses of difference by comparing a group which has undergone a treatment with a group which has not, or with one which has been subjected to a different treatment.

The researcher must be meticulous in his design, methods, and procedures in making such comparisons, to be sure that the significant differences which might be observed are actually the results of the treatments. For example, in attempting to compare two methods of teaching reading by having a given teacher instruct one group by one method and a different group by a second method, if the instructor inadvertently motivates one group, or one of the groups is composed of students who are more able readers to begin with, the difference in performance of the groups might be due to these variables and not be caused by the treatments (methods) at all.

One way of controlling some of the difficulty of intervening variables in "between groups" analysis is to employ two *related* samples in the research design. This approach introduces the notion of "matching" (relating) the elements of the two samples being employed. Matching may be achieved by using each element of the sample as its own control, or by pairing subjects and then assigning each pair to the two treatments under study. If the sample element is to serve as its own control, it is exposed to the treatments under study at different times. If the pairing method is employed, the elements should be matched on the basis of those relevant variables that might have a relatively heavy bearing on the results of the research. One element of each pair, selected by random means, is then assigned to one treatment and its counterpart is assigned to the other treatment.

The method of using each element as its own control is preferable to the pairing method, because the matching of sample units is only as good as the researcher's ability to determine the relevant variables that might affect the research outcomes, his ability to measure these variables, and his ingenuity for providing a design that makes for maximum control of them within and between the matched elements. Many of these problems are avoided when each sample element serves as its own control. No more precise matching is possible than that achieved by employing "identical" (same) elements, and then counter-balancing the order in which they are subjected to the treatments of the experiment.

The *t*-test is the parametric test most frequently employed to compare two related samples. A difference score may be obtained for each matched pair, or from two scores (e.g., "before" and "after" scores) of each subject for the two treatments. The *t*-test should only be employed if these difference scores are measured in at least the interval scale, and are normally and independently distributed in the population from which the sample is drawn. If the researcher should find that these data are not amenable to the assumptions underlying the *t*-test, a nonparametric test for two *related samples* should be employed.* The "Wilcoxon" test is a nonparametric test which can be employed under such circumstances.

### THE WILCOXON SIGNED-RANKS TEST FOR PAIRED OBSERVATIONS

The Wilcoxon Signed-Ranks test considers the *magnitudes and the directions* of the differences $(X_2 - X_1)$ of paired observations. This test not only considers the direction of these differences, but assigns more weight to a pair showing a large difference than to a pair showing a small difference.

Any time the researcher can assign positive $(+)$ or negative $(-)$ *signs* to the differences $(X_2 - X_1)$, *and* then make judgments between any two of the *absolute values* of the differences arising from the set of pairs, the Wilcoxon test may be employed. This procedure requires, in effect, that the researcher have ordinal information *within pairs* and *within the differences* of the pairs. This type of measurement, in strength, is equivalent to *ordered metric scaling* which lies between the ordinal and interval scales of measurement.

We can use the data of Table X to illustrate the rationale and method of the Wilcoxon test. Columns (1) and (2) of Table X show the $X_1$ (before) and $X_2$ (after) scores for 17 paired observations. In column (3) we let $d_i$ equal the difference score $(X_2 - X_1)$ for any matched pair. Thus, each pair has one: $d_i = X_2 - X_1$.

The differences ($d_i$'s) are ranked in terms of their *absolute values*, that is, without regard to algebraic sign, $(+)$ or $(-)$. The ranking process is carried out by *ignoring algebraic signs* and giving the rank of 1 to the $d_i$ of *smallest* magnitude, a rank of 2 to the $d_i$ of the next smallest magnitude, and so on, until each value of the set of $d_i$'s, *except those of $d_i = 0$ that are dropped from the analysis*, has been assigned a *rank*. If two or more $d_i$'s have the same absolute value (e.g., $|-5| = |5| = 5$), they are assigned the *same* rank, which is the *average of the ranks* that would have been assigned if the $d_i$'s had differed in value. Thus, in column (4) of Table X, the $d$'s of $-1$ and $+1$, found in column (3), are assigned the rank of 1.5, because $(1 + 2)/2 = \frac{3}{2} = 1.5$. Since the ranks of 1 and 2 have been used, the rank of 3 is assigned to $d = 2$, and the rank of 5 is given to the $d$'s

---

* It should be recalled at this point that a nonparametric test is a distribution-free test that does not require assumptions about the form of the distribution of measurements under analysis.

Table X
Data to Illustrate the Wilcoxon Signed-Ranks Test for
Paired Observations

| (1) $X_1$ | (2) $X_2$ | (3) $d_i = X_2 - X_1$ | (4) Rank of $d_i$ | (5) Ranks $d_i$ (+) | (6) Ranks $d_i$ (−) |
|---|---|---|---|---|---|
| 2 | 9 | 7 | 13.5 | 13.5 | |
| 6 | 8 | 2 | 3 | 3 | |
| 3 | 9 | 6 | 11.5 | 11.5 | |
| 4 | 7 | 3 | 5 | 5 | |
| 8 | 5 | −3 | 5 | | 5 |
| 5 | 10 | 5 | 9 | 9 | |
| 6 | 1 | −5 | 9 | | 9 |
| 5 | 5 | 0 | | | |
| 7 | 8 | 1 | 1.5 | 1.5 | |
| 6 | 5 | −1 | 1.5 | | 1.5 |
| 1 | 10 | 9 | 16 | 16 | |
| 4 | 9 | 5 | 9 | 9 | |
| 5 | 9 | 4 | 7 | 7 | |
| 2 | 10 | 8 | 15 | 15 | |
| 9 | 3 | −6 | 11.5 | | 11.5 |
| 1 | 8 | 7 | 13.5 | 13.5 | |
| 7 | 4 | −3 | 5 | | 5 |
| | | | | $T_1 = 104.0$ | $T_2 = 32.0$ |

of 3, −3 and −3, because the average of the next three ranks, 4, 5, and 6 is: $(4 + 5 + 6)/3 = \frac{15}{3} = 5$. These procedures are followed until all of the $d$'s in column (3), except that of $d = 0$, are assigned the ranks shown in column (4) of the table.

The ranks appearing in column (5) of Table X are those from column (4) that correspond to the positive (+) $d$'s of column (3), while the ranks shown in column (6) are those that correspond to the negative (−) $d$'s. The total of column (5), designated as $T_1$, is the sum of the ranks corresponding to the positive (+) $d$'s of column (3). Similarly, the total of column (6), designated as $T_2$, is the sum of the ranks corresponding to the negative (−) $d$'s.

Now, if $X_1$, $X_2$, $X_3$, ..., $X_n$ are ranks accorded to $n$ elements of a set, these ranks form an arithmetic series. It can be shown by algebraic means that the sum of the $n$ terms of this arithmetic series is:

$$\sum_{i=1}^{n} X_i = \frac{n(n + 1)}{2} \qquad (2)$$

If all the $d$'s in column (3) of Table X were different, then the ranks assigned to them in column (4) would form an arithmetic series the sum of which would be given by formula (2). Since the practice of giving tied observations the average of the ranks they would have otherwise been assigned has a *negligible* effect on the value of $T_1$, or the value of $T_2$, formula (2) may be applied as a very good approximation, and we may write:

$$T_1 + T_2 = \frac{n(n + 1)}{2} \qquad (2a)$$

where $n$ indicates the number of pairs of differences (in our example, $n = 16$, number of non-zero $d$'s in column (3) Table X).

If the null hypothesis ($H_0$) is supposedly true, that is, if the condition represented by $X_1$ is equivalent to the condition represented by $X_2$, we would expect an approximately equal distribution of large and small ranks for the positive $(+)$ and negative $(-)$ $d$'s. Thus, when we sum the ranks for the positive $(+)$ $d$'s $(T_1)$, and find the total $(T_2)$ for the negative $(-)$ $d$'s, we should expect the two sums, $T_1$ and $T_2$, to be about equal under $H_0$. In other words, if $T_1$ and $T_2$ differ very much, the null hypothesis ($H_0$) is rejected.

Since the expectation under the null hypothesis is that $T_1$ will be equal to $T_2$, the expected total for either $T_1$ or $T_2$ will be the mean of the population of $T$ values, $\mu_T$. The value of $\mu_T$ may be found by formula (3):

$$\mu_T = \frac{n(n + 1)}{4} \tag{3}$$

The standard deviation of the population of values for $T$ is given by formula (4):

$$\sigma_T = \sqrt{\frac{n(n + 1)(2n + 1)}{24}} \tag{4}$$

If the null hypothesis ($H_0$) is true, and if $n \geq 8$, it can be shown that the sum of the ranks, $T$, is practically normally distributed.* Therefore, the normal distribution may be employed for the test of significance, by evaluating formula (5):

$$z = \frac{T - \mu_T}{\sigma_T} = \frac{T - n(n + 1)/4}{\sqrt{n(n+1)(2n+1)/24}} \tag{5}$$

where the value substituted for $T$ may be that of either $T_1$ or $T_2$ (under $H_0$ the distribution of the rank totals $T_1$ and $T_2$ are symmetrical about the expected value $\mu_T$, thus the test of significance by formula (5) can be made with either $T_1$ or $T_2$).

Since the normal distribution is continuous and the distribution of rank totals is discrete, a better approximation of the probability which is sought may be realized if a correction for continuity in the numerator of formula (5) is effected before a value of $z$ is computed. The correction is made by reducing the *absolute value* of the difference $(T - \mu_T)$ by .5. Making this correction for continuity modifies formula (5) as follows:

$$z = \frac{|T - \mu_T| - .5}{\sigma_T} = \frac{|T - n(n + 1)/4| - .5}{\sqrt{n(n + 1)(2n + 1)/24}} \tag{5a}$$

---

* For sample sizes $n < 8$, see Table I of (4b) F. Wilcoxon, *Some Rapid Approximate Statistical Procedures*, p. 13. It should be pointed out that this table gives critical values of $T_1$ or $T_2$, whichever is smaller, for sample sizes beginning with $n = 6$. Since the agreement between the probabilities for the *tabled* values and those obtained for the values by the normal distribution approximation is relatively high, especially for $n \geq 8$, there seems to be no practical reason for not using the normal approximation only.

To this point our discussion of the Wilcoxon test has been concerned only with two-tailed tests of the null hypothesis, that is: $H_0: T_1 = T_2 = \mu_T$, or $H_0: T_1 = \mu_T$. The statistical alternative hypothesis which is accepted if the null is rejected states: $H_1: T_1 \neq T_2$, or $H_1: T_1 \neq \mu_T$. The implication of accepting $H_1$ is that $T_1 > T_2$ or that $T_1 < T_2$.

One-tailed tests of null hypotheses may also be made by the Wilcoxon Signed-Ranks test. If the null hypothesis $H_0: T_1 \geq \mu_T$ is subjected to testing, it can only be rejected if the magnitude of $T_1$ is sufficiently *less* than $\mu_T$ so that the absolute value of the difference $|T_1 - \mu_T|$ in formula (5a) results in a value of $z$ *negative* $(-)$ *in sign* and *numerically* equal to or greater than the critical value $z_\alpha$ which defines the region of rejection in this case. If the null hypothesis $(H_0)$ is rejected in favor of the "alternative" $H_1: T_1 < \mu_T$, then the condition that $T_1 < T_2$ is also implied.

If the null hypothesis $H_0: T_1 \leq \mu_T$ is to be rejected when it is tested, it is necessary that $T_1$ be sufficiently *greater* than $\mu_T$ so that the absolute value of the difference $|T_1 - \mu_T|$ in formula (5a) results in a value which is *positive* $(+)$ *in sign* and *numerically* equal to or greater than the critical value $z_{1-\alpha}$ which defines the region of rejection in this case. If the null hypothesis $(H_0)$ is rejected in favor of the statistical alternative hypothesis: $H_1: T_1 > \mu_T$, then the condition that $T_1 > T_2$ is also implied.

We now present an illustration of the application of the Wilcoxon Signed-Ranks test for paired observations. Suppose that a researcher is attempting to determine if the "Hawthorne Effect" (the tendency of an experimental group to perform differently than the control group merely because of the psychological effect of being termed "experimental") exists in each of six different settings. A model of research is designed for the investigation. In one part of the study, the model is applied to determine if the "effect" exists in a public high school setting. Suppose that the data in Table X are the scores of seventeen matched-pairs of students on a given subject matter examination. One member from each matched pair is assigned, by methods of random selection, to the "control" group. The other member of each pair then automatically becomes a member of the "experimental" group. Both groups are taught the same material by the same teacher in the same classroom, but during different morning class periods. The group which is informed every day, in some fashion, that it is an "experimental group" meets at 9:00 A.M., and the "control group" which is taught in the customary fashion with no reference to group membership meets at 10:00 A.M. Suppose the scores designated as $X_1$ in column (1) of Table X are those of the "control" group, and those in the $X_2$ column are the scores of the "experimental" group.

The inference process associated with the numerical procedures of the Data Processing and Decision elements of the model of research would be as follows:

1. *Null Hypothesis.* $H_0: T_1 = T_2 = \mu_T$; or in statement form: the test scores of the "experimental" and "control" groups do not differ significantly, i.e., they come from the same population with mean $\mu_T$. This statement indicates that the "Hawthorne Effect" does not exist to any significant degree. The statistical

alternative hypothesis is: $H_1: T_1 \neq T_2$; or, the test scores of the "experimental" and "control" groups differ significantly, i.e., they come from populations with different mean values. This statement indicates that the "Effect" does exist to a significant extent.

2. *Statistical Test.* A two-tailed Wilcoxon Signed-Ranks test is chosen as the most appropriate statistical test for this phase of the research which involves two related groups.

3. *Level of Significance*, $\alpha$. The level of significance is set at $\alpha = .05$, and the size of the sample is $n = 16$ (the one case in Table X where $d = 0$ is dropped from the analysis).

4. *Sampling Distribution.* The normal distribution approximation of the Wilcoxon test as given by formula (5a) is the appropriate sampling distribution to be employed.

5. *Critical Region.* The critical region for this two-tailed test under $H_0$ with $\alpha = .05$ is the sets of values $\{z < -1.96\}$ and $\{z > +1.96\}$.

6. *Computing the Statistic.* Substituting the value of $T_2$ (the smaller total of $T_1$ and $T_2$, although $T_1$ would yield the same *numerical* value of $z$) for $T$ in formula (5a), we have:

$$z = \frac{|T - n(n+1)/4| - .5}{\sqrt{n(n+1)(2n+1)/24}} = \frac{|32 - (16)(17)/4| - .5}{\sqrt{(16)(17)(33)/24}}$$

$$z = \frac{|32 - 68| - .5}{\sqrt{(2)(17)(11)}} = \frac{|-36| - .5}{\sqrt{374}} = \frac{-35.5^*}{19.34} = -1.8356$$

7. *Decision concerning $H_0$.* Since $z = -1.8356$ does *not* fall in the critical region, the researcher *cannot reject* the null hypothesis ($H_0$). The decision to *not reject $H_0$* does *not* mean that $H_0$ is *accepted*. Failure to reject a given null hypothesis means only that the hypothesis is tenable—along with many other hypotheses that might have been formulated—and not that it must be true. In fact, in our example the value of $z = -1.8356$ is sufficiently close to the critical value of $z = -1.96$, so that the researcher might well place the null hypothesis ($H_0$) "in doubt," and replicate the experiment with a larger sample of "matched pairs."

### The Kruskal–Wallis $H$ Test for $k$ Independent Samples

Differences between groups may be studied by using either related or independent samples. Although the advantages of using related samples in models of research are great, frequently it is impractical or impossible to do so. When the nature of the variable precludes using the subject as his own control, as in the case where the dependent variable is time duration in solving a particular unfamiliar task (that particular task can only be unfamiliar once), related samples cannot be employed.

When related samples are impractical or impossible to use, independent samples may be employed. Independent samples may be obtained in either

---

\* Note that .5 is subtracted from the *numerical* value of $|-36| = 36$ to obtain 35.5, and *then* the *proper* algebraic sign $(-)$ is affixed.

one of two ways: (1) they may be drawn at random from different populations, or (2) they may be formed by assigning at random different treatments to the individuals of a sample selected in some arbitrary fashion. When independent samples are employed, it is *not* necessary that thev be of the same size $n$ as is necessary in the case of related samples.

In some models of research it becomes necessary to determine whether *several independent samples* have come from the same population or different populations. The usual parametric test employed for making this determination is the $F$-test involving the one-way analysis of variance. The basic assumptions underlying the $F$-test are that the sample observations are independently drawn from normally distributed populations having equal variances, and that the level of measurement of the data be at least of interval scale.

If the assumptions underlying the $F$-test cannot be met, the researcher may employ a nonparametric statistical test for $k$ independent samples. To this point of the discussion of nonparametric tests, we have only covered one test that is capable of analyzing data for $k$ independent samples—the chi-square test. Since the $\chi^2$ test for $k$ independent samples can only be employed in those cases where the data are of the nominal (classificatory) scale of measurement, it becomes necessary to introduce one which may be applied in those cases where the $k$ independent samples present data that are in the ordinal scale of measurement (ranks). The Kruskal–Wallis $H$-test for $k$ independent samples is a nonparametric statistical test which meets the latter requirement.

The Kruskal–Wallis $H$-test, sometimes referred to as "the one-way analysis of variance by ranks," provides an excellent means of determining whether the differences between $k$ independent samples represents merely chance variations expected among several random samples from the same population, or whether the differences between samples is such that it is highly probable that the samples are from different populations.[1] The test assumes that the variable under study has a continuous distribution, and is measured at least at the ordinal scale of measurement.

The first step involved in the application of the Kruskal–Wallis $H$-test is that of assigning a rank to each of the $n$ independent observations composing the total number of cases included in the $k$ samples. Thus, all of the observations from the $k$ independent samples are combined and ranked in a single series, with the observation of smallest value being replaced by rank 1, the next smallest by rank 2, and so on, until all values have been assigned ranks.

After the assignment of ranks is completed, the sum of the ranks for each of the $k$ samples (groups) are found. If the null hypothesis that these $k$ samples have been drawn from the same population or identical populations is true, then the sums of the ranks for the respective samples should not be extremely different in value. This null hypothesis may be tested by the $H$ statistic developed by Kruskal and Wallis, (1952), and given by formula (6):

$$H = \left(\frac{12}{n(n+1)}\right) \cdot \left(\sum_{j=1}^{k} \frac{S_j^2}{n_j}\right) - 3(n+1) \tag{6}$$

where

$k$ = the number of groups, or samples

$n_j$ = the number of observations in the $j$-th sample

$n = \sum n_j$, the total number of observations in all $k$ samples

$S_j^2$ = the "square" of the sum of ranks for the $j$-th group; and

$\sum\limits_{j=1}^{k}$ = indicates the summation over the $k$ groups

Kruskal and Wallis[2] have shown that if the null hypothesis ($H_0$) is true, and if the number of observations in each group is greater than $5$ ($n_j > 5$), then the $H$ statistic is distributed approximately as chi-square with $k - 1$ degrees of freedom; i.e., $df = k - 1$, where $k$ = the number of groups (samples).* Therefore, when there are more than five cases ($n_j > 5$) in each of the $k$ groups, the probability associated with the occurrence of values as large as the observed statistic $H$ under the null hypothesis ($H_0$), may be read from a chi-square table (see Figure 20). If the observed value of the statistic $H$ is equal to or greater than the critical value of $\chi^2$ found under the previously established level of significance and the appropriate number of degrees of freedom ($df = k - 1$), then the null hypothesis may be rejected at that level of significance.

The rejection of the null hypothesis by the $H$ statistic rejects the notion that the $k$ samples come from identical populations, and allows the acceptance of the statistical alternative hypothesis ($H_1$) that the populations are not identical. It should be pointed out here that since most educational research examines population means, and is only concerned with variances and other characteristics of the population, under certain circumstances it is important to know whether the rejection of the null hypothesis ($H_0$) by the Kruskal–Wallis $H$-test allows the researcher in general to conclude that the population means are not equal. Kruskal and Wallis indicate that the $H$-test is relatively insensitive to differences in the population variances. Therefore, in general, it may be inferred that the $H$-test can be used to test differences between population means, without assuming homogeneity of variance.

Before proceeding to an illustrative application of the $H$-test, the matter of adjustments for tied observations should be discussed. When ties occur between two or more observations, the average value of the ranks they would have been assigned had they differed should be given to the cases involved. The value of the $H$ statistic is affected somewhat by ties, and a correction factor must be employed to compensate for the effect. Correction for the effect of ties is realized by dividing formula (6) by the expression:

$$1 - \frac{\sum (t^3 - t)}{n^3 - n} \tag{6a}$$

---

* Kruskal and Wallis give tables for the distribution of $H$ with $k = 3$ samples all having $n_j \leq 5$; see (67a) W. H. Kruskal and W. A. Wallis, Tables for the Distribution of $H$ in "Use of Ranks in One-Criterion Variance Analysis," *Journal of American Statistical Association*, XLVII (1952), pp. 614–17. Also see (155) Siegel, pp. 282–83.

where

$t =$ the number of observations in a group tied for a given rank

$n = \sum n_j$, the number of all the observations in the $k$ samples combined

$\sum (t^3 - t)$ indicates summation over all groups of ties.

This correction factor for tied ranks modifies formula (6) to formula (6b):

$$H = \frac{\left(\dfrac{12}{n(n+1)}\right)\left(\sum\limits_{j=1}^{k} \dfrac{S_j^2}{n_j}\right) - 3(n+1)}{1 - \dfrac{\sum (t^3 - t)}{(n^3 - n)}} \tag{6b}$$

Correcting for ties increases the value of the statistic $H$, and makes the result more significant than one yielded by an uncorrected $H$. In other words, if the null hypothesis ($H_0$) is rejected by an *uncorrected* $H$ statistic formula (6), it will be rejected at an even "higher" level of significance ($\alpha = .03$ is a "higher" level of significance than $\alpha = .05$) by the corrected $H$ given by formula (6b).

As our illustrative example, suppose that a model of research is constructed to test the research hypothesis that secondary school teachers are more inflexible in the matter of attempting experimentation with new teaching methods and curriculum content than are elementary school teachers. Since the elementary school teachers are certified to teach grades $K$–8, and the secondary school teaching certificate covers grades 7–12 in the particular state where the study is being conducted, there is a group of teachers among both the elementary and secondary school teachers that might produce an unpredictable bias in the experimental results. In order to avoid this situation, the researcher decides to examine three teacher groups in the experiment: (1) a group which is composed of elementary school teachers who teach grade levels $K$–6, (2) a hybrid group which is composed of equal numbers of elementary school and intermediate school (secondary) teachers who have taught, and/or are teaching, grades 7 and 8 in elementary and intermediate school settings, respectively, and (3) a group composed of secondary school teachers who teach grade levels 9–12. The measuring instruments are administered to each of the twenty-four participating teachers, and the results are reported in the form of a composite score for each individual. The operational hypothesis advanced is that there will be a difference between the groups' average composite scores.

Suppose that even though the three samples have been drawn independently and randomly, the assumption of their having been drawn from normally distributed populations with equal variances cannot be made. The fictitious data are shown in Table XI, where high scores indicate greater flexibility.

The inference process is as follows:

1. *Null Hypotheses.* $H_0 : Pr(X_3 > X_1) = Pr(X_3 > X_2) = Pr(X_2 > X_1) = \frac{1}{2}$, or in statement form there is no difference between the three groups' average composite scores, i.e., the three groups have been drawn from the same population with mean of $\mu_0$. The statistical alternative hypothesis ($H_1$) calls for

Table XI

"Flexibility" Scores of Three Groups of Teachers

(Fictitious Data)

| Elementary (K–6) | | Elementary and Intermediate (7–8) | | Secondary (9–12) | |
|---|---|---|---|---|---|
| Score $(X_1)$ | Assigned Rank | Score $(X_2)$ | Assigned Rank | Score $(X_3)$ | Assigned Rank |
| 105 | 4 | 101 | 2 | 128 | 8 |
| 130 | 10 | 150 | 13 | 260 | 20 |
| 100 | 1 | 130 | 10 | 247 | 17 |
| 108 | 5 | 142 | 12 | 280 | 23 |
| 103 | 3 | 214 | 14.5 | 266 | 21 |
| 109 | 6 | 247 | 17 | 273 | 22 |
| 121 | 7 | | | 291 | 24 |
| 130 | 10 | | | 256 | 19 |
| | | | | 247 | 17 |
| | | | | 214 | 14.5 |
| $S_1 = 46$ | | $S_2 = 68.5$ | | $S_3 = 185.5$ | |

inequality in at least one of the cases presented by $H_0$ or, the three groups of teachers are not drawn from the same population in terms of their average composite scores.

2. *Statistical Test.* Three independent groups are under study, and a test for $k$ independent samples is needed. The parametric $F$-test cannot be employed, because assumptions of normality of distribution and equality of variance for the hypothetical populations of composite scores for the three classifications of teachers cannot be made by the researcher. Since the composite scores can be considered to be of *at least* the ordinal scale of measurement (they were originally considered to be of the interval level of measurement), the Kruskal–Wallis $H$-test is the most appropriate one for the situation.

3. *Level of significance,* $\alpha$. The level of significance is set at $\alpha = .01$, and the size of the sample is $n = 24$, the total number of teachers participating in the study. The number of elementary teachers (K–6) participating is: $n_1 = 8$. The number of elementary-intermediate (7–8) is: $n_2 = 6$, and the number of secondary teachers (9–12) is: $n_3 = 10$.

4. *Sampling Distribution.* Since $n_j$, the size of the $j$-th group (sample), in each of the three samples involved is greater than 5, the chi-square ($df = 3 - 1 = 2$) approximation of the $H$-test as given by formula (6b) is the appropriate sampling distribution to be employed.

5. *Critical Region.* The critical region consists of all values of the $H$ statistic which are so large that the probability associated with their occurrence under the null hypothesis, for the $\chi^2$ distribution of $df = 3 - 1 = 2$, is equal to or less than $\alpha = .01$.

6. *Computing the Statistic.* Since tied ranks are involved, formula (6b) should be used to find the value of $H$. In order to evaluate (6b), it is first necessary to determine how many groups of ties have occurred and how many scores are tied in each of these groups. The first tie occurred between three scores of 130, which were assigned the tied rank of 10. In this case, the number of tied obser-

vations is $t = 3$, and $t^3 - t = 27 - 3 = 24$. The next tie occurred between two scores of 214, which were assigned the tied rank of 14.5. For this occurrence, $t = 2$, and $t^3 - t = 8 - 2 = 6$. The last of the three groups of ties occurring in the data of Table XI is one between three scores of 247, which were assigned the tied rank of 17. In this case, $t = 3$, and $t^3 - t = 27 - 3 = 24$. From these results, the value of the summation for the three *groups of ties* becomes: $\sum (t^3 - t) = 24 + 6 + 24 = 54$. The value of the correction factor, therefore, is found to be:

$$1 - \frac{\sum (t^3 - t)}{n^3 - n} = 1 - \frac{54}{(24)^3 - 24} = 1 - \frac{54}{(24)(575)} = 1 - .0039 = .9961$$

The value of the $H$ statistic is:

$$H = \frac{\frac{12}{(24)(25)} \left[ \frac{(46)^2}{8} + \frac{(68.5)^2}{6} + \frac{(185.5)^2}{10} \right] - (3)(25)}{.9961}$$

$$= \frac{\frac{1}{50}(264.5 + 782.042 + 3441.025) - 75}{.9961}$$

$$= \frac{89.75 - 75}{.9961} = \frac{14.75}{.9961} = 14.808$$

7. *Decision concerning $H_0$.* Reference to a $\chi^2$ probability table (see Figure 20), indicates that a value of $H \geq 14.808$, under the condition of $df = k - 1 = 3 - 1 = 2$, has a probability of occurrence under the null hypothesis ($H_0$) of $Pr < .01$ (in fact, $Pr < .001$). The researcher would therefore reject $H_0$ in favor of the statistical alternative hypothesis ($H_1$), and infer that there is a difference between the three groups in the trait of "flexibility" as measured by the composite scores.

To establish which groups of the three are different from each other, the researcher may adapt the data to a Kolmogorov–Smirnov two-sample test, or even apply the $H$-test for $k = 2$ independent groups.

*Chapter 26—References*
See Bibliography: 27, 49, 53, 54, 89, 108, 109, 148, 155, 165, 179, 203; 7a, 8a, 11a, 34a, 67a, 82a, 84a, 104a, 116a, 117a; 3b, 4b.

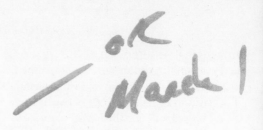

*Chapter Twenty-seven*

# Parametric Statistical Tests—I

## (*The Normal and t-Distributions*)

IN OUR DISCUSSION of *basic concepts of statistics* the properties and principles underlying frequency distributions of measurements and enumerations were pointed out. Since, under certain conditions, estimates derived from measurements and enumerations have frequency distributions of known characteristics, the broad areas of *sampling* and *estimation* used these distributions in several different ways to solve some of the problems associated with determining "representativeness" and "adequacy" of sample along with improving estimates and the process of estimation itself. Finally, the frequency distribution was employed as a *test statistic* (all nonparametric to this point) to provide a vehicle for testing statistical hypotheses. These applications of the frequency distribution are fundamental to all elements of the suggested general model of research, and play an important part in the analytic procedures of the problem, hypothesis, universe, sample, and data collection elements of the model. In fact, the "test statistic" aspect of distributions is the basic structure of the *analytical and numerical procedures* associated with the Data Processing and Decision elements of the research model.

This chapter is concerned with the topic of parametric test statistics. Regardless of whether a test statistic is of the nonparametric or parametric type, it has certain basic characteristics. First, every test statistic has a frequency distribution which can be used as a probability distribution to determine if the observed value of the test statistic is a likely one when the statistical hypothesis under test is assumed to be true. Second, the value of a test statistic is computed from sample data. If it is a nonparametric test, it is evaluated in terms of frequencies, proportions, or ranks derived from the sample. If it is a parametric test, its value is computed from such *sample statistics* as the arithmetic mean ($\overline{X}$), the variance ($S^2$), the correlation coefficient ($r$), and other similar estimates. Third, some test statistics are capable of testing all three of the possible statistical hypotheses (magnitude, difference, and relationship), while others are capable of testing no more than one of them. Finally, each test statistic is based upon assumptions concerning: (1) the continuity of the distribution of the data, (2) the level of measurement of the data, (3) the method of drawing the sample, and (4) the way in which the data are collected.

Nonparametric test statistics are associated with the following distributions:

1. binomial distribution;
2. Poisson distribution;
3. normal probability distribution (as an approximation);
4. chi-square ($\chi^2$) distribution;
5. Kolmogorov–Smirnov probability distribution (for both the one-sample and two-sample cases);
6. Wilcoxon probability distribution; and
7. Kruskal–Wallis $H$ Statistic probability distribution.

The parametric test statistics selected for discussion here are those associated with:

1. the normal probability distribution,
2. the $t$-distribution, and
3. the $z$- or $F$-distribution.

It should be pointed out that test statistics cannot be employed mechanically. They must be applied in keeping with the research problem and the general design of the research model. It should be kept in mind that a test of a statistical hypothesis is, at best, *evidence*, and not proof, of the conditions or treatments involved. The research decision can only be made if the results of the statistical inference process are interpreted in terms of the many factors of the research problem and situation. Unless the research model provides a carefully designed inquiry, which takes all of the elements of the model into account, the effect of bias on the tests of the statistical hypotheses will not be eliminated.

The normal probability distribution was discussed in connection with certain basic concepts of statistics, and during the discussion of the subject of the normal distribution, it was pointed out that if the random sample drawn from the population was sufficiently large, the sampling distribution of the arithmetic mean ($\overline{X}$) would be approximately normally distributed. Under the condition of sufficiently large sample size, the sampling distributions of the differences between two group means ($\overline{X}_2 - \overline{X}_1$), the linear correlation coefficient, and certain other types of measures are also normally distributed. Since the normal probability distribution of these measures cannot actually be employed unless the value of the population variance ($\sigma^2$) is known, in which case there is no need for making an estimate or drawing an inference about the value of the population parameter (i.e., the mean) involved, we shall not discuss the distribution or its possible implications further. In most cases, the value of $\sigma^2$ is not known, and the value of $S^2$ (an estimate of $\sigma^2$) must be used. Under these conditions, the $t$-distribution must be employed. We now discuss that distribution.

### THE $t$-DISTRIBUTION

In the previous section it was pointed out that in order to apply the normal probability distribution as a test statistic to hypotheses of *magnitudes* and *differences* of *population means*, it is necessary to know the value of the population variance. In most research problems, however, the researcher does not work with samples from populations of "known variances," but must estimate these parameters from the data of the sample. The estimate of the population variance $(\sigma^2)$ is the sample variance $(S^2)$, which is found by the formula:

$$S^2 = \frac{\sum X^2 - (\sum X)^2/n}{n - 1}$$

The estimated standard deviation of the sampling distribution of the mean for sample size $n$ drawn from an approximately normal population with estimated variance equal to $S^2$ is:

$$S_{\bar{X}} = \frac{S}{\sqrt{n}} \tag{1}$$

where $S_{\bar{X}}$ is called "the estimate of the standard error of the mean for sample size $n$, $S$ is the standard deviation of the sample, and $n$ is the number of elements in the sample.

The definition of $t$ then becomes:*

$$t = \frac{\bar{X} - \mu_{\bar{X}}}{S_{\bar{X}}} = \frac{\bar{X} - \mu}{S/\sqrt{n}} \tag{2}$$

where $\bar{X}$ is the mean of the sample of size $n$, $S$ is the standard deviation of the sample, and $\mu_{\bar{X}} \approx \mu$ is the value of the mean of the sampling distribution of the mean for sample size $n$.

The $t$-distribution differs from the normal probability distribution in that it is not one distribution but a whole family of distributions one for each value of $n - 1$, where the value $n - 1$ is defined technically as the number of *degrees of freedom* available in the sample set of observations. The concept of *degrees of freedom* can be explained in a number of different ways. One approach that may be used is that the number of degrees of freedom available in a set of $n$ observations depends upon the number of restrictions placed upon the observations, i.e., the number of observations minus the number of population parameters (e.g., arithmetic mean, variance) estimated from the data. To illustrate, in finding the value of the sample variance $S^2$, theoretically, it is first necessary to calculate the mean of the sample $(\bar{X})$, and then find the "differences" of the $n$ observations from the sample mean $(\bar{X})$. Since the sum of these differences (deviations) must be equal to zero, only $n - 1$ of them are *free to vary*, and the value of the last observation must be such (fixed) that it renders the sum of the deviations zero in value. Hence, it is said that the estimate of the population variance (a parameter) is based upon $n - 1$ degrees of freedom. Another explanation of the degrees of freedom concept is that the number of

---

* The general mathematical equation for the $t$-distribution is:

$$Y = C\left(1 + \frac{t^2}{n'}\right) - \frac{(n' + 1)}{2}$$

where $Y$ is the frequency of $t$, $n'$ is the number of *degrees of freedom* used in estimating $S$ and is equal to $(n - 1)$, (one less than the number of elements in the sample), and $C$ is a constant depending upon the value of $n'$.

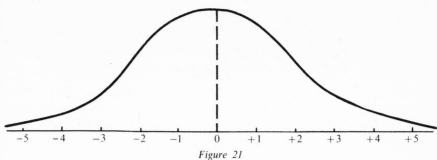

*Figure 21*

*The t-Distribution for n = 4, or n − 1 = 3 Degrees of Freedom*

degrees of freedom is the number of independent comparisons which can be made *between observations* or *between classes of observations*, thus with *n* observations there are *n* − 1 independent comparisons *between observations* that can be made, while if there are *k* classes of observations, *k* − 1 independent comparisons can be made between classes of observations. Finally, in a mathematical sense the term "degrees of freedom" implies the number of independent *variables* involved, i.e., the number of dimensions under consideration that may be assigned values freely.

The curves forming the family of the *t*-distribution are similar to the normal curve to the extent that they are single-peaked at, and symmetrical about, a zero mean. The *t*-curves differ from the normal curve in that they are more peaked at the mean and extend further from the mean than does the normal curve. This condition indicates that for the same values of *t* and *z* (normal deviate), the area beyond that value of *t* is larger than the area beyond the commensurate value of *z*. Hence, the *t*-distribution requires a larger deviate for the 5 per cent and 1 per cent levels of significance than does the normal probability curve. It should be recalled, however, that the values of *t* at all levels of significance, are functions of the number of degrees of freedom, *n* − 1, involved. Figure 21 shows one of the *t*-distributions, and Table XII presents selected critical values of *t* at certain levels of significance (probabilities).

The general characteristics of the *t*-distribution are clearly illustrated in Figure 21. For samples of size *n* > 30 the values of $t = (\bar{X} - \mu_{\bar{x}})/(S/\sqrt{n})$ may be assumed to be approximately normally distributed, but as *n* becomes smaller this is not the case. If hypotheses of magnitudes and differences of population means are to be tested *with small samples, the t-distribution should be used* rather than the normal distribution.

Table XII may be employed for one-tailed and two-tailed *t*-tests of hypotheses of magnitudes and differences of population means, and hypotheses of relationships involving values of the population correlation coefficient ($\rho$), and the random sample values (*r*). Table XII presents certain percentiles for selected *t*-distributions.* The percentiles are shown at the tops of the columns of the

---

* For a complete table of *t*-values see any of the elementary statistics textbooks listed in the references.

Table XII
Selected Percentiles of the $t$-Distribution

| df | t .90 | t .95 | t .975 | t .99 | t .995 |
|---|---|---|---|---|---|
| 1 | 3.078 | 6.314 | 12.706 | 31.821 | 63.657 |
| 2 | 1.886 | 2.920 | 4.303 | 6.965 | 9.925 |
| 3 | 1.638 | 2.353 | 3.182 | 4.541 | 5.841 |
| 4 | 1.533 | 2.132 | 2.776 | 3.747 | 4.604 |
| 5 | 1.476 | 2.015 | 2.571 | 3.365 | 4.032 |
| 6 | 1.440 | 1.943 | 2.447 | 3.143 | 3.707 |
| 7 | 1.415 | 1.895 | 2.365 | 2.998 | 3.499 |
| 8 | 1.397 | 1.860 | 2.306 | 2.896 | 3.355 |
| 9 | 1.383 | 1.833 | 2.262 | 2.821 | 3.250 |
| 10 | 1.372 | 1.812 | 2.228 | 2.764 | 3.169 |
| 12 | 1.356 | 1.782 | 2.179 | 2.681 | 3.055 |
| 15 | 1.341 | 1.753 | 2.131 | 2.602 | 2.947 |
| 18 | 1.330 | 1.734 | 2.101 | 2.552 | 2.878 |
| 20 | 1.325 | 1.725 | 2.086 | 2.528 | 2.845 |
| 22 | 1.321 | 1.717 | 2.074 | 2.508 | 2.819 |
| 25 | 1.316 | 1.708 | 2.060 | 2.485 | 2.787 |
| 27 | 1.314 | 1,703 | 2.052 | 2.473 | 2.771 |
| 28 | 1.313 | 1.701 | 2.048 | 2.467 | 2.763 |
| 29 | 1.311 | 1.699 | 2.045 | 2.462 | 2.756 |
| 30 | 1.310 | 1.697 | 2.042 | 2.457 | 2.750 |
| ∞ | 1.282 | 1.645 | 1.960 | 2.326 | 2.576 |
| df | − t .10 | − t .05 | − t .025 | − t .01 | − t .005 |

table, and the particular $t$-distribution for the selected percentiles are indicated in the first column down the left side of the table by $df$ (degrees of freedom). When the table is read from the bottom row of probabilities, the $t$-values found in the body of the table are to be prefixed with a negative ($-$) sign. The table may be used for both one-tailed and two-tailed tests of hypotheses. To illustrate, if the level of significance for a two-tailed $t$-test is set at $\alpha = .05$, and the size of the sample employed is $n = 30$, the critical value of $t = +2.045$ is found in the $30 - 1 = 29$ $df$ row under the column headed $t.975$ and footed $-t.025$. If a one-tailed $t$-test is to be employed with $\alpha = .01$, and the critical region is in the "upper" (positive) tail of the curve listed for, say, $n - 1 = 12$ $df$, the critical value would be $t = +2.681$. In similar fashion, a one-tailed $t$-test for $\alpha = .05$ in an $n - 1 = 9$ $df$ distribution, in the "lower" (negative) tail of the curve, would show a critical value of $t = -1.833$.

With this background we are now prepared to illustrate the application of the $t$-distribution to hypotheses of magnitudes and differences of population means, and to hypotheses of relationship involving sample values of the correlation coefficient ($r$). In testing hypotheses of relationships involving correlation coefficients, the Pearson Product-Moment correlation coefficient ($r$) and the Spearman Rank correlation coefficient ($\rho_S$) are the only two coefficients that can be correctly employed in the $t$-test formula designed for such tests. It will be recalled from earlier discussions that the "significance" of the $\Phi$ coefficient is more suitably measured by the $\chi^2$ distribution. Other correlation coefficients may be tested by the distribution after undergoing Fisher's $z$ transformation.

### Hypotheses of Magnitude

We have seen that the sampling distribution of the mean for sample size $n$: $z = (\overline{X} - \mu_{\bar{x}})/(\sigma/\sqrt{n})$ can be considered as normally distributed if $\sigma$ is known.

In most research "problems", however, the value of $\sigma$ is not known. In those cases where the value of $\sigma$ is not known, we may estimate it ($\sigma$) with the value of $S$ and use the sampling distribution of: $t = (\overline{X} - \mu_{\bar{x}})/(S/\sqrt{n})$; instead of $z$. In order to select the appropriate sampling distribution of $t$ to conduct the test of $H_0$, it is necessary to know the number of degrees of freedom available in the "problem" under study. Testing hypotheses of the magnitude of a population mean, since only one population parameter (the mean) is being estimated, involves $(n - 1)$ degrees of freedom $(df)$, where $n$ indicates the number of elements composing the independently and randomly selected sample.

Two-tailed and one-tailed tests of appropriate null hypotheses may be conducted by the $t$-test in a fashion similar to that employed by the normal probability distribution in making such tests. The two examples which follow illustrate two-tailed and one-tailed $t$-tests of null hypotheses of magnitudes of population means.

As part of an action research project, a social studies teacher decides to incorporate three field trips into the syllabus of a high-school course in civics. One trip will include a half-day visit to city and county governmental agencies. Another trip will involve the visiting of courts and federal agencies located in the school district, and, finally, a day-long trip to the state capitol will be effected.

The teacher has administered a locally constructed final examination of four parallel forms for the past two years to groups who have taken the civics class when field trips were *not* included in the course offering, and except for knowing the mean score of the total number of pupils who have taken the examination, none of the values of the other parameters of the test population is known. The teacher is unsure of whether the field trips will have a positive or negative affect on the final examination scores of the pupils involved in the "experiment". Hence, the alternative hypothesis that there will be a difference between the "experimental" group's mean score and the population mean score on the final examination is advanced.

Suppose the mean score of the twenty-nine pupils composing the "experimental" group is $\overline{X} = 73$, and the standard deviation is $S = 8$. If the population mean is $\mu = 70$, can the teacher infer that the field trips probably have affected the population mean score ($\mu$) of the final examination? The inference process for testing the appropriate null hypothesis would be as follows:

1. *Null Hypothesis.* $H_0 : \mu_E = 70$. The "experimental" group's scores come from the population composed of the "previous" group's scores. The alternative hypothesis is $H_1 : \mu_E \neq 70$. The experimental group's scores come from a different population than those of the previous groups.

2. *Statistical Test.* Since the population standard deviation ($\sigma$) is not known, its sample estimate: $S = 8$ must be used in the test statistic to be employed. Assuming that the sample of $n = 29$ students' scores was independently and randomly selected from an approximately normally distributed population, the appropriate statistical test under these conditions would be the $t$-test.

3. *Level of Significance*, α. The level of significance for this two-tailed test of $H_0$ is set at $\alpha = .05$, and the sample size of $n = 29$ is found to be adequate for the purposes of the study.

4. *Sampling Distribution.* The appropriate sampling distribution is the following $t$-statistic under $29 - 1 = 28 \, df.$

$$t = \frac{\bar{X} - \mu_{\bar{x}}}{S/\sqrt{n}} = \frac{\bar{X} - 70}{8/\sqrt{29}} = \frac{\bar{X} - 70}{8/5.38} = \frac{\bar{X} - 70}{1.487}$$

5. *Critical Region.* The critical region for this two-tailed $t$-test of $H_0$ with 28 $df$ and $\alpha = .05$ is: $\{t < -2.048\}$ and $(t > +2.048)$.

6. *Computing the Statistic.* Computing the value of $t$, we have:

$$t = \frac{\bar{X} - 70}{1.487} = \frac{73 - 70}{1.487} = \frac{3}{1.487} = +2.017$$

7. *Decision concerning $H_0$.* Since the value of $t = +2.017$ is not in the critical region, the null hypothesis $(H_0)$ cannot be rejected. The value of $t = 2.017$, however, is so close to the critical value of $t = +2.048$ that the teacher should infer that the null $(H_0)$ is "placed in doubt," and thus prepare to conduct the experiment again. As a rule of thumb, the researcher should be prepared to "place the null hypothesis in doubt," if the value of the statistic is such that it falls just within the critical region, or just outside of the critical region, e.g., if $\alpha = .05$, and the probability of occurrence associated with the observed value of the test statistic, say, $z$, or $t$, falls within the range of $.05 \leq Pr \leq .10$, the hypothesis is "placed in doubt" and the experiment is replicated.

To illustrate a one-tailed $t$-test, suppose that the teacher in our previous example decides to conduct the experiment once again with another group of students supposedly chosen independently and randomly. With the knowledge gained from the previous experiment, the teacher decides to advance the "alternative" hypothesis that the experimental group's mean score will be higher than the population mean. Assuming the teacher does not "teach" the examination, and that other factors which might affect the group's mean score are kept under control, the inference process that would be used to make a one-tailed test of the appropriate null hypothesis, if the group's mean score is $\bar{X} = 74$, and the standard deviation is $S = 6.5$, would be as follows:

1. *Null Hypothesis.* $H_0 : \mu_E \leq 70$. The experimental group's scores come from a population of scores that has a mean equal to, or less than, that of the population composed of previous groups' scores. The alternative hypothesis is $H_1$: $\mu_E > 70$.

2. *Statistical Test.* Since the population standard deviation $(\sigma)$ is unknown, its sample estimate $S = 6.5$ must be used in the test statistic to be employed. Assuming that the sample of $n = 31$ students' scores was independently and randomly selected from a population of scores that is approximately normally distributed, the appropriate statistical test under these conditions would be the $t$-test.

3. *Level of Significance,* $\alpha$. The level of significance for this one-tailed test of $H_0$ is set at $\alpha = .05$, and the sample size of $n = 31$ is found to be adequate for the purposes of the study.

4. *Sampling Distribution.* The appropriate sampling distribution is given by formula (2) under the condition of $31 - 1 = 30$ degrees of freedom $(df)$:

$$t = \frac{\overline{X} - \mu_{\overline{X}}}{S/\sqrt{n}} = \frac{\overline{X} - 70}{6.5/\sqrt{31}} = \frac{\overline{X} - 70}{6.5/5.568} = \frac{\overline{X} - 70}{1.167}$$

5. *Critical Region.* The critical region for this one-tailed $t$-test of $H_0$: $\mu_E \leq 70$ with 30 $df$ and $\alpha = .05$ is: $\{t > +1.697\}$.

6. *Computing the Statistic.* Computing the value of $t$, we have:

$$t = \frac{\overline{X} - 70}{1.167} = \frac{74 - 70}{1.167} = \frac{4}{1.167} = +3.428$$

7. *Decision concerning $H_0$.* Since the value of $t = 3.428$ falls in the critical region, the null hypothesis $(H_0)$ is rejected in favor of the "alternative" hypothesis $(H_1)$, and the teacher may infer that the field trips do affect the population mean score, and based upon the findings of this and her previous "experiment," the field trips are factors which appear to increase learning in the civics class. It should be noted here that the examples used to illustrate the one-tailed and two-tailed $t$-tests would probably *not* occur in practice. The fact that there are so many variables at work in such an "experimental" setting would dictate that a more "rigorous" design, accounting for other variables probably at work, be employed. Research problems of this type can best be examined by the analysis-of-variance or analysis-of-covariance techniques which are described in later chapters.

## Hypotheses of Difference

The $t$-distribution may also be employed to test hypotheses of difference involving two population means, providing the randomly and independently selected samples from which the values of $\overline{X}_1$, $\overline{X}_2$, $S_1^2$ and $S_2^2$ are determined have been drawn from approximately normally distributed populations. The statement of the null hypothesis $(H_0)$ involving the population means, $\mu_1$ and $\mu_2$, and the assumption of either the *equality* or *inequality* of the population variances, $\sigma_1^2$ and $\sigma_2^2$, along with a stipulated number of degrees of freedom $(df)$, determines the appropriate $t$-distributed sampling distribution of the difference of two groups' means to be employed.

If the null hypothesis states that the *population means are equal*, regardless of whether a one-tailed or two-tailed test is to be employed, i.e., the hypotheses $H_0 : \mu_1 = \mu_2$; $H_0 : \mu_1 \leq \mu_2$; and $H_0 : \mu_1 \geq \mu_2$; and the respective population variances, $\sigma_1^2$ and $\sigma_2^2$, are *unknown but assumed to be unequal*, then the formula for the appropriate $t$-test is:

$$t = \frac{(\overline{X}_1 - \overline{X}_2) - (\mu_1 - \mu_2)}{\sqrt{S_1^2/n_1 + S_2^2/n_2}} = \frac{\overline{X}_1 - \overline{X}_2}{\sqrt{S_1^2/n_1 + S_2^2/n_2}} \tag{3}$$

where all symbols are defined as in formula (1), and $S_1^2$ and $S_2^2$ are estimates of the respective population variances, $\sigma_1^2$ and $\sigma_2^2$.

If the null hypothesis states that the population means are *equal* for both one-tailed and two-tailed tests, and the respective population variances are *equal*; i.e., $\sigma_1^2 = \sigma_2^2 = \sigma^2$, then the formula for the appropriate $t$-test is:

$$t = \frac{(\overline{X}_1 - \overline{X}_2) - (\mu_1 - \mu_2)}{\sqrt{S_p^2/n_1 + S_p^2/n_2}} = \frac{\overline{X}_1 - \overline{X}_2}{S_p\sqrt{1/n_1 + 1/n_2}} \tag{4}$$

where $S_p^2$ is the *pooled mean-square estimate* of $\sigma^2$ given by:

$$S_p^2 = \frac{(n_1 - 1)S_1^2 + (n_2 - 1)S_2^2}{n_1 + n_2 - 2}$$

with $n_1, n_2, S_1^2$, and $S_2^2$ defined as they are in formula (3).

When the research situation involves *paired* observations or matched subjects, and it becomes necessary to test a hypothesis of difference of two population means ($\mu_1$ and $\mu_2$), the form of the $t$-test which takes into account the possible correlation between the paired observations must be employed. The appropriate $t$-formula is:

$$t = \frac{(\overline{X}_1 - \overline{X}_2) - (\mu_1 - \mu_2)}{\sqrt{(S_1^2/n_1) + (S_2^2/n_2) - (2rS_1S_2/n)}} \tag{5}$$

where $\overline{X}_1, \overline{X}_2, \mu_1, \mu_2$, and $n$ are as previously defined, $r$ is the correlation between paired values $(X_1, X_2)$, and $S_1^2$ and $S_2^2$ are the estimates of the respective population variances, $\sigma_1^2$ and $\sigma_2^2$.

Formula (5) is not as convenient in terms of the number of calculations required as its *identity* form, which is developed as follows:

Let $d$ equal the difference $(\overline{X}_1 - \overline{X}_2)$ between the two elements of any given paired observations, i.e., $d = \overline{X}_1 - \overline{X}_2$. The mean difference $(\overline{d})$ for the sample of $n$ paired observations is:

$$\overline{d} = \frac{\sum\limits_{i=1}^{n} d_i}{n}$$

where $\sum\limits_{i=1}^{n}$ indicates the operation of summing the $n$ $d$'s yielded by the paired observations composing the sample. The deviation of any given $d$ from the mean difference $(\overline{d})$ may then be designated as: $D = (d - \overline{d})$; and to find the sum of squares of this expression we would have:

$$\sum D^2 = \sum (d - \overline{d})^2 = \sum (d^2 - 2d\overline{d} + \overline{d}^2) = \sum d^2 - 2\frac{(\sum d)^2}{n} + n\left(\frac{\sum d}{n}\right)^2$$

$$\therefore \quad \sum D^2 = \sum d^2 - \frac{(\sum d)^2}{n} \tag{6}$$

where $n$ is equal to the number of differences or pairs of observations.

Employing the relationship denoted by formula (6), we find that the variance of the distribution of differences ($d$'s) will be given by:

$$S_D^2 = \frac{\sum d^2 - (\sum d)^2/n}{n-1} = \frac{\sum D^2}{n-1} \tag{7}$$

and the standard deviation of the distribution of the $n$ differences ($d$'s) occurring in the sample will be the square root of the expression in (7), or:

$$S_D = \sqrt{\frac{\sum D^2}{n-1}} \tag{7a}$$

There are $n-1$ degrees of freedom available for $S_D$ in (7a), where $n$ is the number of *paired observations* composing the sample.

Formula (7a) is used to determine an estimate of the population standard deviation of the differences ($d$'s) between the elements of paired observations. The estimate, in turn, is important in determining the *standard error of the difference between the means for paired observations*, $S_{\bar{X}_1 - \bar{X}_2}$, which is equivalent to the denominator found in formula (5) of the $t$-test. Hence, we have:

$$S_{\bar{X}_1 - \bar{X}_2} = \frac{S_D}{\sqrt{n}} \tag{8}$$

where $n$ denotes the number of paired observations in the sample, and the $t$-test statistic *identity* of formula (5) becomes:

$$t = \frac{(\bar{X}_1 - \bar{X}_2) - (\mu_1 - \mu_2)}{S_{\bar{X}_1 - \bar{X}_2}} = \frac{\bar{d} - c}{S_D/\sqrt{n}} \tag{9}$$

where $\bar{d} = \bar{X}_1 - \bar{X}_2$; $c$ is a constant (including 0) which is stipulated in the null hypothesis as the value of the difference between the population means, $\mu_1$ and $\mu_2$; $S_D$ is as defined in (7a); $n$ is the number of paired observations in the sample; and the *number of degrees of freedom available for evaluating $t$ is equal to the number of paired observations minus* 1, i.e., $n-1$.

We shall now present examples which will illustrate the application of formulas (3), (4), and (9) to various one-tailed and two-tailed tests of hypotheses of differences of two population means. It should be pointed out that formula (5) is omitted because its *identity*, formula (9), is more convenient to calculate and, naturally, can be employed in all research situations that present conditions calling for the application of (5).

To illustrate the application of formula (3), suppose that a large city school system is in the process of conducting a vast curriculum research project. In order to determine whether it will be necessary to have different curricular offerings at the same grade level for certain "districts" within the community served by the system, one phase of the total effort is devoted to a field research study of socio-economic backgrounds existing in the geographical area of the school district. In the process of attempting to determine whether the individual districts served by each of two junior high schools were of relatively the same socio-economic level, two pilot study random samples of families were selected, one from each of the records of the two junior high schools. Since the neighborhoods served by the respective schools had been considered to be "similar" in terms of the socio-economic backgrounds of the inhabitants of the respective districts prior to the study, the *null hypothesis* that the two population means, $\mu_1$ and $\mu_2$, are *equal* is advanced; and the "conservative" assumption is made that the population variances, $\sigma_1^2$ and $\sigma_2^2$, are *unequal*,* where the means and variances involved are parameters of the population of composite socio-economic scores resulting from the combining of a standardized socio-economic inventory score with ratings for each family in the sample made by the field research team.

---

* In applying the $t$-test to the hypothesis of the difference between two population means, it is usually implicit in the hypothesis being tested that the variances of the populations from which the samples are drawn are equal. In rejecting the null hypothesis, $H_0: \mu_1 = \mu_2$, being tested, it is implied that the way in which the two populations differ is with respect to their means rather than with respect to their variances. If the researcher wishes to avoid this situation, or *does not wish to assume the inequality of the population variances*, it is possible to test the hypothesis that $\sigma_1^2 = \sigma_2^2$ without involving any hypothesis about the population means. This test is accomplished by comparing two independent estimates $S_1^2$ and $S_2^2$ of the *assumed common population variance*, $\sigma^2$, by means of Fisher's $F$-test which is discussed later.

The $F$-test of the null hypothesis, $H_0: \sigma_1^2 = \sigma_2^2 = \sigma^2$, is accomplished by placing the value of $S_1^2$ or $S_2^2$, *whichever is larger*, in the numerator and the smaller value in the denominator of the ratio, defined as:

$$F = \frac{S_1^2}{S_2^2}; \quad \text{or} \quad F = \frac{S_2^2}{S_1^2}$$

so that the value of $F$ will always be greater than 1.

The distribution of $F$ is known and has been tabled in convenient form. A table of selected values of $F > 1$ which are significant at $\alpha = .05$ and $.01$ *points* for various degrees of freedom, respectively, is found in Chapter 28. To illustrate how the $F$-test is employed in this case, suppose that values of the two independent estimates, $S_1^2$ and $S_2^2$ of the assumed common population variance $\sigma^2$, are found to be 4.03 and 28.21, from random samples of size $n_1 = 16$, and $n_2 = 9$, respectively. Our $F$-ratio then becomes: $F = S_2^2/S_1^2 = 28.21/4.03 = 7.0$. Entering the *column* of Table XIV designated by the value of the number of degrees of freedom of the estimate, $S_2^2$, found in the numerator of the $F$-ratio, i.e., $n_2 - 1 = 9 - 1 = 8$, and proceeding down that column to the *row* designated by the value of the number of degrees of freedom of the estimate, $S_1^2$, in the denominator of the ratio, i.e., $n_1 - 1 = 16 - 1 = 15$, we find the value enclosed in parentheses to be the value of $F$ significant for the .01 point and the other value of $F$ to be the one significant at the .05 *point*. Since, in our sample, we are conducting a two-tailed test of the null; $H_0: \sigma_1^2 = \sigma_2^2$, against $H_1: \sigma_1^2 \neq \sigma_2^2$, we must *double the probability values* given in the table of $F$. Hence, for our example the values in the $F$ table will correspond to the .02 and .10 levels of significance.

For our example with $F = 28.21/4.03 = 7.0$, and 8 degrees of freedom for the numerator along with 15 degrees of freedom for the denominator, we find from Table XIV that a value of $F = 2.64$ is significant at the 10 per cent *level*, and the value of $F = 4.00$ to be significant at the 2 per cent *level*. Although we could find by approximate interpolation the value of $F$ which would be significant at the .05 level, since our value of $F = 7.0$ is greater than $F = 4.00$ for the 2 per cent level, we would reject $H_0$ in favor of $H_1$ and infer that the respective variances of the two populations are significantly different.

Suppose the results of the pilot study for the two samples are as follows:

$$\overline{X}_1 = 61.5 \qquad \overline{X}_2 = 55.9$$
$$S_1^2 = 84.64 \qquad S_2^2 = 16.81$$
$$n_1 = 36 \qquad n_2 = 41$$

The inference process employed would be:

1. *Null Hypothesis.* $H_0: \mu_1 = \mu_2$; or $\mu_1 - \mu_2 = 0$. In statement form the null hypothesis is that the two populations have the same mean. The "alternative" hypothesis is $H_1: \mu_1 \neq \mu_2$, i.e., the two population means are *not* equal.

2. *Statistical Test.* Assuming that the "composite" scores for the districts under study are approximately normally distributed, but not knowing the values of the variances of these populations of scores and therefore planning to use estimates of the variances derived from an independent random sample drawn from each of the two populations, the research team decides that the *t*-test is the appropriate statistical test to employ.

3. *Level of Significance,* $\alpha$. The level of significance for this two-tailed *t*-test of $H_0$ is set at: $\alpha = .05$, and the sample sizes of $n_1 = 36$ and $n_2 = 41$ are found to be adequate for the purposes of the *pilot study*.

4. *Sampling Distribution.* Because the populations' variances are assumed to be unequal (or if they were found to be significantly different by means of the *F*-test),* and the null hypothesis under test is that of the equality of the two population means $(H_0: \mu_1 = \mu_2)$, the appropriate sampling distribution of the *t*-test with $(n_1 + n_2 - 2)$ degrees of freedom is provided by formula (3):

$$t = \frac{(\overline{X}_1 - \overline{X}_2) - (\mu_1 - \mu_2)}{\sqrt{S_1^2/n_1 + S_2^2/n_2}} \tag{3}$$

and since the hypothesis $\mu_1 - \mu_2 = 0$ is being tested, we may substitute 0 for the difference $(\mu_1 - \mu_2)$ in the formula, and rewrite:

$$t = \frac{\overline{X}_1 - \overline{X}_2}{\sqrt{S_1^2/n_1 + S_2^2/n_2}} \tag{3}$$

This formula, under the condition of $n_1 + n_2 - 2 = 36 + 41 - 2 = 75$ degrees of freedom is evaluated to provide the "observed value of *t*."

5. *Critical Region.* The critical region for this two-tailed *t*-test of $H_0$ with $n_1 + n_2 - 2 = 75$ *df* and $\alpha = .05$ is *conservatively speaking*: $\{t < -2.04\}$ and $\{t > +2.04\}$; where the value of $t = 2.04$ is chosen from the 30 *df* row of the table with the knowledge that the "true" critical value of *t* for 75 *df* is somewhat less than 2.04.

---

* In this case: $F = 84.64/16.81 = 5.03$ with $n_1 - 1 = 35$ *df* for the numerator and $n - 1 = 40$ *df* for the denominator, we find from Table XIV that a value of $F = 2.19$ (approx.) is significant at the 2 per cent *level*; we therefore would conclude that the population variances are significantly different.

6. *Calculating the Statistic.* The value of the "observed $t$" for the situation under study would be:

$$t = \frac{\overline{X}_1 - \overline{X}_2}{\sqrt{\dfrac{S_1^2}{n_1} + \dfrac{S_2^2}{n_2}}} = \frac{61.5 - 55.9}{\sqrt{\dfrac{84.64}{36} + \dfrac{16.81}{41}}} = \frac{5.6}{\sqrt{2.76}} = \frac{5.6}{1.66} = 3.37$$

7. *Decision Concerning $H_0$.* Since the observed value of $t = 3.37$ falls in the critical region, the null hypothesis ($H_0$) is rejected in favor of the "alternative" hypothesis ($H_1$), and the research team may infer that the two districts involved in the study are different in socio-economic level *as measured by the composite score* constructed for the study.

Although this example illustrates a two-tailed test conducted by using formula (3), it should be obvious that the same formula could be applied to conduct a one-tail test of the null hypothesis, $H_0 : \mu_1 \geq \mu_2$ or of, $H_0 : \mu_1 \leq \mu_2$. The one-tailed tests would be conducted if the research team has reason to believe that the mean score of one district might be significantly higher, or lower, which ever the case may be, than the mean score of the other district. Since conducting a one-tailed test of $H_0$ by formula (3) should be fairly obvious, an additional example illustrating the procedures will not be included.

In order to illustrate the use of formula (4), *the pooled mean square form of the t-test,* suppose as part of the curriculum research project described in the previous example, teachers in the system are requested to contribute findings to the central research committee resulting from any germane action research projects that they might have conducted. Suppose further that a junior high school mathematics teacher, who teaches in a school located in the inner city, or core area of the municipality, wishes to conduct an experiment involving a "laboratory" approach to the instruction of seventh-grade mathematics. Student achievement and motivation scores are to be used as measures by which effectiveness of the approach will be determined.

Prior to the beginning of the new semester, the teacher procures a list of names of those pupils who will be taking seventh-grade mathematics during that semester. Fifty pupils are chosen to form twenty-five "matched" pairs, where the matching is based upon the pupils' I.Q.'s, previous school achievements in reading and arithmetic, socio-economic levels, permanency of address, and educational backgrounds of parents. By means of random numbers, one pupil of each pair is assigned to the experimental group (laboratory approach class), and the other member of the pair is assigned to the control group (traditional approach class).

Although the experiment could best be analyzed on the basis of a covariance design, suppose that the teacher involved desires only to measure differences between group means by employing an appropriate form of the $t$-test. Since the groups have been formed by random assignment of members composing "matched" pairs, the teacher conducting the experiment assumes that the two sample groups, "control" and "experimental," have come from two populations having the same means and variances, that is, $\mu_1 = \mu_2$, and $\sigma_1^2 = \sigma_2^2 = \sigma^2$. In view of the latter assumption, formula (4) may be employed as the appropriate form of the $t$-test for examining the null hypothesis.

Suppose that the following statistics are produced by the respective groups on the midsemester mathematics achievement examination which was carefully constructed by the teacher-experimenter:

$$
\begin{array}{cc}
\textit{Control Group} & \textit{Experimental Group} \\
\overline{X}_c = 71 & \overline{X}_E = 76 \\
S_c^2 = 12 & S_E^2 = 8 \\
n_c = 22 & n_E = 24
\end{array}
$$

where $n_c = 22$ and $n_E = 24$ occur instead of the original total of 25 in each case, because of absences and loss of group members as a result of pupils' families moving out of the city or out of the district.

In order to apply formula (4), it is necessary to check the assumption of equal variances, i.e., $\sigma_1^2 = \sigma_2^2 = \sigma^2$, by conducting an $F$-test of the null hypothesis that: $\sigma_1^2 - \sigma_2^2 = 0$. Since $F = \frac{12}{8} = 1.5$ is not significant, the null hypothesis cannot be rejected, which means the assumption can be condoned. With the ascertainment of the assumption of equal variances, it becomes necessary to find the value of $S_p^2$, the pooled mean square estimate of $\sigma^2$. The data of this example produce the following value for $S_p^2$:

$$
S_p^2 = \frac{(n_c - 1)S_c^2 + (n_E - 1)S_E^2}{n_c + n_E - 2} = \frac{(22 - 1)(12) + (24 - 1)(8)}{22 + 24 - 2}
$$

$$
S_p^2 = \frac{(21)(12) + (23)(8)}{44} = \frac{109}{11} = 9.9091
$$

Thus,

$$
S_p = \sqrt{9.9091} = 3.148
$$

The statistical inference process employed for this example would be as follows:

1. *Null Hypothesis.* $H_0: \mu_c = \mu_E$, or $\mu_c - \mu_E = 0$. The "alternative" hypothesis would be $H_1: \mu_c \neq \mu_E$.

2. *Statistical Test.* Since the comparatively small random samples are considered to be drawn from approximately normal distributions having equal means and equal variances, i.e., $\mu_1 = \mu_2$, and $\sigma_1^2 = \sigma_2^2 = \sigma^2$, an appropriate form of the $t$-test may be employed to test the null hypothesis ($H_0$) of "no difference" between the respective population means, $\mu_c$ and $\mu_E$.

3. *Level of Significance, $\alpha$.* The level of significance for this two-tailed $t$-test of $H_0$ is set at $\alpha = .05$, and the sample sizes of $n_c = 22$ and $n_E = 24$ are found to be adequate for the purposes of this action research study.

4. *Sampling Distribution.* Since the two population variances can be considered equal, i.e., $\sigma_c^2 = \sigma_E^2 = \sigma^2$ (see *F*-test: $F = \frac{12}{8} = 1.5$), the null hypothesis under test is that of the equality of the two population means, $H_0: \mu_c = \mu_E$, the appropriate sampling distribution of the *t*-test, with $(n_c + n_E - 2)$ degrees of freedom is provided by formula (4):

$$t = \frac{(\overline{X}_E - \overline{X}_c) - (\mu_E - \mu_c)}{S_p\sqrt{1/n_E + 1/n_c}} \tag{4}$$

Since the hypothesis $\mu_E - \mu_c = 0$ is being tested, we may substitute 0 for the difference $(\mu_E - \mu_c)$ in the formula, which results in the expression:

$$t = \frac{\overline{X}_E - \overline{X}_c}{S_p\sqrt{1/n_E - 1/n_c}}$$

and under the condition of $n_E + n_c - 2$ degrees of freedom is evaluated to provide the "observed" value of *t*.

5. *Critical Region.* The critical region for this two-tailed *t*-test of $H_0$ with $n_E + n_c - 2 = 44$ degrees of freedom and $\alpha = .05$ is, *conservatively speaking*: $\{t < -2.04\}$ and $\{t > +2.04\}$; where the value of $t = 2.04$ is chosen from the 30 *df* row of the table with the knowledge that the "true" critical value of *t* for 44 *df* is somewhat less than 2.04.

6. *Calculating the Statistic.* The value of the observed *t* for this example would be:

$$t = \frac{76-71}{3.148\sqrt{\frac{1}{24} + \frac{1}{22}}} = \frac{5}{3.148\sqrt{.0871}} = \frac{5}{.929} = 5.382$$

7. *Decision Concerning $H_0$.* Since the observed value of $t = 5.382$ falls in the critical region, the null hypothesis $(H_0)$ is rejected in favor of the alternative hypothesis $(H_1)$, and the teacher may infer that there is a significant difference between the "laboratory" and traditional approaches of instruction, with the higher mean score being attained by the "laboratory" group.

It should be noted here that the teacher involved in the action research experimentation first conducted a two-tailed test of the null hypothesis; that is, he did not attempt to predict that the "laboratory" (experimental) group would realize a significantly higher group mean score. With this experiment as background, however, it would now be wise for the teacher to replicate the experiment, and test the alternative hypothesis that the laboratory group's mean score is greater than that of the "traditional approach" group, or put in another way, conduct a one-tailed test of the null hypothesis; $H_0: \mu_E \leq \mu_c$ [the mean score of the experimental group is equal to or less than that of the traditional (control) group].

Formula (9) may be employed in those research problems where the data are of at least the interval scale of measurement, and are the results of observations made on paired or matched sample elements. In research projects where elements are paired before actually conducting an experiment or a survey, there is usually some expectation that performance under the experimental or study conditions might be related to an initial level of performance. Hence, consideration should be given to any possible correlation in performance between paired elements under the experimental or study condition. Formula (9) of the *t*-test is an appropriate formula for accomplishing consideration of possible correlation in performance between paired elements composing the random sample.

Suppose that a teacher performing an experiment involving ten children participating in an intensive remedial reading laboratory program hypothesizes that, on parallel forms of a standardized reading examination, each child will improve his initial score by more than two points after two weeks of participation in the program. Suppose the data are as shown in the first two columns of Table XIII. Can the teacher's hypothesis be supported by the data?

Table XIII
Initial and Final Scores of Ten Children
Participating in Remedial Reading
Laboratory Program
(Fictitious Data)

| Child | Initial Score $X_1$ | Final Score $X_2$ | $(X_2 - X_1)$ $d$ | $(X_2 - X_1)^2$ $d^2$ |
|-------|------|------|------|------|
| 1 | 3.4 | 7.1 | 3.7 | 13.69 |
| 2 | 4.7 | 5.0 | 0.3 | .09 |
| 3 | 2.1 | 5.5 | 3.4 | 11.56 |
| 4 | 3.9 | 4.4 | 0.5 | .25 |
| 5 | 4.0 | 7.2 | 3.2 | 10.24 |
| 6 | 4.2 | 6.8 | 2.6 | 6.76 |
| 7 | 3.4 | 7.5 | 4.1 | 16.81 |
| 8 | 2.9 | 6.0 | 3.1 | 9.61 |
| 9 | 3.1 | 7.2 | 4.1 | 16.81 |
| 10 | 2.7 | 6.1 | 3.4 | 11.56 |
| Total | 34.4 | 62.8 | 28.4 | 97.38 |

In order to evaluate formula (9) it is necessary to find first the value of $\sum D^2$. Employing formula (6), we find the value of $\sum D^2$ to be:

$$\sum D^2 = \sum d^2 - \frac{(\sum d)^2}{n}$$

$$\sum D^2 = 97.38 - \frac{(28.4)^2}{10}$$

$$\sum D^2 = 97.38 - \frac{806.56}{10} = 97.38 - 80.656 = 16.724$$

By formula (7) we find the variance of the distribution of differences (*d*'s) to be:

$$S_D^2 = \frac{\sum D^2}{n-1} = \frac{16.724}{9} = 1.858$$

and the standard deviation of the distribution of the $n = 10$ differences ($d$'s) occurring in the sample to be:

$$S_D = \sqrt{\frac{\sum D^2}{n-1}} = \sqrt{1.858} \approx 1.4$$

The standard error of the difference between the means for paired observations, $S_{\bar{x}_1 - \bar{x}_2}$, is related to $S_D$ by formula (8), and the value of it for this example is found to be:

$$S_{\bar{x}_2 - \bar{x}_1} = \frac{S_D}{\sqrt{n}} = \frac{1.4}{\sqrt{10}} = \frac{1.4}{3.1623} \approx .43$$

With these values determined we are now ready to illustrate the statistical inference process that could be employed to test the null hypothesis ($H_0$) resulting from the "alternative" hypothesis ($H_1$) which is directly related to the operational hypothesis (statement) made by the teacher conducting the experiment.

The inference process would be as follows:

1. *Null Hypothesis.* $H_0 : \mu_2 - \mu_1 \leq 2$; or $\bar{d} \leq 2$. The "alternative" hypothesis, a mathematical statement of the operational hypothesis, would be: $H_1 : \mu_2 - \mu_1 > 2$, or $\bar{d} > 2$.

2. *Statistical Test.* Since the reading scores of the population from which the random sample is drawn are considered to be normally distributed, and are measured in the interval scale of measurement, an appropriate form of the $t$-test may be employed for testing the one-tailed null hypothesis ($H_0$) advanced in step 1.

3. *Level of Significance, $\alpha$.* The level of significance $\alpha$ for this one-tailed $t$-test of $H_0$ is set at: $\alpha = .01$, and the sample size of $n = 10$ paired observations is found to be adequate for the purposes of this action research, experimental-survey type of study.

4. *Sampling Distribution.* Since the two samples, the sample of the "before" and the sample of the "after" scores of the ten individuals, are related, formula (9), under $n - 1 = 9$ degrees of freedom, is the appropriate sampling distribution of the $t$-test to employ. Hence:

$$t = \frac{(\bar{X}_2 - \bar{X}_1) - (\mu_2 - \mu_1)}{S_{\bar{x}_1 - \bar{x}_2}} = \frac{\bar{d} - c}{S_D/\sqrt{n}}$$

under $n - 1 = 9$ degrees of freedom is to be evaluated to provide the "observed" value of $t$.

5. *Critical Region.* The critical region for this one-tailed $t$-test of $H_0$ with $n - 1 = 9$ $df$ and $\alpha = .01$ is: $\{t > +2.821\}$.

6. *Calculating the Statistic.* The value of the observed $t$ for the data of this example is:

$$t = \frac{(6.28 - 3.44) - 2}{.43}; \quad \text{or if } (\bar{d} - c) \text{ form is used:} \quad t = \frac{2.84 - 2}{.43};$$

$$t = \frac{2.84 - 2}{.43} = \frac{.84}{.43} = 1.954.$$

7. *Decision Concerning $H_0$.* Since the observed value of $t = 1.954$ does not fall in the defined critical region, the null hypothesis ($H_0$) cannot be rejected, and the teacher cannot infer that the laboratory approach to an intensive remedial reading of two weeks duration will increase participating pupils' scores by more than two points on parallel forms of the standardized reading examination employed in the study. The convenience of employing formula (9) as opposed to formula (5) should be noted at this point. If formula (5) had been employed it would have been necessary to compute the variances of both the initial score and final score sets along with performing the computations necessary to determine the value of the correlation coefficient ($r$) which would indicate the degree of relationship between the paired scores of the ten pupils composing the samples of the study. Although formulas (5) and (9) yield precisely the same results, (9) is by far the more desirable form to employ in the interest of computational time and general efficiency of operation.

We discontinue our discussion of the *t*-test of hypotheses of differences of two population means at this point with the knowledge that we have not discussed the test of the *difference of means for two equated groups*, and tests of difference between *adjusted group means*. The development of these tests of significance are based upon the technique known as the analysis of covariance, a technique which we shall discuss in connection with the *F*-test. In view of this fact, the *t*-tests for differences of *two equated groups* and *adjusted group means* will be discussed in their broader applications when the topic of the analysis of covariance is covered.

### Hypotheses of Relationship

The most convenient measurements to employ in testing hypotheses of relationship are correlation coefficients. We have discussed many different types of correlation coefficients in connection with our treatment of the topic of estimation. The *t*-test may be employed in the testing of hypotheses of relationship when the correlation coefficients being employed as measures of the relationship are either Pearson product-moment coefficients ($r$) or Spearman rank correlation coefficients ($\rho_s$).

The hypothesis of relationship most frequently tested by the *t*-test is the null, which states that the value of the population correlation coefficient, $\rho$, is equal to zero; i.e., $H_0: \rho = 0$. Before discussing the appropriate form of the *t*-test to accomplish the testing of this "null," however, we present a brief treatment of sampling distributions of correlation coefficients.

When the sample size $n$ is large, and the value of $\rho$ (the population correlation coefficient) is not too high, the sampling distribution of the correlation coefficient is approximately normal in form. If the sample size $n$ is small and the population correlation coefficient is high, say, plus or minus .75 (i.e., $\pm.75$), the sampling distribution of the correlation coefficient is highly skew. This condition is easy to understand when consideration is given the fact that the limiting values of the sampling distribution of the correlation coefficient are $+1.00$ and $-1.00$. Obviously, if the value of $\rho$ is, say, .85, then sample values could vary from: $r = -1.00$ to $r = +1.00$, but they would not be able to exceed the population value by more than .15 in one tail of the distribution, while in the opposite direction they could differ as much as 1.85 from the population value of $\rho = .85$.

If the sample employed is as large as $n = 300$, then the limiting conditions of $r = -1.00$ and $r = +1.00$ at the ends of the scale of possible values would not be important factors in determining the sampling distribution of the correlation coefficient. This condition is explained on the basis that sample values of the correlation coefficient based upon a sample size of $n = 300$, even when drawn from a population in which: $\rho = .85$, would be such good estimates of the population value that they would tend not to range more than .05 on either side of the population value. In other words, the sampling distribution would tend to be a leptokurtic "normal." If the population value were, say $\rho = .98$, however, the restriction of $r = +1.00$ would be a factor to consider.

When the population correlation coefficient is $\rho = 0$, the sampling distribution of the correlation coefficient $r$, for samples of size $n < 25$, depart slightly from normality. The deviation from normality, under conditions of small sample size, does not cause serious error if a normal distribution is assumed, but usually, especially when the Pearson product-moment correlation coefficient $r$ is involved, every attempt should be made to procure a sample of $n = 50$, and in any circumstance no less than $n = 25$. The Spearman rank correlation coefficient has the advantage of closely approximating a Pearson $r$ despite a sample size of $n < 25$. Since both of these types of correlation coefficients are measures that can be used to evaluate the $t$-test for testing hypotheses of relationship, it is important that such limitations as previously described be known about them.

The $t$-test formula for testing the null hypothesis of relationship, $H_0: \rho = 0$, assuming that the sample value of $r$ (Pearson), or $\rho_s$ (Spearman rank) is the result of sampling variation, is:

$$t = \frac{r}{\sqrt{1 - r^2}} \sqrt{n - 2} \qquad \text{(Pearson)} \quad \text{(10a)}$$

or

$$t = \frac{\rho_s}{\sqrt{1 - \rho_s^2}} \sqrt{n - 2} \qquad \text{(Spearman-rank)} \quad \text{(10b)}$$

where $t$ denotes the observed $t$ ratio, or statistic, with $n - 2$ degrees of freedom, $r$ denotes the observed sample value of the Pearson product-moment correlation coefficient, $\rho_s$ denotes the observed sample value of the Spearman-rank correlation coefficient, and $n$ denotes the number of paired observations in the sample.

The value of $t$ obtained from either formula (10a) or (10b), depending upon whether a Pearson product-moment or Spearman rank correlation coefficient is being employed as a measure, is distributed as a $t$-distribution of $n - 2$ degrees of freedom, when the null hypothesis of $H_0: \rho = 0$ in the population is true. This condition allows the use of the $t$-table (Table XII) to determine whether the *observed* value of $t$ is significant at the 5 per cent or 1 per cent levels. We shall now present an example to illustrate our discussion of employing a $t$-test of the null hypothesis of relationship, $H_0: \rho = 0$.

Suppose that in a pilot study sample composed of twenty ninth grade pupils drawn at random from the beginning algebra class sections of a particular junior high school, the degree of relationship between the reading scores and algebra readiness test scores of the pupils in the sample is found to be $r = .71$ (the correlation coefficient employed here could be either the Pearson product-moment or the Spearman rank). Suppose further that the pilot study sample had been drawn to provide guide lines for a study of the problem, or need, for teaching reading in the later grades of junior high school as an approach to improving learning in certain "basic" subjects in the junior high school curriculum. The researcher conducting the pilot study decides to test the significance of a correlation coefficient of value $r = .71$. The inference process would be as follows:

1. *Null Hypothesis.* $H_0: \rho = 0$; the population correlation coefficient is zero. The "alternative" hypothesis is $H_1: \rho \neq 0$, that is, either $\rho > 0$ or $\rho < 0$, significantly so.

2. *Statistical Test.* Since the sample size is small ($n = 20$), and the sample value of $r$ may be considered to result from sampling variation or chance so that such values are approximately normal in distribution, the $t$-test may be employed to test the null hypothesis of relationship.

3. *Level of Significance, $\alpha$.* The level of significance ($\alpha$) for this two-tailed $t$-test of $H_0$ is set at: $\alpha = .01$, and the sample size of twenty paired observations is found to be adequate for the purposes of this pilot study.

4. *Sampling Distribution.* The appropriate sampling distribution for this $t$-test of the null hypothesis of relationship, $H_0$, is:

$$t = \frac{r}{\sqrt{1 - r^2}}\sqrt{n - 2} \qquad (10a)$$

where $r$ (Pearson) may be replaced by $\rho_s$ if the correlation coefficient is of Spearman-rank form instead of the Pearson product-moment type, in which case we would be employing formula (10b).

5. *Critical Region.* The critical region for this two-tailed $t$-test of $H_0$ with $n - 2 = 18$ degrees of freedom and $\alpha = .01$ is:

$$\{t < -2.878\} \text{ and } \{t > +2.878\}$$

6. *Calculating the Statistic.* The value of the observed $t$ for the data of this example is:

$$t = \frac{.71}{\sqrt{1 - (.71)^2}}\sqrt{20 - 2} = \frac{.71}{\sqrt{1 - .5041}}\sqrt{18} = \frac{.71\sqrt{18}}{\sqrt{.4959}} \approx 4.2426$$

7. *Decision Concerning $H_0$.* Since the observed value of $t$ falls in the critical region, the null hypothesis ($H_0 : \rho = 0$) is rejected in favor of the "alternative" hypothesis ($H_1 : \rho \neq 0$), and the researcher may infer that a highly significant (beyond .01 level) relationship exists between the paired scores of the defined population. The acceptance of the "alternative hypothesis" ($H_1 : \rho \neq 0$) implies that *either $\rho > 0$ or* that $\rho < 0$. Since the observed value was : $r = +.71$, it follows that a highly significant *positive* relationship exists, i.e., $\rho > 0$.

Although this test of significance of a correlation coefficient is illustrated in terms of the inference process, it should be pointed out that in practice a test of significance of an $r$ is not carried out in such a formal sense. Usually after the value of $r$ (or $\rho_s$) is determined from the sample, the value of $t$ is computed from either formula (10a) or (10b), whichever is appropriate. The observed value of $t$ is then compared to the critical value of $t$ found in the $t$-table in the appropriate $df$ row and probability ($\alpha$) column. If the observed $t$ is larger than the tabled value, $r$ is held to be significant or highly significant depending upon whether $\alpha = .05$ or .01 is used for the value of the level of significance.

This treatment of this topic concludes our discussion of the possibilities of application of the $t$-test in the data processing aspect of our general model of educational research. With this background we are now prepared to discuss the $z$- or $F$-distribution.

*Chapter 27—References*

See Bibliography: 4, 27, 38, 41, 49, 52, 53, 54, 65, 66, 67, 76, 77, 89, 104, 105, 106, 112, 113, 123, 126, 128, 140, 141, 148, 155, 156, 159, 165, 179, 180, 181, 182, 183, 184, 185, 186, 190, 197, 198, 199, 200; 21a, 34a, 62a, 72a, 75a, 104a.

*Chapter Twenty-eight*

# Parametric Statistical Tests—II

### (*The z- or F-Distribution*)

WITH THE DISCUSSION of two distributions commonly employed as parametric tests of statistical hypotheses—the normal and the *t*-distributions—completed, we now consider a more generalized type of distribution, the *z*-distribution, which includes not only the normal and *t*-distributions, but also the chi-square distribution (Chapter 24), as special cases. The *z-distribution*, which was derived by R. A. Fisher, should not be confused with Fisher's *z-transformation* of the correlation coefficient *r*, a topic which is usually discussed in connection with the employment of the normal distribution as a test of statistical hypotheses of relationship.[1]

The *z* statistic (distribution) involves the ratio of two sample variances, $S_1^2$, and $S_2^2$, and is defined as:

$$z = \frac{1}{2} \ln \frac{S_1^2}{S_2^2} \tag{1}$$

where "ln" denotes the *natural* logarithm, and $S_1^2$, and $S_2^2$ are two independent random sample estimates of the same population variance, $\sigma^2$. The *z*-distribution, like the *t* and chi-square distributions, is not one distribution but a family of distributions, wherein each distribution is determined by the number of degress of freedom involved, which in turn depends upon the combination of the respective sample sizes, $n_1$ and $n_2$ associated with $S_1^2$ and $S_2^2$, respectively.

The *z*-test can be simplified by defining a value *F* as:

$$F = \frac{S_1^2}{S_2^2} \tag{2}$$

where from (2) and (1) it may be shown that:

$$F = e^{2z}$$

or

$$z = \tfrac{1}{2} \ln F$$

The critical values of *F* for the 5 per cent and the 1 per cent levels for various degrees of freedom have been tabled by Snedecor[2] and Fisher and Yates.[3] Since the *F*-test does not involve the logarithmic relationship of the sample variances, it is easier to compute and to use than the *z*-test. *For this reason we shall use the F-test instead of the z-test throughout our examples, illustrations and general discussion.*

Excerpts from a table of $F$ values are presented in Table XIV which we shall find useful in later discussions. In order to use the table it is necessary to know the number of degrees of freedom, $n'_1$, corresponding to the *greater variance* (mean square), and the number of degrees of freedom, $n'_2$, corresponding to the *smaller variance* (mean square). The appropriate critical value of $F$ can be found in the "cell" of the table formed by the intersection of the particular $n'_1$ column and $n'_2$ row defined by the conditions (degrees of freedom) of the problem under study. If the *obtained value* of $F$ is larger than the critical value of $F$ at the chosen level of significance, $\alpha = .05$ or $\alpha = .01$, the null hypothesis under test is rejected.

Four conditions must be satisfied in order for the $z$- or $F$-distribution to produce a valid test of a statistical hypothesis. The conditions are:

1. Random sampling must be employed.
2. Estimates of the common population variance must be derived from independent categories, or groups. The existence of this condition means that the occurrence of a score or value in one category, or group, is in no way affected by the occurrence of a score or value in another group.
3. The various subclasses must have a common variance.
4. The variate, $X$, must be normally distributed.

Numerous tests are available to determine if these conditions exist in any given problem under study. Many of the tests discussed previously may be used to determine if the sampling is random. A chi-square test of independence may be employed to determine if the categories are independent. A simple approximate first test of homogeneity of variance (condition 3) may be made by taking the *largest estimate* of the variance (mean square) produced by one of the subclasses (groups) and dividing it by the *smallest estimate* to provide a value of $F$.* If the "observed" value of $F$ is less than the *appropriate* critical value found in the $F$ table, the variances are considered to be homogeneous, that is, the subclasses have a common variance. If the observed value of $F$ is *greater* than the *appropriate* critical $F$ value, a separate test of the hypothesis of homogeneity of variance can be made. This test is Bartlett's test which is accorded a complete description in Edwards.[4] If Bartlett's test is not employed, normal probability paper, or a chi-square goodness of fit test may be adapted to the situation and provide a solution to the problem.

Of the four conditions that must be satisfied in order to employ the $z$- or $F$-distributions as "test statistics," the first two must be met without qualification. In dealing with the third condition, if heterogeneous variances are found in the subclasses, it is possible to select, for testing only, those which are homogeneous, and thus provide a legitimate test of the hypothesis. In connection with the fourth condition, some variation from normality is allowable, but in the case of extreme skewness the test becomes invalid.

---

* See footnote page 344 for example of this test.

Table XIV

Selected Critical Values of *F* for the 5 Per cent and 1 Per cent Levels of Significance

$n_1$ degrees of freedom (for greater mean square)

| $n_2$ | 1 | 2 | 3 | 4 | 5 | 6 | 7 | 8 | 9 | 10 | 12 | 16 | 20 | 30 | 50 | 75 | 100 | 500 | ∞ |
|---|---|---|---|---|---|---|---|---|---|---|---|---|---|---|---|---|---|---|---|
| 1 | 161 (4,052) | 200 (4,999) | 216 (5,403) | 225 (5,764) | 230 (5,764) | 234 (5,859) | 237 (5,928) | 239 (5,981) | 241 (6,022) | 242 (6,056) | 244 (6,106) | 246 (6,169) | 248 (6,208) | 250 (6,258) | 252 (6,302) | 253 (6,323) | 253 (6,334) | 254 (6,361) | 254 (6,366) |
| 2 | 18.51 (98.49) | 19.00 (99.01) | 19.16 (99.17) | 19.25 (99.25) | 19.30 (99.30) | 19.33 (99.33) | 19.36 (99.34) | 19.37 (99.36) | 19.38 (99.38) | 19.39 (99.40) | 19.41 (99.42) | 19.43 (99.44) | 19.44 (99.45) | 19.46 (99.47) | 19.47 (99.48) | 19.48 (99.49) | 19.49 (99.49) | 19.50 (26.14) | 19.50 (26.12) |
| 5 | 6.61 (16.20) | 5.79 (13.27) | 5.41 (12.06) | 5.19 (11.39) | 5.05 (10.97) | 4.95 (10.67) | 4.88 (10.45) | 4.82 (10.27) | 4.78 (10.15) | 4.74 (10.05) | 4.68 (9.89) | 4.60 (9.68) | 4.56 (9.55) | 4.50 (9.38) | 4.44 (9.24) | 4.42 (9.17) | 4.40 (9.13) | 4.37 (9.04) | 4.36 (9.02) |
| 7 | 5.59 (12.25) | 4.74 (9.55) | 4.35 (8.45) | 4.12 (7.85) | 3.97 (7.46) | 3.87 (7.19) | 3.79 (7.00) | 3.73 (6.84) | 3.68 (6.71) | 3.63 (6.62) | 3.57 (6.47) | 3.49 (6.27) | 3.44 (6.16) | 3.38 (5.98) | 3.32 (5.85) | 3.29 (5.78) | 3.28 (5.75) | 3.24 (5.67) | 3.23 (5.65) |
| 10 | 4.96 (10.04) | 4.10 (7.56) | 3.71 (6.55) | 3.48 (5.99) | 3.33 (5.64) | 3.22 (5.39) | 3.14 (5.21) | 3.07 (5.06) | 3.02 (4.95) | 2.97 (4.85) | 2.91 (4.71) | 2.82 (4.52) | 2.77 (4.41) | 2.70 (4.25) | 2.64 (4.12) | 2.61 (4.05) | 2.59 (4.01) | 2.55 (3.93) | 2.54 (3.91) |
| 12 | 4.75 (9.33) | 3.88 (6.93) | 3.49 (5.95) | 3.26 (5.41) | 3.11 (5.06) | 3.00 (4.82) | 2.92 (4.65) | 2.85 (4.50) | 2.80 (4.39) | 2.76 (4.30) | 2.69 (4.16) | 2.60 (3.98) | 2.54 (3.86) | 2.46 (3.70) | 2.40 (3.56) | 2.36 (3.49) | 2.35 (3.46) | 2.31 (3.38) | 2.30 (3.36) |
| 15 | 4.54 (8.60) | 3.68 (6.36) | 3.29 (5.42) | 3.06 (4.89) | 2.90 (4.56) | 2.79 (4.32) | 2.70 (4.14) | 2.64 (4.00) | 2.59 (3.89) | 2.55 (3.80) | 2.48 (3.67) | 2.39 (3.48) | 2.33 (3.36) | 2.25 (3.20) | 2.18 (3.07) | 2.15 (3.00) | 2.12 (2.97) | 2.08 (2.89) | 2.07 (2.87) |
| 16 | 4.49 (8.53) | 3.63 (6.23) | 3.24 (5.29) | 3.01 (4.77) | 2.85 (4.44) | 2.74 (4.20) | 2.66 (4.03) | 2.59 (3.89) | 2.54 (3.78) | 2.49 (3.69) | 2.42 (3.55) | 2.33 (3.37) | 2.28 (3.25) | 2.20 (3.10) | 2.13 (2.96) | 2.09 (2.89) | 2.07 (2.86) | 2.02 (2.77) | 2.01 (2.75) |
| 20 | 4.35 (8.10) | 3.40 (5.85) | 3.10 (4.94) | 2.87 (4.43) | 2.71 (4.10) | 2.60 (3.87) | 2.52 (3.71) | 2.45 (3.56) | 2.40 (3.45) | 2.35 (3.37) | 2.28 (3.23) | 2.18 (3.05) | 2.12 (2.94) | 2.04 (2.77) | 1.96 (2.63) | 1.92 (2.56) | 1.90 (2.53) | 1.85 (2.44) | 1.84 (2.42) |
| 25 | 4.24 (7.77) | 3.38 (5.57) | 2.99 (4.68) | 2.76 (4.18) | 2.60 (3.86) | 2.49 (3.63) | 2.41 (3.46) | 2.34 (3.32) | 2.28 (3.21) | 2.24 (3.13) | 2.16 (2.99) | 2.06 (2.81) | 2.00 (2.70) | 1.92 (2.54) | 1.84 (2.40) | 1.80 (2.32) | 1.77 (2.29) | 1.72 (2.19) | 1.71 (2.17) |
| 30 | 4.17 (7.56) | 3.32 (5.39) | 2.92 (4.51) | 2.69 (4.02) | 2.53 (3.70) | 2.42 (3.47) | 2.34 (3.30) | 2.27 (3.17) | 2.21 (3.06) | 2.16 (2.98) | 2.09 (2.84) | 1.99 (2.66) | 1.93 (2.55) | 1.84 (2.38) | 1.76 (2.24) | 1.72 (2.16) | 1.69 (2.13) | 1.64 (2.03) | 1.62 (2.01) |
| 48 | 4.04 (7.19) | 3.19 (5.08) | 2.80 (4.22) | 2.56 (3.74) | 2.41 (3.42) | 2.30 (3.20) | 2.21 (3.04) | 2.14 (2.90) | 2.08 (2.80) | 2.03 (2.71) | 1.96 (2.58) | 1.86 (2.40) | 1.79 (2.28) | 1.70 (2.11) | 1.61 (1.96) | 1.55 (1.88) | 1.53 (1.84) | 1.47 (1.73) | .45 (1.70) |
| 100 | 3.94 (6.90) | 3.09 (4.82) | 2.70 (3.98) | 2.46 (3.51) | 2.30 (3.20) | 2.19 (2.99) | 2.10 (2.82) | 2.03 (2.69) | 1.97 (2.59) | 1.92 (2.51) | 1.85 (2.36) | 1.75 (2.19) | 1.68 (2.06) | 1.57 (1.89) | 1.48 (1.78) | 1.42 (1.64) | 1.39 (1.59) | 1.30 (1.46) | 1.28 (1.43) |
| 400 | 3.86 (6.70) | 3.02 (4.66) | 2.62 (3.83) | 2.39 (3.36) | 2.23 (3.06) | 2.12 (2.85) | 2.03 (2.69) | 1.96 (2.55) | 1.90 (2.46) | 1.85 (2.37) | 1.78 (2.23) | 1.67 (2.04) | 1.60 (1.92) | 1.49 (1.74) | 1.38 (1.57) | 1.32 (1.47) | 1.28 (1.42) | 1.16 (1.24) | 1.13 (1.19) |
| ∞ | 3.84 (6.64) | 2.99 (4.60) | 2.60 (3.78) | 2.37 (3.32) | 2.21 (3.02) | 2.09 (2.80) | 2.01 (2.64) | 1.94 (2.51) | 1.88 (2.41) | 1.83 (2.32) | 1.75 (2.18) | 1.64 (1.99) | 1.57 (1.87) | 1.46 (1.69) | 1.35 (1.52) | 1.28 (1.41) | 1.24 (1.36) | 1.11 (1.15) | 1.00 (1.00) |

\* *F*-values for one per cent levels are shown in parentheses.

The *z*-or *F*-distribution can be employed to test four general types of hypotheses:

1. The hypothesis that two population variances are equal.
2. The hypothesis that *k* population means are equal.
3. The hypothesis that the regression coefficients in the general form of the regression equation: $Y = a + bX + cX^2 + dX^3 + \cdots$, are significant.
4. The hypothesis that various types of correlation coefficients are significant.

Since we are not concerned here with how the *z*-or *F*-distributions may be employed in testing hypotheses of the significance of regression and correlation coefficients, we shall confine our discussion to how these distributions may be employed in the testing of hypotheses concerning the equality of two population variances and *k* population means.

The technique of *analysis of variance*, which employs the *F*-distribution, is one of the best means for effecting tests of the hypotheses that: (a) two population variances are equal, and (b) that *k* population means are equal. Analysis of variance requires the cross-classification of data by categories so that the initial design of the inquiry is directly reflected; and, providing the sampling is random and the categories are independent, is a technique of considerable practical value to employ in the Data Collection and Data Processing elements of a research model designed to analyze a complex set of data. In view of these facts, we now turn to a discussion of the analysis of variance technique.

### ANALYSIS OF VARIANCE (SINGLE CLASSIFICATION)

Analysis of variance is one of the most powerful techniques employed in statistical inquiry. In general terms, analysis of variance is a technique by which the total variation of a given set of observations is analyzed into components. These components of the total variance are determined by principal causes or factors, one of which is *random* or *residual variation*. The data are interpreted by employing the *F*-distribution to test the significance of values of *ratios* formed by comparing each of the *principal cause components of variation* with that of the *random or residual variation*.

The rationale of analysis of variance is that the total *sum of squares* of a set of observations, resulting from combining the observations for several groups, can be analyzed into specific parts each of which is identifiable with a given source of variation. In the simplest case (single classification), the data are divided into two or more classes of a *single category* with two or more observations within each class. The total sum of squares for all the data may then be analyzed into two parts: a sum of squares for the variation within the classes (groups), and a sum of squares based upon the variation between the class (group) means. From these two sums of squares, independent estimates of the population variance are calculated.

A minimum of two random observations must be available within each class forming the set of classes being analyzed, if an estimate of within classes variation is to be made. It is actually preferable to have more than two observations for each class, particularly in those cases where the variability within a class might be quite large. The point to be made here is that if only one observation exists within each class, it will be impossible to find a within classes estimate of the population variance, and without this estimate no analysis of variance can be made.

*Testing the Hypothesis; $H_0: \mu_1 = \mu_2 = \mu_3 = \cdots = \mu_k$*

The basic assumption of the analysis of variance technique is that the samples composing a total set of observations are random samples that have been drawn from a common normal population, and hence the values of the *within* and *between* groups estimates of the population variance are expected to differ only within the limits of random sampling error. We have already seen (footnote, page 344) how to test a null hypothesis that the variances of two normally distributed populations are equal ($H_0: \sigma_1^2 = \sigma_2^2 = \sigma^2$), by dividing the larger variance by the smaller variance to find the value of the $F$-ratio, and if the observed value of $F$ equals or exceeds the tabled value (Table XIV), then $H_0$ is considered untenable. The same approach may be applied to compare the *within* groups and *between* groups estimates of the common population variance. If the null hypothesis involving the *within* and *between* groups estimates of the population variance is rejected, then the populations from which the samples have been drawn may differ in terms of means or variances or both. If the null hypothesis is not rejected, the variances can be considered to be approximately the same, and only the possibility that the means may differ exists. This situation leads to the examination of the null hypothesis, $H_0: \mu_1 = \mu_2 = \mu_3 = \cdots = \mu_k$; that is, the population means of the $k$ classes (samples) are homogeneous.

The *within* and *between* groups estimates of the population variance are used to test the null hypothesis, $H_0: \mu_1 = \mu_2 = \mu_3 = \cdots = \mu_k$, when the data are for $k$ classes (random samples) composing a single category. To illustrate the general situation, suppose we were to test the hypothesis, $H_0: \mu_1 = \mu_2 = \mu_3 = \mu_4$, on the basis of achievement test scores in reading attained by four groups, each of which had been taught by a different method. In this case there would be $k = 4$ classes (random samples) composing a single category of reading achievement test scores. By methods to be shown later, values for $S_w^2$ and $S_b^2$, *within* and *between* groups estimates of the population variance, would be derived. If the mean scores of the respective classes are subject only to the fluctuations due to random sampling, then, generally speaking, $S_w^2$ will tend to be equal to $S_b^2$, and the value of the $F$-ratio will tend to fluctuate about unity. If, however, the means of the four classes differ greatly, then $S_b^2$ (between groups estimate) will tend to be larger than $S_w^2$ (within groups estimate) and the value of the $F$-ratio will exceed unity. Whether the *observed value* of the $F$-ratio is relatively rare can be determined by referring to an $F$ table (Table XIV) and comparing it with the critical value of $F$ listed under the appropriate number of degrees of freedom. If the randomness of the sampling is not in question and the value of $F$ proves to be one that would occur rarely due to chance alone, the null hypothesis, $H_0: \mu_1 = \mu_2 = \mu_3 = \mu_4$, would be rejected. Although the $F$-test may show that the class means are not homogeneous, that is, it might show that there is a significant difference between class (group) means, this result does not *prove* that any or all of the class means are *actually significantly* different, but rather it presents evidence that the class (group) means are *statistically significantly* different. If the $F$-test value leads to the decision to reject the null hypothesis, $H_0 : \mu_1 = \mu_2 = \mu_3 = \mu_4$, pairs of means, for example, $H_0 : \mu_1 = \mu_2$, or $\mu_1 = \mu_3$, or $\mu_1 = \mu_4$, or $\mu_2 = \mu_3$, will have to be tested by the $t$-test for determining a significant difference between two group means or some other appropriate test such as Scheffe's multiple comparisons test will need to be employed.

*Degrees of Freedom*

We have previously discussed the concept of degrees of freedom in connection with the $\chi^2$ (chi-square) and $t$-distributions. One approach to computing an estimate of the population variance involves the process of finding a sum of the squares of the deviations from a mean for each of the observations composing the samples (classes), and dividing this sum of squares by the appropriate or corresponding number of degrees of freedom. The "corresponding number of degrees of freedom" may be determined in at least two ways. First, the "appropriate" number of degrees of freedom is equal to the number of observations minus the number of population parameters (e.g., the arithmetic mean) which have been estimated from the data. Hence, if the arithmetic mean, or for that matter, the variance, is estimated from the observations, then, in either case, the corresponding number of degrees of freedom is $n - 1$. Second, the appropriate number of degrees of freedom may be determined on the basis of the number of independent comparisons which can be made between observations or between classes (samples) of observations. If we had $n$ observations, $n - 1$ independent comparisons can be made between them. If $k$ classes (samples) exist, $k - 1$ independent comparisons are possible to make between them.

In connection with the *analysis of variance of classes under a single basis for classification, the total number of degrees of freedom is equal to the number of df within classes plus the number of df between classes*. If the situation is such that there is a total of $n$ observations divided into $k$ classes, the arrangement of degrees of freedom is as follows:

$$\text{total } df = \text{within classes } df + \text{between classes } df$$

or

$$n - 1 = n - k + k - 1$$

The total number of degrees of freedom is $n - 1$, the *df* between classes or columns is $k - 1$, while the *df* within classes is $n - k$, which results from the fact that the number of degrees of freedom within *each* of the $k$ classes (samples) is $n_j - 1$, where $n_j$ represents the number of observations within a particular class.

With this background and the added information that the variation *within classes* arises from the sum of the squared differences between each observation $X_{ij}$ and the mean $\overline{X}_j$ of that class, while the variation *between classes* emanates from the sum of the squared differences between each class mean $\overline{X}_j$ and the grand mean $\overline{X}$, we are prepared to examine the mechanics of computing the within groups, between groups, and total sum of squares for a set of observations. The discussion will be presented in terms of an example.

## Analysis of the Sums of Squares

Assume that values presented in the "diagramed" Table XV are test scores for five groups, the first taught by a laboratory method, the second by a lecture method, the third by a project method, the fourth by a discussion method, and the fifth by a teaching machine approach. The number of values used in the example is kept small so that the mechanics of the technique may be emphasized with a minimum of computational effort.

Table XV

Scores ($X$) and Squares of Scores ($X^2$) on a Particular Test for Materials Taught by Laboratory, Lecture, Project, Discussion, and Teaching Machine Methods (Fictitious Data)

| Individual Observations | Five Classes of a Single Category | | | | | | | | | | |
|---|---|---|---|---|---|---|---|---|---|---|---|
| | 1 | | 2 | | 3 | | 4 | | 5 | | |
| | $X$ | $X^2$ | $X$ | $X^2$ | $X$ | $X^2$ | $X$ | $X^2$ | $X$ | $X^2$ | |
| 1 | 8 | 64 | 5 | 25 | 14 | 196 | 3 | 9 | 15 | 225 | |
| 2 | 11 | 121 | 5 | 25 | 12 | 144 | 4 | 16 | 17 | 289 | |
| 3 | 12 | 144 | 6 | 36 | 14 | 196 | 6 | 36 | 13 | 169 | |
| 4 | 11 | 121 | | | 11 | 121 | 2 | 4 | | | |
| 5 | | | | | 15 | 225 | 4 | 16 | | | |
| 6 | | | | | 13 | 169 | | | | | |
| Total | 42 | 450 | 16 | 86 | 79 | 1051 | 19 | 81 | 45 | 683 | $\sum_j \sum_i X_{ij} = 201$ (Col.) (Row) $\sum_i \sum_j X_{ij}^2 = 2351$ |
| Mean | $\overline{X}_1 = \dfrac{42}{4}$ $= 10.5$ | | $\overline{X}_2 = \dfrac{16}{3}$ $= 5.3$ | | $\overline{X}_3 = \dfrac{79}{6}$ $= 13.2$ | | $\overline{X}_4 = \dfrac{19}{5}$ $= 3.8$ | | $\overline{X}_5 = \dfrac{45}{3}$ $= 15$ | | $\overline{X}_{ij} = \dfrac{201}{21} = 9.57$ Grand Mean |

(Within Classes (Groups) — bracket on right side)

←————————Between Classes (Groups)————————→

The *total sum of squares*, which is the sum of the squares of the deviations of all the observations about the grand mean, is partitioned into two components, the *between classes* and the *within classes sums of squares*, just as was the total number of degrees of freedom. The *between classes* component is equal to the total sum of squares of the class (column) means about the grand mean, and the *within classes* component is the total sum of squares of the individual observation's deviations about their own class (column) means.

The rationale of the analysis of the *total sum of squares* can probably be demonstrated best through an algebraic approach. The point of departure of the algebraic analysis is the identity:

$$(X_{ij} - \overline{X}) = (X_{ij} - \overline{X}_j) + (\overline{X}_j - \overline{X}) \tag{3}$$

where $X_{ij}$ is the value of the observation found in the $i$-th row (horizontal) of the $j$-th column (vertical), $\overline{X}_j$ is the arithmetic mean of the $j$-th column (class), and $\overline{X}$ is the *grand mean* of the $n$ observations composing the total (all classes) sample. In expression (3), the term $(X_{ij} - \overline{X})$ represents the deviation of a single observation from the grand mean; $(X_{ij} - \overline{X}_j)$ represents the deviation of a single observation from its class (column) mean, and the term $(\overline{X}_j - \overline{X})$ represents the deviation of a class (column) mean from the grand mean. To illustrate the notion purveyed by (3), suppose in Table XV we select the observation $X_{25} = 17$; i.e., the value in the *second row* of the *fifth column* (class); then substituting appropriate values in (3):

$$(X_{ij} - \overline{X}) = (X_{ij} - \overline{X}_j) + (\overline{X}_j - \overline{X});$$

we would have:

$$(17 - 9.57) = (17 - 15) + (15 - 9.57)$$
$$7.43 = 2 + 5.43$$

or:

$$7.43 = 7.43$$

Noting that (3) will hold for each observation in the total sample, we are now prepared for the second step of our algebraic approach to the analysis of the sums of squares.

If both sides of the identity (3) are "squared," and the resulting expression is summed for all values of $i$ and $j$, we would have for $n$ observations distributed over $k$ classes (in Table XV $n = 21$; $k = 5$):

$$\sum_{j=1}^{k} \sum_{i=1}^{n_j} (X_{ij} - \overline{X})^2 = \sum_{j=1}^{k} \sum_{i=1}^{n_j} (X_{ij} - \overline{X}_j)^2 + 2 \sum_{j=1}^{k} \sum_{i=1}^{n_j} (X_{ij} - \overline{X}_j)(\overline{X}_j - \overline{X})$$
$$+ \sum_{j=1}^{k} n_j(\overline{X}_j - \overline{X})^2 \tag{4}$$

The middle term of the right hand side of equation (4),

$$2 \sum_{j=1}^{k} \sum_{i=1}^{n_j} (X_{ij} - \overline{X}_j)(\overline{X}_j - \overline{X}),$$

becomes zero as the summation operation is performed over *each* of the $k$ classes. To illustrate, let $j = 1$, which means we are considering the first class (column) of the $k$ classes. The "middle" term then becomes:

$$2 \sum_{i=1}^{n_j} (X_{i1} - \overline{X}_1)(\overline{X}_1 - \overline{X}),$$

and since $(\overline{X}_1 - \overline{X})$ is actually a constant, we may rewrite the expression as:

$$2(\overline{X}_1 - \overline{X}) \sum_{i=1}^{n_j} (X_{i1} - \overline{X}_1).$$

But, $\sum_{i=1}^{n_j} (X_{i1} - \overline{X}_1)$ is the sum of the deviations of the observations in the first class (column) from the mean of that column $(\overline{X}_1)$, and is equal to zero. Since the "middle" term would be zero for every value of $j$ from 1 to $k$, the "entire" middle term of the right hand side of equation (4) would be zero. Thus, we would have expression (5), as the *final expression for the analysis of the total sum of squares for k classes of a single basis of classification:*

$$\sum_{j=1}^{k} \sum_{i=1}^{n_j} (X_{ij} - \overline{X})^2 = \sum_{j=1}^{k} \sum_{i=1}^{n_j} (X_{ij} - \overline{X}_j)^2 + \sum_{j=1}^{k} n_j(\overline{X}_j - \overline{X})^2$$

| Total sum of squares of deviations from the grand mean | Sum of squares of deviations of observations from class (column) means | Sum of squares of deviations of class means from grand mean ($n_j$ equals number of observations in a given class) (5) |
|---|---|---|

To illustrate the analysis of the total sum of squares we use the fictitious data of Table XV, and a *short form for computing the sum of squares within classes and between classes.** Finding the *total* sum of squares first, we have:

$$\sum_{j=1}^{k} \sum_{i=1}^{n_j} (X_{ij} - \overline{X})^2 = \sum_{j=1}^{k} \sum_{i=1}^{n_j} X^2 - \frac{\left(\sum_{j}\sum_{i} X\right)^2}{n} = 2351 - \frac{(201)^2}{21}$$

$$= 2351 - 1923.86 \approx 427.14$$

---

* The *total* sum of squares and the *within classes* sum of squares can be computed by using the *general* expression for sum of squares: $\sum X^2 - (\sum X)^2/n$. In the first case (total), the formula is applied to the entire table; in the latter case (within) it is applied to *each* of the $k$ classes of values, and the results of *each* analysis are summed to find the value of *within classes* component of the total sum of squares.

The short form for computing the sum of squares *between classes* is derived as follows: Let $n_1, n_2, n_3, \ldots, n_k$ be the size of the sample in *each* of the $k$ classes, and the corresponding means be $\overline{X}_1, \overline{X}_2, \overline{X}_3, \ldots, \overline{X}_k$. The grand mean will be denoted as $\overline{X}$, and the total sample size $(n)$ will be: $n = \sum n_j$. Then expanding the term

$$\sum_{j=1}^{k} n_j(\overline{X}_j - \overline{X})^2$$

we have:

$$\sum_{j=1}^{k} n_j(\overline{X}_j - \overline{X})^2 = n_1(\overline{X}_1 - \overline{X})^2 + n_2(\overline{X}_2 - \overline{X})^2 + n_3(\overline{X}_3 - \overline{X})^2 + \cdots + n_k(\overline{X}_k - \overline{X})^2$$

Expanding the right hand side of the expression and simplifying we have:

$$\sum_{j=1}^{k} n_j(\overline{X}_j - \overline{X})^2 = \frac{(\sum X_1)^2}{n_1} + \frac{(\sum X_2)^2}{n_2} + \frac{(\sum X_3)^2}{n_3} + \cdots + \frac{(\sum X_k)^2}{n_k} - \frac{(\sum \sum X_{ij})^2}{n}$$

i.e., each class sum is squared and divided by the number of values from which that sum is derived. These $k$ sums are added and a correction term equal to the grand sum of $X$, the quantity squared, divided by the total sample size $n$, is subtracted from the total of the $k$ sums.

The sum of squares *within classes* would be:

$$\sum_{j=1}^{k} \sum_{i=1}^{n_j} (X_{ij} - \bar{X})^2 = \left( \sum_{1}^{n_1} X_1^2 - \frac{(\sum X_1)^2}{n_1} \right) + \left( \sum_{i=1}^{n_2} X_2^2 - \frac{(\sum X_2)^2}{n_2} \right)$$

$$+ \left( \sum_{i=1}^{n_3} X_3^2 - \frac{(\sum X_3)^2}{n_3} \right) + \cdots \left( \sum_{i=1}^{n_k} X_k^2 - \frac{(\sum X_k)^2}{n_k} \right)$$

$$= \left( 450 - \frac{(42)^2}{4} \right) + \left( 86 - \frac{(16)^2}{3} \right) + \left( 1051 - \frac{(79)^2}{6} \right)$$

$$+ \left( 81 - \frac{(19)^2}{5} \right) + \left( 683 - \frac{(45)^2}{3} \right)$$

$$= (450 - 441) + (86 - 85.33) + (1051 - 1040.17)$$

$$+ (81 - 72.2) + (683 - 675)$$

$$= 9 + .67 + 10.83 + 8.8 + 8$$

$$= 37.3$$

The sum of squares *between classes* is:

$$\sum_{i=1}^{n_j} n_j (\bar{X}_j - \bar{X})^2 = \frac{\left( \sum_{i=1}^{n_1} X_1 \right)^2}{n_1} + \frac{\left( \sum_{i=1}^{n_2} X_2 \right)^2}{n_2}$$

$$+ \frac{\left( \sum_{i=1}^{n_3} X_3 \right)^2}{n_3} + \cdots + \frac{\left( \sum_{i=1}^{n_k} X_k \right)^2}{n_k} - \frac{\left( \sum_{j=1}^{k} \sum_{i=1}^{n_j} X_{ij} \right)^2}{n}$$

$$= \frac{(42)^2}{4} + \frac{(16)^2}{3} + \frac{(79)^2}{6} + \frac{(19)^2}{5} + \frac{(45)^2}{3} - \frac{(201)^2}{21}$$

$$= 441 + 85.33 + 1040.17 + 72.2 + 675 - 1923.86$$

$$= 2313.70 - 1923.86$$

$$= 389.84$$

This simple example does not reflect the "true" computational merit of the "short form" approach. In research problems that involve many "entries" of relatively large magnitude, the computational effort is reduced considerably by the approach illustrated in our example. Efficiency in the processes of computation is not the only advantage realized by the employment of the short form approach. The sum of squares computed in this fashion not only provides a "check" on the computations, but reveals how much each class contributes to the *within classes* sum of squares. To illustrate, we note that for the analysis of the sum of squares of the fictitious data in Table XV the figures "check":

$$\text{Total} = \text{within} + \text{between}$$

$$427.14 = 37.30 + 389.84;$$

and that the third class (10.83) contributes more heavily to the within classes sum of squares than do the other four groups.

*Mean Squares*

Each of the sums of squares, *total*, *within*, and *between*, has a specified number of *degrees of freedom* associated with it. The number of degrees of freedom associated with the *total* sum of squares is $n - 1$, where $n$ indicates the number of elements in the total sample. The total sum of squares for the data in Table XV has $21 - 1 = 20$ degrees of freedom. The *within classes* sum of squares component has $n - k$ degrees of freedom, where $n$ is as previously defined and $k$ indicates the number of classes involved. In our example of data from Table XV, the within classes component of the sum of squares has $21 - 5 = 16$ degrees of freedom associated with it. Finally, the *between classes* sum of squares has $k - 1$ degrees of freedom, hence, in our example it would have $5 - 1 = 4$ *df* associated with it.

If the sum of squares within classes is divided by the number of degrees of freedom associated with it, and the sum of squares between groups is divided by its number of degrees of freedom, we shall have *two estimates* of the *common population variance*. The *within classes estimate* will be independent of the variation between class means, while the *between classes estimate* will be independent of the variation within classes. *These estimates of the population variance are called "mean squares,"* and are usually presented in a *variance table*. Table XVI is a variance table which shows the results of the analysis of variance technique as applied to the data of Table XV.

Table XVI
Variance Table of Results of Analysis of Data From Table XV
(Fictitious Data)

| Source of Variation | Degrees of Freedom | Sum of Squares | Mean Square | F-Ratio | Decision Concerning $H_0$ |
|---|---|---|---|---|---|
| Between classes | 4 | 389.84 | 97.46 | $\dfrac{97.46}{2.33} = 41.8$ | Reject |
| Within classes | 16 | 37.30 | 2.33 | | |
| Total | 20 | 427.14 | | | |

From the variance table, we note that the *mean square for between classes* is decidedly greater than the *within classes mean square*, which has certain implications that we shall now discuss.

*The F-Test of Significance*

In our discussion of the *F*-test we pointed out that if two estimates of the population variance were available, the value of *F* could be found by dividing the larger estimate by the smaller one. If the analysis of variance technique is employed to test the null hypothesis of $H_0$: $\mu_1 = \mu_2 = \mu_3 = \cdots = \mu_k$; the hypothesis, in effect, calls for the testing of the *estimated variance between class means* (between classes mean square), in order to determine whether its value is a likely or unusual one. The test of the *between classes mean square* may be accomplished by using as the basis of comparison the *variance estimated from the uncontrolled variation within samples* (classes), i.e., by comparing the *between classes mean square* to the *within classes mean square*. Hence we define the *F*-ratio for use in *this application* of the analysis of variance technique as:

$$F = \frac{\text{mean square between classes}}{\text{mean square within classes}} = \frac{S_b^2}{S_w^2} \qquad (6)$$

In the fifth column of Table XVI we see that the *F*-ratio for the data of our example is:

$$F = \frac{97.46}{2.33} = 41.8$$

To determine whether the value of the *F*-ratio is significant at the 5 or 1 per cent levels, we enter Table XIV in the *column* designated by the *number of degrees of freedom associated with the greater mean square*. In our example, the mean square between classes, with 4 *df*, is the greater of the two mean squares, hence we enter Table XIV through the *column* designated "4 degrees of freedom." We now proceed down the column until we find the *row* entry corresponding to the *degrees of freedom associated with the smaller mean square*. For our example, this approach means that we proceed down the "4 *df* " *column* to the *row* entry corresponding to 16 degrees of freedom, the number associated with the (smaller) mean square within groups. At this point we find the critical (significant) values of *F* to be: *F* = 3.01 at the 5 per cent level, and *F* = 4.77 at the one per cent level.

Since the *observed value* of *F* = 41.8 is much greater than the tabled value of *F* = 4.77 at the 1 per cent level for 4 and 16 degrees of freedom, we may conclude that the observed value is a highly significant one. As a result of this finding, the null hypothesis, $H_0$: $\mu_1 = \mu_2 = \mu_3 = \mu_4 = \mu_5$, will be rejected, and we may infer that the arithmetic means of the classes differ significantly, i.e., they show more variation than can be attributed to random sampling from populations with a common population mean and variance. This conclusion permits the inference that the differences in test scores between the five groups taught by different methods of instruction are indicative of actual or real differences.

In summary, for this application of the analysis of variance technique the *F*-test of significance has been defined as the mean square between classes divided by the mean square within classes. The null hypothesis, $H_0$: $\mu_1 = \mu_2 = \mu_3 \cdots = \mu_k$, is tested under the assumption that the samples employed in the test are random samples drawn from a common, normal population. If the null hypothesis is true under the assumed conditions of sampling, then the mean square between classes and the mean square within classes provide two independent estimates of the common population variance.

Inferences pertaining to the significance of differences between class means can only be drawn if the mean square between classes is "significantly" greater than the mean square within classes. It is for this reason that the mean square between classes is placed in the numerator of the $F$-ratio, the mean square within classes is placed in the denominator, and the test of significance is conducted in the right end of the $F$-distribution.

If the experimental conditions have any systematic effect upon the arithmetic means of the experimental classes, then the *mean square between* classes is expected to be larger than the *mean square within classes*. Hence, if the mean square between classes is equal to or less than the mean square within classes, so that $F \leq 1$ as defined by (6), the null hypothesis will not be rejected. Only if the mean square between classes is greater than the mean square within classes, so that $F > 1$, will the data offer evidence against the "null," $H_0$. If the level of significance is set at $\alpha = .05$, then the null hypothesis will be rejected if the *observed value* of $F$ is greater than the critical value of $F$ found in the table under the appropriate degrees of freedom for the respective mean squares. The test of significance is a one-tailed test conducted in the right end of the $F$-distribution.

## Homogeneity of Variance

The analysis of variance and its accompanying $F$-test of significance assume that the variances *within the classes* are homogeneous, i.e., do not differ significantly among themselves. Usually with random assignment of subjects to experimental classes, the variation within classes is found to be homogeneous.

An approximate first test of homogeneity of *within classes variance* can be effected by finding the values of these estimates and submitting them to a test by means of the $F$-ratio. The values of the "estimates" are found by dividing *each of the separate sums of squares within the respective classes by the corresponding degrees of freedom*, or $n_j - 1$. In our example, the five "estimates" would be:

$$S_1^2 = \frac{9}{3} = 3; \qquad S_2^2 = \frac{.67}{2} = .33; \qquad S_3^2 = \frac{10.83}{5} = 2.17; \qquad S_4^2 = \frac{8.8}{4} = 2.2;$$

and

$$S_5^2 = \tfrac{8}{2} = 4$$

*These are the estimates that are assumed to be homogeneous.*

If an $F$-ratio is established by dividing the "estimate" of the largest value by the estimate of the smallest magnitude in the set of values, an *approximate test* of homogeneity is effected. In our example, the largest estimate is $S_5^2 = 4$, and the smallest is $S_2^2 = .33$. Hence, the $F$-ratio becomes: $F = 4/.33 = 12$, with 2 and 2 degrees of freedom, respectively. From Table XIV, we find that for 2 and 2 degrees of freedom a value of $F = 19.00$ is required for significance at the 10 per cent level, and a value of $F = 99.01$ is necessary at the 2 per cent level.* Since the observed value of $F = 12$ is not greater than that given for the 2 per cent level, the null hypothesis of $H_0 : \sigma_1^2 = \sigma_2^2$ cannot be rejected in favor of the "alternative" $H_1 : \sigma_1^2 \neq \sigma_2^2$.

Usually, if the two extreme estimates do not differ significantly, it can be concluded that homogeneity of variance prevails. It should be noted, however, that if the two extreme estimates did differ significantly, this result does not mean that the complete set of variances are not homogeneous. If the condition of "statistically significant difference" is found to exist by the "approximate" test, then a separate test of the hypothesis of homogeneity of variance, Bartlett's test, should be made. Since Bartlett's test is accorded a complete description in either Edwards,[5] or Dixon and Massey,[6] it will not be discussed further here. The point to be made is that if a nonsignificant value of $F$ is obtained, as in our example, the sample (class) variances are said to be homogeneous, that is, they all are assumed to be estimates of the same population variance. If a significant value of $F$ is found, the sample (class) variances would be assumed to be heterogeneous. To be positive of the inference of heterogeneity, however, Bartlett's test of the homogeneity of variance should be conducted.

### Multiple Comparisons of Means—The Scheffé Test

If the $F$-test associated with the analysis of variance technique indicates that there is a significant difference between the class means, that is, it rejects the null hypothesis, $H_0 : \mu_1 = \mu_2 = \mu_3 = \cdots = \mu_k$, we shall be interested in knowing how the means actually differ. We shall probably want to know the answers to such questions as: Are all the means significantly different from each other? Is there a significant difference between some of the means and not between others?

A variety of methods have been proposed for investigating differences between a set of $k$ class means. These methods are particularly useful for conducting *multiple comparisons* among the class means. One of the best and most general tests, appropriate for making *any* and *all* comparisons of interest between a set of $k$ means, is Scheffé's test. We shall only be interested in applying Scheffé's test to those comparisons involving *selected pairs* of the set of $k$ class means.

Scheffé's test can be conducted in either of two ways. One way involves the use of the analysis of variance; the other employs a *value of minimum significance*. It is the latter method we shall describe here.†

In order to meet the requirements of comparing selected pairs of the set of $k$ class means, Scheffé's test only involves the establishment of *the product* formed

---

* If the null hypothesis, $H_0 : \sigma_1^2 = \sigma_2^2$, is tested against the alternative, $H_1 : \sigma_1^2 \neq \sigma_2^2$, a two-tailed test is being conducted and the values listed at the 5 per cent and 1 per cent levels in the right tail of the $F$-distribution (Table XIV), must be considered to correspond to the 10 per cent and 2 per cent levels, respectively.

† Scheffé's test is general and need not be limited to testing differences between *pairs* of individual means. The test may be employed equally well to test one *group* of means against another group of means, or test a *group* of means against a *single* mean. For a more comprehensive discussion of Scheffé's Test see (54) Allen L. Edwards, *Experimental Design in Psychological Research*, pp. 154–56.

by multiplying a standard error of the difference of two means by a quantity ($F$). *If each of the k class means has been based upon an equal number of n observations, the product provides a value of minimum significance* which may be used to evaluate the difference between any selected pair of the original set of $k$ class means. If each of the $k$ means has been based upon a different number of observations, i.e., $n_1 \neq n_2 \neq n_3 \neq \cdots n_k$, etc., a new value for the standard error of the difference of two means will be found for each of the selected pairs, and hence a new value of minimum significance will also be derived. Obviously the computations for Scheffé's test, not to mention the computations for the analysis of variance and the computations for the test of homogeneity of variances, are simplified if all the classes (samples) are of the same size $n$. An additional reason for selecting classes (samples) of equal size $n$ is an expected improvement in the estimate of the standard error of the difference of two means.[7] In order to demonstrate efficiently certain computational procedures associated with the analysis of variance, we have employed as an example, Table XV, wherein some of the classes (samples) include a different number of observations, i.e., $n_1 = 4$, $n_2 = 3$, $n_3 = 6$, $n_4 = 5$, and $n_5 = 3$. We shall use this example to illustrate Scheffé's test, and to demonstrate how much the computational procedures are increased as a result of not having all classes (samples) of the same size $n$. Before proceeding to the example, however, it is necessary to become familiar with certain general formulas.

*If an analysis of variance has been conducted,* the standard error of the difference between any two (or pair) of the class means may be found most simply and quickly by formula (7):

$$S_{\bar{X}_A - \bar{X}_B} = \sqrt{S_w^2 \left( \frac{1}{n_A} + \frac{1}{n_B} \right)} \tag{7}$$

where $S_w^2$ is the within classes mean square, $n_A$ is the number of observations in class $A$, and $n_B$ is the number of observations in class $B$.

The quantity ($F$) may be found by formula (8):

$$(F) = \sqrt{(k - 1) F_{.05(k-1, n')}} \tag{8}$$

where $k$ is the number of classes in the analysis of variance, $n'$ is the number of degrees of freedom associated with the within classes mean square, and $F_{.05(k-1, n')}$ is the *tabled value* of the $F$-ratio at the .05 level with $k - 1$ and $n'$ degrees of freedom. If we wished, we could have used $F_{.01(k-1, n')}$ instead of $F_{.05}$, but since Scheffé's test is a conservative one, $F_{.05}$ is almost always used.

The product giving the value of minimum significance is expressed by formula (9):

$$\text{value of minimum significance} = (F)(S_{\bar{X}_A - \bar{X}_B}) \tag{9}$$

where the *value* will change as $S_{\bar{X}_A - \bar{X}_B}$ changes in value for a given pair of class means because the $k$ set of classes were of *different sizes*, $n_j$, or the *value* will remain fixed if each of the $k$ classes included the same number ($n$) of observations.

With this background, we shall now illustrate Scheffé's test by applying it to the data of Table XV. The value of $(F)$ for this example would be by formula (8):

$$(F) = \sqrt{(5-1)(3.01)} = \sqrt{12.04} \approx 3.47$$

where the value of $F_{.05(4,16)} = 3.01$ is read from Table XIV on the basis that from the analysis of variance the within classes mean square with $df = 16$ was found to be the *smaller* of the two.

If the researcher were interested in making comparisons of all the *different pairs* of class means that exist within the set of $k = 5$ classes, he would have ten such comparisons. These comparisons would be: 1 vs. 2, 1 vs. 3, 1 vs. 4, 1 vs. 5, 2 vs. 3, 2 vs. 4, 2 vs. 5, 3 vs. 4, 3 vs. 5, 4 vs. 5. Since only two of the groups (2 and 5) have the same number of observations ($n = 3$), it will be necessary to determine the different values of $S_{\bar{X}_A - \bar{X}_B}$ for each of the different *pairs* of means being compared involving groups that have different numbers of observations $(n_j)$.

If the means of class 1 (laboratory method) and class 2 (lecture method) are to be compared, we would have:

$$S_{\bar{X}_1 - \bar{X}_2} = \sqrt{2.33(\tfrac{1}{4} + \tfrac{1}{3})} = 1.167$$

which is also the value of $S_{\bar{X}_1 - \bar{X}_5}$, because the sample sizes involved, $n_1 = 4$ and $n_5 = 3$, are the same as those used in finding the value of $S_{\bar{X}_1 - \bar{X}_2}$. Thus, the *value of minimum significance* for Scheffé's test, as applied to the difference between means of class 1 and class 2; and class 1 and class 5 (teaching machine method) is:

$$(F)(S_{\bar{X}_1 - \bar{X}_2}) = (3.47)(1.167) \approx 4.0$$

If the *absolute values* of the differences $(\bar{X}_1 - \bar{X}_2)$ and $(\bar{X}_1 - \bar{X}_5)$ are as large as, or larger than, 4.0, then a significant difference between each of the pair of class means under examination exists. Since:

$$|\bar{X}_1 - \bar{X}_2| = |10.5 - 5.3| = 5.2$$

and

$$|\bar{X}_1 - \bar{X}_5| = |10.5 - 15| = 4.5$$

We may infer that there *is a significant difference* between the means of class 1 and class 2, and between the means of class 1 and class 5, *at the .05 level of significance.* If we had wished to conduct the test at the .01 level instead of the .05 level of significance, we would have used the value of $F_{.01(k-1,n')}$ in formula (8) instead of $F_{.05(k-1,n')}$, and found a different *value of minimum significance*. It should be noted again that the .05 level $(F_{.05})$ is sufficient for almost all of the problems found in educational research.

In order to test for differences between the means of class 1 and class 3 (project method), the value of $S_{\bar{X}_1 - \bar{X}_3}$ must be determined. Employing formula

(7) we find:

$$S_{\bar{X}_1 - \bar{X}_3} = \sqrt{2.33(\tfrac{1}{4} + \tfrac{1}{6})} = .989$$

and the *value of minimum significance* at the .05 level becomes:

$$(F)(S_{\bar{X}_1 - \bar{X}_3}) = (3.47)(.989) \approx 3.43$$

Since $|\bar{X}_1 - \bar{X}_3| = |10.5 - 13.2| = 2.7$, we infer that there is *not* a significant difference between the means of class 1 and class 3.

Testing for a significant difference between the means of class 1 and class 4 (discussion method) we would find:

$$S_{\bar{X}_1 - \bar{X}_4} = \sqrt{2.33(\tfrac{1}{4} + \tfrac{1}{5})} \approx 1.02$$

and the *value of minimum significance* at the .05 level to be:

$$(F)(S_{\bar{X}_1 - \bar{X}_4}) = (3.47)(1.02) = 3.54$$

Since the value of $|\bar{X}_1 - \bar{X}_4| = 6.7$ we would infer that the means of class 1 (laboratory method) is significantly different from the mean of class 4 (discussion method).

Since the sample size of class 2 (lecture) and class 5 (teaching machine) are the same, i.e., $n_2 = n_5 = 3$, we know that: (a) $S_{\bar{X}_2 - \bar{X}_3} = S_{\bar{X}_3 - \bar{X}_5}$; (b) $S_{\bar{X}_2 - \bar{X}_4} = S_{\bar{X}_4 - \bar{X}_5}$; and, naturally (c) $S_{\bar{X}_2 - \bar{X}_5} = S_{\bar{X}_5 - \bar{X}_2}$. The values of these respective "standard errors" are:

$$S_{\bar{X}_2 - \bar{X}_3} = \sqrt{2.33(\tfrac{1}{3} + \tfrac{1}{6})} \approx 1.08$$

$$S_{\bar{X}_2 - \bar{X}_4} = \sqrt{2.33(\tfrac{1}{3} + \tfrac{1}{5})} \approx 1.11$$

and

$$S_{\bar{X}_2 - \bar{X}_5} = \sqrt{2.33(\tfrac{1}{3} + \tfrac{1}{3})} \approx 1.20$$

Thus, the respective *values of minimum significance* at the .05 level become:

$$(F)(S_{\bar{X}_2 - \bar{X}_3}) = (3.47)(1.09) \approx 3.75$$

$$(F)(S_{\bar{X}_2 - \bar{X}_4}) = (3.47)(1.11) \approx 3.85$$

and

$$(F)(S_{\bar{X}_2 - \bar{X}_5}) = (3.47)(1.20) \approx 4.16$$

Now, since $|\bar{X}_2 - \bar{X}_3| = 7.9$ is greater than 3.75, and $|\bar{X}_3 - \bar{X}_5| = 1.8$ is less than 3.75 we may infer that the means of class 2 (lecture) and class 3 (project) *are* significantly different, but that those of class 3 and class 5 (teaching machine) are *not* significantly different. By the same approach we note that $|\bar{X}_2 - \bar{X}_4| = |5.3 - 3.8| = 1.5$ is less than 3.85, while $|\bar{X}_4 - \bar{X}_5| = |3.8 - 15| = 11.2$ is greater than 3.85. Hence, we may infer that the mean of class 2 is *not* significantly different from that of class 4 (discussion method), but that the mean of class 4 is significantly different from that of class 5.

Finally, to complete our analysis of all the different pairs of class means, we find $S_{\bar{X}_3 - \bar{X}_4}$ to be:

$$S_{\bar{X}_3 - \bar{X}_4} = \sqrt{2.33(\tfrac{1}{6} + \tfrac{1}{5})} \approx .92$$

and the *value of minimum significance* at the .05 level to be:

$$(F)(S_{\bar{X}_3 - \bar{X}_4}) = (3.47)(.98) \approx 3.40$$

Since the value of $|\bar{X}_3 - \bar{X}_4| = 13.2 - 3.8| = 9.4$ is greater than 3.4, we may infer that the mean of class 3 is significantly different from that of class 4.

Scheffé's test is a conservative one. If a significant difference between a pair of class means is indicated by Scheffé's test, regardless of the number of pairs of class means involved, the researcher can be quite sure that the difference between the pair being tested really is significant. On the other hand, if the *t*-test for significant difference between two independent group means is applied to a random selection of two means from, say, the five of our examples in Table XV, and a significant difference at the .05 level is found, the significance might be spurious. This statement is based upon the fact that there are ten possible *pairs* of means that might be selected, and if all the possible ten *t*-tests were made, we could *expect*, when the null hypothesis is actually true, that 5 per cent of these *t*'s, or with rounding, approximately one, could be significant at the .05 level by chance alone.*

It should be emphasized at this point that Scheffé's test need not be restricted to testing the significance of the difference between individual means. The method is general, and if it suited the purposes of the research, tests could be conducted of one group of means against another group of means, or a group of means against a single mean. The same basic reasoning is applied, but in view of our purposes these approaches need not be discussed here.†

*Outline of Analysis of Variance Test (Single Classification)*

To summarize our discussion of the analysis of variance single variable of classification technique, the following outline is presented:

1. *Null Hypothesis.* $H_0: \mu_1 = \mu_2 = \mu_3 = \cdots = \mu_k$. The $k$ population means are *all* equal. The alternative hypothesis ($H_1$) is that *all* of the $k$ means are not equal.

2. *Statistical Test.* The $F$-ratio statistical test is chosen as the appropriate one under the assumption that the elements included in the sample have been randomly and independently drawn from a common population, which further implies a common variance, i.e., $\sigma_1^2 = \sigma_2^2 = \sigma_3^2 = \cdots = \sigma_k^2 = \sigma^2$.

3. *Level of Significance,* $\alpha$. In compliance with usual research practices, the level of significance is set at $\alpha = .05$ or $\alpha = .01$, whichever is most desirable.

---

* For a more detailed discussion of this point see (53) Allen L. Edwards, *Statistical Methods for Behavioral Sciences*, pp. 329–30.

† See footnote, page 368.

and an adequate sample size, $n$, is distributed randomly and independently over the $k$ classes forming the classification.

4. *Sampling Distribution.* The appropriate sampling distribution of the $F$-ratio formed by dividing the mean square between classes by the mean square within classes will be: $F_{.05(k-1,n')}$; or $F_{.01(k-1,n')}$ where $k-1$ indicates the degrees of freedom for the mean square between classes, and $n'$ indicates the *df* of the mean square within classes.

5. *Critical Region.* The critical region is composed of all the values of the observed $F$-statistic equal to or greater than the critical value of $F$ found in the appropriate cell of the $F$-table (Table XIV).

6. *Computing the Value of the Statistic.* By finding the between classes sum of squares, the within classes sum of squares, and dividing each by the appropriate numbers of degrees freedom; the mean square between classes, and the mean square within classes are found. The value of the $F$-ratio is then found by the formula:

$$F = \frac{\text{mean square between classes}}{\text{mean square within classes}}$$

7. *Decision.* The null hypothesis ($H_0$) is rejected, or not rejected, as the observed value of $F$ falls, or does not fall, in the critical region.

In the process of carrying out the analysis of variance test, it is necessary to know whether a condition of homogeneity of variance exists. An approximate test of this condition can be conducted by determining whether the $F$-ratio, formed by dividing the *largest* mean square of all the $k$ respective classes by the *smallest* mean square of these classes, is a significant one. If it is not significant, homogeneity of variance can be assumed to prevail. If it is significant, Bartlett's test should be conducted to ascertain the "true" condition.

If the hypothesis: $H_0 : \mu_1 = \mu_2 = \mu_3 = \cdots = \mu_k$ is true, both $S_w^2$ and $S_b^2$ are independent estimates of $\sigma^2$, the common population variance. If in fact $H_0$ is not true and some of the $\mu$'s are unequal, the mean square between classes, $S_b^2$, will be significantly larger than the mean square within classes, $S_w^2$, which will be indicated by a significant $F$-ratio.

When a significant value of the $F$-ratio is found, $H_0$ is rejected, and a significant difference between class means is inferred. In order to determine whether every mean is significantly different from every other mean, or if there are significant differences between some of the means and not between others, Scheffé's test of multiple comparisons is applied to all possible *pairs* of class means.

Scheffé's test is greatly simplified, and more valid, if there is an equal number ($n_j$) of observations in each of the classes composing the total sample $n = \sum n_j$. The test is a conservative one, however, and may be applied to classes of unequal size with complete confidence at the $\alpha = .05$ level. Finally, the method is general and need not be limited to testing pairs of individual means. It can be applied with equal effectiveness to test one group of means against another group of means, or to test a group of means against a single mean.

With this background we are prepared to discuss the analysis of variance for *multiple bases of classification*. The analysis of variance for multiple bases of classification technique is particularly useful in those situations where it is desirable to study the effects of several variables in a given experiment.

*Chapter 28—References*

See Bibliography: 4, 38, 49, 53, 54, 65, 66, 67, 76, 77, 89, 104, 113, 123, 141, 148, 159, 179, 183, 191; 31a, 38a, 42a, 67a, 107a; 1b.

# Parametric Statistical Tests—III

## (Analysis of Variance Multiple Bases of Classification)

WHEN THE RESEARCH PROBLEM is concerned with the influence of two or more independent variables (*factors*) on a dependent variable, a more complicated application of the analysis of variance than that used for a single variable of classification is necessary. The number of categories in which a factor (variable) is placed is the number of *levels* of the factor under consideration. Thus, if a factor is categorized in two ways, it is said to have two levels, and a factor varied (categorized) in three ways is said to have three levels. If the situation is such that two or more factors each with two or more levels are under consideration, a *treatment* consists of a combination of one level for each factor. When an *equal number of observations* are made for all possible combinations of levels, a *factorial design with equal replications* is produced. In research involving two or more variables it is not always possible to study all combinations of levels. For example, an experimental research model might be designed to examine the effects of four teaching methods. If there are eleven classes of students available for testing the four methods, assignment of each of the methods to two of the classes of students (thus involving eight of the eleven classes) could be made at random, resulting in two *replications* of each method.* This situation would create a completely randomized design of a study of the four methods. On the other hand, if the four methods were randomly assigned to four groups of students in each of seven schools, a *randomized-block design* is produced. In the latter example, the schools are considered to be the "blocks."

Assumptions underlying the analysis of variance for two or more bases of classification are: (1) random sampling prevails; (2) population variables are approximately normally distributed; (3) the subclasses are independent in terms of the variables; (4) the subclasses have equal variances, and (5) additivity of effects prevails. The assumption of additivity of effects means that a cell value $X_{jg}$ is equal to a common effects $W$, plus a row effect $X_g$, plus a column effect

---

* In the analysis of variance, a given set of observations consisting of one observation for each treatment is called a *replication*. For example, if there are $k = 3$ treatments with $n = 25$ observations *for each* treatment, the experiment being conducted would have 25 replications. Behavioral science research problems usually involve many factors, each with many levels. If an experiment involved 5 factors, each at 3 levels, one replication of the factorial experiment would require $3^5 = 243$ observations. To obtain an *error mean square based upon a within-treatments sum of squares*, at least one additional replication (243 more observations) would be required. If the observations were associated with subjects, a total of 486 persons would be needed for the two replications of the design.

$X_j$, and a random variation $W_{jg}$, i.e., $X_{jg} = W + X_g + X_j + W_{jg}$. These effects are assumed to be uncorrelated, and in addition the average value of $W_{jg}$ is zero.

We shall now develop the analysis of variance computational procedure for a factorial design two-way classification of observations by working through a numerical example. The fictitious data in Table XVII represent the case where one observation $X_{jg}$ has been made for each combination of levels. There are $k = 4$ columns (treatments), and $r = 3$ rows (varieties), forming 12 cells in the table. The $\bar{X}_r$'s are the means of the rows (schools), the $\bar{X}_k$'s the means of the columns (methods), and $\bar{X}$ is the grand mean of the table.

Table XVII
Analysis of Variance for Two-Way Classification Factorial Design
(Fictitious Data)

| | | First Variable (Treatments) $k$ Methods | | | | | |
| | | 1 | 2 | 3 | 4 | Total | Means |
|---|---|---|---|---|---|---|---|
| Second variable | A | $X_{11} = 9$ | $X_{21} = 7$ | $X_{31} = 8$ | $X_{41} = 7$ | 31 | $\bar{X}_{1r} = 7.75$ |
| (Varieties) | B | $X_{12} = 3$ | $X_{22} = 2$ | $X_{32} = 3$ | $X_{42} = 2$ | 10 | $\bar{X}_{2r} = 2.5$ |
| $r$ Schools | C | $X_{13} = 4$ | $X_{23} = 6$ | $X_{33} = 4$ | $X_{43} = 5$ | 19 | $\bar{X}_{3r} = 4.75$ |
| Total | | 16 | 15 | 15 | 14 | 60 | |
| Means | | $\bar{X}_{1k} = 5.33;$ | $\bar{X}_{2k} = 5.0;$ | $\bar{X}_{3k} = 5.0;$ | $\bar{X}_{4k} = 4.66$ | | $\bar{X} = 5.0$ |

The total variation of the observations in Table XVII is caused not only by the variance of the common population from which the sample is selected, and basic experimental errors (e.g., measurement) that are always present, but from differences that may be caused by a difference in *treatments* (first variable of classification, methods) or a difference in *varieties* (second variable of classification, schools). In the analysis of variance for a single variable of classification, one of the two independent estimates of the common population variance was obtained from the between classes (columns) mean square. In the two-way classification technique an independent estimate of the population variance is also obtained from the *row* means.

*Sums of Squares*

1. Total:

$$9^2 + 3^2 + 4^2 + 7^2 + 2^2 \cdots + 7^2 + 2^2 + 5^2 - \frac{(60)^2}{12} = 362 - 300 = 62$$

2. Between column means:

$$\frac{(16)^2}{3} + \frac{(15)^2}{3} + \frac{(15)^2}{3} + \frac{(14)^2}{3} - \frac{(60)^2}{12} = 300.67 - 300 = .67$$

3. Between row means:

$$\frac{(31)^2}{4} + \frac{(10)^2}{4} + \frac{(19)^2}{4} - \frac{(60)^2}{12} = 355.5 - 300 = 55.5$$

4. Interaction (residual)

The interaction (residual) sum of squares can be found by subtracting the sum of squares for column means and row means from the total sum of squares:

$$62 - 55.5 - .67 = 5.83$$

Table XVIII shows the analysis of variance for the data of Table XVII. The number of degrees of freedom for the component of the total variation due to column means is $(k - 1) = 4 - 1 = 3$. The $df$ for the row means component is: $(r - 1) = 3 - 1 = 2$. The number of degrees of freedom for the component of variation allocated to interaction (residual) is: $(k - 1)(r - 1) = (3)(2) = 6$.

Table XVIII
Summary of Analysis of Variance for Data of Table XVII

| Source of Variation | df | Sum of Squares | Mean Square | F-ratio | Decision |
|---|---|---|---|---|---|
| Between column means | 3 | .67 | .223 | .229 | Do not reject $H_0$ |
| Between row means | 2 | 55.50 | 27.75 | 28.55 | Reject $H_0$ |
| Interaction (residual) | 6 | 5.83 | .972 | | |
| Total | 11 | 62.00 | | | |

The values of the $F$-ratios shown in the fourth column of Table XVIII are used to test the significance of the difference between column means and the difference between row means, respectively. The $F$-ratio for testing the significance of the difference between column means is formed by dividing the *mean square for between column means* by the interaction (residual) mean square. Similarly, the significance of the difference between row means is tested by dividing the *mean square for between row means* by the interaction mean square. In our example, the value of the $F$-ratio for "between column means" is:

$$F = \frac{.223}{.972} = .229,$$

and for "between row means" is:

$$F = \frac{27.75}{.972} = 28.55$$

Since the value of the $F$-ratio for the between column means test $(F = .229)$ is less than one $(F < 1)$, the null hypothesis of no significant difference between *column* means, is *not* rejected. The $F$-ratio $(F = 28.55)$ for the between row means test, however, is greater than the critical value found at the .05 level in Table XIV, $[F_{.05(2,8)} = 4.46]*$, hence the null hypothesis is rejected.

---

* If the level of significance ($\alpha$) had been set at the .01 level instead of the .05 level, the null hypothesis ($H_0$) would still have been rejected because the observed value of $F = 28.55$ exceeds the critical value $F_{.01(2,8)} = 8.65$ found in Table XIV.

The discussion of the previous example describes the computational procedures associated with the analysis of variance for a two-way classification, single observation, factorial design. We shall now express in general terms the analysis of the number of degrees of freedom and the sum of squares for a two-way classification in which there is one value per cell, and more than one *but an equal number* of values per cell.*

1. General expressions for degrees of freedom:

    (a) One observation per cell.

| | |
|---|---:|
| Between $k$ classes (columns) | $k - 1$ |
| Between $r$ classes (rows) | $r - 1$ |
| Interaction (residual) of $r$ and $k$ classes | $(k - 1)(r - 1)$ |
| Total | $n - 1$ |

    (b) More than one, but an equal number ($c$) of observations per cell, and hence the total size of $n$ observations is: $n = krc.$†

| | |
|---|---:|
| Between $k$ classes (columns) | $k - 1$ |
| Between $r$ classes (rows) | $r - 1$ |
| Interaction between $k$ and $r$ classes | $(k - 1)(r - 1)$ |
| Within classes | $kr(c - 1)$ |
| Total | $n - 1$ |

2. General expressions for sums of squares:

    (a) One observation per cell.

        Assume the data are classified within each of two categories, and there is a single observation in each of the cells of the table so that $n = rk$. If we then let $j$ represent any class by columns, and $g$ any class by rows; then $X_{jg}$ is a cell value, $\overline{X}_j$ is the mean of the $j$-th class (column), $\overline{X}_g$ is the mean of the $g$-th class (row), while $\overline{X}$ is the grand mean of the table. Starting with the identity:

$$(X_{jg} - \overline{X}) = (X_{jg} - \overline{X}_j - \overline{X}_g + \overline{X}) + (\overline{X}_j - \overline{X}) + (\overline{X}_g - \overline{X})$$

We square and sum it for all values of $j$ and $g$, where $j$ assumes values from 1 to $k$ (the number of columns in the table) and $g$ takes on values

---

* For a discussion of the case involving *any number of values per cell* see: (148) A. C. Rosander, *Elementary Principles of Statistics*, pp. 546–52.

† In testing the hypothesis of difference of class means, the best estimate of the common population variance can be obtained from measurements repeated under similar conditions. If in our example of two-way classification of treatments and varieties, for every combination of treatment and variety, we have more than one value, we say the design of the investigation has been *replicated*, or repeated. This replication makes possible a more thorough analysis of the data than is otherwise possible. Only the case of an equal number of replications in each cell is considered here. The analysis associated with an unequal number of replications is a modification of the one for an equal number; however, for simplification of computational procedures and better unbiased estimates of variance, every effort should be made to provide an equal number of replications in each cell.

from 1 to $r$ (the number of rows in the table). Since the value of the "summed" cross products of the squared result are zero, the following formula represents the respective sums of squares:

$$\sum_{g=1}^{r} \sum_{j=1}^{k} (X_{jg} - \overline{X})^2 = \sum_{g=1}^{r} \sum_{j=1}^{k} (X_{jg} - \overline{X}_j - \overline{X}_g + \overline{X})^2$$

$$\text{Total} \qquad\qquad \underset{\text{(residual)}}{\underset{\text{Interaction}}{}}$$

$$+ r \sum_{j=1}^{k} (\overline{X}_j - \overline{X})^2 + k \sum_{g=1}^{r} (\overline{X}_g - \overline{X})^2 \qquad (1)$$

$$\underset{\text{means}}{\underset{k \text{ Column}}{}} \qquad\qquad \underset{\text{means}}{\underset{r \text{ Row}}{}}$$

The term on the left-hand side of the equation is the total sum of squares of the individual values about the grand mean $\overline{X}$. Three components of the total sum of squares form the right-hand side of equation (1): the sum of squares due to the interaction between the $k$ and $r$ classes, frequently called the "residual"; the sum of squares due to the $r$ row means; and the sum of squares for the $k$ column means.

(b) More than one, but an equal number ($c$) of observations per cell, thus $n = krc$ in total sample. When there is the same number of values per cell, but the number is two or more, i.e., $c > 1$, there is a fourth component of the total sum of squares—*the sum of squares within classes*—which is symbolized as:

$$\sum_{g}^{r} \sum_{j}^{k} \sum_{i}^{n_{jg}} (X_{ijg} - \overline{X}_{jg})^2 \qquad (2)$$

where $\overline{X}_{jg}$ is the mean of any cell, and $X_{ijg}$ is any value within that cell. Thus, expression (2) gives the sum of squares of the cell values about their respective *cell* means. The total sum of squares for the entire table of values can be expressed simply by adding the term given by (2) to a slightly modified form of (1), the modification being the substitution of $\overline{X}_{jg}$ (the cell mean) for $X_{jg}$ in the first term on the right-hand side of equation (1). The modified expression is:

$$\sum_{g=1}^{r} \sum_{j=1}^{k} \sum_{i=1}^{n_{jg}} (X_{ijg} - \overline{X})^2 = \sum_{g=1}^{r} \sum_{j=1}^{k} \sum_{i=1}^{n_{jg}} (X_{ijg} - \overline{X}_{jg})^2$$

$$\text{Total} \qquad\qquad\qquad \text{Within}$$

$$+ \sum_{g=1}^{r} \sum_{j=1}^{k} (\overline{X}_{jg} - \overline{X}_j - \overline{X}_g + \overline{X})^2$$

$$\text{Interaction}$$

$$+ r \sum_{j=1}^{k} (\overline{X}_j - \overline{X})^2 + k \sum_{g=1}^{r} (\overline{X}_g - \overline{X})^2 \qquad (3)$$

$$\underset{\text{means}}{\underset{\text{Column}}{}} \qquad\qquad \underset{\text{means}}{\underset{\text{Row}}{}}$$

The "interaction" term in (3) is different from the "interaction (residual)" term of (1). The "within classes" sum of squares component in (3) provides the means of finding a better estimate (the within classes mean square) of the common population variance ($\sigma^2$), than does the "interaction" sum of squares. Under the condition of one observation per cell, the condition for which (1) holds, the best sum of squares component to transform into a mean square estimate of $\sigma^2$, in order to test the significance of the difference between class means, is that of "interaction (residual)."

Equation (3) demonstrates that when two or more replications per cell are employed in the factorial design, the total sum of squares is analyzed into four parts: (1) the within-class sum of squares; (2) the sum of squares for interaction; (3) the sum of squares for column means; and (4) the row means sum of squares. In both case A (one observation per cell) and case B (more than one, but an equal number of observations per cell), the sum of squares between classes is computed as shown in our numerical example of the two-way classification analysis, that is, the method of calculation is applied separately to $k$ classes (columns) and to the $r$ classes (rows). Similarly, the sum of squares within classes does not involve any new principles. The same basic expression involving the sum of the "squares" of $X$, i.e., $\sum X^2$, and the square of the sum of $X$, i.e., $(\sum X)^2$, is employed. The sum of squares due to interaction, however, does demand introduction of a new concept and a new method of calculation, at least in those cases where there are simple sets of data. In cases where more complex sets of data are involved, however, the interaction sum of squares is usually found by subtraction since the total sum of squares can be readily calculated in all cases. Because of its importance to the analysis of variance technique for multiple bases of classification, we now discuss certain aspects of interaction.

## Interaction (Residual)

The term *interaction*, as applied to a two-way table of observations, refers to the extent to which the differences between successive values in a class of one of the variables of classification are maintained from one class to another. If these differences are constant, or maintained exactly, then the interaction is zero. If, on the other hand, the differences are not constant, the degree of variation is measured by the sum of squares divided by the appropriate number of degrees of freedom just as with any other source of variance. The interaction (residual) sum of squares term in (1) will be zero, if, *for every cell value*, the following condition is satisfied:

$$X_{jg} - \bar{X}_j - \bar{X}_g + \bar{X} = 0 \tag{4}$$

or, rewriting in another form: $X_{jg} + \bar{X} = \bar{X}_j + \bar{X}_g$. If condition (4) exists for every cell value $(X_{jg})$, *for the case of one observation per cell*, or for the *cell mean* $(\bar{X}_{jg})$, if there is *more than one value per cell*, then the sum of squares due to the interaction of the two variables of classification will be zero.

The following example of one observation per cell $(X_{jg})$ illustrates a condition of zero interaction for *every cell*, which causes the sum of squares and the mean square (variance) for the interaction component to vanish, i.e., be equal to zero. The variation which does exist is accounted for by the sums of squares between classes (rows and columns). In Table XIX each value in a column ( $j$ class) is one more than the preceding value, which creates a situation that satisfies condition (4) and hence the requirements for zero interaction.

*A special linear relationship must exist between adjacent pairs of column values for the interaction to be zero.* Thus, if $X_{12} = X_{11} + a$; and $X_{13} = X_{12} + b$; and $X_{14} = X_{13} + c$, then the table (set) made up of these values will have zero interaction.

Table XIX
Fictitious Data Illustrating Zero Interaction

| $r$ Classes | $k$ Classes | | | | | |
|---|---|---|---|---|---|---|
| | 1 | 2 | 3 | 4 | Total | $\overline{X}_g$ |
| A | $X_{11} = 2$ | $X_{21} = 6$ | $X_{31} = 10$ | $X_{41} = 14$ | 32 | 8 |
| B | $X_{12} = 3$ | $X_{22} = 7$ | $X_{32} = 11$ | $X_{42} = 15$ | 36 | 9 |
| C | $X_{13} = 4$ | $X_{23} = 8$ | $X_{33} = 12$ | $X_{43} = 16$ | 40 | 10 |
| Total | 9 | 21 | 33 | 45 | 108 | |
| $\overline{X}_j$ | 3 | 7 | 11 | 15 | | $\overline{X} = 9$ |

The interaction in a two-way table will be a *maximum* if all of the values of the $\overline{X}_j$'s and the $\overline{X}_g$'s are identical. When this condition prevails, the sums of squares between both sets of class means (columns and rows) are zero, and the *total sum of squares* will be due to *interaction*. The situation is illustrated by Table XX.

Table XX
Fictitious Data Illustrating Maximum Interaction

| $r$ Classes | $k$ Classes | | | | | |
|---|---|---|---|---|---|---|
| | 1 | 2 | 3 | 4 | Total | $\overline{X}_g$ |
| A | $X_{11} = 6$ | $X_{21} = 7$ | $X_{31} = 8$ | $X_{41} = 7$ | 28 | 7 |
| B | $X_{12} = 7$ | $X_{22} = 5$ | $X_{32} = 6$ | $X_{42} = 10$ | 28 | 7 |
| C | $X_{13} = 8$ | $X_{23} = 9$ | $X_{33} = 7$ | $X_{43} = 4$ | 28 | 7 |
| Total | 21 | 21 | 21 | 21 | 84 | |
| $\overline{X}_j$ | 7 | 7 | 7 | 7 | | $\overline{X} = 7$ |

Total sum of squares:

$$6^2 + 7^2 + 8^2 + 7^2 + 5^2 + 9^2 + 8^2 + \cdots + 10^2 + 4^2 - \frac{(84)^2}{12}$$

$$= 618 - 588 = 30$$

Between column means:

$$\frac{(21)^2 + (21)^2 + (21)^2 + (21)^2}{3} - \frac{(84)^2}{12} = 588 - 588 = 0$$

Between row means:

$$\frac{(28)^2 + (28)^2 + (28)^2}{4} - \frac{(84)^2}{12} = 588 - 588 = 0$$

Interaction (residual):

$$\frac{1}{2}\left[\left(149 - \frac{(21)^2}{3}\right) + \left(155 - \frac{(21)^2}{3}\right) + \left(149 - \frac{(21)^2}{3}\right) + \left(165 - \frac{(21)^2}{3}\right)\right.$$
$$\left. + \left(198 - \frac{(28)^2}{4}\right) + \left(210 - \frac{(28)^2}{4}\right) + \left(210 - \frac{(28)^2}{4}\right)\right] = \frac{60}{2} = 30$$

The value of the interaction sum of squares could have been found by subtracting the sums of squares for the between column and between row means from the total sum of squares; however, the interaction sum of squares should be calculated independently in order to have a "check" on the other computations employed. Only if the work of calculation becomes too costly should the interaction sum of squares be found by subtraction.

### Interaction (*More than One, but an Equal Number of Observations per Cell*)

In those two-way tables where there is more than one, but an equal number of values per cell, there is a variance *within cells* as well as between classes. The method of computing the interaction sum of squares for this type of table can be illustrated by the simple case in which there are two values per cell, as shown in Table XXI.

Table XXI
Fictitious Data Illustrating Interaction for More Than One,
But an Equal Number of Values Per Cell

| $r$ Classes | $k$ Classes | | | | |
|---|---|---|---|---|---|
| | 1 | 2 | 3 | Total | $\bar{X}_g$ |
| $A$ | $X_{111} = 5$<br>$X_{112} = 6$<br>Cell<br>mean: $\bar{X}_{11} = 5.5$ | $X_{211} = 3$<br>$X_{212} = 4$<br>Cell<br>mean: $\bar{X}_{21} = 3.5$ | $X_{311} = 1$<br>$X_{312} = 2$<br>Cell<br>mean: $\bar{X}_{31} = 1.5$ | 21<br>Cell<br>mean: 7.0 | 3.5 |
| $B$ | $X_{121} = 9$<br>$X_{122} = 10$<br>Cell<br>mean: $\bar{X}_{12} = 9.5$ | $X_{221} = 7$<br>$X_{222} = 8$<br>Cell<br>mean: $\bar{X}_{22} = 7.5$ | $X_{321} = 11$<br>$X_{322} = 12$<br>Cell<br>mean: $\bar{X}_{32} = 11.5$ | 57<br>Cell<br>mean: 19.0 | 9.5 |
| Total | 30<br>Cell<br>mean: 15.0 | 22<br>Cell<br>mean: 11.0 | 26<br>Cell<br>mean: 13.0 | 78<br>Cell<br>mean: 13.0 | |
| $\bar{X}_j$ | 7.5 | 5.5 | 6.5 | | $\bar{X} = 6.5$ |

Total sum of squares:

$$5^2 + 6^2 + 9^2 + 10^2 + 3^2 + 4^2 + 7^2 + \cdots + 11^2 + 12^2 - \frac{(78)^2}{12}$$

$$= 650 - 507 = 143$$

Between column means:

$$\frac{30^2 + 22^2 + 26^2}{4} - \frac{(78)^2}{12} = 515 - 507 = 8$$

Between row means:

$$\frac{21^2 + 57^2}{6} - \frac{(78)^2}{12} = 615 - 507 = 108$$

Interaction between $k = 3$ and $r = 2$ classes: $= 24$ (see explanation below).
Within cells: 66 (.5 per cell) $= 3$ (see explanation below).

The interaction sum of squares can be computed directly by employing the second term on the right-hand side of equation (3), and substituting the values of each set of cell means into the expression, making sure to weigh each sum of squares by the number of cases in the cell. Thus, substituting in the expression: $(n_{ijg})(\bar{X}_{jg} - \bar{X}_j - \bar{X}_g + \bar{X})^2$ and adding the results for each cell, we have:

| | | | |
|---|---|---|---|
| Cell $A1$: | $2(5.5 - 7.5 - 3.5 + 6.5)^2 = 2(1)^2$ | $=$ | 2 |
| Cell $A2$: | $2(3.5 - 5.5 - 3.5 + 6.5)^2 = 2(1)^2$ | $=$ | 2 |
| Cell $A3$: | $2(1.5 - 6.5 - 3.5 + 6.5)^2 = 2(-2)^2$ | $=$ | 8 |
| Cell $B1$: | $2(9.5 - 7.5 - 9.5 + 6.5)^2 = 2(-1)^2$ | $=$ | 2 |
| Cell $B2$: | $2(7.5 - 5.5 - 9.5 + 6.5)^2 = 2(-1)^2$ | $=$ | 2 |
| Cell $B3$: | $2(11.5 - 6.5 - 9.5 + 6.5)^2 = 2(2)^2$ | $=$ | 8 |

Total interaction sum of squares $= 24$

Whenever the work of calculation is not too costly, the interaction sum of squares should be computed independently instead of being found by subtracting the sum of the between rows classes, the between columns classes, and the within cells sum of squares from the total sum of squares. The approach of independent calculation has the advantage of providing a "check" on the other computational work involved.

The within cells sum of squares may be found by applying the general form $\left[\sum X^2 - \frac{(\sum X)^2}{n_{ijg}}\right]$ to each cell of the table. Thus, in our example, we would have:

$$\text{Cell } A1: \quad 5^2 + 6^2 - \frac{(11)^2}{2} = 61 - 60.5 = .5$$

$$\text{Cell } A2: \quad 3^3 + 4^2 - \frac{(7)^2}{2} = 25 - 24.5 = .5$$

$$\text{Cell } A3: \quad 1^2 + 2^2 - \frac{(3)^2}{2} = 5 - 4.5 = .5$$

$$\text{Cell } B1: \quad 9^2 + 10^2 - \frac{(19)^2}{2} = 181 - 180.5 = .5$$

$$\text{Cell } B2: \quad 7^2 + 8^2 - \frac{(15)^2}{2} = 113 - 112.5 = .5$$

$$\text{Cell } B3: \ 11^2 + 12^2 - \frac{(23)^2}{2} = 265 - 264.5 = \underline{0.5}$$

$$\text{Total within cells sum of squares} = 3.0$$

As a "check" on the calculations on the sums of squares, the following equation should be satisfied:

Total = between $k$ classes (cols.) + between $r$ classes (rows) + interaction + within

substituting, we find:

$$143 = 8 + 108 + 24 + 3 = 143$$

We can therefore conclude, with a reasonable degree of certainty, that the calculations have produced accurate results.

*Mean Squares (Estimates of Variance)*

The analysis of variance technique involving two variables of classification and a single observation per cell, providing the values of the observations are independently and normally distributed, produce three unbiased estimates (mean squares) of the population variance ($\sigma^2$). These three estimates (mean squares) are derived from: (a) the $k$ (column) classes, (b) the $r$ (row) classes, and (c) the interaction (residual) component of the sums of squares. The mean square of the $k$ classes is found by dividing the sum of squares for the $k$ classes by the appropriate number of degrees of freedom, $(k - 1)$. The mean square of the $r$ classes is derived by dividing the $r$ classes sum of squares by $(r - 1)$, and, finally, the interaction (residual) square is calculated by dividing the interaction (residual) sum of squares by $(r - 1)(k - 1)$ degrees of freedom. Expressed in algebraic terms the three estimates (mean squares) of the common population variance ($\sigma^2$) are:

From $k$ classes (columns):

$$S_k^2 = \frac{r \sum (\bar{X}_j - \bar{X})^2}{k - 1},$$

From $r$ classes (rows):

$$S_r^2 = \frac{k \sum (\bar{X}_g - \bar{X})^2}{r - 1}, \quad \text{and}$$

From the interaction (residual) between the $k$ and $r$ classes:

$$S_I^2 = \frac{\sum\sum (X_{jg} - \bar{X}_j - \bar{X}_g + \bar{X})^2}{(r - 1)(k - 1)}$$

where $S_k^2$, $S_r^2$, and $S_I^2$ denote an estimate of the population variance ($\sigma^2$) from the indicated sources (e.g., rows, columns) and all other symbols are as previously defined in our earlier discussions.

A better estimate of the population variance is obtained from two variables of classification, if the measurements, or observations, are repeated under similar conditions. If this procedure is followed in the process of conducting an experiment, the experiment is said to have been *replicated*, or repeated. Replications of the "design" makes possible a more complete analysis of the data than otherwise would be possible, and provides four unbiased estimates (mean squares) of the *experimental error* ($\sigma^2$) of the common population: (a) the $k$ (columns) classes mean square; (b) the $r$ (rows) classes mean square; (c) the interaction mean square; and (d) the within cells mean square.* Expressed in algebraic terms the four estimates (mean squares) of the common population variance ($\sigma^2$) are:

From $k$ classes (columns):

$$S_k^2 = \frac{r\sum(\overline{X}_j - \overline{X})^2}{k-1}$$

From $r$ classes (rows):

$$S_r^2 = \frac{k\sum(\overline{X}_g - \overline{X})^2}{r-1}$$

From interaction between $k$ and $r$ classes:

$$S_I^2 = \frac{\sum\sum(\overline{X}_{jg} - \overline{X}_j - \overline{X}_g + \overline{X})^2}{(r-1)(k-1)}, \quad \text{and}$$

From within cells:

$$S_w^2 = \frac{\sum\sum\sum(X_{ijg} - \overline{X}_{jg})^2}{kr(c-1)}$$

where $c$ denotes the *equal* number of observations in each cell of the table, $S_w^2$ denotes an estimate of the population variance ($\sigma^2$) from the indicated source, and all other symbols are as previously defined.

The rationale of the analysis of variance test of class means associated with a two-way classification schema is based on the assumption that the observations form a random sample drawn from a homogeneous normal population; and that these values are arranged in the two-way table on a purely arbitrary basis. If this assumption holds, then the estimated variances or mean squares (three in the case of one entry per cell, and four in the other case) will tend to vary from one another only because of fluctuations due to random selection; hence values of ratios ($F$-ratios) established to compare mean squares with one another are not expected to vary too far from unity. Put in another way, no *significant* test is expected if one mean square (estimate of common population variance, $\sigma^2$) is compared (by the operation of division) with another. If one or both of the

---

* The mean squares referred to here are derived from an equal number of replications in each cell of the table. The analysis would be modified for an unequal number of replications. For discussion of the latter point, consult Johnson (104) and/or Cochran and Cox (38).

two variables of classification, however, are sources of variation in the values, then one or both of the estimated variances derived from the category (variable of classification) class means will be higher than it otherwise would be. Under these conditions a *significant* value of the ratio (test) may be obtained when *each* of the between classes estimates (mean square of $k$ classes and mean square of $r$ classes) is compared with either that obtained from the interaction, or that obtained from the variance estimate (mean square) within cells. Which "measuring stick" to employ, i.e., the interaction mean square, or the within cells mean square, is discussed later.

As a limited illustration of our discussion, consider Table XVIII, which is a variance table for the data of Table XVII. It should be noted at this point that Table XVII depicts a two-way classification *single observation per cell* factorial design, where it is assumed that observations have been drawn at random from an approximately normal (homogeneous) population, and the rows and columns of the table are purely arbitrary arrangements of the values selected.

The three mean squares, shown in the fourth column of Table XVIII represent three independent estimates of the population variance, $\sigma^2$. In order to test the hypotheses concerning significant difference between the $k$ column class means and the $r$ row class means, we test whether the mean squares are significantly different or whether they could represent random fluctuations due to sampling. The latter condition is anticipated because of the basic assumption of random selection and arbitrary arrangement of the observations in the table. In the case of the single variable of classification analysis of variance technique, the basis of the $F$-test was the estimate based upon the uncontrolled variance *within classes*. In the two-way classification example under consideration, there is but one value (observation) per cell, and the only measure of random variation is the estimated variance or mean square due to interaction (residual). Since the interaction mean square (.972) is larger than the mean square for the between column means (.223), there is no statistical evidence for rejecting the notion of random fluctuation in favor of the idea of the existence of significant differences between column means. This condition would indicate that the statistical analysis was in harmony with the logical bases upon which the data were selected and tabulated. On the other hand, the interaction mean square (.972) is considerably smaller than the mean square between row means (27.75). The value of the $F$-ratio formed by dividing the mean square between rows (27.75) by the mean square due to interaction (.972) is 28.55, a value considerably larger than the critical value of $F_{.05(2,8)} = 4.46$, which allows us to reject the notion of random fluctuation and accept, with high probability of being correct, the idea of the existence of significant differences between row class means.

If we had employed an example which involved a two-way classification with more than one, but an equal number of observations per cell, we would have had four estimates of the common population variance $\sigma^2$, two of which might well serve as measures of random variation, namely: the mean square due to interaction, and the mean square due to the within cells component. This condition creates the important problem of which estimated variance or mean square should be employed as the "measuring stick" in testing a particular hypothesis as well as the problem of how many and what kinds of hypotheses can be tested in applying the analysis of variance technique to a two-way table of classification of data.

*Mean Square to Use in Testing Hypotheses.*

The problem of selecting the appropriate mean square "measuring stick" is frequently referred to as the "*valid measure of error problem.*" The problem can be adequately covered, for our purposes, by considering three cases.

*Case 1.* Single variable of classification. To test the null hypothesis, $H_0$: $\mu_1 = \mu_2 = \mu_3 = \cdots = \mu_k$; i.e., there is no significant difference between $k$ class means; employ the *mean square* within classes as the denominator of the $F$-ratios involved.

*Case 2.* Multiple (two *or more*) bases (variables) of classification with one observation per cell. The significance of the categories of classification is tested by employing the *highest order interaction mean square*, which is the one involving all of the categories, as the denominator of the $F$-ratios employed.

*Case 3.* Multiple (two or more) bases (variables) of classification with more than one, but an equal number of observations per cell. If we are only interested in testing the *differential* relation between the *main effects* of the variables of classification, the *highest order interaction mean square* is employed as the denominator of the $F$-ratios. If the within cells mean square merely represents the stratification of the population, testing main effects and interactions categories of the variables of classification may be accomplished by employing *either* the *within cells mean square* or the *highest order interaction mean square* as the denominator of the $F$-ratios. Where a choice is possible, it is preferable to use that *mean square which is based upon the larger number of degrees of freedom.*

Cases 1 and 2 have already been illustrated by examples, and will not be discussed further. The data in Table XXI and the accompanying sums of squares can be used to illustrate Case 3.

If we were to apply an outline of the inference process associated with the analysis-of-variance test for two variables of classification with more than one, but an equal number of observations per cell, to the data in Table XXI we would have, expressed in general terms:

1. *Null Hypotheses. Hypothesis 1.* For the $k$ column means, $H_0: \mu_1 = \mu_2 = \cdots = \mu_k$ or in other words, *the $k$ column effects are zero.* The test of this hypothesis is made independent of the row and interaction effects; under the assumption that the observations in the cell formed by the $j$-th column and $g$-th row are random samples from a normal population with a mean (for the cell) defined as: $\mu_{jg} = \mu + k_j + r_g + I_{jg}$, where $\mu$ (the population mean) is the same for all cells, $k_j$ is the same effect for all cells in the $j$-th *column*, $r_g$ is the same effect for all cells in the $g$-th *row*, but $I_{jg}$, the effect due to the interaction of the two effects ($k_j \times r_g = I_{jg}$), may be different for each cell of the table. If the $k$ column effects are zero, and if the $r$ row effects are zero (tested in *Hypothesis 2*), then $\sum I_{jg} = 0$, and we should expect the null hypothesis, $H_0: \mu_1 = \mu_2 = \cdots \mu_k$, to be true.

For the data of Table XXI we would have:

$$H_0 : \mu_1 = \mu_2 = \mu_3$$

*Hypothesis 2.* The null hypothesis for the $r$ row means of the data in Table XXI is: $H_0 : \mu_A = \mu_B$, or in statement form, *the $r$ row effects are zero.* The test of this hypothesis is made independent of the column and interaction effects, under the same assumptions made for testing *Hypothesis 1.*

*Hypothesis 3.* The null hypothesis to be tested in order to determine if the $(j \times g)$ interaction effects are zero for the data in Table XXI is: $H_0 : \mu_{A_1} = \mu_{A_2} = \mu_{A_3} = \mu_{B_1} = \mu_{B_2} = \mu_{B_3}$. The test of this hypothesis is made independent of the $k$ column and $r$ row effects, under the same assumptions made for testing *Hypothesis 1.*

2. *Select the Proper Statistical Test.* Assuming that the variance is the same for each of the normally distributed populations involved, and assuming further that the values appearing in the various cells of Table XXI were randomly and independently selected from the populations which they represent, the $F$-test, in association with the analysis of variance technique, is the most appropriate statistical test to employ.

3. *Specify ($\alpha$) and ($n$).* In order to test the three hypotheses listed under the category of "null hypothesis," the level of significance is set at: $\alpha = .05$ for this sample of $n = 12$ replications (cell entries).

4. *Determine the Sampling Distribution.* Supposing that each of the null hypotheses being tested (*Hypotheses 1, 2, and 3*) is true, the appropriate sampling distribution for testing *Hypothesis 1* is: $F_{.05[k-1, kr(c-1)]}$; or $F_{.05(2,6)}$; for *Hypothesis 2* it becomes: $F_{.05[r-1, kr(c-1)]}$; or $F_{.05(1,6)}$, and, finally, for *Hypothesis 3*: $F_{.05[(k-1)(r-1), kr(c-1)]}$; or $F_{.05(2,6)}$.

5. *The Critical Region.* The critical region for *Hypothesis 1* is: $F > F_{.05(2,6)}$; or $\{F > 5.14\}$; the critical region for *Hypothesis 2* is: $F > F_{.05(1,6)}$; or $\{F > 5.99\}$; and, finally, the critical region for *Hypothesis 3* is: $F > F_{.05(2,6)}$; or $\{F > 5.14\}$.

6. *Compute the Value of the Statistic.* Employing the values of the respective sums of squares of the components of variation involved, we establish the following variance table for the data of Table XXI:

Variance Table for Data of Table XXI

| Source of Variation | df | Sum of Squares | Mean Square | F-ratio | Decision |
|---|---|---|---|---|---|
| Main Effects: | | | | | |
| Column means | 2 | 8 | 4 | $\frac{4}{.5} = 8$ | Reject $H_0$ of Hypothesis 2 |
| Row means | 1 | 108 | 108 | $\frac{108}{.5} = 216$ | Reject $H_0$ of Hypothesis 1 |
| Interaction | 2 | 24 | 12 | $\frac{12}{.5} = 24$ | Reject $H_0$ of Hypothesis 3 |
| Within cells | 6 | 3 | .5 | | — |
| Total | 11 | 143 | | | |

7. *Decision.* According to the results shown in the "Decision" column of the variance table in Step 6, all of the null hypotheses are rejected in favor of their respective "alternative" hypotheses; and thus it can be inferred that there is a significant difference between the $k$ class means and the $r$ class means, and that the $j \times g$ interaction effects are significant. It should be noted here that a test for homogeneity of variance (e.g., Bartlett's Test) has not been conducted, and before a definite decision could be made about the results of the analysis, it would be necessary to conduct such a test. In order to preserve the continuity of our discussion of analysis of variance for multiple bases of comparison, we shall not attempt to demonstrate the test of homogeneity of variance here, but instead refer the reader to Edwards.[1]

The variance table in step 6 shows a "partitioning" of the total sum of squares into four segments: (1) the sum of squares of column means, which measures the variability from one column to another; (2) the analogous sum of squares for row means; (3) the interaction sum of squares, a measure of the lack of additivity of column and row effects; and, (4) the "within-cells" sum of squares, which measures the variances of the six populations, one per each cell of the table. In our example, we used the "within-cells" mean square as the "measuring stick" of variability. This component of variability is used as a measuring stick when the researcher is interested not only in the main effects (differences in column means averaged over all rows, and differences in row means averaged over all columns), but in whether the combination of row and column effects (interaction), produces a significantly large result.

If the research problem is not concerned with the significance of the "interaction" component, a combination of the "interaction" and "within-cells" components may improve the estimate of the common population variance, $\sigma^2$. To combine these two components of variation, we add the "interaction" sum of squares to that of the "within-cells" to get a "residual" sum of squares. The appropriate number of degrees of freedom for the "residual" component is found by adding the respective degrees of freedom for the "interaction" and "within-cells" components together. The "residual" mean square is found by dividing the "residual" sum of squares by the appropriate (residual) number of degrees of freedom. The "residual" mean square is then used as the denominator of the $F$-ratio in testing for column and row main effects.

If the researcher were testing for main effects only, the analysis of variance table in Step 6 would be modified as follows:

Modified Variance Table of Step 6

| Source of Variation | df | Sum of Squares | Mean Square | F-ratio | Decision |
|---|---|---|---|---|---|
| Main Effects | | | | | |
| Column means | 2 | 8 | 4 | $\frac{4}{3.375} \approx 1.18$ | Do not reject $H_0$ of Hypothesis 1 |
| Row means | 1 | 108 | 108 | $\frac{108}{3.375} = 32$ | Reject $H_0$ of Hypothesis 2 |
| Residual | 8 | 27 | 3.375 | | |
| Total | 11 | 143 | | | |

To test for column means effects, we compare the observed $F \approx 1.18$ with the critical value of: $F_{.05(2.8)} = 4.46$. This comparison shows the observed value of $F \approx 1.18$ is not significant, and that the null hypothesis ($H_0$) of *Hypothesis 1* cannot be rejected. The observed, $F = 32$, for the test of row means effects, is greater than the critical value of: $F_{.05(1.8)} = 5.32$, and is therefore significant. In view of this fact, the null hypothesis ($H_0$) of *Hypothesis 2* is rejected in favor of the "alternative" ($H_1$) which indicates that there is a significant difference between the row class means.

To this point we have restricted our discussion of multiple bases of classification to factorial designs involving only two variables of classification. If the factorial design is applied to an experiment, it is possible to design a factorial experiment having an equal number of observations (replications) for every combination of categories included in the variables of classification. Thus, for a two variable experiment, in which each variable has been classified into two categories, we would design a 2 × 2 factorial experiment. Similarly, if we had a three variable experiment, and the first variable was divided into two categories, and the second into three categories, and the third into four categories, we could establish a 2 × 3 × 4 factorial experiment. The analysis of variance technique applied to such a design, would be one constructed for analyzing multiple bases of comparison [in this case three bases (variables) of classification]. If we wished to extend the number of variables under consideration to, say, five, we might have a 2 × 2 × 3 × 4 × 4 factorial experiment where the numbers (2 × 2 × 3 × 4 × 4) denote the number of categories (levels) included in each variable. The analysis of variance technique could be applied to this design, and could be used to test "main effects" and "interactions," or be modified to test "main effects" only. Employing this terminology, we shall now present an example of a 2 × 3 × 5 factorial experiment (three variables, the first having two categories, the second having three categories, and the third having five categories), in order to illustrate a further application of the analysis of variance technique.

### A 2 × 3 × 5 Factorial Experiment

The analysis of variance, multiple bases of classification, technique is modified as it is applied to the investigation of factors (variables) that include several levels (categories). In this example, methods for the direct calculation of any interaction, regardless of the number of variables or the number of categories included in the variables involved in the interaction, will be discussed. From the discussion and description of this example, it should be possible for the reader to generalize to any particular factorial experiment that might occur in connection with models of experimental research in education.

Assume that an experiment in the instruction of mathematics involving three factors (variables) has been conducted. Suppose one factor under investigation is that of "method," another is that of "intelligence," and the third is that of "sex." Suppose further that the "method" factor has *five* levels, "intelligence" has *three* levels, and "sex," naturally, has *two* levels. Under these circumstances the experiment would have involved $(5)(3)(2) = 30$ different treatments. If a *randomized groups* design is used, where each cell (treatment combination) of the table has the same number of observations, and, say, $n = 3$ observations have been included in each treatment (cell), we would then have a total of $(30)(3) = 90$ observations in the whole table. The total sum of squares, which would have 89 degrees of freedom associated with it, could be partitioned into the following components:

| *Component* | *Degrees of Freedom* |
|---|---|
| Error (within cells) | |
| (30) (2) | 60 |
| Second order interaction | |
| (3 Factors: methods × intelligence × sex) | 8 |
| (4)        (2)        (1) | |
| First order interactions | |
| (2 Factors: methods × intelligence) | 8 |
| (4)        (2) | |
| (2 Factors: methods × sex) | 4 |
| (4)        (1) | |
| (2 Factors: intelligence × sex) | 2 |
| (2)        (1) | |
| Main effects | |
| (Methods) | 4 |
| (4) | |
| (Intelligence) | 2 |
| (2) | |
| (Sex) | 1 |
| (1) | |
| Total | 89 |

With this background, suppose that the fictitious data of Table XXII are standardized test score results of the random sample of students who could meet the "requirements" of the treatment combinations (cells) of the "grid." For example, the scores of 9, 7, 5 in the cell in the upper left-hand corner of the table were selected at random from the set of scores produced by *boys* who were rated *high in intelligence* and had been taught by Method I. The scores and their accompanying "squares" shown in parentheses have been confined to small values so that computational procedures would be minimized and interfere as little as possible with the discussion pertaining to the direct calculation of any interaction, regardless of the number of variables or the number of categories included in the variables involved in the interaction.

The variable of "intelligence" has been divided arbitrarily by the experimenter into three categories: H—high; A—average; L—low;

Table XXII
A $2 \times 3 \times 5$ Factorial Design Experiment in Mathematics Instruction—$n = 3$
Observations Per Cell
(Fictitious Data)

| Intelligence | H | | A | | L | | |
|---|---|---|---|---|---|---|---|
| Sex | M | F | M | F | M | F | |
| Score | $X$ $X^2$ | $X$ $X^2$ | $X$ $X^2$ | $X$ $X^2$ | $X$ $X^2$ | $X$ $X^2$ | Total |
| Method | | | | | | | |
| I | 9 (81) | 6 (36) | 5 (25) | 6 (36) | 6 (36) | 1 (1) | 33 (215) |
| | 7 (49) | 9 (81) | 4 (16) | 6 (36) | 3 (9) | 1 (1) | 30 (192) |
| | 5 (25) | 8 (64) | 5 (25) | 5 (25) | 1 (1) | 2 (4) | 26 (144) |
| II | 6 (36) | 5 (25) | 3 (9) | 5 (25) | 2 (4) | 0 (0) | 21 (99) |
| | 4 (16) | 3 (9) | 4 (16) | 6 (36) | 1 (1) | 0 (0) | 18 (78) |
| | 7 (49) | 4 (16) | 1 (1) | 2 (4) | 0 (0) | 1 (1) | 15 (71) |
| III | 9 (81) | 8 (64) | 7 (49) | 8 (64) | 5 (25) | 6 (36) | 43 (319) |
| | 9 (81) | 9 (81) | 7 (49) | 6 (36) | 5 (25) | 4 (16) | 40 (288) |
| | 8 (64) | 8 (64) | 6 (36) | 6 (36) | 4 (16) | 5 (25) | 37 (241) |
| IV | 9 (81) | 5 (25) | 6 (36) | 5 (25) | 4 (16) | 5 (25) | 34 (208) |
| | 6 (36) | 5 (25) | 5 (25) | 5 (25) | 5 (25) | 6 (36) | 32 (172) |
| | 4 (16) | 8 (64) | 6 (36) | 6 (36) | 4 (16) | 4 (16) | 32 (184) |
| V | 9 (81) | 8 (64) | 7 (49) | 8 (64) | 3 (9) | 4 (16) | 39 (283) |
| | 9 (81) | 8 (64) | 6 (36) | 5 (25) | 4 (16) | 0 (0) | 32 (222) |
| | 9 (81) | 9 (81) | 4 (16) | 6 (36) | 0 (0) | 5 (25) | 33 (239) |
| Total | 110 (858) | 103 (763) | 76 (424) | 85 (509) | 47 (199) | 44 (202) | |

$$\sum_m \sum_i \sum_s \sum_n X = 465$$
$$\sum_m \sum_i \sum_s \sum_n X^2 = 2955$$

the variable of "sex" into two categories: M—male; and F—female; and since five methods of instruction were involved in the experiment, the variable of "methods" is partitioned into five categories, I–V, and, finally, each cell contains $n = 3$ standardized test scores $X$. The standardized test score for each individual included in the table is symbolized as: $X_{misn}$, and the total sum of these scores (omitting the subscript on $X$) is: $\sum_m \sum_i \sum_s \sum_n X$, where $\sum_m$ indicates that the scores should be summed over the five *methods*; $\sum_i$ indicates summation of scores over the three categories of intelligence; $\sum_s$ denotes summation over the two categories of sex; and $\sum_n$ indicates summation of the $n = 3$ entries in each cell of the table. Similarly, the symbolization $\sum_m \sum_i \sum_s \sum_n X^2$ denotes the total sum of "squared" scores in the table.

## CALCULATION OF SUMS OF SQUARES

### Total Sum of Squares

The analysis of the sums of squares is conducted as illustrated in previous examples. We first find the *total sum of squares*. The total sum of squares for this example is:

$$\text{Total} = \sum_m \sum_i \sum_s \sum_n X^2 - \frac{(\sum \sum \sum \sum X)^2}{90}$$

or in arithmetic form:

$$\text{Total} = (9)^2 + (7)^2 + (5)^2 + (6)^2 + (4)^2 + \cdots + (4)^2 + (0)^2 + (5)^2$$

$$-\frac{(465)^2}{90} = 2955 - 2402.5 = 552.50$$

This method of calculating the total sum of squares can be applied to any table, regardless of the number of variables (factors) or the number of categories (levels) included in them. Thus, for a four variable (factor) factorial experiment with an equal number of $n$ entries in each cell, the general formula for the total sum of squares would be:

$$\sum_a \sum_b \sum_c \sum_d \sum_n X^2 - \frac{(\sum_a \sum_b \sum_c \sum_d \sum_n X)^2}{N_{abcdn}}$$

where $\sum_a, \sum_b, \sum_c, \sum_d$, denote summation over variable (factor) $a$, $b$, $c$, and $d$, respectively; $\sum_n$ denotes summation of the equal number of $n$ observations of $X$ in each cell of the table; and $N_{abcdn}$ denotes the total number of observations in the table. For a five variable (factor) factorial experiment, the formula would become:

$$\sum_a \sum_b \sum_c \sum_d \sum_e \sum_n X^2 - \frac{(\sum_a \sum_b \sum_c \sum_d \sum_e \sum_n X)^2}{N_{abcden}};$$

and for an $r$ variable (factor) experiment the formula would become:

$$\sum_a \sum_b \sum_c \sum_d \sum_e \cdots \sum_{r-1} \sum_r \sum_n X^2 - \frac{(\sum_a \sum_b \sum_c \sum_d \sum_e \cdots \sum_{r-1} \sum_r \sum_n X)^2}{N_{abcde...(r-1)rn}}.$$

*Error (Within Cells) Sum of Squares*

The error (within cells) component sum of squares can be calculated in either one of two ways. One possibility is that of calculating the total sum of squares and the sum of squares between treatments and then obtaining the sum of squares within cells (error) by subtraction. The other possibility, and the one recommended for purposes of "cross-checking" various values and computational procedures of the total process, is that of calculating the sum of squares within each cell (treatment group) separately and then summing these sums of squares to find the error (within cells) sum of squares. Following the "direct" method of calculation, the formula,

$$\sum_n X_{misn}^2 - \frac{(\sum X_{misn})^2}{n}$$

where $X_{misn}$ indicates an individual's score in a given cell, and $n$ denotes the equal number of observations in each cell of the table, is applied to each cell of the table to produce the error (within cells) component sum of squares. Although the method illustrated here applies to a three-factor (variable) analysis with $n = 3$ entries in each cell, *the procedure is general and can be applied to obtain the "error" component for a table constructed on the basis of any number of variables (factors), each of which can be partitioned into any number of categories (levels), and where each cell of the table includes the same number of n entries.*

For this example, the error (within cells) sum of squares is found to be:

(1) $\sum_n X_{IMH}^2 - \dfrac{(\sum X_{IMH})^2}{3} = 9^2 + 7^2 + 5^2 - \dfrac{(21)^2}{3} = 155 - 147 \quad = 8.00$

(2) $\sum_n X_{IIMH}^2 - \dfrac{(\sum X_{IIMH})^2}{3} = 6^2 + 4^2 + 7^2 - \dfrac{(17)^2}{3} = 101 - \quad 96.33 = 4.67$

(3) $\sum_n X_{IIIMH}^2 - \dfrac{(\sum X_{IIIMH})^2}{3} = 9^2 + 9^2 + 8^2 - \dfrac{(26)^2}{3} = 226 - 225.33 = .67$

(4) $\sum_n X_{IVMH}^2 - \dfrac{(\sum X_{IVMH})^2}{3} = 9^2 + 6^2 + 4^2 - \dfrac{(19)^2}{3} = 133 - 120.33 = 12.67$

(5) $\sum_n X_{VMH}^2 - \dfrac{(\sum X_{VMH})^2}{3} = 9^2 + 9^2 + 9^2 - \dfrac{(27)^2}{3} = 243 - 243 \quad = .00$

(6) $\sum_n X_{IFH}^2 - \dfrac{(\sum X_{IFH})^2}{3} = 6^2 + 9^2 + 8^2 - \dfrac{(23)^2}{3} = 181 - 176.33 = 4.67$

(7) $\sum_n X_{IIFH}^2 - \dfrac{(\sum X_{IIFH})^2}{3} = 5^2 + 3^2 + 4^2 - \dfrac{(12)^2}{3} = \quad 50 - 48 \quad = 2.00$

$\vdots \qquad\qquad \vdots \qquad\qquad \vdots \qquad\qquad \vdots \qquad \vdots \qquad \vdots \quad \vdots$

(26) $\sum_n X_{ILF}^2 - \dfrac{(\sum X_{ILF})^2}{3} = 1^2 + 1^2 + 2^2 - \dfrac{(4)^2}{3} = \quad 6 - \quad 5.33 = .67$

(27) $\sum_n X_{IILF}^2 - \dfrac{(\sum X_{IILF})^2}{3} = 0^2 + 0^2 + 1^2 - \dfrac{(1)^2}{3} = \quad 1 - \quad .33 = .67$

(28) $\sum_n X_{IIILF}^2 - \dfrac{(\sum X_{IIILF})^2}{3} = 6^2 + 4^2 + 5^2 - \dfrac{(15)^2}{3} = \quad 77 - 75 \quad = 2.00$

(29) $\sum_n X_{IVLF}^2 - \dfrac{(\sum X_{IVLF})^2}{3} = 5^2 + 6^2 + 4^2 - \dfrac{(15)^2}{3} = \quad 77 - 75 \quad = 2.00$

(30) $\sum_n X_{VLF}^2 - \dfrac{(\sum X_{VLF})^2}{3} = 4^2 + 0^2 + 5^2 - \dfrac{(9)^2}{3} = \quad 41 - 27 \quad = 14.00$

---

Total: $\displaystyle\sum_m\sum_i\sum_s\sum_n X^2 - \dfrac{\sum_m\sum_i\sum_s\left[\sum_{n=3} X\right]^2}{3}$ ; (within cells) sum of squares—

$$2955 - \dfrac{8527}{3} = 112.67$$

The "direct" method of calculating the error component of the sum of squares may be shortened considerably by merely evaluating the "total" summations appearing at the end of the table. The individual cell computation approach was presented here for the purpose of explanation only; in practice, as we shall see later, the "total" summation formula is employed extensively.

*Interactions Sums of Squares*

In a three-factor (variable) experiment, as illustrated in our example, it is necessary to calculate a second-order interaction (one involving three factors), and three first-order interactions (each one involving two factors). If a four-factor (variable) experiment was to be analyzed, it would be necessary to calculate a third-order interaction (composed of four factors), four second-order interactions (each one involving three factors), and six first-order interactions (two factors in each). In similar fashion, the analysis of a five factor experiment would involve a fourth-order interaction composed of the five factors, five third-order interactions, ten second-order interactions, and ten first-order interactions. For the analysis of an experiment of, say, $r$ factors, there would be one $(r - 1)$ order interaction, $r$ interactions of the $(r - 2)$ order, $r(r - 1)/2$ interactions of $(r - 3)$ order, $r(r - 1)(r - 2)/6$ interactions of the $(r - 4)$ order, $r(r - 1)(r - 2)(r - 3)/24$ interactions of the $(r - 5)$ order, and so on to the point of $r(r - 1)(r - 2)(r - 3)/24$ third-order interactions, $r(r - 1)(r - 2)/6$ second-order interactions, and, finally, $r(r - 1)/2$ first-order interactions.

The procedure for calculating directly the sum of squares for a second-order interaction (three factors) *is perfectly general and can be applied to obtain an interaction of any order.* Regardless of the number of variables (factors) and the number of categories (levels) included in them, the procedure to be illustrated here can be applied to find all the interactions of different order sums of squares which might occur in any given analysis.

The initial phase of the procedure for finding the values of sums of squares for interactions of various orders deals with the establishment of a set of tables derived by first summing the scores in the original table over the levels (categories) of one of the variables, then over the levels of two of the variables, and so on until tables for each of the variables involved are derived. Since a second-order (or greater, depending upon the number of variables involved) interaction sum of squares may be found from many different "summed" tables, it pays the researcher to examine the data to determine that set of tables which will require the least effort in terms of calculations to be made.

Applying the first phase of the procedure to our example, we would have the following set of tables established:

## Table XXII(S)
### Tables for the Calculation of the Interactions Sums of Squares
#### Table (1)—$\sum\limits_{n} X$ and $(\sum\limits_{n} X)^2$

| Intelligence | H | | A | | L | | Total |
|---|---|---|---|---|---|---|---|
| Sex | M | F | M | F | M | F | |
| Score | $\sum\limits_{n} X\ (\sum\limits_{n} X)^2$ | $\sum\limits_{n} X\ (\sum\limits_{n} X)^2$ | $\sum\limits_{n} X\ (\sum\limits_{n} X)^2$ | $\sum\limits_{n} X\ (\sum\limits_{n} X)^2$ | $\sum\limits_{n} X\ (\sum\limits_{n} X)^2$ | $\sum\limits_{n} X\ (\sum\limits_{n} X)^2$ | |
| Method | | | | | | | |
| I | 21 (441) | 23 (529) | 14 (196) | 17 (289) | 10 (100) | 4 (16) | 89 (1571) |
| II | 17 (289) | 12 (144) | 8 (64) | 13 (169) | 3 (9) | 1 (1) | 54 (676) |
| III | 26 (676) | 25 (625) | 20 (400) | 20 (400) | 14 (196) | 15 (225) | 120 (2522) |
| IV | 19 (361) | 18 (324) | 17 (289) | 16 (256) | 13 (169) | 15 (225) | 98 (1624) |
| V | 27 (729) | 25 (625) | 17 (289) | 19 (361) | 7 (49) | 9 (81) | 104 (2134) |
| Total | 110 (2496) | 103 (2247) | 76 (1238) | 85 (1475) | 47 (523) | 44 (548) | $\sum\limits_{m}\sum\limits_{i}\sum\limits_{s}[\sum\limits_{n} X]$ $= 465$ $\sum\limits_{m}\sum\limits_{i}\sum\limits_{s}[\sum\limits_{n} X]^2$ $= 8527$ |

#### Table (2)—$\sum\limits_{m}\sum\limits_{n} X$ and $(\sum\limits_{m}\sum\limits_{n} X)^2$

| Intelligence | H | | A | | L | | Total |
|---|---|---|---|---|---|---|---|
| Sex | M | F | M | F | M | F | |
| Score | $\sum\limits_{m}\sum\limits_{n} X (\sum\limits_{m}\sum\limits_{n} X)^2$ | $\sum\limits_{m}\sum\limits_{n} X (\sum\limits_{m}\sum\limits_{n} X)^2$ | $\sum\limits_{m}\sum\limits_{n} X (\sum\limits_{m}\sum\limits_{n} X)^2$ | $\sum\limits_{m}\sum\limits_{n} X (\sum\limits_{m}\sum\limits_{n} X)^2$ | $\sum\limits_{m}\sum\limits_{n} X (\sum\limits_{m}\sum\limits_{n} X)^2$ | $\sum\limits_{m}\sum\limits_{n} X (\sum\limits_{m}\sum\limits_{n} X)^2$ | |
| Total | 110 (12,100) | 103 (10,609) | 76 (5776) | 85 (7225) | 47 (2209) | 44 (1936) | $\sum\limits_{i}\sum\limits_{s}[\sum\limits_{m}\sum\limits_{n} X]$ $= 465$ $\sum\limits_{i}\sum\limits_{s}[\sum\limits_{m}\sum\limits_{n} X]^2$ $= 39,855$ |

#### Table (3)—$\sum\limits_{s}\sum\limits_{n} X$ and $(\sum\limits_{s}\sum\limits_{n} X)^2$

| Intelligence | H | | A | | L | | |
|---|---|---|---|---|---|---|---|
| Score | $\sum\limits_{s}\sum\limits_{n} X$ | $(\sum\limits_{s}\sum\limits_{n} X)^2$ | $\sum\limits_{s}\sum\limits_{n} X$ | $(\sum\limits_{s}\sum\limits_{n} X)^2$ | $\sum\limits_{s}\sum\limits_{n} X$ | $(\sum\limits_{s}\sum\limits_{n} X)^2$ | Total |
| Method | | | | | | | |
| I | 44 | (1936) | 31 | (961) | 14 | (196) | 89 (3093) |
| II | 29 | (841) | 21 | (441) | 4 | (16) | 54 (1298) |
| III | 51 | (2601) | 40 | (1600) | 29 | (841) | 120 (5042) |
| IV | 37 | (1369) | 33 | (1089) | 28 | (784) | 98 (3242) |
| V | 52 | (2704) | 36 | (1296) | 16 | (256) | 104 (4256) |
| Total | 213 | (9451) | 161 | (5387) | 91 | (2093) | $\sum\limits_{m}\sum\limits_{i}[\sum\limits_{s}\sum\limits_{n} X]$ $= 465$ $\sum\limits_{m}\sum\limits_{i}[\sum\limits_{s}\sum\limits_{n} X]^2$ $= 16,931$ |

Table (4)—$\sum_i\sum_n X$ and $(\sum_i\sum_n X)^2$

| Sex | M | | F | | |
|---|---|---|---|---|---|
| Score | $\sum_i\sum_n X$ | $(\sum_i\sum_n X)^2$ | $\sum_i\sum_n X$ | $(\sum_i\sum_n X)^2$ | Total |
| **Method** | | | | | |
| I | 45 | (2025) | 44 | (1936) | 89 (3961) |
| II | 28 | (784) | 26 | (676) | 54 (1460) |
| III | 60 | (3600) | 60 | (3600) | 120 (7200) |
| IV | 49 | (2401) | 49 | (2401) | 98 (4802) |
| V | 51 | (2601) | 53 | (2809) | 104 (5410) |
| Total | 233 | (11,411) | 232 | (11,422) | $\sum_m\sum_s\lvert\sum_i\sum_n X\rvert = 465$ $\sum_m\sum_s\lvert\sum_i\sum_n X\rvert^2 = 22{,}833$ |

Table (5)—$\sum_m\sum_i\sum_n X$ and $(\sum_m\sum_i\sum_n X)^2$

| Sex | M | | F | | |
|---|---|---|---|---|---|
| Score | $\sum_m\sum_i\sum_n X$ | $(\sum_m\sum_i\sum_n X)^2$ | $\sum_m\sum_i\sum_n X$ | $(\sum_m\sum_i\sum_n X)^2$ | Total |
| Total | 233 | (54,289) | 232 | (53,824) | $\sum_s[\sum_m\sum_i\sum_n X] = 465$ $\sum_s[\sum_m\sum_i\sum_n X]^2 = 108{,}113$ |

Table (6)—$\sum_s\sum_i\sum_n X$ and $(\sum_s\sum_i\sum_n X)^2$

| Method | I | II | III | IV | V | Total |
|---|---|---|---|---|---|---|
| Score | $\sum_s\sum_i\sum_n X(\sum_s\sum_i\sum_n X)^2$ | $\sum_s\sum_i\sum_n X(\sum_s\sum_i\sum_n X)^2$ | $\sum_s\sum_i\sum_n X(\sum_s\sum_i\sum_n X)^2$ | $\sum_s\sum_i\sum_n X(\sum_s\sum_i\sum_n X)^2$ | $\sum_s\sum_i\sum_n X(\sum_s\sum_i\sum_n X)^2$ | Total |
| Total | 89 (7921) | 54 (2916) | 120 (14,400) | 98 (9604) | 104 (10,816) | $\sum_m[\sum_s\sum_i\sum_n X] = 465$ $\sum_m[\sum_s\sum_i\sum_n X]^2 = 45{,}657$ |

Table (7)—$\sum_m\sum_s\sum_n X$ and $(\sum_m\sum_s\sum_n X)^2$

| Intelligence | H | | A | | L | | Total |
|---|---|---|---|---|---|---|---|
| Score | $\sum_m\sum_s\sum_n X$ | $(\sum_m\sum_s\sum_n X)^2$ | $\sum_m\sum_s\sum_n X$ | $(\sum_m\sum_s\sum_n X)^2$ | $\sum_m\sum_s\sum_n X$ | $(\sum_m\sum_s\sum_n X)^2$ | Total |
| Total | 213 | (45,369) | 161 | (25,921) | 91 | (8281) | $\sum_i[\sum_m\sum_s\sum_n X] = 465$ $\sum_i[\sum_m\sum_s\sum_n X]^2 = 79{,}571$ |

In Table XXII, $\sum_m \sum_i \sum_s \sum_n X = 465$. As a form of "check," the total of the observations in each of the seven "working" tables was found to be 465. The values of interest to the computation of interaction components, however, are the total sums of "squared" scores found in each table. We shall now consider the equations for deriving values of the sums of squares associated with the different orders of interaction which might occur in any given analysis.

The equations for finding the values of the components of sums of squares associated with different orders of interaction result from certain algebraic manipulations, and can be proved by methods employed by Edwards.[2] It is not necessary for the reader to know the algebraic manipulations or their associated proofs to derive the equations that will produce the values of the components of sums of squares associated with any given order of interaction which may be under consideration. A mechanical procedure may be employed to produce the desired equation. The mechanical approach will now be presented by applying it to our example with accompanying explanatory remarks.

In order to find the value of the component of sums of squares associated with the second-order interaction composed of the three factors (variables), methods × intelligence × sex, we must evaluate the following summations equation:

$$\frac{\sum_m \sum_i \sum_s (\sum_n X)^2}{3} - \left( \frac{\sum_m \sum_s (\sum_i \sum_n X)^2}{9} + \frac{\sum_m \sum_i (\sum_s \sum_n X)^2}{6} + \frac{\sum_i \sum_s (\sum_m \sum_n X)^2}{15} \right)$$

$$+ \left( \frac{\sum_m (\sum_s \sum_i \sum_n X)^2}{18} + \frac{\sum_i (\sum_m \sum_s \sum_n X)^2}{30} + \frac{\sum_s (\sum_m \sum_i \sum_n X)^2}{45} \right) - \frac{(\sum_m \sum_i \sum_s \sum_n X)^2}{90} \quad (1)$$

Substituting the appropriate values from the seven "working" tables, we would have:

$$\frac{8527}{3} - \left( \frac{22{,}833}{9} + \frac{16{,}931}{6} + \frac{39{,}855}{15} \right) + \left( \frac{45{,}657}{18} + \frac{79{,}571}{30} + \frac{108{,}113}{45} \right)$$

$$- \frac{(465)^2}{90}$$

or:

$$2842.33 - (2537 + 2821.83 + 2657) + (2536.5 + 2652.37 + 2402.51)$$

$$- 240.5 = 15.38$$

Thus, the value of the component of the sums of squares associated with the second-order interaction formed by the three variables, method × intelligence × sex, is 15.38.

The summations (sum of squares) equation (1), which produces the appropriate value for the sum of squares component associated with the second-order interaction effect of the combination of, methods × intelligence × sex, may be derived mechanically as follows:

1. The first term of equation (1) is the summation over the three factors of the second-order interaction, namely, methods, intelligence, and sex. Symbolically, the summation is shown as: $\sum\sum\sum\limits_{m\ i\ s}$. The measurement, or observation, to be summed is that of the square of the summation over the $n$ entries* in each cell of the table, namely, $[\sum\limits_{n}X]^2$. Hence, in symbolic form, the first term of equation (1) becomes:

$$\frac{\sum\sum\sum\limits_{m\ i\ s\ n}[\sum X]^2}{3}$$

where division by 3 is necessitated because in our example there are $n = 3$ entries in each cell of Table XXII. The value for the numerator of the fraction, $\sum\sum\sum\limits_{m\ i\ s\ n}[\sum X]^2$, is read from "working" table (1) of Table XXII(S). Thus, evaluating the first term of equation (1), we have:

$$\frac{\sum\sum\sum\limits_{m\ i\ s\ n}[\sum X]^2}{3} = \frac{8527}{3} = 2842.33$$

2. The second term of equation (1) *is always a polynomial* (an expression containing more than one term), and is *always subtracted from the first term of the equation*. Since there are three different combinations of three different things taken two at a time, the polynomial forming the second term of the summations equation (1) *of a second order interaction will always contain three terms*. In our illustration, the symbolic representations of the sums within the polynomial are: $\sum\sum\limits_{m\ i}$; $\sum\sum\limits_{m\ s}$; and $\sum\sum\limits_{i\ s}$. The measurement to be summed is that of the *square* of the summation over the $n$ entries in each cell *and* the summation of these sums over each category (level) of the variable not appearing in the "external" summation signs. Thus, for the first expression $\sum\sum\limits_{m\ i}$, the squared observation would be $[\sum\limits_{n}\sum X]^2$; for $\sum\sum\limits_{m\ s}$, the squared observation would be $[\sum\limits_{s\ n}\sum X]^2$; and finally, for $\sum\sum\limits_{i\ s}$, the squared observation would be $[\sum\limits_{m\ n}\sum X]^2$.

---

* It should be noted here that the total discussion of Within Cells (Error) components, proof, algebraic manipulation, and mechanical procedures is based upon the fundamental fact that *each cell of the original table* (or grid) includes the same number of entries, $n$. In the present illustration, each cell contains $n = 3$ entries. It should further be pointed out that if in our example employing Table XXII, there had been $n = 1$ entries in each cell of the table instead of $n = 3$ as shown, it would not have been possible to calculate a Within Cells (Error) component of the sums of squares; and the highest ordered interaction, the second order in this illustration, sum of squares would have included *as the first term* of equation (1) the expression: $\sum\sum\sum\limits_{m\ i\ s}X^2$. Another fact of significance associated with the condition of $n = 1$ entry per each cell of the table is that when the "measuring stick" of the variance components is employed (see later discussion of variance tables) under such conditions, it (the measuring stick) must be the highest ordered interaction component of variance. When there are more than $n = 1$ entries in each cell of the table, however, the Within Cells (Error) component of variance is employed as the measuring stick.

Hence, the polynomial forming the second term of equation (1), and which is to be subtracted from the first term, becomes:

$$-\left(\frac{\sum\limits_{m}\sum\limits_{i}[\sum\limits_{s}\sum\limits_{n}X]^2}{6}+\frac{\sum\limits_{m}\sum\limits_{s}[\sum\limits_{i}\sum\limits_{n}X]^2}{9}+\frac{\sum\limits_{i}\sum\limits_{s}[\sum\limits_{m}\sum\limits_{n}X]^2}{15}\right)$$

where the 6 dividing the first term is derived from the product formed by multiplying the two categories of sex by the three entries in each cell of the table ($s \times n = 2 \times 3 = 6$); the 9 dividing the second term results from the product formed by multiplying the three categories of intelligence by the three entries in each cell of the table ($i \times n = 3 \times 3 = 9$); and, finally, the 15 dividing the third term results from the product of five categories of methods being multiplied by three entries in each cell of the table ($m \times n = 5 \times 3 = 15$). The values of the numerators of the fractions composing the polynomial are read from working tables (2), (3), and (4) of Table XXII(S), and the value of each term in the polynomial is found to be:

$$\frac{\sum\limits_{m}\sum\limits_{i}[\sum\limits_{s}\sum\limits_{n}X]^2}{6}=\frac{16,931}{6}=2821.83;$$

$$\frac{\sum\limits_{m}\sum\limits_{s}[\sum\limits_{i}\sum\limits_{n}X]^2}{9}=\frac{22,833}{9}=2537;$$

and

$$\frac{\sum\limits_{i}\sum\limits_{s}[\sum\limits_{m}\sum\limits_{n}X]^2}{15}=\frac{39,855}{15}=2657.$$

3. The third term of equation (1) is always a polynomial, and is always added to the first two terms of the equation. Since there are three different combinations of three different things taken one at a time, the polynomial forming the third term of the summations equation (1) *of a second-order interaction will always contain three terms*. In our illustration, the symbolic representations of the sums within the polynomial are: $\sum\limits_{m}$; $\sum\limits_{i}$; $\sum\limits_{s}$. The measurement to be summed is that of the *square* of the summation over the $n$ entries in each cell, the summation of these sums over each category of *one* of the variables not appearing in the "external" summation sign; and, finally, the summation of these double sums over each category of the *other* variable not appearing in the external summation sign. Thus, for the first expression $\sum\limits_{m}$, the squared observation or measurement would be $[\sum\limits_{i}\sum\limits_{s}\sum\limits_{n}X]^2$; for $\sum\limits_{i}$, the squared observation would be $[\sum\limits_{i}\sum\limits_{s}\sum\limits_{n}X]^2$; and finally, for $\sum\limits_{s}$, the squared observation would be $[\sum\limits_{m}\sum\limits_{s}\sum\limits_{n}X]^2$. Hence, the polynomial forming the second term of equation (1),

and which is to be added to the first two terms of the equation, becomes:

$$+ \left( \frac{\sum\limits_{m}(\sum\limits_{s}\sum\limits_{i}\sum\limits_{n}X)^2}{18} + \frac{\sum\limits_{i}(\sum\limits_{m}\sum\limits_{s}\sum\limits_{n})^2}{30} - \frac{\sum\limits_{s}(\sum\limits_{m}\sum\limits_{i}\sum\limits_{n}X)^2}{45} \right)$$

where the 18 dividing the first term results from: $i \times s \times n = 3 \times 2 \times 3 = 18$ category-entries to be accounted for; the 30 dividing the second term is derived from: $m \times s \times n = 5 \times 2 \times 3 = 30$ category-entries involved; and, finally, the 45 dividing the third term is based upon the product: $m \times i \times n = 5 \times 3 \times 3 = 45$ category-entries of concern.

The values of the numerators of the fractions composing the polynomial are read from working tables (5), (6), and (7) of Table XXII(S), and the value of each term in the polynomial is found to be:

$$\frac{\sum\limits_{m}[\sum\limits_{s}\sum\limits_{i}\sum\limits_{n}X]^2}{18} = \frac{45,657}{18} = 2536.5$$

$$\frac{\sum\limits_{i}[\sum\limits_{m}\sum\limits_{s}\sum\limits_{n}X]^2}{30} = \frac{79,571}{30} = 2652.37$$

$$\frac{\sum\limits_{s}[\sum\limits_{m}\sum\limits_{i}\sum\limits_{n}X]^2}{45} = \frac{108,113}{45} = 2402.51$$

4. The fourth and final term of equation (1) is, like the first term of the expression, a monomial (a single term). Frequently called the "correction term" in discussions of the technique of the analysis of variance, the fourth, and last, term of equation (1) is the observation, or measurement, resulting from the squaring of the total summation of the original scores over the $n$ entries and all categories of the variables (factors) included in Table XXII. In symbolic form the final term becomes: $[\sum\limits_{m}\sum\limits_{i}\sum\limits_{s}\sum\limits_{n}X]^2/90$; where division by 90 is necessitated by the fact that there are 90 category-entries in the total table. The evaluation of the final term is as follows:

$$\frac{[\sum\limits_{m}\sum\limits_{i}\sum\limits_{s}\sum\limits_{n}X]^2}{90} = \frac{(465)^2}{90} = 2402.5$$

In the "summations" equation (1), for a *second-order interaction*, the "correction" (final) term is always subtracted from the *algebraic* sum of the first three terms of the equation.

5. In order to generalize our discussion to interactions of different orders, and at the same time illustrate the application of the suggested mechanical procedures, we shall agree to designate in any "interaction" analysis, the highest order summation process by the letter $A$ (in our example we would have designed $A$ as: $\sum\limits_{m}\sum\limits_{i}\sum\limits_{s}[\sum\limits_{n}X]^2/3$); the next highest summation processes by

a subscripted letter $B$ (in our illustration) we would have assigned:

$$B_1 = \frac{\sum_m \sum_i [\sum_s \sum_n X]^2}{6}$$

$$B_2 = \frac{\sum_m \sum_s [\sum_i \sum_n X]^2}{9}$$

and

$$B_3 = \frac{\sum_i \sum_s [\sum_m \sum_n X]^2}{15}$$

the next highest summation processes by a subscripted letter $C$ (to illustrate, we could have assigned):

$$C_1 = \frac{\sum_m [\sum_s \sum_i \sum_n X]^2}{18}$$

$$C_2 = \frac{\sum_i [\sum_m \sum_s \sum_n X]^2}{30}$$

and

$$C_3 = \frac{\sum_s [\sum_m \sum_i \sum_n X]^2}{45}$$

the next highest summation process by a subscripted letter $D$ (in our illustration of a *second-order interaction* summation (sum of squares) equation, we would have used $D$ as the designator of the final term of the equation, and thus would not have used a subscript, i.e.,

$$D = \frac{[\sum_m \sum_i \sum_s \sum_n X]^2}{90}$$

If a *third or fourth order interaction sum of squares* equation were being written, however, $D$ would have the number of subscripts necessary to carry out the symbolization of the equation, and the next highest summation process by a subscripted letter $E$, and so on, until the total equation for the order of interaction under consideration is completed to its "correction" (final) term.

To illustrate the application of the method described here, equation (1) which reads:

$$\frac{\sum_m \sum_i \sum_s [\sum_n X]^2}{3} - \left( \frac{\sum_m \sum_i [\sum_s \sum_n X]^2}{6} + \frac{\sum_m \sum_s [\sum_i \sum_n X]^2}{9} + \frac{\sum_i \sum_s [\sum_m \sum_n X]^2}{15} \right)$$

$$+ \left( \frac{\sum_m [\sum_s \sum_i \sum_n X]^2}{18} + \frac{\sum_i [\sum_m \sum_s \sum_n X]^2}{30} + \frac{\sum_s [\sum_m \sum_i \sum_n X]^2}{45} \right) - \frac{[\sum_m \sum_i \sum_s \sum_n X]^2}{90}$$

would become:

$$A - (B_1 + B_2 + B_3) + (C_1 + C_2 + C_3) - D \qquad (2)$$

or for further brevity:

$$A - \sum_{i=1}^{3} B_i + \sum_{i=1}^{3} C_i - D \qquad (3)$$

From equations (2) and (3), the pattern of starting with a negative sign after the first term and alternating the algebraic ($+$ and $-$) signs when the letter designators change, becomes somewhat more obvious than it was in equation (1).

6. The method described in the first five steps for calculating the sum of squares for a second-order (three-factor) interaction can be varied to find the value of the three first-order (two-factor) interactions associated with our illustrative example.

The three first-order interactions of our example are: (1) method $\times$ intelligence; (2) method $\times$ sex; and (3) intelligence $\times$ sex. The appropriate sum of squares equation for the first-order interaction of *methods* $\times$ *intelligence* is:

$$B_1 - (C_1 + C_2) + D = \frac{\sum_{m}\sum_{i}[\sum_{s}\sum_{n}X]^2}{6} - \left( \frac{\sum_{m}(\sum_{s}\sum_{i}\sum_{n}X]^2}{18} + \frac{\sum_{i}[\sum_{m}\sum_{s}\sum_{n}X]^2}{30} \right)$$

$$+ \frac{[\sum_{m}\sum_{i}\sum_{s}\sum_{n}X]^2}{90}$$

$$= 2821.83 - (2536.5 + 2652.37) + 2402.5$$

$$= 35.46$$

It should be noted that the mechanical pattern of always subtracting the second term of the equation ($C_1 + C_2$) from the first term ($B_1$), still holds, and that the third term of the equation ($D$) is, according to the mechanical method, added to the first two terms of the equation. In similar fashion, the appropriate sums of squares equation for the first-order interaction of *methods* $\times$ *sex* is found to be:

$$B_2 - (C_1 + C_3) + D = \frac{\sum_{m}\sum_{s}(\sum_{i}\sum_{n}X)^2}{9} - \left( \frac{\sum_{m}(\sum_{s}\sum_{i}\sum_{n}X)^2}{18} + \frac{\sum_{s}(\sum_{m}\sum_{i}\sum_{n}X)^2}{45} \right)$$

$$+ \frac{(\sum_{m}\sum_{i}\sum_{s}\sum_{n}X)^2}{90}$$

$$= 2537 - (2536.5 + 2402.51) + 2402.5$$

$$= .49$$

Although the value of the sum of squares for this interaction is small, there is no reason to believe that an error has been made. The mechanical procedure has been applied for establishing the sum of squares equation for this particular first-order interaction, and the working tables, from which the values of the respective squared summations were taken, "cross-check" in the totals with other related tables. Finally, the sum of squares equation for the third first-order interaction of the two factors of *intelligence* × *sex* is found to be:

$$B_3 - (C_2 + C_3) + D = \frac{\sum_i\sum_s(\sum_m\sum_n X)^2}{15} - \left(\frac{\sum_i(\sum_m\sum_s\sum_n X)^2}{30} + \frac{\sum_s(\sum_m\sum_i\sum_n X)^2}{45}\right)$$

$$+ \frac{(\sum_m\sum_i\sum_s\sum_n X)^2}{90}$$

$$= 2657 - (2652.37 + 2402.51) + 2402.5$$

$$= 4.62$$

The examples presented here show how the mechanical procedure is varied to produce first-order (two-factor) interactions. We shall now consider how the mechanical procedures can be modified to produce values for the *main effects* (zero-order interactions).

7. The sum of squares equations for the three *main effects* (zero-order one-variable interactions) of our illustrative example can also be produced by application of the suggested mechanical method. The three *main effects* (factors) of our example are: (1) methods, (2) intelligence, and (3) sex. The appropriate sum of squares equation for the *methods* variable (factor) is:

$$C_1 - D = \frac{\sum_m[\sum_s\sum_i\sum_n X]^2}{18} - \frac{[\sum_m\sum_i\sum_s\sum_n X]^2}{90} = 2536.5 - 2402.5 = 134.0$$

and the appropriate sum of squares equation for the factor (variable) of *intelligence* is found to be:

$$C_2 - D = \frac{\sum_i[\sum_m\sum_s\sum_n X]^2}{30} - \frac{[\sum_m\sum_i\sum_s\sum_n X]^2}{90} = 2652.37 - 2402.5 = 249.87$$

and, finally, the appropriate sum of squares equation for the factor of *sex* is found to be:

$$C_3 - D = \frac{\sum_s[\sum_m\sum_i\sum_n X]^2}{45} - \frac{[\sum_m\sum_i\sum_s\sum_n X]^2}{90} = 2402.51 - 2402.5 = .01$$

With these values established for the *one second-order* interaction sum of squares, the *three first-order* sums of squares, and the *three main effects* sums of squares, we are ready to develop a variance table and establish tests of significance of the various interactions, and main effects. Before proceeding to this point, however, we present a summary table of the interaction sums of squares equations, for our illustrative example, developed by application of the suggested mechanical method.

Although the mechanical method for calculating the sum of squares inter-action equations, described earlier in seven steps, has been illustrated by application to an example that demanded equations for no more than second-order (three-variable) interactions, by very slight modification the "method" can be employed to calculate sum of squares equations for any order inter-action desired. In order to explicate this point more fully we delay our intended discussion of the variance table, and illustrate as briefly as possible how the mechanical method could be employed to calculate sums of squares for dif-ferent orders of interaction that might occur in problems of educational re-search.

Table XXIII
Summary Table of Interaction Sums of Squares Equations

| Interactions | Designator Equations | Actual Summations |
|---|---|---|
| 1. Methods × intelligence × sex | $A - \sum\limits_{i=1}^{3} B_i + \sum\limits_{i=1}^{3} C_i - D$ | (see page 398) |
| 2. Methods × intelligence | $B_1 - (C_1 + C_2) + D$ | (see page 403) |
| 3. Methods × sex | $B_2 - (C_1 + C_3) + D$ | (see page 403) |
| 4. Intelligence × sex | $B_3 - (C_2 + C_3) + D$ | (see page 404) |
| *Main Effects* | | |
| 5. Methods | $C_1 - D$ | (see page 404) |
| 6. Intelligence | $C_2 - D$ | (see page 404) |
| 7. Sex | $C_3 - D$ | (see page 404) |

Suppose that it were necessary to calculate a sum of squares equation of a *fifth-order* (six factors) *interaction* for a table with an equal number of $n$ entries in each cell of the table. Applying the mechanical method, we would proceed as follows:

1. Let

$$A = \frac{\sum\limits_{a}\sum\limits_{b}\sum\limits_{c}\sum\limits_{d}\sum\limits_{e}\sum\limits_{f}[\sum\limits_{n} X]^2}{n}$$

where $a, b, c, d, e, f$ represent the six factors (variables) involved, $n$ is the same number of entries in each cell of the original table, or grid, and $X$ is the obser-vation or measurement being analyzed.

2. Since there are six different combinations of six different things taken five at a time:

$$\overset{6}{\underset{5}{C}} = \frac{6!}{5!(6-5)!} = \frac{6\,\cancel{5}!}{\cancel{5}!\,(1)!} = 6;$$

the second term of the sum of squares equation to be formed would be a poly-nomial including six summations. The "second term" polynomial would be *subtracted* from the first term $A$. Put in the form of letter designators, we could have:

$$B_1 = \frac{\sum\limits_{a}\sum\limits_{b}\sum\limits_{c}\sum\limits_{d}\sum\limits_{e}[\sum\limits_{f}\sum\limits_{n} X]^2}{(f_0)(n)}$$

where the product $[(f_0)(n)]$ is equal in value to the *number of categories* [(levels) $(f_0)$] included in the factor $f$ multiplied by $n$ the "equal number" of entries in each cell of the original table;

$$B_2 = \frac{\sum_a \sum_b \sum_c \sum_d \sum_f [\sum_e \sum_n X]^2}{(e_0)(n)}$$

where the product $[(e_0)(n)]$ is equal to the *number of categories* $[(e_0)(n)]$ included in the factor $e$ multiplied by $n$;

$$B_3 = \frac{\sum_a \sum_b \sum_c \sum_e \sum_f [\sum_d \sum_n X]^2}{(d_0)(n)}$$

where $d_0$ is equal to the number of categories included in the factor $d$;

$$B_4 = \frac{\sum_a \sum_b \sum_d \sum_e \sum_f [\sum_c \sum_n X]^2}{(c_0)(n)}$$

with $c_0$ equal in value to the number of categories included in factor $c$;

$$B_5 = \frac{\sum_a \sum_c \sum_d \sum_e \sum_f [\sum_b \sum_n X]^2}{(b_0)(n)}$$

where $b_0$ is the number of categories included in factor $b$; and

$$B_6 = \frac{\sum_b \sum_c \sum_d \sum_e \sum_f [\sum_a \sum_n X]^2}{(a_0)(n)}$$

with $a_0$ equal to the number of categories included in factor $a$.

3. The $\overset{6}{\underset{4}{C}} = \frac{6!}{4!2!} = 15$ different combinations of six different sums taken four at a time, compose the polynomial forming the third term of the sum of squares equations in question. The "third term" of the sum of squares equation will be added to the second term of the expression, resulting in a form of the equation for the fifth order interaction as follows:

$$A - \sum_{i=1}^{6} B_i + \sum_{i=1}^{15} C_i$$

The fifteen different summations would be:

$$C_1 = \frac{\sum_a \sum_b \sum_c \sum_d [\sum_e \sum_f \sum_n X]^2}{(e_0)(f_0)(n)}$$

$$C_3 = \frac{\sum_a \sum_b \sum_d \sum_e [\sum_c \sum_f \sum_n X]^2}{(c_0)(f_0)(n)}$$

$$C_5 = \frac{\sum_b \sum_c \sum_d \sum_e [\sum_a \sum_f \sum_n X]^2}{(a_0)(f_0)(n)}$$

$$C_2 = \frac{\sum_a \sum_b \sum_c \sum_e [\sum_d \sum_f \sum_n X]^2}{(d_0)(f_0)(n)}$$

$$C_4 = \frac{\sum_a \sum_c \sum_d \sum_e [\sum_b \sum_f \sum_n X]^2}{(b_0)(f_0)(n)}$$

$$C_6 = \frac{\sum_a \sum_b \sum_c \sum_f [\sum_d \sum_e \sum_n X]^2}{(d_0)(e_0)(n)}$$

$$C_7 = \frac{\underset{abdf}{\sum\sum\sum}[\underset{cen}{\sum\sum\sum}X]^2}{(c_0)(e_0)(n)} \qquad C_{10} = \frac{\underset{abef}{\sum\sum\sum}[\underset{cdn}{\sum\sum\sum}X]^2}{(c_0)(d_0)(n)} \qquad C_{13} = \frac{\underset{bdef}{\sum\sum\sum}[\underset{acn}{\sum\sum\sum}X]^2}{(a_0)(c_0)(n)}$$

$$C_8 = \frac{\underset{acdf}{\sum\sum\sum}[\underset{ben}{\sum\sum\sum}X]^2}{(b_0)(e_0)(n)} \qquad C_{11} = \frac{\underset{acef}{\sum\sum\sum}[\underset{bdn}{\sum\sum\sum}X]^2}{(b_0)(d_0)(n)} \qquad C_{14} = \frac{\underset{bcef}{\sum\sum\sum}[\underset{adn}{\sum\sum\sum}X]^2}{(a_0)(d_0)(n)}$$

$$C_9 = \frac{\underset{bcdf}{\sum\sum\sum}[\underset{aen}{\sum\sum\sum}X]^2}{(a_0)(e_0)(n)} \qquad C_{12} = \frac{\underset{adef}{\sum\sum\sum}[\underset{bcn}{\sum\sum\sum}X]^2}{(b_0)(c_0)(n)} \qquad C_{15} = \frac{\underset{cdef}{\sum\sum\sum}[\underset{abn}{\sum\sum\sum}X]^2}{(a_0)(b_0)(n)}$$

Where $a_0$, $b_0$, $c_0$, $d_0$, $e_0$, $f_0$, and $n$ are as indicated in Step 2.

4. The fourth term of the sum of squares equation for a fifth-order interaction is a polynomial *subtracted from the third term of the expression*, and is composed of 20 different combinations of six different sums taken three at a time, i.e.,

$$\underset{3}{\overset{6}{C}} = \frac{6!}{3!3!} = 20$$

The sum of squares equation for the fifth order interaction, *to this point*, would be:

$$A - \sum_{i=1}^{6} B_i + \sum_{i=1}^{15} C_i - \sum_{i=1}^{20} D_i$$

The twenty different summations would be:

$$D_1 = \frac{\underset{abc}{\sum\sum\sum}[\underset{defn}{\sum\sum\sum}X]^2}{(d_0)(e_0)(f_0)(n)} \qquad D_8 = \frac{\underset{abf}{\sum\sum\sum}[\underset{cden}{\sum\sum\sum}X]^2}{(c_0)(d_0)(e_0)(n)} \qquad D_{15} = \frac{\underset{bef}{\sum\sum\sum}[\underset{acdn}{\sum\sum\sum}X]^2}{(a_0)(c_0)(d_0)(n)}$$

$$D_2 = \frac{\underset{abd}{\sum\sum\sum}[\underset{cefn}{\sum\sum\sum}X]^2}{(c_0)(e_0)(f_0)(n)} \qquad D_9 = \frac{\underset{acf}{\sum\sum\sum}[\underset{bden}{\sum\sum\sum}X]^2}{(b_0)(d_0)(e_0)(n)} \qquad D_{16} = \frac{\underset{bdf}{\sum\sum\sum}[\underset{acen}{\sum\sum\sum}X]^2}{(a_0)(c_0)(e_0)(n)}$$

$$D_3 = \frac{\underset{adc}{\sum\sum\sum}[\underset{befn}{\sum\sum\sum}X]^2}{(b_0)(e_0)(f_0)(n)} \qquad D_{10} = \frac{\underset{bcf}{\sum\sum\sum}[\underset{aden}{\sum\sum\sum}X]^2}{(a_0)(d_0)(e_0)(n)} \qquad D_{17} = \frac{\underset{bde}{\sum\sum\sum}[\underset{acfn}{\sum\sum\sum}X]^2}{(a_0)(c_0)(f_0)(n)}$$

$$D_4 = \frac{\underset{bcd}{\sum\sum\sum}[\underset{aefn}{\sum\sum\sum}X]^2}{(a_0)(e_0)(f_0)(n)} \qquad D_{11} = \frac{\underset{def}{\sum\sum\sum}[\underset{abcn}{\sum\sum\sum}X]^2}{(a_0)(b_0)(c_0)(n)} \qquad D_{18} = \frac{\underset{cef}{\sum\sum\sum}[\underset{abdn}{\sum\sum\sum}X]^2}{(a_0)(b_0)(d_0)(n)}$$

$$D_5 = \frac{\underset{abe}{\sum\sum\sum}[\underset{cdfn}{\sum\sum\sum}X]^2}{(c_0)(d_0)(f_0)(n)} \qquad D_{12} = \frac{\underset{ade}{\sum\sum\sum}[\underset{bcfn}{\sum\sum\sum}X]^2}{(b_0)(c_0)(f_0)(n)} \qquad D_{19} = \frac{\underset{cdf}{\sum\sum\sum}[\underset{aben}{\sum\sum\sum}X]^2}{(a_0)(b_0)(e_0)(n)}$$

$$D_6 = \frac{\underset{ace}{\sum\sum\sum}[\underset{bdfn}{\sum\sum\sum}X]^2}{(b_0)(d_0)(f_0)(n)} \qquad D_{13} = \frac{\underset{adf}{\sum\sum\sum}[\underset{bcen}{\sum\sum\sum}X]^2}{(b_0)(c_0)(e_0)(n)} \qquad D_{20} = \frac{\underset{cde}{\sum\sum\sum}[\underset{abfn}{\sum\sum\sum}X]^2}{(a_0)(b_0)(f_0)(n)}$$

$$D_7 = \frac{\underset{bce}{\sum\sum\sum}[\underset{adfn}{\sum\sum\sum}X]^2}{(a_0)(d_0)(f_0)(n)} \qquad D_{14} = \frac{\underset{aef}{\sum\sum\sum}[\underset{bcdn}{\sum\sum\sum}X]^2}{(b_0)(c_0)(d_0)(n)}$$

5. The fifth term of the sum of squares equation in question is a polynomial *added* to the fourth term of the expression, and is composed of $\overset{6}{\underset{2}{C}} = \dfrac{6!}{2!4!} = 15$ different combinations of six different sums taken two at a time. The sum of squares equation, *to this point* would be:

$$A - \sum_{i=1}^{6} B_i + \sum_{i=1}^{15} C_i - \sum_{i=1}^{20} D_i + \sum_{i=1}^{15} E_i$$

The fifteen different summations would be:

$$E_1 = \frac{\sum_{ab}\sum[\sum\sum\sum\sum_{cdefn}X]^2}{(c_0)(d_0)(e_0)(f_0)(n)}$$

$$E_2 = \frac{\sum_{ac}\sum[\sum\sum\sum\sum_{bdefn}X]^2}{(b_0)(d_0)(e_0)(f_0)(n)}$$

$$E_3 = \frac{\sum_{bc}\sum[\sum\sum\sum\sum_{adefn}X]^2}{(a_0)(d_0)(e_0)(f_0)(n)}$$

$$E_4 = \frac{\sum_{ad}\sum[\sum\sum\sum\sum_{bcefn}X]^2}{(b_0)(c_0)(e_0)(f_0)(n)}$$

$$E_5 = \frac{\sum_{bd}\sum[\sum\sum\sum\sum_{acefn}X]^2}{(a_0)(c_0)(e_0)(f_0)(n)}$$

$$E_6 = \frac{\sum_{ae}\sum[\sum\sum\sum\sum_{bcdfn}X]^2}{(b_0)(c_0)(d_0)(f_0)(n)}$$

$$E_7 = \frac{\sum_{be}\sum[\sum\sum\sum\sum_{acdfn}X]^2}{(a_0)(c_0)(d_0)(f_0)(n)}$$

$$E_8 = \frac{\sum_{af}\sum[\sum\sum\sum\sum_{bcden}X]^2}{(b_0)(c_0)(d_0)(e_0)(n)}$$

$$E_9 = \frac{\sum_{bf}\sum[\sum\sum\sum\sum_{acden}X]^2}{(a_0)(c_0)(d_0)(e_0)(n)}$$

$$E_{10} = \frac{\sum_{cd}\sum[\sum\sum\sum\sum_{abefn}X]^2}{(a_0)(b_0)(e_0)(f_0)(n)}$$

$$E_{11} = \frac{\sum_{ce}\sum[\sum\sum\sum\sum_{abdfn}X]^2}{(a_0)(b_0)(d_0)(f_0)(n)}$$

$$E_{12} = \frac{\sum_{de}\sum[\sum\sum\sum\sum_{abcfn}X]^2}{(a_0)(b_0)(c_0)(f_0)(n)}$$

$$E_{13} = \frac{\sum_{cf}\sum[\sum\sum\sum\sum_{abden}X]^2}{(a_0)(b_0)(d_0)(e_0)(n)}$$

$$E_{14} = \frac{\sum_{df}\sum[\sum\sum\sum\sum_{abcen}X]^2}{(a_0)(b_0)(d_0)(e_0)(n)}$$

$$E_{15} = \frac{\sum_{ef}\sum[\sum\sum\sum\sum_{abcdn}X]^2}{(a_0)(b_0)(c_0)(d_0)(n)}$$

Where $a_0, b_0, c_0, d_0, e_0, f_0$, and $n$ are defined as in previous steps.

6. The sixth term of the sum of squares equation for a fifth-order interaction is a polynomial *subtracted* from the fifth term of the expression, and is composed of: $\overset{6}{\underset{1}{C}} = \dfrac{6!}{1!5!} = 6$ different combinations of six different sums taken one at a time. The sum of squares equation *including the sixth term* would be:

$$A - \sum_{i=1}^{6} B_i + \sum_{i=1}^{15} C_i - \sum_{i=1}^{20} D_i + \sum_{i=1}^{15} E_i - \sum_{i=1}^{6} F_i$$

The six different summations would be:

$$F_1 = \frac{\sum[\underset{a}{\sum}\underset{b}{\sum}\underset{c}{\sum}\underset{d}{\sum}\underset{e}{\sum}\underset{f}{\sum}\underset{n}{\sum}X]^2}{(b_0)(c_0)(d_0)(e_0)(f_0)(n)} \qquad F_4 = \frac{\sum[\underset{d}{\sum}\underset{a}{\sum}\underset{b}{\sum}\underset{c}{\sum}\underset{e}{\sum}\underset{f}{\sum}\underset{n}{\sum}X]^2}{(a_0)(b_0)(c_0)(e_0)(f_0)(n)}$$

$$F_2 = \frac{\sum[\underset{b}{\sum}\underset{a}{\sum}\underset{c}{\sum}\underset{d}{\sum}\underset{e}{\sum}\underset{f}{\sum}\underset{n}{\sum}X]^2}{(a_0)(c_0)(d_0)(e_0)(f_0)(n)} \qquad F_5 = \frac{\sum[\underset{e}{\sum}\underset{a}{\sum}\underset{b}{\sum}\underset{c}{\sum}\underset{d}{\sum}\underset{f}{\sum}\underset{n}{\sum}X]^2}{(a_0)(b_0)(c_0)(d_0)(f_0)(n)}$$

$$F_3 = \frac{\sum[\underset{c}{\sum}\underset{a}{\sum}\underset{b}{\sum}\underset{d}{\sum}\underset{e}{\sum}\underset{f}{\sum}\underset{n}{\sum}X]^2}{(a_0)(b_0)(d_0)(e_0)(f_0)(n)} \qquad F_6 = \frac{\sum[\underset{f}{\sum}\underset{a}{\sum}\underset{b}{\sum}\underset{c}{\sum}\underset{d}{\sum}\underset{e}{\sum}\underset{n}{\sum}X]^2}{(a_0)(b_0)(c_0)(d_0)(e_0)(n)}$$

7. The seventh, and final term, of the sum of squares equation in question is a single term:

$$G = \frac{[\underset{a}{\sum}\underset{b}{\sum}\underset{c}{\sum}\underset{d}{\sum}\underset{e}{\sum}\underset{f}{\sum}\underset{n}{\sum}X]^2}{(a_0)(b_0)(c_0)(d_0)(e_0)(f_0)(n)}$$

which is *added* to the sixth term of the expression, and produces the following sum of squares equation for a *fifth-order interaction*:

$$A - \sum_{i=1}^{6} B_i + \sum_{i=1}^{15} C_i - \sum_{i=1}^{20} D_i + \sum_{i=1}^{15} E_i - \sum_{i=1}^{6} F_i + G$$

A table of the sum of squares equations for the "error" term and all interactions of a six-factor table with an equal number of $n$ entries in each cell of the original "grid" (table) can be produced from the summations set forth in the seven steps describing the formation of a sum of squares equation for a fifth-order interaction. Letting

$$Z = \underset{a}{\sum}\underset{b}{\sum}\underset{c}{\sum}\underset{d}{\sum}\underset{e}{\sum}\underset{f}{\sum}\underset{n}{\sum}X^2$$

the sum of squares equations for the total analysis would appear as in Table XXIV.

In order to obtain the appropriate values for the various summations appearing in the different interaction sum of squares equations, a set of tables like those associated with our example of a $2 \times 3 \times 5$ three-factor "grid" (table) shown in Table XXII(S) must be prepared. In our example, it was necessary to construct seven "working" tables. Obviously, if a research problem were such that more factors (variables) than three might be involved, a greater number of "working" tables would be required.

If computer facilities are available a great deal of time and energy may be saved by programing the particular analysis of variance pattern being employed. It should be noted, however, that each "program" is unique in terms of the number of variables (factors), and the number of categories (levels) in each of the respective factors being analyzed. To illustrate, different programs must be written for three-factor problems of $2 \times 3 \times 5$ and $3 \times 3 \times 4$ levels; or for a

Table XXIV

Sum of Squares Equations and Accompanying Degrees of Freedom for Error Term and All Interactions of a Six-Factor Research Problem, with $n$ Equal Entries in Each Cell of Original Table

| Source of Variation | Degrees of Freedom | Sum of Squares Equations |
|---|---|---|
| 1. Error (within cells − $n$ equal entries per cell) Interactions | $(a_0)(b_0)(c_0)(d_0)(e_0)(f_0)(n-1)$ | $Z - A$ |
| 2. (fifth order) (1) $\underline{a \times b \times c \times d \times e \times f}$ | $(a_0-1)(b_0-1)(c_0-1)(d_0-1)(e_0-1)(f_0-1)$ | $A - \sum_{i=1}^{6} B_i + \sum_{i=1}^{15} C_i - \sum_{i=1}^{20} D_i + \sum_{i=1}^{15} E_i - \sum_{i=1}^{6} F_i + G$ |
| 3. (fourth orders) (6) $\underline{a \times b \times c \times d \times e}$ | $(a_0-1)(b_0-1)(c_0-1)(d_0-1)(e_0-1)$ | $B_1 - (C_1 + C_2 + C_3 + C_4 + C_5) + (D_1 + D_2 + D_3 + D_4 + D_5 + D_6 + D_7 + D_{12} + D_{17} + D_{20}) - (E_1 + E_2 + E_3 + E_4 + E_5 + E_6 + E_7 + E_{10} + E_{11} + E_{12}) + (F_1 + F_2 + F_3 + F_4 + F_5) - G$ |
| 4. $a \times b \times c \times d \times f$ | $(a_0-1)(b_0-1)(c_0-1)(d_0-1)(f_0-1)$ | $B_2 - (C_1 + C_6 + C_7 + C_8 + C_9) + (D_1 + D_2 + D_3 + D_4 + D_8 + D_9 + D_{10} + D_{13} + D_{16} + D_{19}) - (E_1 + E_2 + E_3 + E_4 + E_5 + E_8 + E_9 + E_{10} + E_{13} + E_{14}) + (F_1 + F_2 + F_3 + F_4 + F_6) - G$ |
| 5. $a \times b \times c \times e \times f$ | $(a_0-1)(b_0-1)(c_0-1)(e_0-1)(f_0-1)$ | $B_3 - (C_2 + C_6 + C_{10} + C_{11} + C_{14}) + (D_1 + D_5 + D_6 + D_7 + D_8 + D_9 + D_{10} + D_{14} + D_{15} + D_{18}) - (E_1 + E_2 + E_3 + E_6 + E_7 + E_8 + E_9 + E_{11} + E_{13} + E_{15}) + (F_1 + F_2 + F_3 + F_5 + F_6) - G$ |
| 6. $a \times b \times d \times e \times f$ | $(a_0-1)(b_0-1)(d_0-1)(e_0-1)(f_0-1)$ | $B_4 - (C_3 + C_7 + C_{10} + C_{12} + C_{13}) + (D_2 + D_5 + D_8 + D_{11} + D_{12} + D_{13} + D_{14} + D_{15} + D_{16} + D_{17}) - (E_1 + E_4 + E_5 + E_6 + E_7 + E_8 + E_9 + E_{12} + E_{14} + E_{15}) + (F_1 + F_2 + F_4 + F_5 + F_6) - G$ |
| 7. $a \times c \times d \times e \times f$ | $(a_0-1)(c_0-1)(d_0-1)(e_0-1)(f_0-1)$ | $B_5 - (C_4 + C_8 + C_{11} + C_{12} + C_{15}) + (D_3 + D_6 + D_9 + D_{11} + D_{12} + D_{13} + D_{14} + D_{18} + D_{19} + D_{20}) - (E_2 + E_4 + E_6 + E_8 + E_{10} + E_{11} + E_{12} + E_{13} + E_{14} + E_{15}) + (F_1 + F_3 + F_4 + F_5 + F_6) - G$ |
| 8. $b \times c \times d \times e \times f$ | $(b_0-1)(c_0-1)(d_0-1)(e_0-1)(f_0-1)$ | $B_6 - (C_5 + C_9 + C_{13} + C_{14} + C_{15}) + (D_4 + D_7 + D_{10} + D_{11} + D_{15} + D_{16} + D_{17} + D_{18} + D_{19} + D_{20}) - (E_3 + E_5 + E_7 + E_9 + E_{10} + E_{11} + E_{12} + E_{13} + E_{14} + E_{15}) + (F_2 + F_3 + F_4 + F_5 + F_6) - G$ |
| 9. (third orders) (15) $a \times b \times c \times d$ | $(a_0-1)(b_0-1)(c_0-1)(d_0-1)$ | $C_1 - (D_1 + D_2 + D_3 + D_4) + (E_1 + E_2 + E_3 + E_4 + E_5 + E_{10}) - (F_1 + F_2 + F_3 + F_4) + G$ |

Table XXIV (*contd.*)

| Source of Variation | Degrees of Freedom | Sum of Squares Equations |
|---|---|---|
| 10. $a \times b \times c \times e$ | $(a_0 - 1)(b_0 - 1)(c_0 - 1)(e_0 - 1)$ | $C_2 - (D_1 + D_5 + D_6 + D_7) + (E_1 + E_2 + E_3 + E_6 + E_7 + E_{11}) - (F_1 + F_2 + F_3 + F_5) + G$ |
| 11. $a \times b \times d \times e$ | $(a_0 - 1)(b_0 - 1)(d_0 - 1)(e_0 - 1)$ | $C_3 - (D_2 + D_5 + D_{12} + D_{17}) + (E_1 + E_4 + E_5 + E_6 + E_7 + E_{12}) - (F_1 + F_2 + F_4 + F_5) + G$ |
| 12. $a \times c \times d \times e$ | $(a_0 - 1)(c_0 - 1)(d_0 - 1)(e_0 - 1)$ | $C_4 - (D_3 + D_6 + D_{12} + D_{20}) + (E_2 + E_4 + E_6 + E_{10} + E_{11}) - (F_1 + F_3 + F_4 + F_5) + G$ |
| 13. $b \times c \times d \times e$ | $(b_0 - 1)(c_0 - 1)(d_0 - 1)(e_0 - 1)$ | $C_5 - (D_4 + D_7 + D_{17} + D_{20}) + (E_3 + E_5 + E_7 + E_{10} + E_{11}) - (F_2 + F_3 + F_4 + F_5) + G$ |
| 14. $a \times b \times c \times f$ | $(a_0 - 1)(b_0 - 1)(c_0 - 1)(f_0 - 1)$ | $C_6 - (D_1 + D_8 + D_9 + D_{10}) + (E_1 + E_2 + E_3 + E_8 + E_9 + E_{13}) - (F_1 + F_2 + F_3 + F_6) + G$ |
| 15. $a \times b \times d \times f$ | $(a_0 - 1)(b_0 - 1)(d_0 - 1)(f_0 - 1)$ | $C_7 - (D_2 + D_8 + D_{13} + D_{16}) + (E_1 + E_4 + E_5 + E_8 + E_9 + E_{14}) - (F_1 + F_2 + F_4 + F_6) + G$ |
| 16. $a \times c \times d \times f$ | $(a_0 - 1)(c_0 - 1)(d_0 - 1)(f_0 - 1)$ | $C_8 - (D_3 + D_9 + D_{13} + D_{19}) + (E_2 + E_4 + E_8 + E_{10} + E_{13} + E_{14}) - (F_1 + F_3 + F_4 + F_6) + G$ |
| 17. $b \times c \times d \times f$ | $(b_0 - 1)(c_0 - 1)(d_0 - 1)(f_0 - 1)$ | $C_9 - (D_4 + D_{10} + D_{16} + D_{19}) + (E_3 + E_5 + E_9 + E_{10} + E_{13} + E_{14}) - (F_2 + F_3 + F_4 + F_6) + G$ |
| 18. $a \times b \times e \times f$ | $(a_0 - 1)(b_0 - 1)(e_0 - 1)(f_0 - 1)$ | $C_{10} - (D_5 + D_8 + D_{14} + D_{15}) + (E_1 + E_6 + E_7 + E_8 + E_9 + E_{15}) - (F_1 + F_2 + F_5 + F_6) + G$ |
| 19. $a \times c \times e \times f$ | $(a_0 - 1)(c_0 - 1)(e_0 - 1)(f_0 - 1)$ | $C_{11} - (D_6 + D_9 + D_{14} + D_{18}) + (E_2 + E_6 + E_8 + E_{11} + E_{13}) - (F_1 + F_3 + F_5 + F_6) + G$ |
| 20. $a \times d \times e \times f$ | $(a_0 - 1)(d_0 - 1)(e_0 - 1)(f_0 - 1)$ | $C_{12} - (D_{11} + D_{12} + D_{13} + D_{14}) + (E_4 + E_6 + E_8 + E_{12} + E_{14}) - (F_1 + F_4 + F_5 + F_6) + G$ |
| 21. $b \times d \times e \times f$ | $(b_0 - 1)(d_0 - 1)(e_0 - 1)(f_0 - 1)$ | $C_{13} - (D_{11} + D_{15} + D_{16} + D_{17}) + (E_5 + E_7 + E_9 + E_{12} + E_{14}) - (F_2 + F_4 + F_5 + F_6) + G$ |
| 22. $b \times c \times e \times f$ | $(b_0 - 1)(c_0 - 1)(e_0 - 1)(f_0 - 1)$ | $C_{14} - (D_7 + D_{10} + D_{15} + D_{18}) + (E_3 + E_7 + E_9 + E_{11} + E_{13}) - (F_2 + F_3 + F_5 + F_6) + G$ |
| 23. $c \times d \times e \times f$ | $(c_0 - 1)(d_0 - 1)(e_0 - 1)(f_0 - 1)$ | $C_{15} - (D_{11} + D_{18} + D_{19} + D_{20}) + (E_{10} + E_{11} + E_{12} + E_{13} + E_{14}) - (F_3 + F_4 + F_5 + F_6) + G$ |
| (second orders) (20)<br>24. $a \times b \times c$ | $(a_0 - 1)(b_0 - 1)(c_0 - 1)$ | $D_1 - (E_1 + E_2 + E_3) + (F_1 + F_2 + F_3) - G$ |

Table XXIV (*contd.*)

| Source of Variation | Degrees of Freedom | Sum of Squares Equations |
|---|---|---|
| 25. $a \times b \times d$ | $(a_0 - 1)(b_0 - 1)(d_0 - 1)$ | $D_2 - (E_1 + E_4 + E_5) + (F_1 + F_2 + F_4) - G$ |
| 26. $a \times c \times d$ | $(a_0 - 1)(c_0 - 1)(d_0 - 1)$ | $D_3 - (E_2 + E_4 + E_{10}) + (F_1 + F_3 + F_4) - G$ |
| 27. $b \times c \times d$ | $(b_0 - 1)(c_0 - 1)(d_0 - 1)$ | $D_4 - (E_3 + E_5 + E_{10}) + (F_2 + F_3 + F_4) - G$ |
| 28. $a \times b \times e$ | $(a_0 - 1)(b_0 - 1)(e_0 - 1)$ | $D_5 - (E_1 + E_6 + E_7) + (F_1 + F_2 + F_5) - G$ |
| 29. $a \times c \times e$ | $(a_0 - 1)(c_0 - 1)(e_0 - 1)$ | $D_6 - (E_2 + E_6 + E_{11}) + (F_1 + F_3 + F_5) - G$ |
| 30. $b \times c \times e$ | $(b_0 - 1)(c_0 - 1)(e_0 - 1)$ | $D_7 - (E_3 + E_7 + E_{11}) + (F_2 + F_3 + F_5) - G$ |
| 31. $a \times b \times f$ | $(a_0 - 1)(b_0 - 1)(f_0 - 1)$ | $D_8 - (E_1 + E_8 + E_9) + (F_1 + F_2 + F_6) - G$ |
| 32. $a \times c \times f$ | $(a_0 - 1)(c_0 - 1)(f_0 - 1)$ | $D_9 - (E_2 + E_8 + E_{13}) + (F_1 + F_3 + F_6) - G$ |
| 33. $b \times c \times f$ | $(b_0 - 1)(c_0 - 1)(f_0 - 1)$ | $D_{10} - (E_3 + E_9 + E_{13}) + (F_2 + F_3 + F_6) - G$ |
| 34. $d \times e \times f$ | $(d_0 - 1)(e_0 - 1)(f_0 - 1)$ | $D_{11} - (E_{12} + E_{14} + E_{15}) + (F_4 + F_5 + F_6) - G$ |
| 35. $a \times d \times e$ | $(a_0 - 1)(d_0 - 1)(e_0 - 1)$ | $D_{12} - (E_4 + E_6 + E_{12}) + (F_1 + F_4 + F_5) - G$ |
| 36. $a \times d \times f$ | $(a_0 - 1)(d_0 - 1)(f_0 - 1)$ | $D_{13} - (E_4 + E_8 + E_{14}) + (F_1 + F_4 + F_6) - G$ |
| 37. $a \times e \times f$ | $(a_0 - 1)(e_0 - 1)(f_0 - 1)$ | $D_{14} - (E_6 + E_8 + E_{15}) + (F_1 + F_5 + F_6) - G$ |
| 38. $b \times e \times f$ | $(b_0 - 1)(e_0 - 1)(f_0 - 1)$ | $D_{15} - (E_7 + E_9 + E_{15}) + (F_2 + F_5 + F_6) - G$ |
| 39. $b \times d \times f$ | $(b_0 - 1)(d_0 - 1)(f_0 - 1)$ | $D_{16} - (E_5 + E_9 + E_{14}) + (F_2 + F_4 + F_6) - G$ |
| 40. $b \times d \times e$ | $(b_0 - 1)(d_0 - 1)(e_0 - 1)$ | $D_{17} - (E_5 + E_7 + E_{12}) + (F_2 + F_4 + F_5) - G$ |
| 41. $c \times e \times f$ | $(c_0 - 1)(e_0 - 1)(f_0 - 1)$ | $D_{18} - (E_{11} + E_{13} + E_{15}) + (F_3 + F_5 + F_6) - G$ |
| 42. $c \times d \times f$ | $(c_0 - 1)(d_0 - 1)(f_0 - 1)$ | $D_{19} - (E_{10} + E_{13} + E_{14}) + (F_3 + F_4 + F_6) - G$ |
| 43. $c \times d \times e$ | $(c_0 - 1)(d_0 - 1)(e_0 - 1)$ | $D_{20} - (E_{10} + E_{11} + E_{12}) + (F_3 + F_4 + F_5) - G$ |
| (first orders) (15) | | |
| 44. $a \times b$ | $(a_0 - 1)(b_0 - 1)$ | $E_1 - (F_1 + F_2) + G$ |
| 45. $a \times c$ | $(a_0 - 1)(c_0 - 1)$ | $E_2 - (F_1 + F_3) + G$ |

# Table XXIV (*contd.*)

Parts of the *mechanical method for writing sums of squares equations* for different orders of interaction which should be noted are:

1. The first term of the equation must have the same factors in the "external" sums as those stated in the "Source of Variation." For example, the first-order interaction in line 48 of Table XXIV is that of: $b \times d$. The first term of the sum of squares equation for the interaction of $b \times d$ is

$$E_5 = \frac{\sum_b \sum_d |\sum_a \sum_c \sum_e \sum_f \sum_n X|^2}{(a_0)(c_0)(e_0)(f_0)(n)}$$

2. The second term of the equation, always in some form of a polynomial except for the "Main Effects—zero-order interactions," *and always subtracted from the first term of the equation*, must show in combination, or singularly, the same factors in its "external" sums that are given in the source of variation. Returning to our example of line 48 we find as the *second term of the equation*:

$$-(F_2 + F_4) = -\left( \frac{\sum_b |\sum_a \sum_c \sum_d \sum_e \sum_f \sum_n X|^2}{(a_0)(c_0)(d_0)(e_0)(f_0)(n)} + \frac{\sum_d |\sum_a \sum_b \sum_c \sum_e \sum_f \sum_n X|^2}{(a_0)(b_0)(c_0)(e_0)(f_0)(n)} \right)$$

Using line 37 as an example of what occurs in connection with equations for second-order interactions, we find the interaction of $a \times e \times f$; and the first and second terms of its equation to be: $D_{14} - (E_6 + E_8 + E_{15})$; or expressed in summations:

$$\frac{\sum_a \sum_e \sum_f |\sum_b \sum_c \sum_d \sum_n X|^2}{(b_0)(c_0)(d_0)(n)} - \left( \frac{\sum_a \sum_e |\sum_b \sum_c \sum_d \sum_f \sum_n X|^2}{(b_0)(c_0)(d_0)(f_0)(n)} + \frac{\sum_a \sum_f |\sum_b \sum_c \sum_d \sum_e \sum_n X|^2}{(b_0)(c_0)(d_0)(e_0)(n)} + \frac{\sum_e \sum_f |\sum_a \sum_b \sum_c \sum_d \sum_n X|^2}{(a_0)(b_0)(c_0)(d_0)(n)} \right)$$

3. The *odd numbered terms* (first, third, fifth, seventh, etc.) of an interaction sum of squares equation are always positive ($+$) in algebraic sign. The *even numbered terms* (second, fourth, sixth, eighth, etc.) of the interaction equations are always negative ($-$) in algebraic sign. To illustrate, we use the equation associated with line 37 of the table:

$$\underset{\substack{1\text{st} \\ \text{term}}}{D_{14}} - \underset{\substack{2\text{nd} \\ \text{term}}}{(E_6 + E_8 + E_{15})} + \underset{\substack{3\text{rd} \\ \text{term}}}{(F_1 + F_5 + F_6)} - \underset{\substack{4\text{th} \\ \text{term}}}{G}$$

4. The *second to last term* of any interaction sum of squares equation always shows the interacting factors of the "Source of Variation" as *single* "external" sums. For example, in line 37, the second to last term of the equation is: $+(F_1 + F_5 + F_6)$, which when expressed in summation form becomes:

$$\frac{\sum_a |\sum_b \sum_c \sum_d \sum_e \sum_f \sum_n X|^2}{(b_0)(c_0)(d_0)(e_0)(f_0)(n)} + \frac{\sum_e |\sum_a \sum_b \sum_c \sum_d \sum_f \sum_n X|^2}{(a_0)(b_0)(c_0)(d_0)(f_0)(n)} + \frac{\sum_f |\sum_a \sum_b \sum_c \sum_d \sum_e \sum_n X|^2}{(a_0)(b_0)(c_0)(d_0)(e_0)(n)}$$

5. The last term of every interaction sum of squares equation is called the "correction term." It is always a monomial (single term), and is positive ($+$) in algebraic sign or negative ($-$) in algebraic sign, depending upon whether it is an odd numbered term (first, third, fifth, seventh, etc.) or an even numbered term (second, fourth, sixth, eighth, etc.), respectively, of the "equation." The "correction" term in Table XXIV is:

$$G = \frac{|\sum_a \sum_b \sum_c \sum_d \sum_e \sum_f \sum_n X|^2}{(a_0)(b_0)(c_0)(d_0)(e_0)(f_0)(n)}$$

and in line 2 of the table, as the *seventh term* of the interaction sum of squares equation, is positive ($+$) in algebraic sign; and in line 5 as the *sixth term* of the equation, is negative ($-$) in algebraic sign; while in line 44 as the *third term* of the equation is positive ($+$) in sign.

## Table XXIV (contd.)

| Source of Variation | Degrees of Freedom | Sum of Squares Equations |
|---|---|---|
| 46. $b \times c$ | $(b_0 - 1)(c_0 - 1)$ | $E_3 - (F_2 + F_3) + G$ |
| 47. $a \times d$ | $(a_0 - 1)(d_0 - 1)$ | $E_4 - (F_1 + F_4) + G$ |
| 48. $b \times d$ | $(b_0 - 1)(d_0 - 1)$ | $E_5 - (F_2 + F_4) + G$ |
| 49. $a \times e$ | $(a_0 - 1)(e_0 - 1)$ | $E_6 - (F_1 + F_5) + G$ |
| 50. $b \times e$ | $(b_0 - 1)(e_0 - 1)$ | $E_7 - (F_2 + F_5) + G$ |
| 51. $a \times f$ | $(a_0 - 1)(f_0 - 1)$ | $E_8 - (F_1 + F_6) + G$ |
| 52. $b \times f$ | $(b_0 - 1)(f_0 - 1)$ | $E_9 - (F_2 + F_6) + G$ |
| 53. $c \times d$ | $(c_0 - 1)(d_0 - 1)$ | $E_{10} - (F_3 + F_4) + G$ |
| 54. $c \times e$ | $(c_0 - 1)(e_0 - 1)$ | $E_{11} - (F_3 + F_5) + G$ |
| 55. $d \times e$ | $(d_0 - 1)(e_0 - 1)$ | $E_{12} - (F_4 + F_5) + G$ |
| 56. $c \times f$ | $(c_0 - 1)(f_0 - 1)$ | $E_{13} - (F_3 + F_6) + G$ |
| 57. $d \times f$ | $(d_0 - 1)(f_0 - 1)$ | $E_{14} - (F_4 + F_6) + G$ |
| 58. $e \times f$ | $(e_0 - 1)(f_0 - 1)$ | $E_{15} - (F_5 + F_6) + G$ |
| **Main Effects (or zero orders) (6)** | | |
| 59. $a$ | $(a_0 - 1)$ | $F_1 - G$ |
| 60. $b$ | $(b_0 - 1)$ | $F_2 - G$ |
| 61. $c$ | $(c_0 - 1)$ | $F_3 - G$ |
| 62. $d$ | $(d_0 - 1)$ | $F_4 - G$ |
| 63. $e$ | $(e_0 - 1)$ | $F_5 - G$ |
| 64. $f$ | $(f_0 - 1)$ | $F_6 - G$ |
| Total | $(a)(b)(c)(d)(e)(f)(n) - 1$ | $Z - G$ |

See page 414 for footnotes to Table XXIV.

three-factor problem and a four-factor problem. Since, in most cases, a "programmer" from the computation laboratory is assigned to a "job" as it is accepted by the laboratory, the researcher need not be too worried about the details of the analysis performed by the computer. It should be noted, however, that a format of the respective sum of squares equations as shown in Table XXIV would be of immeasurable help to personnel assigned the chore of writing a program for an analysis of variance (or covariance) of a multi-factor and multi-level problem.

### Calculation of Variance (*Mean Squares*)

The mean squares (variances) for the Error (Within Cells), Main Effects, and various interaction variations of our $2 \times 3 \times 5$ factorial experiment are calculated by dividing the value of the sum of squares equation for a given source of variation by its number of degrees of freedom. The most convenient and efficient presentation of the respective variances (mean squares) is that of the analysis of variance table. In effect, the "variance table" is an extension of the sums of squares equations table, and differs from it to the extent that it presents numerical data, as opposed to the presentation of algebraic forms of the various sums of squares equations. The variance table for the $2 \times 3 \times 5$ factorial experiment is as shown in Table XXV.

Check points of the analysis of variance are the total number of degrees of freedom, and the total of the sums of squares. The total of 89 degrees of freedom is consistent for the original table of 90 entries. The total of the sums of squares, 552.50, "cross-checks" precisely with the value computed from the formula for the total sum of squares:

$$\sum_{m}\sum_{i}\sum_{s}\sum_{n}X^2 - \frac{[\sum_{m}\sum_{i}\sum_{s}\sum_{n}X]^2}{90} = 2955 - 2402.5 = 552.50$$

The value of each $F$-ratio appearing in the table is calculated by dividing the mean square of each source of variation by the mean square of the "error" term. For example, the $F$-ratio for the interaction *methods* $\times$ *intelligence* is:

$$F = \frac{4.4325}{1.878} = 2.36$$

Table XXV
Summary of Analysis of Variance for Fictitious Data of Table XXII

| Source of Variation | df | Sum of Squares | Mean Square | F-Ratio | Decision |
|---|---|---|---|---|---|
| Error (Within Cells) | 60 | 112.67 | 1.878 | — | — |
| Methods × intelligence × sex | 8 | 15.38 | 1.9225 | 1.02 | Do not reject $H_0$ |
| Methods × intelligence | 8 | 35.46 | 4.4325 | 2.36 | Reject $H_0$ at .05 level |
| Methods × sex | 4 | .49 | .1225 | — | Do not reject $H_0$ |
| Intelligence × sex | 2 | 4.62 | 2.310 | 1.23 | Do not reject $H_0$ |
| Methods | 4 | 134.0 | 33.500 | 17.838 | Reject $H_0$ at .01 level |
| Intelligence | 2 | 249.87 | 124.935 | 66.525 | Reject $H_0$ at .01 level |
| Sex | 1 | .01 | .01 | — | Do not reject $H_0$ |
| Total | 89 | 552.50 | | | |

Where the value of the $F$-ratio is obviously less than one, which readily indicates that the factor, or factors, of that source of variation cannot be significant, the calculation is omitted. Such are the cases of the *interaction* of *methods* × *sex*, and the *main effect* of *sex*. If the value of the $F$-ratio is not greater than the critical value of $F$ found under the appropriate number of degrees of freedom in Table XIV, the null hypothesis ($H_0$) cannot be rejected. The null hypothesis in our example was *not* rejected in the following cases: (1) methods × intelligence × sex; (2) methods × sex; (3) intelligence × sex; and (4) sex. The null hypothesis ($H_0$), to the effect that the variables, or factors, in a given interaction (line of the table) are not significant in their effect upon differences of the arithmetic means under consideration, *is rejected* in the following cases: (1) methods × intelligence, at the .05 level; (2) *methods*, at the .01 level; and (3) *intelligence*, at the .01 level.

When the null hypothesis ($H_0$) is rejected in connection with a main effect (one of the factors), a significant difference between the arithmetic means of the categories (levels) included in that factor is indicated. In these cases, Scheffé's test (see page 368) is applied to determine more precisely between which "category" means of the factor in question significant differences exist. In our example, Scheffé's test could be applied to the main effects (factors) of *methods* and *intelligence*. After Scheffé's test had been applied to the factor of *methods*, the researcher should know precisely which differences among the arithmetic mean scores of the five methods under study are significant ones; and after the application of the test to the arithmetic mean scores for each of the three levels (categories) of intelligence, the researcher should know precisely where significant differences among the categories of that factor exist. The application of Scheffé's test in this example is left as an exercise for the reader.

The techniques employed in calculating the mean squares and $F$-ratios, and making the decision to *reject*, or *not* reject, the null hypothesis ($H_0$), in connection with our example of a $2 \times 3 \times 5$ factorial experiment, are general in nature and with proper modification and extension could be applied to any multi-factorial experiment. Since these techniques and procedures have been illustrated and discussed in detail throughout the presentation, further time and space will not be accorded the generalizations that can be made by analogy.

It should be pointed out that a test for homogeneity of variances was not conducted in our example, and the value of .01 for the mean square of the factor of *sex* is highly suspect. Bartlett's test should be conducted at this point, but in the interest of preserving continuity and keeping the discussion moving in the present universe of discourse, it is *assumed* that the variances are homogeneous.

In closing our discussion of the analysis of variance technique as one of the more excellent analytical and numerical procedures associated with the "processing of data" and "decision" aspects of the suggested analog model of educational research, it should be pointed out that only two forms of the analysis of variance technique have been discussed here, those of *factorial designs* and *randomized groups* design. These two forms of the technique were chosen because of their excellent possibilities for wide and, if the word can be used properly here, "profound" (depth) applications throughout the realm of problems occurring in educational research. Some of the other forms of the analysis of variance technique with more limited possibilities for application, which were not discussed, are: (1) randomized blocks; (2) trend analysis; (3) Latin square designs; and (4) Greco-Latin squares. For the reader interested in the latter forms of the analysis of variance technique, excellent treatments of these topics may be found in (54) Edward's *Experimental Design in Psychological Research*. Almost all of the multi-factor problems confronting the worker in educational research, however, can be adequately analyzed by the randomized groups and general factorial design experiment techniques that have been presented here.

*Chapter 29—References*

See Bibliography: 8, 38, 41, 49, 53, 54, 65, 66, 67, 76, 77, 89, 104, 112, 113, 141, 148, 158, 159, 183; 31a, 38a, 42a, 67a, 82a, 104a, 107a; 1b.

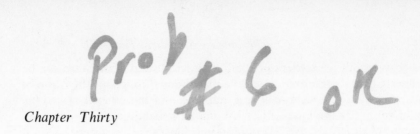

*Chapter Thirty*

# Parametric Statistical Tests—IV

### Analysis of Covariance

CERTAIN TYPES of educational research problems call for the matching of subjects and repeated treatment of them by the variables under investigation. The object of such an approach is increased precision of the experiment, that is, deriving a more accurate estimate of the error term of the experiment by reducing the magnitude of errors in the experimental comparison. Matching also equates the arithmetic means of the groups being matched.

A design and method of analysis of an experiment which results in increased precision and equated group means, *but does not require the matching of subjects, is that of the analysis of covariance.* The covariance design increases precision and equates group means by employing a *supplementary* measure $X^*$ which is known to be correlated with the $Y$ measure obtained on the dependent variable of the experiment. The $X$ measures are obtained under uniform conditions *prior to the application* of the treatments, and therefore cannot be affected by the treatments. The $Y$ measures are then adjusted, or "corrected," by eliminating the variability due to differences between subjects on the $X$ measures which were taken prior to the experiment. The adjustment of the dependent variable $Y$ for initial differences among subjects on the supplementary measure $X$ is usually carried out through employment of the regression equation of $Y$ on $X$.

The statistical definition of *covariance*, the technical term for covariation, or varying together, involves two measures, $X$ and $Y$, and results in an expression analogous to that of the variance of $X$. Where the population variance $(\sigma^2)$ of the measure $X$ may be *estimated* by the expression $\sum (X - \overline{X})^2/(n - 1)$ with $\overline{X}$ denoting the arithmetic mean of a sample of size $n$, the covariance of the bivariate population involving $X$ and $Y$ measures may be *estimated* by summing the products of the paired deviations, $\sum (X_i - \overline{X}) \cdot (Y_i - \overline{Y})$, and dividing the sum by the total number of degrees of freedom $n - 1$, the same as that for the variance of $X$. In algebraic form, the *mean product* estimate of covariance is expressed as in (1):

$$\text{Covariance } X \text{ and } Y = \frac{\sum\limits_{i=1}^{n} (X_i - \overline{X})(Y_i - \overline{Y})}{n - 1} \tag{1}$$

---

\* The supplementary measure is not itself of experimental interest, but is considered to be a concomitant measure or observation.

Although (1) provides an estimate of the bivariate population covariance, it is rarely if ever used as the basis of tests of significance. Since the analysis of covariance technique is a method which combines analysis of variance, correlation, and regression, tests of significance are conducted in terms of the sums of squares and products resulting from the computations associated with these three statistical concepts.

## Sums of Products

It will be recalled that the analysis of variance technique for a randomized groups design with $n_j$ measurements $(X)$ for each group was applied by first analyzing the *total* sum of squares into two components: (1) the sum of squares *between* groups, and (2) the sum of squares *within* groups. In similar fashion, the analysis of covariance technique for a randomized groups design with $n_j$ *paired* measurements $(X, Y)$ for each group not only first analyzes the total sums of squares for each of the variables $X$ and $Y$ into *between* and *within* components sums of squares, respectively, but resolves the *total sum of products* into two components: (1) the *between groups sum of products*; and (2) the *within groups sum of products*. It should be further noted that, as in the case of the application of the analysis of variance technique, the analysis of covariance technique for *randomized groups does not require that equal $n_j$'s exist in each of the treatment groups*. It should be pointed out, however, that the computation procedures for unequal $n_j$'s are far more time-consuming than those associated with the analysis for equal $n_j$'s, and thus if given the choice, the wise researcher should make every effort to employ the design involving equal $n_j$'s in each of the treatment groups.

Since the partitioning of the total sum of squares into a *between groups* component and a *within groups* component has been accorded a thorough discussion in Chapter 28, we concentrate our discussion at this point on the matter of resolving the total sum of products into between groups and within groups components. We begin our discussion of "product sums" by considering the fact that the deviation of the $i$-th pair of values in the $j$-th group $(X_{ij}, Y_{ij})$ from the grand means $(\bar{X}, \bar{Y})$ may be expressed in the form of the identity:

$$(X_{ij} - \bar{X}) \cdot (Y_{ij} - \bar{Y}) = (X_{ij} - \bar{X}_j + \bar{X}_j - \bar{X}) \cdot (Y_{ij} - \bar{Y}_j + \bar{Y}_j - \bar{Y})$$

$$= [(X_{ij} - \bar{X}_j) + (\bar{X}_j - \bar{X})][(Y_{ij} - \bar{Y}_j) + (\bar{Y}_j - \bar{Y})] \quad (2)$$

where $\bar{X}_j$ and $\bar{Y}_j$ are *means for the j-th group*. Multiplying the right hand side of equation (2), summing over the $n_j$ observations in a single group, and then summing over the $k$ groups, we find:

$$\sum_{j=1}^{k} \sum_{i=1}^{n_j} (X_{ij} - \bar{X})(Y_{ij} - \bar{Y}) = \sum_{j=1}^{k} \sum_{i=1}^{n_j} (X_{ij} - \bar{X}_j)(Y_{ij} - \bar{Y}_j) + \sum_{j=1}^{k} \sum_{i=1}^{n_j} (\bar{X}_j - \bar{X})$$

$$\times (\bar{Y}_j - \bar{Y}) + \sum_{j=1}^{k} \sum_{i=1}^{n_j} (X_{ij} - \bar{X}_j)(\bar{Y}_j - \bar{Y}) + \sum_{j=1}^{k} \sum_{i=1}^{n_j} (\bar{X}_j - \bar{X})(Y_{ij} - \bar{Y}) \quad (3)$$

where the differences $(\bar{X}_j - \bar{X})$ and $(\bar{Y}_j - \bar{Y})$ are constants for any given one of the $k$ groups, and hence each of the last two terms on the right side of equation (3) involve a constant times the sum of deviations about a mean. Since we know that in each one of the $k$ groups the sum of deviations about the group mean is zero, i.e.,

$$\sum_{i=1}^{n_j} (X_{ij} - \overline{X}) = \sum_{i=1}^{n_j} (Y_{ij} - \overline{Y}) = 0$$

the third and fourth terms on the right hand side of (3) become zero, and therefore may be dropped from the expression. Expression (4), which is finally derived, relates the *total* sum of *products* of deviations from the variate means, the sum of *products between* groups, and the sum of *products within* groups, as follows:

$$\sum_{j=1}^{k} \sum_{i=1}^{n_j} (X_{ij} - \overline{X})(Y_{ij} - \overline{Y}) = n_j \sum_{j=1}^{k} (\overline{X}_j - \overline{X})(\overline{Y}_j - \overline{Y})$$

$$\underset{\text{Total sum}}{} \qquad \qquad \underset{\text{Between groups}}{}$$
$$\underset{\text{of products}}{} \qquad \qquad \underset{\text{sum of products}}{}$$

$$+ \sum_{j=1}^{k} \sum_{i=1}^{n_j} (X_{ij} - \overline{X}_j)(Y_{ij} - \overline{Y}) \tag{4}$$

$$\underset{\text{Within groups}}{}$$
$$\underset{\text{sum of products}}{}$$

The value of the *total* sum of products is obtained by evaluating the right hand side of equation (5):

$$\sum_{j=1}^{k} \sum_{i=1}^{n_j} (X_{ij} - \overline{X})(Y_{ij} - \overline{Y}) = \sum_{j=1}^{k} \sum_{i=1}^{n_j} X_{ij}Y_{ij} - \frac{\left(\sum\limits_{j=1}^{k} \sum\limits_{i=1}^{n_j} X_{ij}\right)\left(\sum\limits_{j=1}^{k} \sum\limits_{i=1}^{n_j} Y_{ij}\right)}{n} \tag{5}$$

$$\underset{\text{Total sum of products}}{}$$

where $n$ denotes the number of *pairs* of observation $(X_{ij}, Y_{ij})$ in the *entire* table, the subscript $ij$ denotes the $i$-th pair of observations in the $j$-th group; and there are $n_j$ pairs in each of the $k$ groups.

The values of the *between* groups and *within* groups "product sums" may be obtained from equations (6) and (7):

$$n_j \sum_{j=1}^{k} (\overline{X}_j - \overline{X})(\overline{Y}_j - \overline{Y}) = \frac{\left(\sum\limits_{1}^{n_1} X_{i1}\right)\left(\sum\limits_{1}^{n_1} Y_{i1}\right)}{n_1} + \frac{\left(\sum\limits_{1}^{n_2} X_{i2}\right)\left(\sum\limits_{1}^{n_2} Y_{i2}\right)}{n_2} + \cdots$$

$$+ \frac{\left(\sum\limits_{1}^{n_k} X_{ik}\right)\left(\sum\limits_{1}^{n_k} Y_{ik}\right)}{n_k} - \frac{\left(\sum\limits_{j=1}^{k} \sum\limits_{i=1}^{n_j} X_{ij}\right)\left(\sum\limits_{j=1}^{k} \sum\limits_{i=1}^{n_j} Y_{ij}\right)}{n} \tag{6}$$

$$\underset{\text{Between groups}}{}$$
$$\underset{\text{"product sum"}}{}$$

where $n_1, n_2, n_3, \ldots, n_k$ indicate the number of pairs of observation in *each* of the $k$ groups and the last term of the expression is the same as the last term of (5). The value of the product sum within groups is found from equation (7) by first finding:

$$\sum_{j=1}^{k}\sum_{i=1}^{n_j}(X_{ij}-\bar{X}_j)(Y_{ij}-\bar{Y}_j) = \sum_{j=1}^{k}\left[\sum_{i=1}^{n_j}X_{ij}Y_{ij} - \frac{\left(\sum_{i=1}^{n_j}X_{ij}\right)\left(\sum_{i=1}^{n_j}Y_{ij}\right)}{n_j}\right] \quad (7)$$

Within group "product sum"

the product sum for *each* of the *k* groups, by applying the expression inside the brackets to the *pairs* of measures $(X_{ij}, Y_{ij})$ composing the respective groups, and then summing over all *k* groups.

If the researcher is not concerned with "checking" his calculations, he can also obtain the value of the *within groups product sum* by subtraction. If such a procedure is to be followed, the value of the *total product sum* is found by (5) and the *between* groups product sum by (6); then since the sum of the product sums between groups and within groups must equal the total product sum, we know:

Within groups product sum = Total product sum − Between product sum

In order to insure a "check" of calculations, the usual research practice is to employ formulas (5), (6), and (7) to find the values of the product sums under discussion.

*Degrees of Freedom*

The number of degrees of freedom associated with the various components of sums of squares and sums of products of deviations involved in the analysis of covariance technique are determined in a fashion very similar to the one associated with the analysis of variance technique. Suppose in a research problem there are *k* groups being compared in terms of *paired observations* (X, Y) for each of *n* subjects composing the total sample selected for the study, and each of the *k* groups is made up of $n_j$ *pairs of observations*. The *total* number of degrees of freedom to *associate* with *each* one of the three analyses, i.e., (1) total sum of squares for *X*; (2) total sum of squares for *Y*; and (3) total sum of products of *X* and *Y*, is $n-1$. The number of degrees of freedom for *each* of the *X*, *Y*, and "products" of *X* and *Y*, *between groups components* is $k-1$; while the number of degrees of freedom for *each* of the three analyses (X, Y, and "products" of *X* and *Y*) associated with the *within groups components* is $kn_j - k$. Thus, algebraically, we have equation (8) to check the analysis of the number of degrees of freedom allocated to each component of the sums of squares of *X*, sums of squares of *Y*, and the sum of the products of the deviations of *X* and *Y*.

$$(n-1) = (k-1) + (kn_j - k) \quad (8)$$

Total    Between    Within

*Covariance and Correlation*

The linear correlation coefficient *r* may be expressed in terms of the products of deviations from the means of *X* and *Y*, and the *sample* standard deviations of the two variables $X$ and $Y$. After a slight algebraic manipulation of $n$, the number of *pairs* of values involved, the expression for $r$ may be written as:

$$r = \frac{\sum(X - \bar{X})(Y - \bar{Y})}{\sqrt{\sum(X - \bar{X})^2 \sum(Y - \bar{Y})^2}}$$

Thus, the correlation coefficient $r$ is the covariance of $X$ and $Y$ divided by the square root of the product of the sample variance of $X$ times the sample variance of $Y$.

The regression coefficient $b$ is given by the expression:

$$b = \frac{\sum(X - \bar{X})(Y - \bar{Y})}{\sum(X - \bar{X})^2}$$

which is the covariance of $X$ and $Y$ divided by the variance of the independent variable $X$.

Since there is a set of sums of squares and products associated with the *total* sample of paired values $(X, Y)$, another set of sums of squares and products associated with the *between groups* component, and still another set associated with the *within groups* component, three different values of the regression coefficient $b$ can be calculated. Realizing that the *within groups component* values of $r$ and $b$ are considered to be the best estimates of the population parameters $\rho$ and $B$, the expressions, where the summation of $i$ is over 1 to $n_j$ paired observations and the summation of $j$ is over 1 to $k$ groups, are summarized as follows:

| *Component* — | *Correlation Coefficient r* | *Regression Coefficient b* |
|---|---|---|
| 1. Total | $\dfrac{\sum\sum(X_{ij} - \bar{X})(Y_{ij} - \bar{Y})}{\sqrt{\sum\sum(X_{ij} - \bar{X})^2 \sum\sum(Y_{ij} - \bar{Y})^2}}$ | $\dfrac{\sum\sum(X_{ij} - \bar{X})(Y_{ij} - \bar{Y})}{\sum\sum(X_{ij} - \bar{X})^2}$ |
| 2. Between Groups | $\dfrac{\sum\sum(\bar{X}_j - \bar{X})(\bar{Y}_j - \bar{Y})}{\sqrt{\sum\sum(\bar{X}_j - \bar{X})^2 \sum\sum(\bar{Y}_j - \bar{Y})^2}}$ | $\dfrac{\sum\sum(\bar{X}_j - \bar{X})(\bar{Y}_j - \bar{Y})}{\sum\sum(\bar{X}_j - \bar{X})^2}$ |
| 3. Within Groups | $\dfrac{\sum\sum(X_{ij} - \bar{X}_j)(Y_{ij} - \bar{Y}_j)}{\sqrt{\sum\sum(X_{ij} - \bar{X}_j)^2 \sum\sum(Y_{ij} - \bar{Y}_j)^2}}$ | $\dfrac{\sum\sum(X_{ij} - \bar{X}_j)(Y_{ij} - \bar{Y}_j)}{\sum\sum(X_{ij} - \bar{X}_j)^2}$ |

With this background we now are prepared to discuss the matter of adjusting the dependent variable $Y$ for initial differences among subjects measured in terms of the independent variable $X$.

*Adjustment*

There are mainly two ways in which the analysis of covariance technique is used in educational research. The first case arises when the researcher has measures of the subjects on the *supplementary*, or concomitant variable, $X$, i.e., on a variable which could affect the *dependent*, or experimental, variable $Y$;

and uses the covariance technique to account for, or control, the effect of the supplementary variable. To illustrate, a researcher conducting an experiment in reading is aware of the fact that differences in the verbal aptitudes of subjects might affect the experimental findings, and through the use of existing verbal aptitude scores for the subjects, applies the covariance technique to control statistically this supplementary variable. The second way in which the analysis of covariance technique is used is in those situations where there is no measure of the supplementary variable $X$, and in order to procure measures of X, subjects are given whatever test is to be used to measure the dependent (experimental) variable $Y$, *before* the experimental treatments are applied; then by the analysis of covariance technique these pre-experimental measures $X$ are used to *adjust* the post-experimental measures for initial differences. In principle, both cases are the same, and only differ to the extent that in the first case the supplementary variable is specifically named and statistically controlled, while in the second case it is assumed that a score of an individual on a test before application of the experimental treatment(s) is a measure of his "initial capacity" in that area which the test is purported to measure, and this measure can be used to account for initial differences among subjects in the area which it measures. The essential point of both cases is that initial differences between groups, in terms of the supplementary variable $X$, can be "partialed out" of the dependent (experimental) variable $Y$ by the analysis of covariance technique, and a more precise test of the significance of the difference between the "adjusted" group means ($\hat{Y}$'s) can be made than otherwise would have been possible.

Adjustment formulae that are employed frequently in the analysis of covariance technique are: (1) the adjustment of the variability in $Y$, and (2) the adjustment of sample means on the dependent variable $Y$ for initial differences among subjects on the supplementary variable $X$. Equation (9) expresses the adjustment of variability in $Y$, and equation (10) expresses the adjustment of sample means on the dependent variable $Y$'s*

1. Adjusted Total Variance in

$$Y = \sum_{j=1}^{k} \sum_{i=1}^{n_j} (Y_{ij} - \overline{Y})^2 - \frac{\left[\sum_{1}^{k} \sum_{1}^{n_j} (X_{ij} - \overline{X})(Y_{ij} - \overline{Y})\right]^2}{\sum_{1}^{k} \sum_{1}^{n_j} (X_{ij} - \overline{X})^2} \qquad (9)$$

2. Adjusted *Between Groups* Variance in

$$Y = \sum_{j=1}^{k} \sum_{i=1}^{n_j} (\overline{Y}_j - \overline{Y})^2 - \frac{\left[n_j \sum_{1}^{k} (\overline{X}_j - \overline{X})(\overline{Y}_j - \overline{Y})\right]^2}{\sum_{1}^{k} \sum_{1}^{n_j} (\overline{X}_j - \overline{X})^2}$$

---

* For an excellent discussion of the derivation of formulas (9) and (10), see William S. Ray,[143] *An Introduction to Experimental Design,* pp. 111–13, and 119–21.

3. Adjusted *Within Groups* Variance in

$$Y = \sum_{j=1}^{k} \sum_{i=1}^{n_j} (Y_{ij} - \overline{Y}_j)^2 - \frac{\left[ \sum_{1}^{k} \sum_{1}^{n_j} (X_{ij} - \overline{X}_j)(Y_{ij} - \overline{Y}_j) \right]^2}{\sum_{1}^{k} \sum_{1}^{n_j} (X_{ij} - \overline{X}_j)^2} \qquad \begin{array}{l}(9)\\ (\text{cont.})\end{array}$$

Although three adjustment formulas are shown in equations (9), the formula is a general one and can be applied to adjust any component of variance in $Y$, including the various forms associated with interactions components in problems involving two or more factors. Equation (10) can be written in its most general form as:

$$\text{Adjusted } \overline{Y}_k = \hat{Y}_k = \overline{Y}_k - b(\overline{X}_k - \overline{X}) \qquad (10)$$

which indicates how the sample mean $\overline{Y}_k$ of the $k$-th group can be adjusted. Obviously as $k = 1, 2, 3, \ldots k$, equation (10) is being applied to *adjust* the sample means $\overline{Y}_1, \overline{Y}_2, \overline{Y}_3, \ldots, \overline{Y}_k$, respectively. Equation (10) expresses how each sample mean expressed in dependent variable form, $\overline{Y}_1, \overline{Y}_2, \overline{Y}_3 \ldots \overline{Y}_k$, respectively, is adjusted by an amount calculated on the basis of the initial deviation of the sample mean ($\overline{X}_j$, in general form) from the total mean ($\overline{X}$) of the adjusting variable.

It should be noted before proceeding to an illustrative example that the *within groups* adjustment of the variability in $Y$, and the *within groups* value of the regression coefficient $b$ are used most frequently in practice as the basis for adjusting variability and sample means. This fact will be demonstrated in the examples which we shall present and discuss later.

*Homogeneity of Variances*

In the discussion of the analysis of variance technique for a single variable of classification, a simple $F$-test of the homogeneity of the sample variances was presented. The same test can be applied in connection with the analysis of covariance technique.

When some form of biased error is associated with the *supplementary* measure (adjusting variable) $X$ of the paired measures $(X, Y)$, the correlation between $X$ and the dependent variable $Y$ for the sample involved will be affected. This condition may well result in heterogeneous sample regressions and hence heterogeneous components of variance. Since a biased estimate of the population variance results when the components of the estimate are heterogeneous, a test of significance of the observed regressions' homogeneity should be performed.

The test of homogeneity of regressions calls for the computation of the adjusted sum of squares for each separate sample, or group. That is, the adjustment:

$$\sum_{i=1}^{n_j} (Y_{ij} - \overline{Y}_j)^2 - \frac{\left[ \sum_{1}^{n_j} (X_{ij} - \overline{X}_j)(Y_{ij} - \overline{Y}_j) \right]^2}{\sum_{1}^{n_j} (X_{ij} - \overline{X}_j)^2} \qquad (11)$$

is applied to each group (sample) separately, thus producing an adjusted sum of squares for each group. *These adjusted sums of squares for the respective groups are then added together to produce the combined adjusted sums of squares for the groups composing the total sample of the study. This quantity shall be designated as $C_i$.*

Employing the symbol $SS_{aw}$ to denote the within groups adjusted sum of squares, the value of which is found by applying formula (11) to the combined sums of squares and products of the individual groups *before* "*adjusting*" *each group individually,* a measure of the heterogeneity of the several group regressions may be found by subtracting $C_i$ from $SS_{aw}$. In algebraic form the expression becomes:

$$SS_{aw} - C_i$$

It should be noted that the within groups adjusted sum of squares occurs in the main analysis and in the test of significance of the regression as well.

The $F$-ratio provides the test of significance. The numerator of the ratio is the variance calculated by the expression:

$$\frac{SS_{aw} - C_i}{k - 1}$$

where $SS_{aw}$ and $C_i$ are as previously defined, and $k - 1$ indicates the appropriate number of degrees of freedom, with $k$ designating the number of groups involved in the total sample. Hence, the $F$-ratio to be employed is:

$$F = \frac{(SS_{aw} - C_i)/(k - 1)}{C_i/(n - 2k)}$$

It should be noted that if the experiment, or research, has been conducted properly, with measures on the $X$ variable being obtained under uniform conditions, the $X$ measures will contain only sampling errors, and consequently it should not be necessary to test the group variance in $X$ for heterogeneity. In other words, in the analysis of covariance technique, providing the experiment has been properly conducted, only a test of the homogeneity of regressions, as discussed here, should be necessary.

*Examples of the Analysis of Covariance Technique*

Only two examples will be employed to illustrate the analysis of covariance technique. The first example is a simple illustration of the application of the procedures associated with the analysis of covariance which have been discussed previously. The second example demonstrates the application of the analysis covariance design to a five factor (variable) research problem.

The examples of the analysis of covariance technique presented here are not the only applications of the approach. The analysis of covariance has application in many other designs, and the reader who is interested in pursuing the subject in greater depth and scope should investigate treatments of the topic by W. G. Cochran and G. M. Cox;[38] Allen Edwards;[54] P. O. Johnson;[104] P. L. Lindquist;[113] William Ray;[143] and George Snedecor.[159]

*Example 1*

In this example, it should be remembered that the subjects are randomly selected and assigned to the three groups composing the total sample. The null hypothesis under test is that the differences between the *adjusted* means ($\hat{Y}$'s) of the groups involved in the experiment are not significant, and the hope is that this "null" ($H_0$) can be rejected in favor of the "alternative" hypothesis ($H_1$) which states that some, or all, of the differences between the adjusted means *are* significant. It should also be noted that the experimenter *expects* a difference between the *unadjusted* means ($\bar{Y}$'s) of the groups to exist because of the imposition of the experimental treatments. He does not, however, expect differences between the pre-experimental means ($\bar{X}$'s) of the groups, because the $X$ measures were made prior to the experimental treatment of the subjects.

The analysis of covariance technique is applied by making allowances for uncontrolled sources of difference by "partialing out" differences due to the known correlation, or degree of relationship, between the respective groups. This action provides a greater precision in the estimate of the "error" (variance) terms than is possible under simpler statistical test designs. The number of subjects employed in this example has been kept small purposely to avoid computational frustrations, and to allow for concentrated discussion of the processes and procedures associated with the analysis of covariance technique.

Suppose a research worker is interested in determining if there are significant differences between three methods of teaching the subject of economics. The three methods to be investigated are: I—Lecture, II—Large Group, and III—Small Group approaches. Suppose further that differences between the methods had been found previously, but at the time of these findings there was reason to believe that factors other than the methods may well have been operating to provide the differences. The measurements to be taken on the subjects are the scores of these persons on an appropriate standardized test of good reliability, validity, objectivity, and discrimination.

The investigator, before beginning the experiment, assigned numbers to all the eleventh grade pupils in the school where the study was to be conducted. He then selected *at random* fifteen pupils from the supply of subjects, and assigned each of them *at random* to one of the three methods under investigation. These fifteen subjects were then given an appropriate test in economics which provided a set of pre-experimental measures ($X$) on the participating subjects. The experimental treatments are imposed over a period of six months, and at the end of that time, the fifteen students are given another test in economics, parallel to the first test, and of appropriate difficulty for the work covered during the period of experimentation. The fictitious data for both testings are presented below, with $X$ representing the pre-experimental measures and $Y$ the post-experimental scores.

A test of the significant differences between the three groups' mean scores, the computation of the three possible correlation coefficients, the three possible regression coefficients, and the interpretation of these results, are presented below:

Methods

| | I | | | | | II | | | | | III | | | | |
| | X | $X^2$ | Y | $Y^2$ | XY | X | $X^2$ | Y | $Y^2$ | XY | X | $X^2$ | Y | $Y^2$ | XY |
|---|---|---|---|---|---|---|---|---|---|---|---|---|---|---|---|
| | 12 | 144 | 12 | 144 | 144 | 6 | 36 | 9 | 81 | 54 | 12 | 144 | 15 | 225 | 180 |
| | 11 | 121 | 12 | 144 | 132 | 9 | 81 | 9 | 81 | 81 | 10 | 100 | 12 | 144 | 120 |
| | 10 | 100 | 11 | 121 | 110 | 11 | 121 | 13 | 169 | 143 | 4 | 16 | 9 | 81 | 36 |
| | 12 | 144 | 10 | 100 | 120 | 14 | 196 | 14 | 196 | 196 | 4 | 16 | 8 | 64 | 32 |
| | 10 | 100 | 12 | 144 | 120 | 2 | 4 | 5 | 25 | 10 | 8 | 64 | 11 | 121 | 88 |

| | | | | | | | | | | | | | | | |
|---|---|---|---|---|---|---|---|---|---|---|---|---|---|---|---|
| $\sum X$: | 55 | | | | | 42 | | | | | 38 | | | | |
| $\sum Y$: | | | 57 | | | | | 50 | | | | | 55 | | |
| $(\sum X)^2$: | 3025 | | | | | 1764 | | | | | 1444 | | | | |
| $(\sum Y)^2$: | | | 3249 | | | | | 2500 | | | | | 3025 | | |
| $\bar{Y}$ | 11.0 | | | | | 8.4 | | | | | 7.6 | | | | |
| $\bar{X}$ | | | 11.4 | | | | | 10.0 | | | | | 11.0 | | |

| | | | |
|---|---|---|---|
| $\sum X_t = 135$ | $\sum Y_t = 162$ | $\sum X_t^2 = 1387$ |
| $(\sum X_t)^2 = 18{,}225$ | $(\sum Y_t)^2 = 26{,}244$ | $\sum Y_t^2 = 1840$ |
| | $\sum X Y_t = 1566$ | |
| $\sum X_1 Y_t = 626$ | $\sum X_{II} Y_{II} = 484$ | $\sum X_{III} Y_{III} = 456$ |

Grand Means: $\bar{X} = 9$; $\bar{Y} = 10.8$

*Step 1.* Compute the sums of squares for $X$.

$$\text{Total sum of squares } X = \sum X_t^2 - \frac{(\sum X_t)^2}{15} = 1387 - \frac{18{,}225}{15}$$

$$= 1387 - 1215 = 172$$

$$\text{Between groups sum of squares } X = \frac{(\sum X_1)^2 + (\sum X_{II})^2 + (\sum X_{III})^2}{5} - \frac{(\sum X_t)^2}{15}$$

$$= \frac{3025 + 1764 + 1444}{5} - 1215$$

$$= 1246.6 - 1215 = 31.60$$

$$\text{Within groups sum of squares } X = \text{total} - \text{between}$$

$$= 172 - 31.60 = 140.40$$

(Note: This value can be checked by a direct computation of within groups sum of squares.)

Variance Table X

| Source | df | Sum of Squares | Mean Square (Variance) | F-ratio |
|---|---|---|---|---|
| Between | 2 | 31.60 | 15.80 | $F = \dfrac{15.8}{11.7} = 1.35$ |
| Within | 12 | 140.40 | 11.70 | (Do not reject $H_0$) |
| Total | 14 | 172.00 | | |

*Step* 2. Compute the sums of squares for Y.

$$\text{Total sum of squares } Y = \sum Y_t^2 - \frac{(\sum Y_t)^2}{15} = 1840 - \frac{26{,}244}{15}$$

$$= 1840 - 1749.60 = 90.40$$

$$\text{Between groups sum of squares } Y = \frac{(\sum Y_I)^2 + (\sum Y_{II})^2 + (\sum Y_{III})^2}{5} - \frac{(\sum Y_t)^2}{15}$$

$$= \frac{3249 + 2500 + 3025}{5} - \frac{26{,}244}{15}$$

$$= 1754.80 - 1749.60 = 5.20$$

$$\text{Within groups sum of squares } Y = \text{total} - \text{between}$$

$$= 90.40 - 5.20 = 85.20$$

Variance Table Y

| Source | df | Sum of Squares | Mean Square (Variance) | F-ratio |
|--------|-----|----------------|------------------------|---------|
| Between | 2 | 5.20 | 2.6 | $F = \frac{2.6}{7.1}$ |
| Within | 12 | 85.20 | 7.1 | (Do not reject $H_0$:) |
| Total | 14 | 90.40 | | |

*Step* 3. Compute the sums of products $XY$.

Total sum of products $XY$

$$= \sum X Y_t - \frac{(\sum X_t)(\sum Y_t)}{15}$$

$$= 1566 - \frac{(135)(162)}{15}$$

$$= 1566 - \frac{21{,}870}{15} = 1566 - 1458 = 108$$

Between groups sum of products $XY$

$$= \frac{(\sum X_I)(\sum Y_I) + (\sum X_{II})(\sum Y_{II}) + (\sum X_{III})(\sum Y_{III})}{5} - 1458$$

$$= \frac{(55)(57) + (42)(50) + (38)(55)}{5} - 1458$$

$$= 1465 - 1458 = 7$$

Within groups sum of products $XY$

$$= \text{total} - \text{between}$$
$$= 108 - 7 = 101$$

The within groups sum of products $XY$ may be computed directly as follows:

Within groups $XY$

$$= \sum X_1 Y_1 - \frac{(\sum X_1)(\sum Y_1)}{5} + \sum X_{II} Y_{II} - \frac{(\sum X_{II})(\sum Y_{II})}{5} + \sum X_{III} Y_{III} - \frac{(\sum X_{III})(\sum Y_{III})}{5}$$

$$= 626 - 627 + 484 - 420 + 456 - 418 = 101$$

Summary Table of Sums of Squares and Products

| Source | df | $\sum x^2 = \sum (X - \bar{X})^2$ | $\sum y^2 = \sum (Y - \bar{Y})^2$ | $\sum xy = \sum (X - \bar{X})(Y - \bar{Y})$ |
|---|---|---|---|---|
| Between | 2 | 31.60 | 5.20 | 7.00 |
| Within | 12 | 140.40 | 85.20 | 101.00 |
| Total | 14 | 172.00 | 90.40 | 108.00 |

*Step 4.* Compute errors of estimate (adjusted $Y$ sums of squares)
In the following discussion:

$$y = (Y - \bar{Y}); \quad x = (X - \bar{X}); \quad \text{hence, } xy = (X - \bar{X})(Y - \bar{Y});$$
$$y^2 = (Y - \bar{Y})^2; \quad \text{and } x^2 = (X - \bar{X})^2$$

Total:

$$\sum (y - bx)^2 = \sum y_t^2 - \frac{(\sum xy_t)^2}{\sum x_t^2} = 90.40 - \frac{(108)^2}{172} = 90.40 - 67.81 = 22.59$$

Within:

$$\sum (y - bx)^2 = \sum y_w^2 - \frac{(\sum xy_w)^2}{\sum x_w^2} = 85.20 - \frac{(101)^2}{140.4} = 85.20 - 72.66 = 12.54$$

Between:

$$\text{Between} = \text{total} - \text{within}$$
$$= 22.59 - 12.54 = 10.05$$

Summary Table of Adjusted $Y$ Sums of Squares and Variances*

| Source | df | Sums of Squares of Errors of Estimate (Adj. Y) | Mean Square or Variance | F-ratio |
|---|---|---|---|---|
| Adjusted Y Between Groups | 2 | 10.05 | 5.03 | $F = \dfrac{5.03}{1.14} = 4.41$ |
| Adjusted Y Within Groups | 11 | $E_w = 12.54$ | $S_{Y.X}^2 = 1.14$ | Decision: Reject $H_0$: at .05 level |
| Adjusted Y Total | 13 | 22.59 | | |

---

* Note that the total and within groups *Variance* each have one degree of freedom less than before. This condition is caused by using one degree of freedom for *each* computation of the total and within *errors of estimate*.

*Step 5.* Compute values for correlation and regression coefficients.

Total:

$$r_t = \frac{\sum xy_t}{\sqrt{\sum x_t^2 \sum y_t^2}} = \frac{108}{\sqrt{(172)(904)}} = \frac{108}{124.69} = .866;$$

$$b_t = \frac{\sum xy_t}{\sum x_t^2} = \frac{108}{172} = .628$$

Between groups:

$$r_b = \frac{\sum xy_b}{\sqrt{\sum x_b^2 \sum y_b^2}} = \frac{7}{\sqrt{(31.6)(5.2)}} = \frac{7}{12.82} = .55;$$

$$b_b = \frac{\sum xy_b}{\sum x_b^2} = \frac{7}{31.6} = .222$$

Within groups:

$$r_w = \frac{\sum xy_w}{\sqrt{\sum x_w^2 \sum y_w^2}} = \frac{101}{\sqrt{(140.4)(852)}} = \frac{101}{109.37} = .92;$$

$$b_w = \frac{\sum xy_w}{\sum x_w^2} = \frac{101}{140.4} = .719$$

The five steps presented to this point give the necessary computations for applying the analysis of covariance to three groups with pre-treatment measures $X$ and post-treatment measures $Y$. The following steps outline the procedure employed.

*Step 1.* The analysis of variance technique was applied to the $X$ measures to obtain sums of squares for the total and its two components: the between groups component and the within groups component.

*Step 2.* The analysis of variance technique was applied to the $Y$ measures to obtain sums of squares for the between groups components, the within groups component, and the total.

*Step 3.* The sums of products $XY$ for the between groups component, the within groups component, and the total are calculated by employing the procedures of the ordinary analysis of variance technique.

*Step 4.* With the sums of squares of $X$ and $Y$, and the sums of products $XY$, the respective *errors of estimate* (adjusted $Y$ sums of squares) are computed. The errors of estimate are derived from the formula for the standard error of estimate which is a prediction formula. The quantities that are employed in the formula are *sums of squares* of errors of estimate which are calculated from what is called "*the residual variance.*" The residual variance is defined to be that amount of variance which remains in the $Y$ measures after the variance in the

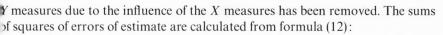

$Y$ measures due to the influence of the $X$ measures has been removed. The sums of squares of errors of estimate are calculated from formula (12):

$$\sum(y - bx)^2 = \sum y^2 - \frac{(\sum xy)^2}{\sum x^2} \tag{12}$$

where the symbol $\sum(y - bx)^2$ denotes the *residual sum of squares of errors of estimate*; $\sum y^2$ denotes the *sum of squares* of $Y$ measures; and $(\sum xy)^2/\sum x^2$ denotes the *variance in Y accounted for by X*.

Formula (12) is employed to derive the values of the total and within groups estimates of error. The *adjusted within groups* sum of squares is used to compute a within groups estimate of the population variance (error). This within groups estimate of variance is used as a "measuring stick" term to test the significance of the adjusted between groups variance which results from the differences between the three groups $Y$-means after they have been "adjusted" (corrected) for the initial influence of $X$.

The *adjusted between groups* sum of squares is calculated by subtracting the *adjusted within groups* sum of squares from the *adjusted total* sum of squares. This between groups component is called "adjusted" because it has been corrected (adjusted) for the variation in it due to the pre-treatment $X$ variable. The summary table of the adjusted sums of squares (errors of estimate), page 429, shows the total and within groups variance each with one degree of freedom less than it had before. The degree of freedom which has been "lost" has been used to compute the value of the within groups regression coefficient which in turn is used to adjust the respective sums of squares. Since the adjusted between groups component of the sums of squares is obtained by subtracting the adjusted within groups component from the adjusted total, the degrees of freedom for the between groups component remains the same.

*Step 5.* A summary table of the analysis of variance is constructed to determine if the adjusted between groups variance is significantly greater than the adjusted within groups estimate. If the adjusted between groups variance is significantly greater than the adjusted within groups component, a significant difference between the *adjusted Y-means* ($\hat{Y}$'s) of the respective groups may be inferred to exist. This result means that there is a significant difference between the $Y$-means of the groups *when the differences existing prior* to the treatments (in the $X$ variable) are partialed out (controlled). Put in another way, the group means differed, but not significantly, before imposition of the experimental treatments. They also differed, but again not significantly, after the application of the experimental treatments. The finding of significant differences between adjusted group means ($\hat{Y}$'s) indicates that the not significant initial differences between means were of sufficient magnitude to obscure differences due to the experimental treatments as measured by the *unadjusted* $\bar{Y}$'s. To find which of the three possible differences between adjusted group means: $(\hat{Y}_I - \hat{Y}_{II})$, $(\hat{Y}_I - \hat{Y}_{III})$, and $(\hat{Y}_{II} - \hat{Y}_{III})$, is significant, or whether all of them are significant, the appropriate $t$-test must be applied. Before proceeding to the $t$-test for adjusted means, however, consideration must be given to the actual process of adjusting the means.

*Step 6.* From the sums of squares in $x$ and $y$ and the sums of products in $xy$ the total, between groups, and within groups correlation coefficients and regression coefficients are computed. The general formula for the correlation coefficient is:

$$r = \frac{\sum xy}{\sqrt{\sum x^2 \sum y^2}}$$

Substituting the appropriate sums of squares values, a correlation coefficient estimate can be found on the bases of the total sum $r_t$, the between groups sum $r_b$, and the within groups sum $r_w$.

The within groups correlation, $r_w = .92$, is a better measure of the relationship between $X$ and $Y$ than is the total correlation, $r_t = .866$, because systematic differences between means have been eliminated from the within groups measure, $r_w$. The high correlation between $X$ and $Y$ accounts for the significance between $Y$-means when the variability in $X$ has been "partialed out." If the within groups correlation is *high*, and the between groups correlation is *low*, the analysis of covariance technique will frequently lead to a significant $F$-ratio while the analysis of variance does not, and hence does not reveal significant differences between the $Y$-means (unadjusted). Thus, the between groups coefficient $r_b$ and the within groups coefficient may be used in a "preliminary estimative" way to determine if the application of the analysis of covariance technique is worthwhile. The more exact test, the significance of the regression is discussed later.

The general expression for the regression coefficient is:

$$b = \frac{\sum xy}{\sum x^2}$$

Regression coefficients may be computed on the basis of the total, between group means, and within groups sums of squares. The within groups regression coefficient $b_w$ is the most nearly unbiased estimate of the regression of $Y$ on $X$, because any systematic bias due to differences between group means have been removed. For this reason, $b_w$ is used as the regression coefficient in calculating the values of the *adjusted* $Y$-means, $\hat{Y}_k$'s, of the respective groups.

*Step 7.* The $Y$-means of the respective groups can be adjusted directly for differences in the $X$-means by employing formula (10):

$$\text{Adjusted } \overline{Y}_k = \hat{Y}_k = \overline{Y}_k - b(\overline{X}_k - \overline{X}) \tag{10}$$

The value substituted for $b$ in the equation is that of the *within groups coefficient*, which in our example is: $b_w = .719$. The symbol $\overline{Y}_k$ denotes the *unadjusted* $Y$-mean of the $k$-th group, $\overline{X}_k$ is the corresponding $X$-mean of that group, and $\overline{X}$ is the *grand*, or *total*, mean of *all* $X$ measures.

The significant $F$-ratio in the Adjusted Sums of Squares and Variances Table, page 429, indicates that at least *one* of the *adjusted* $Y$-means ($\hat{Y}$'s) of the groups differs significantly from one of the other *adjusted* means. In order to determine which of the differences between the adjusted group $Y$-means are significant, it is necessary to compute the values of the adjusted $Y$-means of the respective groups, and then test these differences by an appropriate form of the $t$-test.

The adjustment of the $Y$-mean for Group I in our example is:

$$\hat{Y}_I = \bar{Y}_I - b_w(\bar{X}_I - \bar{X}) = 11.4 - .719(11 - 9) = 11.4 - 1.438 = 9.962$$

In similar fashion, the adjustment of the $Y$-mean for Group II becomes:

$$\hat{Y}_{II} = \bar{Y}_{II} - b_w(\bar{X}_{II} - \bar{X}) = 10 - .719(8.4 - 9) = 10.4314$$

and the adjustment of the $Y$-mean for Group III is:

$$\hat{Y}_{III} = \bar{Y}_{III} - b_w(\bar{X}_{III} - \bar{X}) = 11 - .719(7.6 - 9) = 12.0066$$

*Step 8.* Formula (13) is the appropriate form of the $t$-test to employ in order to determine which of the *differences* between the *adjusted means* ($\hat{Y}$'s) of the respective groups are *significant*. In order to employ formula (13) the following conditions should be satisfied: (1) the $k$ groups are composed of $n_j$ sampling units which have been *selected at random* from the population and *assigned at random* to them, (2) measurements in terms of $X$ are made on all subjects prior to the imposition of the experimental (or differential) treatment, (3) measurements are made on all subjects after the imposition of the experimental treatment, (4) the pre-experimental measures in $X$ are assumed to be correlated linearly with the post-experimental measures $Y$, (5) the data are analyzed by the analysis of covariance technique, and (6) the group means in $Y$ are adjusted by formula (10) for the initial variation in $X$, i.e., by employing the regression equation of $Y$ on $X$. If these six conditions prevail the appropriate form of the $t$-test is:

$$t = \frac{\hat{Y}_{k_1} - \hat{Y}_{k_2}}{\sqrt{S_{Y \cdot X}^2 \left[ \dfrac{1}{n_1} + \dfrac{1}{n_2} + \dfrac{(\bar{X}_{k_1} - \bar{X}_{k_2})^2}{\sum x_w^2} \right]}} \tag{13}$$

where $\hat{Y}_{k_1}$ and $\hat{Y}_{k_2}$ are the *adjusted means* of the respective groups under consideration; $S_{Y \cdot X}^2$ is the *adjusted* within groups mean square (variance), which estimates the adjusted population variance $\sigma_{Y \cdot X}^2$; $n_1$ is the number of sampling units in the one group, and $n_2$ is the number of sampling units in the second group; $\bar{X}_{k_1}$ is the mean of the $k_1$ group in the pre-experimental variable $X$, and $\bar{X}_{k_2}$ is the same type of mean for the $k_2$ group; and $\sum x_w^2$ is the *within groups sums of squares* for $X$. The complexity of formula (13) derives from the consideration given to the standard error [the denominator of (13)] of the difference between two adjusted means. This standard error is developed on the basis of regression theory.*

---

* For further treatment of this point, see W. G. Cochran and C. M. Cox,[38] *Experimental Designs*, pp. 74–82.

Applying formula (13) to the three differences of the adjusted group means occurring in our example, we find by a two-tailed test for:

1. Groups I and II:

$$t = \frac{\hat{Y}_I - \hat{Y}_{II}}{\sqrt{S_{Y \cdot X}^2 \left[\dfrac{1}{n_I} + \dfrac{1}{n_{II}} + \dfrac{(\bar{X}_I - \bar{X}_{II})^2}{\sum x_w^2}\right]}} = \frac{9.962 - 10.4314}{\sqrt{1.14\left[\dfrac{1}{5} + \dfrac{1}{5} + \dfrac{(11 - 8.4)^2}{140.4}\right]}} =$$

$$t = \frac{-.4694}{\sqrt{1.14(.4 + .048)}} = \frac{-.4694}{.7146} \approx -.657$$

entering the $t$-table with 11 degrees of freedom, the number of $df$ associated with the adjusted within groups mean square (variance, $S_{Y \cdot X}^2$, see Summary Table, page 429), the critical value of $t$ at the .05 level of this two-tailed test is found to be: $t = \pm 2.201$. Since the observed value of $t = -.657$ does not fall in the critical region

$$\begin{Bmatrix} t < -2.201 \\ t > +2.201 \end{Bmatrix}$$

the null hypothesis of no significant difference between the adjusted means of Group I and II *cannot be rejected.*

2. Group I and III:

$$t = \frac{\hat{Y}_I - \hat{Y}_{III}}{\sqrt{S_{Y \cdot X}^2 \left[\dfrac{1}{n_I} + \dfrac{1}{n_{III}} + \dfrac{(\bar{X}_I - \bar{X}_{III})^2}{\sum x_w^2}\right]}} = \frac{9.962 - 12.0066}{\sqrt{1.14\left[\dfrac{1}{5} + \dfrac{1}{5} + \dfrac{(11 - 7.6)^2}{140.4}\right]}}$$

$$t = \frac{-2.0446}{\sqrt{1.14(.4 + .082)}} = \frac{-2.0446}{.741} \approx -2.76$$

Since the observed value of $t \approx -2.76$ falls in the critical region

$$\begin{Bmatrix} t < -2.201 \\ t > +2.201 \end{Bmatrix}$$

the null hypothesis ($H_0$) *is rejected* in favor of the "alternative" hypothesis ($H_1$) that a significant difference (at the .05 level) between the *adjusted* means of Groups I and III does exist.

3. Groups II and III

$$t = \frac{10.4314 - 12.0066}{\sqrt{1.14\left[\dfrac{1}{5} + \dfrac{1}{5} + \dfrac{(8.4 - 7.6)^2}{140.4}\right]}}$$

$$= \frac{-1.5752}{\sqrt{1.14(.4 + .0045)}} = \frac{-1.5752}{.68} \approx -2.32$$

Since the observed value of $t \approx -2.32$ falls in the critical region

$$\begin{cases} t < -2.201 \\ t > +2.201 \end{cases}$$

the null hypothesis is *rejected* in favor of the "alternative" hypothesis. Since the adjusted mean score of Group III ($\hat{Y}_{III} = 12.0066$) is greater than that of Group II ($\hat{Y}_{II} = 10.4314$), the experimenter could conclude that the Small Group approach (Group III) is significantly better than the Large Group approach (Group II).

*Step 9.* The analysis of covariance technique terminates with the application of the *t*-test for determining the significance of the differences between the adjusted means of the respective groups; however, the results of the analysis must then be interpreted in terms of the research problem and hypotheses. In our example, by reference to the findings produced in Step 8, it should be clear that since the difference between the adjusted means for Group I and II is not statistically significant it can be concluded that the data of this experiment failed to support the notion that a significant difference between a Lecture and Large Group approach might exist. On the other hand, based upon the *t*-test results of Step 8, the data of the experiment support the hypotheses of a significant difference existing between: (1) the Lecture method of Group I and the Small Group approach of Group III, and (2) the Large Group (Group II) and Small Group (Group III) approaches. Since the Small Group approach showed a significantly higher value in the form of an adjusted mean, if the experimenter wishes to base his conclusions solely on the data of this experiment, he could conclude that the Small Group approach to teaching economics was superior to the other two approaches, and recommend its adoption. In actual practice, however, a more cautious approach would be employed by reporting the findings of the current experiment, and recommending further experimentation with the dimensions involved.

## Significance of Regression

A test of the significance of the regression of the dependent variable $Y$ on the adjusting variable $X$ is usually conducted *before* proceeding with the main analysis. The discussion here has not followed this procedure because it was felt that any deviation from the text dealing with the topics of the main analysis might have tended to confuse the issues instead of clarifying them. For this reason, but keeping in mind that *the significance of regression is usually tested before conducting the main analysis*, a discussion of the topic and its associated computational procedures will now be presented.

The use of the $X$ measure to eliminate error, and hence "adjust" (correct) the $Y$ measure assumes the existence of a relationship between $X$ and $Y$. If the two variables are independent (uncorrelated), there will be no advantage in employing the analysis of covariance technique.

The significance of the relationship between $Y$ and $X$, in the form of the regression of $Y$ on $X$, should be examined as it appears in the data, before proceeding with any part of the main analysis. If it is discovered that the two variables are correlated, the analysis of covariance should be employed including the adjustment of the $Y$ variable. If the variables are found to be uncorrelated (independent), the analysis of covariance should not be employed, but the analysis of variance technique for independent samples should be used.

The test of significance of the regression of $Y$ on $X$ is accomplished by:

(a) computing the value of a *within group predicted sum of squares*:

$$P_w = \frac{(\sum xy_w)^2}{\sum x_w^2}$$

for our example:

$$P_w = \frac{(101)^2}{140.4} = 72.66$$

(b) computing the value of the *within group error of estimate*, $E_w$, (the within "adjusted" $Y$ sums of squares):

$$E_w = \sum y_w^2 - \frac{(\sum xy_w)^2}{\sum x_w^2}$$

for our example:

$$E_w = 85.20 - \frac{(101)^2}{140.4} = 85.20 - 72.66 = 12.54$$

(see Summary Table, page 429)

(c) calculating the value of the *predicted mean square* (variance), $MS_{pw}$, by dividing the value of $P_w$ by one degree of freedom. For our example:

$$MS_{pw} = \frac{P_w}{1} = \frac{72.66}{1} = 72.66$$

(d) calculating the values of the *within groups error mean square* (variance), $S_{Y \cdot X}^2$, by dividing the value of $E_w$ by $(n - k - 1)$ degrees of freedom, where $n$ denotes the number of subjects in the total sample and $k$ denotes the number of groups (samples) involved. In our example the value of $S_{Y \cdot X}^2$ becomes:

$$S_{Y \cdot X}^2 = \frac{E_w}{n - k - 1} = \frac{12.54}{15 - 3 - 1} = \frac{12.54}{11} = 1.14$$

(see Summary Table, page 429)

(e) compute the value of the $F$-ratio employed as the test of significance of the regression of $Y$ on $X$. For our example:

$$F = \frac{MS_{pw}}{S^2_{Y \cdot X}} = \frac{72.66}{1.14} = 63.74; \quad \text{and}$$

(f) determine if the observed value of $F$ exceeds the critical value of $F$ for the appropriate numbers of degrees of freedom. In our example, the critical value of $F$ for 1 and 11 degrees of freedom is 4.84 at the .05 point and 9.65 at the .01 point.

If the observed value of $F$ exceeds the critical value, we reject the null hypothesis in favor of the alternative that a significant correlation (degree of relationship) exists between the two variables $X$ and $Y$, and the use of the $X$ variable for adjusting $Y$ is worthwhile in partially eliminating error from the data. In our example, the value of $F = 63.74$ does exceed the critical value of $F$ at the 5 per cent point (in fact, at the 1 per cent point), and we therefore would reject the null hypothesis in favor of the alternative that a significant regression, and hence a significant relationship, exists between $X$ and $Y$.

In closing our discussion, it should be pointed out that the ratio formed by the within group predicted sums of squares, $P_w$, and the "unadjusted" within group sum of squares on $Y$, is the proportion of error variability eliminated. In our example, the proportion is: $72.66/85.20 = .8528$. It is interesting to note that the value of the within groups correlation coefficient $r_w$, measuring the degree of relationship between $X$ and $Y$ is:

$$r_w = \sqrt{.8528} = .92$$

*Example 2.* This example illustrates how the analysis of covariance technique can be applied to factorial designs of experiments. In general terms, the approach includes the procurement of a number of random samples of subjects. The exact number of samples will be determined by the number of combinations of treatments (categories in the factors) included in the factorial design. An adjusting variable $X$, which is linearly correlated with the dependent variable $Y$ is chosen, and all subjects in the several samples are measured under uniform conditions in terms of adjusting variable $X$ prior to the imposition of experimental treatments. The treatment combinations are then assigned randomly to the samples (groups), and the experimentation is carried out. After the imposition of the experimental treatments, final observations on the dependent variable $Y$ are made. By employing the regression of $Y$ on $X$, the part of the variability associated with initial differences among the participating subjects is removed from the final observations ($Y$'s). The remaining variation is analyzed into interaction components and main treatment effects. These interactions and main effects are then evaluated (tested for significance) by employing the $F$-ratio comparison, which involves the components under study, and an estimate of the population error (variance), which is assumed to exist because of chance factors in the experimentation.

Although factorial designs may be constructed for any number of factors (variables, or classifications) which include any number of levels (categories), two-factor and three-factor designs are employed most frequently. Occasionally there is a need for a design with more than three factors, but since third (four factors) and higher order interactions are usually considered to have little practical significance, the difficulty of managing designs incorporating more than three factors can be avoided by defining and delimiting the research problem so that only three or fewer factors are studied at one time. Our example composed of five factors is one of those problems that occur occasionally in research. It is presented here because of its potential for the discussion of many ramifications of the application of analysis of covariance to factorial designs.

Although the procedures are not included in the discussion, in actual practice the experimenter would be expected to test the significance of the regression, and the homogeneity of the sample variances, before conducting the main analysis. These tests are conducted as previously described, and are left as exercises to be carried out by the reader.

The example discussed here is *based* upon the topic of an unpublished doctoral dissertation, and is presented in the form of a model of experimental research.* Permission of the author to adjust various aspects of the study so that an "adapted" model of experimental research could be illustrated is gratefully acknowledged.

## MODEL OF EXPERIMENTAL RESEARCH

| THE PROBLEM |

*(The problem of the study is stated briefly in terms of background, purpose and significance.)*

### Background of Study

A problem of great concern to the discipline of physical education is that of the development of certain types of motor skills in the individual. Despite the great concern, and comparatively recent advancements in the scientific approach to the analysis of problems of motor skill learning in physical education, there has been little time devoted to the study of the potential importance of the *mental aspects* of motor learning. Although there has been little study of the problem, it is a fact that more knowledge of the role that mental activity plays in developing certain motor skills would greatly enhance the efforts of physical educators in the processes of instruction. The variable of mental activity in motor learning, however, is one which is difficult to isolate and measure. At best, it can only be compared roughly to its counterpart, physical activity, in the motor learning process. The very sparseness of references to this concept in the literature shows a need for studying this problem.

Although limited in number, available studies (references are omitted here) provide sufficient evidence to support the notion that "mental practice," or mind rehearsal in the development of a motor skill, may produce enough improvement to warrant further and more intensive investigation

---

* L. Verdelle Clark, *The Effect of Mental Practice on the Development of a Certain Motor Skill.* Doctoral Dissertation (Detroit: Wayne State University, 1958).

of its potential effect. It would be most difficult to attempt an accurate evaluation, especially in one experiment, of all the variables affecting the development (learning) of any given motor skill. For this reason, the problem of the present research was delimited to the careful investigation of the effect of substituting mental practice for physical practice in the development of a certain motor skill.

*Purpose of Study*

The broad purpose of the study was to investigate the effect of mental practice as compared with that of physical practice in the development of a certain motor skill. Specifically, the purpose of the study was to investigate the effect of mental practice when substituted for physical practice in the development of the Pacific Coast one-hand foul shot motor skill, while considering factors of arm strength, group, intelligence, experience, school, and the influences of the various possible interactions of these factors.

*Significance of Study*

(*The significance of the study is described by considering significance in terms of who, what, when, where, why, and how.*)

The study has particular significance for high school physical educators to the extent that it provides information about motor learning which can be employed in the development of more efficient teaching techniques in the field of physical education. The findings of the study could contribute to the development of techniques of instruction that have application in athletics, recreation, and the activities aspect of physical education.

## THE HYPOTHESES

(*The hypotheses of the study are presented in terms of the research hypotheses, operational hypotheses, and statistical hypotheses.*)

*Research Hypotheses*

Categorical statements of the research hypotheses of the study could be:

1. There is a significant difference between the levels (categories) of the main effects (factors) in the experiment. For example, there is a significant difference between the mental practice group and the physical practice group in the development of the motor skill of the Pacific Coast one-hand foul shot.

2. The interactions of the main effects (factors) contribute significantly to the development of the motor skill of the Pacific Coast one-hand foul shot. For example, the research hypothesis involving arm strength × intelligence × school × group is that there is a significant interaction between arm strength, intelligence, school, and group, which means that this interaction contributes significantly to the development of the motor skill of the Pacific Coast one-hand foul shot.

*Operational Hypotheses*

The appropriate operational hypotheses for the various research hypotheses which could be stated categorically as in (1) and (2) above would include a definition of the measuring device being employed and a definition of the expected conditions expressed in terms of the measurements. For example, there is a significant difference between the mean scores of the mental and physical practice groups, where the score of an individual is defined to be the number of shots made out of twenty-five attempts while exclusively employing the Pacific-Coast one-hand foul shot.

*Statistical Hypotheses*

Appropriate statistical alternative hypotheses ($H_1$) can be developed from the operational hypotheses, and since "direction" is not defined in either the research hypotheses or the operational hypotheses, a two-tailed test would be employed. A typical statistical alternative hypothesis, and its corresponding null hypothesis, would be: $H_1 : \mu_p \neq \mu_m$; i.e., the mean score of the population of the physical practice group, $\mu_p$, is not equal to that of the mental practice group, $\mu_m$; and the corresponding null hypothesis submitted to test would be: $H_0 : \mu_p = \mu_m$; i.e., there is no significant difference between the mean scores of the respective populations.

## THE UNIVERSE

*(The universe, or source of data, is described, and the study sample is discussed in terms of: how selected, representativeness, and adequacy.)*

The source of data for the study was limited by definition to those male high school students who would volunteer to participate in the experiment, and who were attending high schools in the public school system of the local city. Only those high schools with adequate gymnasium facilities, and whose departments of physical education were in favor of helping to conduct the experiment, were considered eligible for inclusion in the universe of the study. At the time the experiment was conducted, only eighteen high schools were considered to have adequate gymnasium facilities for participation in the effort. Of these eighteen schools, only ten were in favor of implementing the experimentation.

Since the city system contained basically four different types of high schools, and each of these types was included in the ten which had volunteered to participate, it was decided that a judgment quota sample composed of four schools, one school representing each one of the four types, should be drawn from the ten available. Male students in each of the four schools selected would then be provided the opportunity to volunteer for participation in the research effort.

## STUDY SAMPLE

The actual study sample was selected from the available male students who fit the requirements of a five-factor, 144 cell factorial grid which had been prepared for the application of the analysis of covariance technique. The grid, which is shown below, was designed to consider the factors of: schools, classes (categories) of experience (Varsity, Junior Varsity, Novice), arm strength (high, average, low), intelligence (high, low), and groups (mental practice and physical practice). Each of the three categories of experience included 12 subjects, thus yielding a total of 36 subjects per school, and with the inclusion of four schools, a total of 144 subjects. Under these circumstances, a statistically adequate sample was employed as the study sample. In those cases where more than one subject was eligible for inclusion in one of the cells of the factorial table, a random numbers table was employed to select the cell entry.

Prior to assigning entries to the cells of the factorial table, the factors of arm strength and intelligence were equated by a paired-groups technique for each of the participating subjects. Random selection was then employed to assign the "equated" subjects to the mental and physical practice groups.

In the factorial grid the four *schools* involved in the experiment are denoted by the Roman numerals, I–IV; the *classes* (experience) are designated as V–Varsity; J.V.—Junior Varsity, and N—Novice; the two groups are indicated by M—mental practice, and P—physical practice; *intelligence* is treated in terms of $\alpha$ (high) and $\beta$ (low); and finally *arm strength* is partitioned into three levels (categories) as H—high, A—average, and L—low. The subjects employed to provide scores for the cells of the table which they (the subjects) "fit," also were used to provide "introspective analysis" data. The latter topic is discussed under the Data Collection and Data Processing elements of the model.

## DATA COLLECTION

*(The aspect of the model dealing with data collection is concerned with the instrumentalities and methods employed under the existing conditions. The points of "methods" and "conditions" are frequently described in practice as "procedures.")*

*Instrumentalities*

The instrumentalities of data collection employed in the study were:

1. Frederick Rand Rogers' Formula for Strength Index—a measure of arm strength;
2. the California Mental Maturity Test—Short Form;
3. an author-prepared interview schedule; and
4. a rating device, developed by participating athletic coaches, used to classify experience as varsity, junior varsity, or novice level.

Five-Factor Factorial Grid showing Initial Measurements X and Final Measurements Y of a Given Motor Skill

| Schools | | | I | | | | | | II | | | | | | III | | | | | | IV | | | |
|---|---|---|---|---|---|---|---|---|---|---|---|---|---|---|---|---|---|---|---|---|---|---|---|---|
| Classes | | | V | | JV | | N | | V | | JV | | N | | V | | JV | | N | | V | | JV | | N |
| Scores | | | X | Y | X | Y | X | Y | X | Y | X | Y | X | Y | X | Y | X | Y | X | Y | X | Y | X | Y | X | Y |
| Arm Strength | Intelligence | Groups | | | | | | | | | | | | | | | | | | | | | | | |
| H | α | M | 19 | 16 | 16 | 15 | 11 | 12 | 13 | 17 | 8 | 11 | 17 | 17 | 8 | 17 | 19 | 21 | 15 | 21 | 14 | 19 | 10 | 16 | 10 | 11 |
| | | P | 9 | 20 | 13 | 13 | 11 | 12 | 5 | 17 | 10 | 16 | 10 | 16 | 17 | 20 | 10 | 18 | 8 | 15 | 16 | 18 | 17 | 21 | 8 | 18 |
| | β | M | 12 | 14 | 16 | 13 | 11 | 13 | 14 | 16 | 5 | 5 | 7 | 15 | 14 | 20 | 10 | 17 | 8 | 12 | 8 | 18 | 6' | 15 | 14 | 16 |
| | | P | 9 | 19 | 13 | 13 | 6 | 14 | 15 | 19 | 8 | 13 | 8 | 13 | 18 | 18 | 18 | 15 | 7 | 7 | 16 | 19 | 14 | 17 | 15 | 15 |
| A | α | M | 14 | 9 | 16 | 12 | 7 | 10 | 13 | 19 | 14 | 19 | 11 | 11 | 19 | 20 | 17 | 19 | 12 | 12 | 17 | 19 | 12 | 15 | 6 | 10 |
| | | P | 14 | 13 | 4 | 10 | 15 | 15 | 13 | 16 | 10 | 12 | 7 | 13 | 17 | 17 | 18 | 18 | 9 | 16 | 20 | 20 | 16 | 18 | 5 | 15 |
| | β | M | 20 | 16 | 16 | 15 | 6 | 9 | 16 | 17 | 15 | 14 | 17 | 15 | 18 | 21 | 11 | 21 | 9 | 10 | 16 | 16 | 13 | 13 | 10 | 11 |
| | | P | 24 | 21 | 9 | 13 | 11 | 10 | 13 | 15 | 16 | 13 | 8 | 14 | 18 | 13 | 16 | 18 | 14 | 15 | 15 | 18 | 8 | 16 | 7 | 14 |
| L | α | M | 18 | 16 | 14 | 14 | 7 | 7 | 13 | 21 | 9 | 9 | 8 | 7 | 15 | 19 | 7 | 17 | 8 | 8 | 12 | 17 | 5 | 9 | 6 | 10 |
| | | P | 11 | 18 | 13 | 17 | 6 | 4 | 12 | 17 | 11 | 14 | 13 | 9 | 13 | 22 | 15 | 22 | 11 | 16 | 20 | 20 | 14 | 15 | 6 | 11 |
| | β | M | 17 | 12 | 13 | 14 | 2 | 11 | 13 | 15 | 10 | 14 | 11 | 18 | 18 | 18 | 11 | 16 | 12 | 11 | 15 | 18 | 9 | 12 | 7 | 16 |
| | | P | 24 | 21 | 7 | 10 | 6 | 8 | 18 | 19 | 11 | 11 | 5 | 13 | 17 | 20 | 14 | 20 | 7 | 12 | 18 | 18 | 16 | 19 | 12 | 14 |

*Procedures (Methods and Conditions)*

Although the researcher realized that the best measure of intelligence could not be obtained through group testing, the number of subjects involved in the testing program, prior to the selection of the 144 of them which "fit" the cells of the factorial grid, plus the factors of cost and time, prohibited the use of such individual intelligence tests as the Standard–Binet. In addition to this fact, the research findings available at that time showed relatively little relationship existing between *group intelligence test scores* and measurements of an *individual's motor ability*. However, the possibility that this particular experiment, dealing strongly with the mental aspects of motor learning, might cause the intelligence factor, despite its mode of measurements, to appear in a new light in its relationship with motor skill, dictated its inclusion in the study.

The experiment was started in each of the four schools on the same date. Two schools were visited by the researcher in the morning, and the other two schools were visited in the afternoon of the same day. Every effort was made to carry out the procedures of the experiment in identical fashion in each of the participating schools. The 36 subjects in each of the schools were instructed to read a group introduction to the experiment. Printed information on the technique for shooting the Pacific Coast one-hand foul shot was read by each of the subjects. The next step was a demonstration in which the 36 subjects positioned themselves in a line facing the instructor. The line extended across the gymnasium, but each of the subjects was within good hearing distance of the instructor. Using a basketball, the researcher instructed the group in the shooting technique to be employed during the experiment. During the instructional period the subjects were requested to pose through the sequence of positions of the body, arms, and legs, without a basketball, as the instructor described and demonstrated the intricacies of the shooting technique. Heavy emphasis was placed upon three factors: (1) *knowing*, understanding mentally and physically the specific motions involved; (2) *seeing*, mentally picturing oneself and the instructor while posing through the successive positions of the technique; and (3) *feeling*, witnessing the kinesthetic sensations associated with the activity, first with the eyes open and then with eyes closed. After a question and answer session, the total instructional period was repeated with each subject handling a basketball. Each subject then shot

25 consecutive practice "foul" shots during which time the instructor corrected any mistakes that were noted in the individual's employment of the technique. After the instructions were repeated again, the subjects were instructed to shoot 25 foul shots, striving to make the best score possible. Each subject was informed that this would be his initial score $(X)$ for the experiment and that a final score $(Y)$ would be obtained at the termination of the experiment in order to measure improvement. The number of shots made out of 25 attempts was recorded on physical practice group and mental practice group record sheets.

Each subject was then notified of the group to which he had been assigned, but great care was taken to avoid mentioning anything that would let those subjects who were assigned to the physical practice group know that there would be a mental practice group. To assure this objective, the mental practice group was referred to only as the experimental group. The subjects composing the mental practice group were told of their role in the experiment in private and requested not to discuss the matter with anybody. In similar fashion, members of the physical practice group were advised of their role in the experiment.

The physical practice group and the experimental (mental practice) group were invited to compete with each other. Subjects were reminded of the fact that many basketball games are won and lost at the foul line. The point was made that each subject might well improve his foul shooting skill through serious, competitive participation in the experiment.

The first day of the experiment was brought to a close with the physical practice group being instructed to shoot 5 "warm-up" shots and then 25 shots for a test score for each of the fourteen school days devoted to the experiment. The group was also informed that four weeks from the date of this, the first day of the experiment, a final test was scheduled which would involve 25 "warm-ups" and then 25 shots for a final test score. No further instructions were given to the physical practice group throughout the course of the experiment after the first day.

The second day of the experiment, the experimental (mental practice) group met in private with the instructor (researcher). Subjects were given a written introduction to the mental practice technique. Once again the group was reminded of the importance of maintaining secrecy about the mental practice procedure. Subjects were requested to compete against the physical practice group by employing mental practice frequently throughout each day of the experiment. A brief description of the motor theory of consciousness, as discussed by E. Jacobson in his article, "Muscular Phenomenon During Imagining," found in the *American Journal of Psychology* 49 (1932), 677–94, was distributed to the subjects to support a demonstration included in the written introductory materials on the mental practice technique.

The subjects composing the experimental group were requested to read carefully through the mental practice instruction sheets each day at the beginning of the "serious" mental practice session despite the fact that the contents might become well memorized after a few readings. The rationale of this procedure was that the subject's thinking would be channeled and thus prevent lack of constant attendance to the task to be learned, a phenomenon reported to have occurred frequently in previous mental practice experiments.

The members of the mental practice (experimental) group were instructed to engage in "serious" mental practice once each day of the fourteen school days devoted to the experiment by imagining to shoot 5 "warm-up" shots and then 25 foul shots for the "test" score of that particular day. The final score of the subjects in the experimental group were obtained by the same method used for the physical practice group—the actual shooting of 25 "warm-ups" and then 25 shots for score. No further instructions were given to the mental practice group after the second day of the experiment.

The experimental procedure previously described was employed in each of the four participating high schools. In order to avoid the possible biased error which might accrue to the personalities and instructional skills of different types of instructors, the researcher handled all of the instructional periods himself.

*Introspective Analysis*

Introspective analysis was employed in the experiment to examine the subjects' mental reaction to the experimentation. Introspection, as employed in this study, was defined as the examination of one's mental states or processes.

A major criticism of the method of introspective analysis is the lack of overt behavior that can be measured and tested for reliability and, in some cases, validity. The method was employed at the end of the experimentation, however, with the hope that the introspective analyses of the subjects' experiences might provide data that could yield important clues to mental practice which then could be tested in further research on the technique.

## DATA PROCESSING

(*The element of "data processing" in the research model provides for the sorting, classifying, and analyzing of the data and the reporting of the findings.*)

*Sorting and Classifying*

The data of the experiment were sorted into two categories. The first category was composed of those data that were "foul shot" scores. The second category was composed of data produced by the employment of the method of introspective analysis. These data were in statement form, and were reported as such.

Classification of the data was carried out in terms of the importance of the particular types of data to making the decision about the research hypothesis. The data considered most important to the research decision in this study were those of the foul shot scores. The data yielded by introspective analysis were considered to be of relatively little importance to the decision concerning acceptance or rejection of the research hypothesis. Although the results of the analysis of the "score" data were the most significant to the decisions made in the study, we shall report the results of the introspective analyses first, so that our purpose—the demonstration of the analysis of covariance technique—will not be confused by unrelated matters (e.g., introspective analysis), and will thus receive the emphasis originally intended.

*Findings from Introspective Analyses*

The 72 subjects in the mental practice group were asked to introspectively analyze the introductory training period of the experiment in terms of its effect upon their utilization of basic perceptual abilities in developing the motor skills associated with the Pacific Coast one-hand foul shot activity. All of the reports were favorable. Each subject reported that his initial score was higher than that which he had been accustomed to shooting. The results of the introspective analyses also indicated that the subjects apparently represented a wide range of ability in visualizing and imagining the movements involved in the basketball shooting skill being performed.

The analyses also showed that some of the subjects experienced hallucinations involving the shooting technique. For example, one subject reported mentally attempting to bounce the ball preparatory to shooting only to imagine that it would not bounce and was stuck to the floor. This disturbance "blocked" him in his attempt to visualize successfully the shooting technique. He stated that he avoided the difficulty by picturing himself shooting the ball without first bouncing it.

Another subject reported that he had difficulty as a result of imagining that he was bouncing the ball and catching it in rapid succession just prior to shooting it. The strength of the "picture" of bouncing the ball was so strong that he had difficulty visualizing the completion of the shot.

Another subject who reported having difficulty visualizing the shooting technique claimed that instead of imagining arching the ball in a normal trajectory, he imagined that his shots veered decidedly to the left and then would swerve suddenly back into the basket. The same subject reported that he also had the impulse to shoot as soon as he had the imaginary ball in his hands. This impulse became a physical manifestation when the subject took his final (physical) test shots. He rarely took time to set, aim, and shoot as the average participant did.

All of the mental practice subjects reported a growth in the ability to visualize the shooting technique, and all but six of them reported an increased confidence in actually shooting a basketball. The same subjects who reported increased confidence in their shooting also reported the development of an acute sense of instantly recognizing mistakes in physically carrying out the shooting technique during the final tests. All 72 participants felt that they had improved, to some degree at least, in the instant recognition of errors in carrying out the shooting technique physically.

*Analysis of Covariance and Findings*

The five-factor, 144 cell factorial grid was analyzed by the analysis of covariance technique. After the 32 sums of squares equations were evaluated and "adjusted," 31 sources of interaction "adjusted" *variation* were submitted to the *F*-ratio test of significance by comparing them with the *adjusted mean square* (variance) *of the highest ordered interaction* available.

The original factorial table is shown on page 441. In Figure 22 illustrations of four of the thirty-two "work" tables necessary for the evaluation of the unadjusted sums of squares and products equations are shown.

*FIGURE 22*

Sample of Work Tables for Determining Values of Sums Appearing in Sums of Squares
and Sums of Products Equations

Table 1.   SQUARES AND CROSS PRODUCTS

| Schools | | | I | | | | | | II | | | | |
|---|---|---|---|---|---|---|---|---|---|---|---|---|---|
| Classes | | | V | | | JV | | | N | | | V | | |
| Scores | | | $X^2$ | $Y^2$ | $XY$ | $X^2$ | $Y^2$ | $XY$ | $X^2$ | $Y^2$ | $XY$ | ... |

**Schools I and II**

| Arm Strength | Intelligence | Groups | I-V $X^2$ | $Y^2$ | $XY$ | I-JV $X^2$ | $Y^2$ | $XY$ | I-N $X^2$ | $Y^2$ | $XY$ | II-V $X^2$ | $Y^2$ | $XY$ | II-JV $X^2$ | $Y^2$ | $XY$ | II-N $X^2$ | $Y^2$ | $XY$ |
|---|---|---|---|---|---|---|---|---|---|---|---|---|---|---|---|---|---|---|---|---|
| H | α | M | 361 | 256 | 304 | 256 | 225 | 240 | 121 | 144 | 132 | 169 | 289 | 221 | 64 | 121 | 88 | 289 | 289 | 289 |
| | | P | 81 | 400 | 180 | 169 | 169 | 169 | 121 | 144 | 132 | 25 | 289 | 85 | 100 | 256 | 160 | 100 | 256 | 160 |
| | β | M | 144 | 196 | 168 | 256 | 169 | 208 | 121 | 169 | 143 | 196 | 256 | 224 | 25 | 25 | 25 | 49 | 225 | 105 |
| | | P | 81 | 361 | 171 | 169 | 169 | 169 | 36 | 196 | 84 | 225 | 361 | 285 | 64 | 169 | 104 | 64 | 169 | 104 |
| A | α | M | 196 | 81 | 126 | 256 | 144 | 192 | 49 | 100 | 70 | 169 | 361 | 247 | 196 | 361 | 266 | 121 | 121 | 121 |
| | | P | 196 | 169 | 182 | 16 | 100 | 40 | 225 | 225 | 225 | 169 | 256 | 208 | 100 | 144 | 120 | 49 | 169 | 91 |
| | β | M | 400 | 256 | 320 | 256 | 225 | 240 | 36 | 81 | 54 | 256 | 289 | 272 | 225 | 196 | 210 | 289 | 225 | 255 |
| | | P | 576 | 441 | 504 | 81 | 169 | 117 | 121 | 100 | 110 | 324 | 225 | 270 | 256 | 169 | 208 | 64 | 196 | 112 |
| L | α | M | 324 | 256 | 288 | 196 | 196 | 196 | 49 | 49 | 49 | 169 | 441 | 273 | 81 | 81 | 81 | 64 | 49 | 56 |
| | | P | 121 | 324 | 198 | 169 | 289 | 221 | 36 | 16 | 24 | 144 | 289 | 204 | 121 | 196 | 154 | 169 | 81 | 117 |
| | β | M | 289 | 144 | 204 | 169 | 196 | 182 | 4 | 121 | 22 | 169 | 225 | 195 | 100 | 196 | 140 | 121 | 324 | 198 |
| | | P | 576 | 441 | 504 | 49 | 100 | 70 | 36 | 64 | 48 | 324 | 361 | 342 | 121 | 121 | 121 | 25 | 169 | 65 |

TABLE 1—continued

**Schools III and IV**

| Arm Strength | Intelligence | Groups | III-V $X^2$ | $Y^2$ | $XY$ | III-JV $X^2$ | $Y^2$ | $XY$ | III-N $X^2$ | $Y^2$ | $XY$ | IV-V $X^2$ | $Y^2$ | $XY$ | IV-JV $X^2$ | $Y^2$ | $XY$ | IV-N $X^2$ | $Y^2$ | $XY$ |
|---|---|---|---|---|---|---|---|---|---|---|---|---|---|---|---|---|---|---|---|---|
| H | α | M | 64 | 289 | 136 | 361 | 441 | 399 | 225 | 441 | 315 | 196 | 361 | 266 | 100 | 256 | 160 | 100 | 121 | 110 |
| | | P | 289 | 400 | 340 | 100 | 324 | 180 | 64 | 225 | 120 | 256 | 324 | 288 | 289 | 441 | 357 | 64 | 324 | 144 |
| | β | M | 196 | 400 | 280 | 100 | 289 | 170 | 64 | 144 | 96 | 64 | 324 | 144 | 36 | 225 | 90 | 196 | 256 | 224 |
| | | P | 324 | 324 | 324 | 324 | 225 | 270 | 49 | 49 | 49 | 256 | 361 | 304 | 196 | 289 | 238 | 225 | 225 | 225 |
| A | α | M | 361 | 400 | 380 | 289 | 361 | 323 | 144 | 144 | 144 | 289 | 361 | 323 | 144 | 225 | 180 | 36 | 100 | 60 |
| | | P | 289 | 289 | 289 | 324 | 324 | 324 | 81 | 256 | 144 | 400 | 400 | 400 | 256 | 324 | 288 | 25 | 225•75 | |
| | β | M | 324 | 441 | 378 | 121 | 441 | 231 | 81 | 100 | 90 | 256 | 256 | 256 | 169 | 169 | 169 | 100 | 121 | 110 |
| | | P | 324 | 169 | 234 | 256 | 324 | 288 | 196 | 225 | 210 | 225 | 324 | 270 | 64 | 256 | 128 | 49 | 196 | 98 |
| L | α | M | 225 | 361 | 285 | 49 | 289 | 119 | 64 | 64 | 64 | 144 | 289 | 204 | 25 | 81 | 45 | 36 | 100 | 60 |
| | | P | 169 | 484 | 286 | 225 | 484 | 330 | 121 | 256 | 176 | 400 | 400 | 400 | 196 | 225 | 210 | 36 | 121 | 66 |
| | β | M | 324 | 324 | 324 | 121 | 256 | 176 | 144 | 121 | 132 | 225 | 324 | 270 | 81 | 144 | 108 | 49 | 256 | 112 |
| | | P | 289 | 400 | 340 | 196 | 400 | 280 | 49 | 144 | 84 | 324 | 324 | 324 | 256 | 361 | 304 | 144 | 196 | 168 |

Values of sums determined from Table 1; where $a$ = arm strength, $i$ = intelligence, $c$ = class, $s$ = school, and $g$ = group, are:

$$A_1 = \sum_{a}\sum_{i}\sum_{c}\sum_{s}\sum_{g} Y^2 = 34{,}728; \qquad A_2 = \sum_{a}\sum_{i}\sum_{c}\sum_{s}\sum_{g} X^2 = 24{,}371; \qquad A_3 = \sum_{a}\sum_{i}\sum_{c}\sum_{s}\sum_{g} XY = 27{,}950$$

Table 2.   Part I—$(\sum_a X ; \sum_a Y$—Original Scores Summed Over "Arm Strength" Factor)

| Schools | | I | | | | | | II | | | | |
|---|---|---|---|---|---|---|---|---|---|---|---|---|
| Classes | | V | | JV | | N | | V | | JV | | N |
| Scores | | $\sum_a X$ | $\sum_a Y$ | $\sum_a X$ | $\sum_a Y$ | $\sum_a X$ | $\sum_a Y$ | $\sum_a X$ | $\sum_a Y$ | $\sum_a X$ | $\sum_a Y$ | $\sum_a X$ | $\sum_a Y$ |
| Intelligence | Groups | | | | | | | | | | | | |
| $\alpha$ | M | 51 | 41 | 46 | 41 | 25 | 29 | 39 | 57 | 31 | 39 | 36 | 35 |
| | P | 34 | 51 | 30 | 40 | 32 | 31 | 30 | 50 | 31 | 42 | 30 | 38 |
| $\beta$ | M | 49 | 42 | 45 | 42 | 19 | 33 | 43 | 48 | 30 | 33 | 35 | 48 |
| | P | 57 | 61 | 29 | 36 | 23 | 32 | 51 | 53 | 35 | 37 | 21 | 40 |

TABLE 2—PART I—continued

| Schools | | III | | | | | | IV | | | | |
|---|---|---|---|---|---|---|---|---|---|---|---|---|
| Classes | | V | | JV | | N | | V | | JV | | N |
| Scores | | $\sum_a X$ | $\sum_a Y$ | $\sum_a X$ | $\sum_a Y$ | $\sum_a X$ | $\sum_a Y$ | $\sum_a X$ | $\sum_a Y$ | $\sum_a X$ | $\sum_a Y$ | $\sum_a X$ | $\sum_a Y$ |
| Intelligence | Groups | | | | | | | | | | | | |
| $\alpha$ | M | 42 | 56 | 43 | 57 | 35 | 41 | 43 | 55 | 27 | 40 | 22 | 31 |
| | P | 47 | 59 | 43 | 58 | 28 | 47 | 56 | 58 | 47 | 54 | 19 | 44 |
| $\beta$ | M | 50 | 59 | 32 | 54 | 29 | 33 | 39 | 52 | 28 | 40 | 31 | 43 |
| | P | 53 | 51 | 48 | 53 | 28 | 34 | 49 | 55 | 38 | 52 | 34 | 43 |

Table 2.   Part II—(Squares and Cross Products Employing $\sum_a X$ and $\sum_a Y$ as Measures.)

| Schools | | I | | | | | | | | |
|---|---|---|---|---|---|---|---|---|---|---|
| Classes | | V | | | JV | | | N | | |
| Scores | | $(\sum_a X)^2$ | $(\sum_a Y)^2$ | $(\sum_a X)(\sum_a Y)$ | $(\sum_a X)^2$ | $(\sum_a Y)^2$ | $(\sum_a X)(\sum_a Y)$ | $(\sum_a X)^2$ | $(\sum_a Y)^2$ | $(\sum_a X)(\sum_a Y)$ |
| Intelligence | Groups | | | | | | | | | |
| $\alpha$ | M | 2601 | 1681 | 2091 | 2116 | 1681 | 1886 | 625 | 841 | 725 |
| | P | 1156 | 2601 | 1734 | 900 | 1600 | 1200 | 1024 | 961 | 992 |
| $\beta$ | M | 2401 | 1764 | 2058 | 2025 | 1764 | 1890 | 361 | 1089 | 627 |
| | P | 3249 | 3721 | 3497 | 841 | 296 | 1044 | 529 | 1024 | 736 |

TABLE 2—PART II—continued

| Schools | | II | | | | | | | | |
|---|---|---|---|---|---|---|---|---|---|---|
| Classes | | V | | | JV | | | N | | |
| Scores | | $(\sum_a X)^2$ | $(\sum_a Y)^2$ | $(\sum_a X)(\sum_a Y)$ | $(\sum_a X)^2$ | $(\sum_a Y)^2$ | $(\sum_a X)(\sum_a Y)$ | $(\sum_a X)^2$ | $(\sum_a Y)^2$ | $(\sum_a X)(\sum_a Y)$ |
| Intelligence | Groups | | | | | | | | | |
| $\alpha$ | M | 1521 | 3249 | 2223 | 961 | 1521 | 1209 | 1296 | 1225 | 1260 |
| | P | 900 | 2500 | 1500 | 961 | 1764 | 1302 | 900 | 1444 | 1140 |
| $\beta$ | M | 1849 | 2304 | 2064 | 900 | 1089 | 990 | 1225 | 2304 | 1680 |
| | P | 2611 | 2809 | 2703 | 1225 | 1369 | 1295 | 441 | 1600 | 840 |

TABLE 2—PART II—continued

| Schools | | III | | | | | | | | |
|---|---|---|---|---|---|---|---|---|---|---|
| Classes | | V | | | JV | | | N | | |
| Scores | | $(\sum\limits_a X)^2$ | $(\sum\limits_a Y)^2$ | $(\sum\limits_a X)(\sum\limits_a Y)$ | $(\sum\limits_a X)^2$ | $(\sum\limits_a Y)^2$ | $(\sum\limits_a X)(\sum\limits_a Y)$ | $(\sum\limits_a X)^2$ | $(\sum\limits_a Y)^2$ | $(\sum\limits_a X)(\sum\limits_a Y)$ |
| Intelligence | Groups | | | | | | | | | |
| $\alpha$ | M | 1764 | 3136 | 2352 | 1849 | 3249 | 2451 | 1225 | 1681 | 1435 |
| | P | 2209 | 3481 | 2773 | 1849 | 3364 | 2494 | 784 | 2209 | 1316 |
| $\beta$ | M | 2500 | 3431 | 2956 | 1024 | 2916 | 1728 | 841 | 1089 | 957 |
| | P | 2809 | 2601 | 2703 | 2304 | 2809 | 2544 | 784 | 1156 | 952 |

TABLE 2—PART II—continued

| Schools | | IV | | | | | | | | |
|---|---|---|---|---|---|---|---|---|---|---|
| Classes | | V | | | JV | | | N | | |
| Scores | | $(\sum\limits_a X)^2$ | $(\sum\limits_a Y)^2$ | $(\sum\limits_a X)(\sum\limits_a Y)$ | $(\sum\limits_a X)^2$ | $(\sum\limits_a Y)^2$ | $(\sum\limits_a X)(\sum\limits_a Y)$ | $(\sum\limits_a X)^2$ | $(\sum\limits_a Y)^2$ | $(\sum\limits_a X)(\sum\limits_a Y)$ |
| Intelligence | Groups | | | | | | | | | |
| $\alpha$ | M | 1849 | 3025 | 2365 | 729 | 1600 | 1080 | 484 | 961 | 682 |
| | P | 3136 | 3364 | 3248 | 2209 | 2916 | 2538 | 361 | 1936 | 836 |
| $\beta$ | M | 1521 | 2704 | 2028 | 784 | 1600 | 1120 | 961 | 1849 | 1333 |
| | P | 2401 | 3025 | 2695 | 1444 | 2704 | 1976 | 1156 | 1849 | 1462 |

Values of sums determined from Table 2, Part II, are:

$$B_{15} = \frac{\sum\limits_i \sum\limits_c \sum\limits_s \sum\limits_g [\sum\limits_a Y]^2}{3} = \frac{101,906}{3} = 33,968\tfrac{2}{3}; \qquad B_{25} = \frac{\sum\limits_i \sum\limits_c \sum\limits_s \sum\limits_g [\sum\limits_a X]^2}{3} = \frac{69,585}{3} = 23,195;$$

$$B_{35} = \frac{\sum\limits_i \sum\limits_c \sum\limits_s \sum\limits_g [\sum\limits_a X][\sum\limits_a Y]}{3} = \frac{82,684}{3} = 27,561\tfrac{1}{3}$$

Table 3. ($\sum\limits_s \sum\limits_a X$; $\sum\limits_s \sum\limits_a Y$—Original Scores Summed Over Factors of "School" and "Arm Strength" and Squares and Cross Products of These Measures.)

| Classes | | V | | | | |
|---|---|---|---|---|---|---|
| Score | | $\sum\limits_s \sum\limits_a X$ | $(\sum\limits_s \sum\limits_a X)^2$ | $\sum\limits_s \sum\limits_a Y$ | $(\sum\limits_s \sum\limits_a Y)^2$ | $(\sum\limits_s \sum\limits_a X)(\sum\limits_s \sum\limits_a Y)$ |
| Intelligence | Group | | | | | |
| $\alpha$ | M | 175 | 30,625 | 209 | 43,681 | 36,575 |
| | P | 167 | 27,889 | 218 | 47,524 | 36,406 |
| $\beta$ | M | 181 | 32,761 | 201 | 40,401 | 36,381 |
| | P | 210 | 44,100 | 220 | 48,400 | 46,200 |

| Classes | | JV | | | | |
|---|---|---|---|---|---|---|
| Score | | $\sum\limits_s \sum\limits_a X$ | $(\sum\limits_s \sum\limits_a X)^2$ | $\sum\limits_s \sum\limits_a Y$ | $(\sum\limits_s \sum\limits_a Y)^2$ | $(\sum\limits_s \sum\limits_a X)(\sum\limits_s \sum\limits_a Y)$ |
| Intelligence | Group | | | | | |
| $\alpha$ | M | 147 | 21,609 | 177 | 31,329 | 26,019 |
| | P | 151 | 22,801 | 194 | 37,636 | 29,294 |
| $\beta$ | M | 135 | 18,225 | 169 | 28,561 | 22,815 |
| | P | 150 | 22,500 | 178 | 31,684 | 26,700 |

TABLE 3—continued

| Classes | | N | | | | |
|---|---|---|---|---|---|---|
| Scores | | $\sum_{s}\sum_{a}X$ | $(\sum_{s}\sum_{a}X)^2$ | $\sum_{s}\sum_{a}Y$ | $(\sum_{s}\sum_{a}Y)^2$ | $(\sum_{s}\sum_{a}X)(\sum_{s}\sum_{a}Y)$ |
| Intelligence | Groups | | | | | |
| $\alpha$ | M | 118 | 13,924 | 136 | 18,496 | 16,048 |
| | P | 109 | 11,881 | 160 | 25,600 | 17,440 |
| $\beta$ | M | 114 | 12,996 | 157 | 24,649 | 17,898 |
| | P | 106 | 11,236 | 149 | 22,201 | 15,794 |

Values of sums determined from Table 3 are:

$$C_{18} = \frac{\sum_{i}\sum_{c}\sum_{g}[\sum_{s}\sum_{a}Y]^2}{12} = \frac{400,162}{12} = 33,346\tfrac{5}{6}; \quad C_{28} = \frac{\sum_{i}\sum_{c}\sum_{g}[\sum_{s}\sum_{a}X]^2}{12} = \frac{270,547}{12} = 22,545\tfrac{7}{12};$$

$$C_{38} = \frac{\sum_{i}\sum_{c}\sum_{g}[\sum_{s}\sum_{a}X][\sum_{s}\sum_{a}Y]}{12} = \frac{327,570}{12} = 27,297\tfrac{1}{2}$$

Table 4. ($\sum_{a}\sum_{s}\sum_{c}X$ ; $\sum_{a}\sum_{s}\sum_{c}Y$—Original Scores Summed Over Factors of "Arm Strength," "School," and "Class"; and Squares and Cross Products of These Measures.)

| Scores | | $\sum_{a}\sum_{s}\sum_{c}X$ | $(\sum_{a}\sum_{s}\sum_{c}X)^2$ | $\sum_{a}\sum_{s}\sum_{c}Y$ | $(\sum_{a}\sum_{s}\sum_{c}Y)^2$ | $(\sum_{a}\sum_{s}\sum_{c}X)(\sum_{a}\sum_{s}\sum_{c}Y)$ |
|---|---|---|---|---|---|---|
| Intelligence | Groups | | | | | |
| $\alpha$ | M | 440 | 193,600 | 522 | 272,484 | 229,680 |
| | P | 427 | 182,329 | 572 | 327,184 | 244,244 |
| $\beta$ | M | 430 | 184,900 | 527 | 277,729 | 226,610 |
| | P | 466 | 217,156 | 547 | 299,209 | 254,902 |

Values of sums determined from Table 4 are:

$$D_{16} = \frac{\sum_{i}\sum_{g}[\sum_{a}\sum_{s}\sum_{c}Y]^2}{36} = \frac{1,176,606}{36} = 32,683\tfrac{1}{2}; \quad D_{26} = \frac{\sum_{i}\sum_{g}[\sum_{a}\sum_{s}\sum_{c}X]^2}{36} = \frac{777,985}{36} = 21,610\tfrac{25}{36}$$

$$D_{36} = \frac{\sum_{i}\sum_{g}[\sum_{a}\sum_{s}\sum_{c}X][\sum_{a}\sum_{s}\sum_{c}Y]}{36} = \frac{955,436}{36} = 26,539\tfrac{8}{9}$$

All of the values shown below were found in the manner demonstrated by the illustration of the "working" tables presented in Figure 22. The values of these sums are substituted in the equations for the sums of squares and sums of cross products of the various interactions and main effects involved in the analysis. The "sums" equations are presented in Table XXVI, p. 450.

$$A_1 = \sum_{a}\sum_{i}\sum_{g}\sum_{c}\sum_{s}Y^2 = 34,728$$

(where $a$ denotes 3 levels of "arm strength"; $i$ denotes 2 levels of "intelligence"; $g$ denotes 2 levels of "group"; $c$ denotes 3 levels of "class"; and $s$ denotes 4 levels of "school.")

$$A_2 = \sum_{a}\sum_{i}\sum_{g}\sum_{c}\sum_{s}X^2 = 24,371$$

$$A_3 = \sum_{a}\sum_{i}\sum_{g}\sum_{c}\sum_{s}XY = 27,950$$

$$B_{11} = \frac{\sum_{a}\sum_{i}\sum_{g}\sum_{c}[\sum_{s}Y]^2}{4} = 33,667$$

$$B_{21} = \frac{\sum_{a}\sum_{i}\sum_{g}\sum_{c}[\sum_{s}X]^2}{4} = 22,939\tfrac{1}{4}$$

$$B_{12} = \frac{\sum_{a}\sum_{i}\sum_{g}\sum_{s}[\sum_{c}Y]^2}{3} = 33,256\tfrac{2}{3}$$

$$B_{22} = \frac{\sum_{a}\sum_{i}\sum_{g}\sum_{s}[\sum_{c}X]^2}{3} = 22,227\tfrac{2}{3}$$

$$B_{13} = \frac{\sum_{a}\sum_{i}\sum_{s}\sum_{c}[\sum_{g}Y]^2}{2} = 34,187$$

$$B_{23} = \frac{\sum_{a}\sum_{i}\sum_{c}\sum_{s}[\sum_{g}X]^2}{2} = 23,429\tfrac{1}{2}$$

$$B_{14} = \frac{\sum_{a}\sum_{g}\sum_{c}\sum_{s}[\sum_{i}Y]^2}{2} = 34,231$$

$$B_{24} = \frac{\sum_{a}\sum_{g}\sum_{c}\sum_{s}[\sum_{i}X]^2}{2} = 23,566\tfrac{1}{2}$$

$$B_{15} = \frac{\sum_{i}\sum_{g}\sum_{c}\sum_{s}[\sum_{a}Y]^2}{3} = 33,968\tfrac{2}{3}$$

$$B_{25} = \frac{\sum_{i}\sum_{g}\sum_{c}\sum_{s}[\sum_{a}X]^2}{3} = 23,195$$

$$B_{31} = \frac{\sum_{a}\sum_{i}\sum_{g}\sum_{c}[\sum_{s}X][\sum_{s}Y]}{4} = 27,449$$

$$B_{32} = \frac{\sum\sum\sum_{a\ i\ g\ s}[\sum X]_c[\sum Y]_c}{3} = 26{,}735\tfrac{2}{3}$$

$$B_{33} = \frac{\sum\sum\sum\sum_{a\ i\ c\ s\ g}[\sum X]_g[\sum Y]}{2} = 27{,}683\tfrac{1}{2}$$

$$B_{34} = \frac{\sum\sum\sum\sum_{a\ g\ c\ s\ i}[\sum X]_i[\sum Y]_i}{2} = 27{,}686$$

$$B_{35} = \frac{\sum\sum\sum\sum_{i\ g\ c\ s\ a}[\sum X]_a[\sum Y]_a}{3} = 27{,}561\tfrac{1}{3}$$

$$C_{10} = \frac{\sum\sum\sum_{a\ i\ s\ g\ c}[\sum\sum Y]^2}{6} = 33{,}062$$

$$C_{11} = \frac{\sum\sum\sum_{a\ i\ g\ c\ s}[\sum\sum Y]^2}{12} = 32{,}771\tfrac{1}{6}$$

$$C_{12} = \frac{\sum\sum\sum_{a\ i\ c\ g\ s}[\sum\sum Y]^2}{8} = 33{,}495\tfrac{1}{4}$$

$$C_{13} = \frac{\sum\sum\sum_{a\ c\ s\ i\ g}[\sum\sum Y]^2}{4} = 33{,}833$$

$$C_{14} = \frac{\sum\sum\sum_{a\ g\ s\ i\ c}[\sum\sum Y]^2}{6} = 33{,}104\tfrac{1}{3}$$

$$C_{15} = \frac{\sum\sum\sum_{a\ g\ c\ i\ s}[\sum\sum Y]^2}{8} = 33{,}500$$

$$C_{16} = \frac{\sum\sum\sum_{i\ c\ s\ a\ g}[\sum\sum Y]^2}{6} = 33{,}749\tfrac{2}{3}$$

$$C_{17} = \frac{\sum\sum\sum_{i\ g\ s\ a\ c}[\sum\sum Y]^2}{9} = 33{,}005\tfrac{1}{9}$$

$$C_{18} = \frac{\sum\sum\sum_{i\ g\ c\ a\ s}[\sum\sum Y]^2}{12} = 33{,}346\tfrac{5}{6}$$

$$C_{19} = \frac{\sum\sum\sum_{g\ c\ s\ a\ i}[\sum\sum Y]^2}{6} = 33{,}807\tfrac{2}{3}$$

$$C_{20} = \frac{\sum\sum\sum_{a\ i\ s\ c\ g}[\sum\sum X]^2}{6} = 21{,}879\tfrac{1}{6}$$

$$C_{21} = \frac{\sum\sum\sum_{a\ i\ g\ c\ s}[\sum\sum X]^2}{12} = 21{,}785\tfrac{1}{12}$$

$$C_{22} = \frac{\sum\sum\sum_{a\ i\ c\ g\ s}[\sum\sum X]^2}{8} = 22{,}754\tfrac{7}{8}$$

$$C_{23} = \frac{\sum\sum\sum_{a\ c\ s\ i\ g}[\sum\sum X]^2}{4} = 22{,}988\tfrac{1}{4}$$

$$C_{24} = \frac{\sum\sum\sum_{a\ g\ s\ i\ c}[\sum\sum X]^2}{6} = 21{,}985\tfrac{1}{2}$$

$$C_{25} = \frac{\sum\sum\sum_{a\ g\ c\ i\ s}[\sum\sum X]^2}{8} = 22{,}760\tfrac{3}{8}$$

$$C_{26} = \frac{\sum\sum\sum_{i\ c\ s\ a\ g}[\sum\sum X]^2}{6} = 22{,}785\tfrac{1}{6}$$

$$C_{27} = \frac{\sum\sum\sum_{i\ g\ s\ a\ c}[\sum\sum X]^2}{9} = 21{,}806\tfrac{5}{9}$$

$$C_{28} = \frac{\sum\sum\sum_{i\ g\ c\ a\ s}[\sum\sum X]^2}{12} = 22{,}545\tfrac{7}{12}$$

$$C_{29} = \frac{\sum\sum\sum_{g\ c\ s\ a\ i}[\sum\sum X]^2}{6} = 22{,}871\tfrac{1}{6}$$

$$C_{30} = \frac{\sum\sum\sum\sum_{a\ i\ s\ c\ g}[\sum X]_{cg}[\sum\sum Y]}{6} = 26{,}681\tfrac{5}{6}$$

$$C_{31} = \frac{\sum\sum\sum\sum_{a\ i\ g\ c\ s}[\sum X]_{cs}[\sum\sum Y]}{12} = 26{,}594\tfrac{5}{6}$$

$$C_{32} = \frac{\sum\sum\sum\sum_{a\ i\ c\ g\ s}[\sum X]_{gs}[\sum\sum Y]}{8} = 27{,}340\tfrac{1}{4}$$

$$C_{33} = \frac{\sum\sum\sum\sum_{a\ c\ s\ i\ g}[\sum X]_{ig}[\sum\sum Y]}{4} = 27{,}528$$

$$C_{34} = \frac{\sum\sum\sum\sum_{a\ g\ s\ i\ c}[\sum X]_{ic}[\sum\sum Y]}{6} = 26{,}682\tfrac{1}{2}$$

$$C_{35} = \frac{\sum\sum\sum\sum_{a\ g\ c\ s\ i}[\sum X]_{is}[\sum\sum Y]}{8} = 27{,}400\tfrac{1}{2}$$

$$C_{36} = \frac{\sum\sum\sum\sum_{i\ c\ s\ a\ g}[\sum X]_{ag}[\sum\sum Y]}{6} = 27{,}447\tfrac{1}{2}$$

$$C_{37} = \frac{\sum\sum\sum\sum_{i\ g\ s\ a\ c}[\sum X]_{ac}[\sum\sum Y]}{9} = 26{,}659\tfrac{7}{9}$$

$$C_{38} = \frac{\sum\sum\sum\sum_{i\ g\ c\ a\ s}[\sum X]_{as}[\sum\sum Y]}{12} = 27{,}297\tfrac{1}{2}$$

$$C_{39} = \frac{\sum\sum\sum\sum_{g\ c\ s\ a\ i}[\sum X]_{ai}[\sum\sum Y]}{6} = 27{,}502$$

$$D_{10} = \frac{\sum\sum_{a\ i\ g\ c\ s}[\sum\sum\sum Y]^2}{24} = 32{,}716\tfrac{5}{12}$$

$$D_{11} = \frac{\sum\sum_{a\ s\ i\ g\ c}[\sum\sum\sum Y]^2}{12} = 32{,}938\tfrac{2}{3}$$

$$D_{12} = \frac{\sum\sum_{a\ g\ i\ c\ s}[\sum\sum\sum Y]^2}{24} = 32{,}716\tfrac{2}{3}$$

$$D_{13} = \frac{\sum\sum_{a\ c\ i\ g\ s}[\sum\sum\sum Y]^2}{16} = 33{,}376\tfrac{7}{8}$$

$$D_{14} = \frac{\sum\sum_{i\ s\ a\ g\ c}[\sum\sum\sum Y]^2}{18} = 32{,}918\tfrac{2}{3}$$

$$D_{15} = \frac{\sum\sum_{i\ c\ a\ g\ s}[\sum\sum\sum Y]^2}{24} = 33{,}286\tfrac{1}{3}$$

$$D_{16} = \frac{\sum\sum_{i\ g\ a\ c\ s}[\sum\sum\sum Y]^2}{36} = 32{,}683\tfrac{1}{2}$$

$$D_{17} = \frac{\sum\sum_{c\ s\ a\ i\ g}[\sum\sum\sum Y]^2}{12} = 33{,}647\tfrac{1}{3}$$

$$D_{18} = \frac{\sum\sum_{g\ s\ a\ i\ c}[\sum\sum\sum Y]^2}{18} = 32{,}952\tfrac{5}{9}$$

$$D_{19} = \frac{\sum\sum_{g\ c\ a\ i\ s}[\sum\sum\sum Y]^2}{24} = 33{,}307\tfrac{1}{4}$$

$$D_{20} = \frac{\sum\sum_{a\ i\ g\ c\ s}[\sum\sum\sum X]^2}{24} = 21{,}698\tfrac{1}{8}$$

$$D_{21} = \frac{\sum\sum_{a\ s\ i\ g\ c}[\sum\sum\sum X]^2}{12} = 21{,}769\tfrac{3}{4}$$

$$D_{22} = \frac{\sum\limits_{a\ g}\sum[\sum\sum\sum\limits_{i\ c\ s}X]^2}{24} = 21,698\tfrac{1}{8}$$

$$D_{23} = \frac{\sum\limits_{a\ c}\sum[\sum\sum\sum\limits_{i\ g\ s}X]^2}{16} = 22,660\tfrac{1}{16}$$

$$D_{24} = \frac{\sum\limits_{i\ s}\sum[\sum\sum\sum\limits_{a\ g\ c}X]^2}{18} = 21,657\tfrac{17}{18}$$

$$D_{25} = \frac{\sum\limits_{i\ c}\sum[\sum\sum\sum\limits_{a\ g\ s}X]^2}{24} = 22,491\tfrac{19}{24}$$

$$D_{26} = \frac{\sum\limits_{i\ g}\sum[\sum\sum\sum\limits_{a\ c\ s}X]^2}{36} = 21,610\tfrac{25}{36}$$

$$D_{27} = \frac{\sum\limits_{c\ s}\sum[\sum\sum\limits_{a\ i\ g}X]^2}{12} = 22,582\tfrac{5}{12}$$

$$D_{28} = \frac{\sum\limits_{g\ s}\sum[\sum\sum\limits_{a\ i\ c}X]^2}{18} = 21,764\tfrac{17}{18}$$

$$D_{29} = \frac{\sum\limits_{g\ c}\sum[\sum\sum\limits_{a\ i\ s}X]^2}{24} = 22,459\tfrac{23}{24}$$

$$D_{30} = \frac{\sum\limits_{a\ i}\sum[\sum\sum\sum\limits_{g\ c\ s}X][\sum\sum\sum\limits_{g\ c\ s}Y]}{24} = 26,566\tfrac{5}{24}$$

$$D_{31} = \frac{\sum\limits_{a\ s}\sum[\sum\sum\sum\limits_{g\ i\ c}X][\sum\sum\sum\limits_{g\ i\ c}Y]}{12} = 26,631\tfrac{7}{12}$$

$$D_{32} = \frac{\sum\limits_{a\ g}\sum[\sum\sum\sum\limits_{i\ c\ s}X][\sum\sum\sum\limits_{i\ c\ s}Y]}{24} = 26,565\tfrac{11}{12}$$

$$D_{33} = \frac{\sum\limits_{a\ c}\sum[\sum\sum\sum\limits_{i\ g\ s}X][\sum\sum\sum\limits_{i\ g\ s}Y]}{16} = 27,325$$

$$D_{34} = \frac{\sum\limits_{i\ s}\sum[\sum\sum\sum\limits_{a\ g\ c}X][\sum\sum\sum\limits_{a\ g\ c}Y]}{18} = 26,617\tfrac{1}{2}$$

$$D_{35} = \frac{\sum\limits_{i\ c}\sum[\sum\sum\sum\limits_{a\ g\ s}X][\sum\sum\sum\limits_{a\ g\ s}Y]}{24} = 27,275\tfrac{5}{12}$$

$$D_{36} = \frac{\sum\limits_{i\ g}\sum[\sum\sum\sum\limits_{a\ c\ s}X][\sum\sum\sum\limits_{a\ c\ s}Y]}{36} = 26,539\tfrac{8}{9}$$

$$D_{37} = \frac{\sum\limits_{c\ s}\sum[\sum\sum\limits_{a\ i\ g}X][\sum\sum\limits_{a\ i\ g}Y]}{12} = 27,424\tfrac{1}{4}$$

$$D_{38} = \frac{\sum\limits_{g\ s}\sum[\sum\sum\limits_{a\ i\ c}X][\sum\sum\limits_{a\ i\ c}Y]}{18} = 26,666\tfrac{1}{2}$$

$$D_{39} = \frac{\sum\limits_{g\ c}\sum[\sum\sum\limits_{a\ i\ s}X][\sum\sum\limits_{a\ i\ s}Y]}{24} = 27,293\tfrac{3}{8}$$

$$E_{11} = \frac{\sum\limits_{a}[\sum\sum\sum\sum\limits_{i\ g\ c\ s}Y]^2}{48} = 32,672\tfrac{5}{24}$$

$$E_{12} = \frac{\sum\limits_{i}[\sum\sum\sum\sum\limits_{a\ g\ c\ s}Y]^2}{72} = 32,643\tfrac{2}{9}$$

$$E_{13} = \frac{\sum\limits_{g}[\sum\sum\sum\sum\limits_{a\ i\ c\ s}Y]^2}{72} = 32,674\tfrac{17}{36}$$

$$E_{14} = \frac{\sum\limits_{c}[\sum\sum\sum\sum\limits_{a\ i\ g\ s}Y]^2}{48} = 33,271\tfrac{1}{2}$$

$$E_{15} = \frac{\sum\limits_{s}[\sum\sum\sum\sum\limits_{a\ i\ g\ c}Y]^2}{48} = 32,881\tfrac{1}{2}$$

$$E_{21} = \frac{\sum\limits_{a}[\sum\sum\sum\sum\limits_{i\ g\ c\ s}X]^2}{48} = 21,660\tfrac{15}{16}$$

$$E_{22} = \frac{\sum\limits_{i}[\sum\sum\sum\sum\limits_{a\ g\ c\ s}X]^2}{72} = 21,590\tfrac{25}{72}$$

$$E_{23} = \frac{\sum\limits_{g}[\sum\sum\sum\sum\limits_{a\ i\ c\ s}X]^2}{72} = 21,588\tfrac{43}{72}$$

$$E_{24} = \frac{\sum\limits_{c}[\sum\sum\sum\sum\limits_{a\ i\ g\ s}X]^2}{48} = 22,437\tfrac{11}{48}$$

$$E_{25} = \frac{\sum\limits_{s}[\sum\sum\sum\sum\limits_{a\ i\ g\ c}X]^2}{36} = 21,647\tfrac{11}{18}$$

$$E_{31} = \frac{\sum\limits_{a}[\sum\sum\sum\sum\limits_{i\ g\ c\ s}X][\sum\sum\sum\sum\limits_{i\ g\ c\ s}Y]}{48} = 26,536\tfrac{1}{24}$$

$$E_{32} = \frac{\sum\limits_{i}[\sum\sum\sum\sum\limits_{a\ g\ c\ s}X][\sum\sum\sum\sum\limits_{a\ g\ c\ s}Y]}{72} = 26,538\tfrac{11}{12}$$

$$E_{33} = \frac{\sum\limits_{g}[\sum\sum\sum\sum\limits_{a\ i\ c\ s}X][\sum\sum\sum\sum\limits_{a\ i\ c\ s}Y]}{72} = 26,554\tfrac{1}{8}$$

$$E_{34} = \frac{\sum\limits_{c}[\sum\sum\sum\sum\limits_{a\ i\ g\ s}X][\sum\sum\sum\sum\limits_{a\ i\ g\ s}Y]}{48} = 27,276\tfrac{1}{2}$$

$$E_{35} = \frac{\sum\limits_{s}[\sum\sum\sum\sum\limits_{a\ i\ g\ c}X][\sum\sum\sum\sum\limits_{a\ i\ g\ c}Y]}{36} = 26,618\tfrac{19}{96}$$

$$F_1 = \frac{[\sum\sum\sum\sum\limits_{a\ i\ c\ g\ s}Y]^2}{144} = 32,640\tfrac{4}{9}$$

$$F_2 = \frac{[\sum\sum\sum\sum\sum\limits_{a\ i\ c\ g\ s}X]^2}{144} = 21,584\tfrac{73}{144}$$

$$F_3 = \frac{[\sum\sum\sum\sum\sum\limits_{a\ i\ c\ g\ s}X][\sum\sum\sum\sum\sum\limits_{a\ i\ c\ g\ s}Y]}{144} = 26,542\tfrac{17}{18}$$

Table XXVI

Equations for Sums of Squares and Sums of Cross Products of the Interactions and Main Effects Involved in the Research Problem

| Source of Variation | df | $\Sigma y^2$ | $\Sigma x^2$ | $\Sigma xy$ |
|---|---|---|---|---|
| 1. Arm strength × intelligence × school × class × group | 12 | $A_1 - \sum_{11}^{15} B_{ii} + \sum_{10}^{19} C_{ii} - \sum_{10}^{15} D_{ii} + \sum_{11}^{15} E_{ii} - F_1$ | $A_2 - \sum_{21}^{25} B_{ii} + \sum_{20}^{29} C_{ii} - \sum_{20}^{25} D_{ii} + \sum_{21}^{25} E_{ii} - F_2$ | $A_3 - \sum_{31}^{35} B_{ii} + \sum_{30}^{39} C_{ii} - \sum_{30}^{35} D_{ii} + \sum_{31}^{35} E_{ii} - F_3$ |
| 2. Arm strength × intelligence × class × group | 4 | $B_{11} - (C_{11} + C_{12} + C_{15} + C_{18}) + (D_{10} + D_{12} + D_{13} + D_{15} + D_{16} + D_{19}) - (E_{11} + E_{12} + E_{13} + E_{14}) + F_1$ | $B_{21} - (C_{21} + C_{22} + C_{25} + C_{28}) + (D_{20} + D_{22} + D_{23} + D_{25} + D_{26} + D_{29}) - (E_{21} + E_{22} + E_{23} + E_{24}) + F_2$ | $B_{31} - (C_{31} + C_{32} + C_{35} + C_{38}) + (D_{30} + D_{32} + D_{33} + D_{35} + D_{36} + D_{39}) - (E_{31} + E_{32} + E_{33} + E_{34}) + F_3$ |
| 3. Arm strength × intelligence × school × group | 6 | $B_{12} - (C_{10} + C_{11} + C_{14} + C_{17}) + (D_{10} + D_{11} + D_{12} + D_{14} + D_{16} + D_{18}) - (E_{11} + E_{12} + E_{13} + E_{15}) + F_1$ | $B_{22} - (C_{20} + C_{21} + C_{24} + C_{27}) + (D_{20} + D_{21} + D_{22} + D_{24} + D_{26} + D_{28}) - (E_{21} + E_{22} + E_{23} + E_{25}) + F_2$ | $B_{32} - (C_{30} + C_{31} + C_{34} + C_{37}) + (D_{30} + D_{31} + D_{32} + D_{34} + D_{36} + D_{38}) - (E_{31} + E_{32} + E_{33} + E_{35}) + F_3$ |
| 4. Arm strength × intelligence × school × class | 12 | $B_{13} - (C_{10} + C_{12} + C_{13} + C_{16}) + (D_{10} + D_{11} + D_{13} + D_{14} + D_{15} + D_{17}) - (E_{11} + E_{12} + E_{14} + E_{15}) + F_1$ | $B_{23} - (C_{20} + C_{22} + C_{23} + C_{26}) + (D_{20} + D_{21} + D_{23} + D_{24} + D_{25} + D_{27}) - (E_{21} + E_{22} + E_{24} + E_{25}) + F_2$ | $B_{33} - (C_{30} + C_{32} + C_{33} + C_{36}) + (D_{30} + D_{31} + D_{33} + D_{34} + D_{35} + D_{37}) - (E_{31} + E_{32} + E_{34} + E_{35}) + F_3$ |
| 5. Arm strength × school × class × group | 12 | $B_{14} - (C_{13} + C_{14} + C_{15} + C_{19}) + (D_{12} + D_{13} + D_{17} + D_{18} + D_{19}) - (E_{11} + E_{13} + E_{14} + E_{15}) + F_1$ | $B_{24} - (C_{23} + C_{24} + C_{25} + C_{29}) + (D_{22} + D_{23} + D_{27} + D_{28} + D_{29}) - (E_{21} + E_{23} + E_{24} + E_{25}) + F_2$ | $B_{34} - (C_{33} + C_{34} + C_{35} + C_{39}) + (D_{32} + D_{33} + D_{37} + D_{38} + D_{39}) - (E_{31} + E_{33} + E_{34} + E_{35}) + F_3$ |
| 6. Intelligence × school × class × group | 6 | $B_{15} - (C_{16} + C_{17} + C_{18} + C_{19}) + (D_{15} + D_{16} + D_{17} + D_{18} + D_{19}) - (E_{12} + E_{13} + E_{14} + E_{15}) + F_1$ | $B_{25} - (C_{26} + C_{27} + C_{28} + C_{29}) + (D_{25} + D_{26} + D_{27} + D_{28} + D_{29}) - (E_{22} + E_{23} + E_{24} + E_{25}) + F_2$ | $B_{35} - (C_{36} + C_{37} + C_{38} + C_{39}) + (D_{35} + D_{36} + D_{37} + D_{38} + D_{39}) - (E_{32} + E_{33} + E_{34} + E_{35}) + F_3$ |
| 7. Arm strength × intelligence × school | 6 | $C_{10} - (D_{10} + D_{11} + D_{14}) + (E_{11} + E_{12} + E_{15}) - F_1$ | $C_{20} - (D_{20} + D_{21} + D_{24}) + (E_{21} + E_{22} + E_{25}) - F_2$ | $C_{30} - (D_{30} + D_{31} + D_{34}) + (E_{31} + E_{32} + E_{35}) - F_3$ |
| 8. Arm strength × intelligence × group | 2 | $C_{11} - (D_{10} + D_{12} + D_{16}) + (E_{11} + E_{13}) - F_1$ | $C_{21} - (D_{20} + D_{22} + D_{26}) + (E_{21} + E_{23}) - F_2$ | $C_{31} - (D_{30} + D_{32} + D_{36}) + (E_{31} + E_{33}) - F_3$ |
| 9. Arm strength × intelligence × class | 4 | $C_{12} - (D_{10} + D_{13} + D_{15}) + (E_{11} + E_{14}) - F_1$ | $C_{22} - (D_{20} + D_{23} + D_{25}) + (E_{21} + E_{24}) - F_2$ | $C_{32} - (D_{30} + D_{33} + D_{35}) + (E_{31} + E_{34}) - F_3$ |
| 10. Arm strength × school × class | 12 | $C_{13} - (D_{11} + D_{13} + D_{17}) + (E_{11} + E_{14}) - F_1$ | $C_{23} - (D_{21} + D_{23} + D_{27}) + (E_{21} + E_{24}) - F_2$ | $C_{33} - (D_{31} + D_{33} + D_{37}) + (E_{31} + E_{34}) - F_3$ |
| 11. Arm strength × school × group | 6 | $C_{14} - (D_{11} + D_{12} + D_{18}) + (E_{11} + E_{13}) - F_1$ | $C_{24} - (D_{21} + D_{22} + D_{28}) + (E_{21} + E_{23}) - F_2$ | $C_{34} - (D_{31} + D_{32} + D_{38}) + (E_{31} + E_{33}) - F_3$ |
| 12. Arm strength × class × group | 4 | $C_{15} - (D_{12} + D_{13} + D_{19}) + (E_{11} + E_{13}) - F_1$ | $C_{25} - (D_{22} + D_{23} + D_{29}) + (E_{21} + E_{23}) - F_2$ | $C_{35} - (D_{32} + D_{33} + D_{39}) + (E_{31} + E_{33}) - F_3$ |
| 13. Intelligence × school × class | 6 | $C_{16} - (D_{14} + D_{15} + D_{17}) + (E_{12} + E_{14}) - F_1$ | $C_{26} - (D_{24} + D_{25} + D_{27}) + (E_{22} + E_{24}) - F_2$ | $C_{36} - (D_{34} + D_{35} + D_{37}) + (E_{32} + E_{34}) - F_3$ |
| 14. Intelligence × school × group | 3 | $C_{17} - (D_{14} + D_{16} + D_{18}) + (E_{12} + E_{13}) - F_1$ | $C_{27} - (D_{24} + D_{26} + D_{28}) + (E_{22} + E_{23}) - F_2$ | $C_{37} - (D_{34} + D_{36} + D_{38}) + (E_{32} + E_{33}) - F_3$ |

Table XXVI (continued)

| Source of Variation | df | $\sum y^2$ | $\sum x^2$ | $\sum xy$ |
|---|---|---|---|---|
| 15. Intelligence × class × group | 2 | $C_{18} - (D_{15} + D_{16} + D_{10}) + (E_{12} + E_{13} + E_{14}) - F_1$ | $C_{28} - (D_{25} + D_{26} + D_{29}) + (E_{22} + E_{23} + E_{24}) - F_2$ | $C_{38} - (D_{35} + D_{36} + D_{39}) + (E_{32} + E_{33} + E_{34}) - F_3$ |
| 16. School × class × group | 6 | $C_{19} - (D_{17} + D_{18} + D_{10}) + (E_{13} + E_{14} + E_{15}) - F_1$ | $C_{29} - (D_{27} + D_{28} + D_{29}) + (E_{23} + E_{24} + E_{25}) - F_2$ | $C_{39} - (D_{37} + D_{38} + D_{39}) + (E_{33} + E_{34} + E_{35}) - F_3$ |
| 17. Arm strength × intelligence | 2 | $D_{10} - (E_{11} + E_{12}) + F_1$ | $D_{20} - (E_{21} + E_{22}) + F_2$ | $D_{30} - (E_{31} + E_{32}) + F_3$ |
| 18. Arm strength × school | 6 | $D_{11} - (E_{11} + E_{15}) + F_1$ | $D_{21} - (E_{21} + E_{25}) + F_2$ | $D_{31} - (E_{31} + E_{35}) + F_3$ |
| 19. Arm strength × group | 2 | $D_{12} - (E_{11} + E_{13}) + F_1$ | $D_{22} - (E_{21} + E_{23}) + F_2$ | $D_{32} - (E_{31} + E_{33}) + F_3$ |
| 20. Arm strength × class | 4 | $D_{13} - (E_{11} + E_{14}) + F_1$ | $D_{23} - (E_{21} + E_{24}) + F_2$ | $D_{33} - (E_{31} + E_{34}) + F_3$ |
| 21. Intelligence × school | 3 | $D_{14} - (E_{12} + E_{15}) + F_1$ | $D_{24} - (E_{22} + E_{25}) + F_2$ | $D_{34} - (E_{32} + E_{35}) + F_3$ |
| 22. Intelligence × class | 2 | $D_{15} - (E_{12} + E_{14}) + F_1$ | $D_{25} - (E_{22} + E_{24}) + F_2$ | $D_{35} - (E_{32} + E_{34}) + F_3$ |
| 23. Intelligence × group | 1 | $D_{16} - (E_{12} + E_{13}) + F_1$ | $D_{26} - (E_{22} + E_{23}) + F_2$ | $D_{36} - (E_{32} + E_{33}) + F_3$ |
| 24. School × class | 6 | $D_{17} - (E_{14} + E_{15}) + F_1$ | $D_{27} - (E_{24} + E_{25}) + F_2$ | $D_{37} - (E_{34} + E_{35}) + F_3$ |
| 25. School × group | 3 | $D_{18} - (E_{13} + E_{15}) + F_1$ | $D_{28} - (E_{23} + E_{25}) + F_2$ | $D_{38} - (E_{33} + E_{35}) + F_3$ |
| 26. Class × Group | 2 | $D_{19} - (E_{13} + E_{14}) + F_1$ | $D_{29} - (E_{23} + E_{24}) + F_2$ | $D_{39} - (E_{33} + E_{34}) + F_3$ |
| 27. Arm strength (a) | 2 | $E_{11} - F_1$ | $E_{21} - F_2$ | $E_{31} - F_3$ |
| 28. Intelligence (i) | 1 | $E_{12} - F_1$ | $E_{22} - F_2$ | $E_{32} - F_3$ |
| 29. Group (g) | 1 | $E_{13} - F_1$ | $E_{23} - F_2$ | $E_{33} - F_3$ |
| 30. Class (c) | 2 | $E_{14} - F_1$ | $E_{24} - F_2$ | $E_{34} - F_3$ |
| 31. School (s) | 3 | $E_{15} - F_1$ | $E_{25} - F_2$ | $E_{35} - F_3$ |
| Total | 143 | $A_1 - F_1$ | $A_2 - F_2$ | $A_3 - F_3$ |

The sums of squares equations and the sums of products equations shown in Table XXVI can be derived by the "mechanical method" for determining sums of squares, and sums of products for different orders of interactions described in Chapter 29.

After the sums of squares and sums of products equations for the various orders of interaction and for the main effects have been determined, they may be evaluated by substituting the values of the appropriate sums (see pages 447–49) into the equations and then performing the indicated operations (addition and subtraction). The values of the sums of squares and sums of cross products for the interactions and main effects of our example are shown in Table XXVII, along with the corresponding mean squares (variances) and the respective tests of significance of the *adjusted mean squares.*

The procedure employed for determining the values of the adjusted *sums of squares* and their corresponding *adjusted mean squares* is such that *one degree of freedom is lost in the "error"* (highest order interaction) *term.* This fact, explained in detail later, accounts for the change in the value of *df* for that term from 12 to 11.

Table XXVII

Tests of Significance of Interactions and Main Effects

| Source of Variation | df | $\sum y^2$ | $\sum x^2$ | $\sum xy$ | df | Adjusted $\sum y^2$ | Adjusted Mean Square | F-Ratio | Null Hypothesis |
|---|---|---|---|---|---|---|---|---|---|
| (Error Term) 1. Arm strength × intelligence × school × class × group | 12 | 51 | 122 | 45 | 11 | 34.41 | 3.128 | — | — |
| 2. Arm strength × intelligence × class × group | 4 | 20 | 20 | 19 | 4 | 7.75 | 1.938 | — | Not rejected |
| 3. Arm strength × intelligence × school × group | 6 | 10 | 68 | −1 | 6 | 16.40 | 2.733 | — | Not rejected |
| 4. Arm strength × intelligence × school × class | 12 | 104 | 131 | 99 | 12 | 38.63 | 3.219 | 1.03 | Not rejected |
| 5. Arm strength × school × class × group | 12 | 66 | 147 | 37 | 12 | 57.60 | 4.800 | 1.53 | Not rejected |
| 6. Intelligence × school × class × group | 6 | 25 | 75 | 26 | 6 | 16.00 | 2.667 | — | Not rejected |
| 7. Arm strength × intelligence × school | 6 | 45 | 68 | 17 | 6 | 41.38 | 6.897 | 2.20 | Not rejected |
| 8. Arm strength × intelligence × group | 2 | 4 | 33 | 9 | 2 | 1.78 | .890 | — | Not rejected |
| 9. Arm strength × intelligence × class | 4 | 62 | 9 | −18 | 4 | 73.03 | 18.258 | 5.84 | Rejected (.01) |
| 10. Arm strength × school × class | 12 | 55 | 137 | 35 | 12 | 100.88 | 8.407 | 2.69 | In doubt |
| 11. Arm strength × school × group | 6 | 84 | 65 | −16 | 6 | 96.10 | 16.017 | 5.13 | Rejected (.01) |
| 12. Arm strength × class × group | 4 | 77 | 44 | 40 | 4 | 50.07 | 12.518 | 4.00 | Rejected (.05) |
| 13. Intelligence × school × class | 6 | 53 | 143 | 21 | 6 | 53.29 | 8.881 | 2.84 | In doubt |
| 14. Intelligence × school × group | 3 | 9 | 14 | 4 | 3 | 7.94 | 2.647 | — | Not rejected |
| 15. Intelligence × class × group | 2 | 19 | 14 | 15 | 2 | 9.12 | 4.560 | 1.46 | Not rejected |
| 16. School × class × group | 6 | 88 | 152 | 24 | 6 | 87.22 | 14.537 | 4.56 | Rejected (.05) |
| 17. Arm strength × intelligence | 2 | 41 | 31 | 34 | 2 | 16.80 | 8.400 | 2.69 | In doubt |
| 18. Arm strength × school | 6 | 25 | 46 | 20 | 6 | 16.44 | 2.740 | — | Not rejected |
| 19. Arm strength × group | 2 | 10 | 34 | 19 | 2 | .33 | .165 | — | Not rejected |
| 20. Arm strength × class | 4 | 74 | 146 | 55 | 4 | 53.28 | 13.320 | 4.26 | Rejected (.05) |
| 21. Intelligence × school | 3 | 34 | 4 | 3 | 3 | 32.31 | 10.770 | 3.44 | In doubt |
| 22. Intelligence × class | 2 | 12 | 49 | 13 | 2 | 8.92 | 4.460 | 1.43 | Not rejected |
| 23. Intelligence × group | 1 | 6 | 17 | −10 | 1 | 13.78 | 13.780 | 4.41 | In doubt |
| 24. School × class | 6 | 135 | 82 | 72 | 6 | 84.49 | 14.081 | 4.50 | Rejected (.05) |
| 25. School × group | 3 | 37 | 114 | 37 | 3 | 25.10 | 8.367 | 2.67 | In doubt |
| 26. Class × group | 2 | 2 | 19 | 6 | 2 | .14 | .070 | — | Not rejected |
| 27. Arm strength$^2$ | 2 | 31 | 77 | −6 | 2 | 39.95 | 19.975 | 6.39 | Rejected (.05) |
| 28. Intelligence$^2$ | 1 | 3 | 6 | −4 | 1 | 6.46 | 6.460 | 2.06 | Not rejected |
| 29. Group$^2$ | 1 | 34 | 4 | 2 | 1 | 33.06 | 33.060 | 10.57 | Rejected (.01) |
| 30. Class$^2$ | 2 | 631 | 853 | 734 | 2 | 585.35 | 292.675 | 93.57 | Rejected (.01) |
| 31. School$^2$ | 3 | 241 | 63 | 76 | 3 | 178.45 | 59.483 | 19.02 | Rejected (.01) |
| Total | 143 | 2088 | 2787 | 1407 | 142 | 1786.46 | | | |

1. The null hypothesis under test concerns the variation in the row under consideration. For example, the hypothesis regarding arm strength × intelligence × school × group (line 3 above) is that there is no significant effect as the result of the interaction between the factors of arm strength, intelligence, school, and group after the variation of the initial foul shooting score has been partialled out.

2. The null hypothesis under test in the rows showing main effects only (rows 27, 28, 29, 30 and 31) is: there is no significant difference between the mean scores of the factors (main effects) after the variation of the initial scores has been partialled out.

Since the original factorial grid is of the form which includes but one entry for each cell of the table, the error term to be employed as the denominator of each $F$-ratio test is the highest ordered interaction mean square in Table XXVII. The value of the adjusted mean square of the highest ordered interaction term for our example is: 3.128. In the column of Table XXVII entitled "F-ratio," only those values of the ratio which were found to be greater than unity are shown. If the value of the ratio was reasonably close to that of the critical value found at the intersection of the appropriate columns and rows of degrees of freedom in Table XIV, the null hypothesis under test was *not rejected* but was *placed in doubt*. The effect of placing the null hypothesis "in doubt" is that of implying that the data of the current experimentation are not of sufficient strength to reject $H_0$, additional investigation, or further experimentation, should be carried out in order to derive a definite decision concerning those sources of variation that have been placed "in doubt." Although the level of significance employed in the study was $\alpha = .05$, whenever the value of the $F$-ratio exceeded the appropriate critical value at the $\alpha = .01$ point, the matter was indicated in the column headed "Null Hypothesis."

The method of "adjusting" $\sum y^2$ (sum of squares of $y$) for each interaction and main effect was accomplished by employing the error term $\sum y^2$, $\sum x^2$, and $\sum xy$ values in each adjustment. Since each adjustment was based upon the "best" estimate of the value of the population regression coefficient, i.e., the "error" term regression coefficient, only one degree of freedom (in the error term) is lost for all of the adjustments that are made.

The mechanics of the adjustment of $\sum y^2$ for each interaction and main effect are based upon the formula: $\sum y^2 - (\sum xy)^2/\sum x^2$. The procedures of the adjustment are illustrated by "adjusting" $\sum y^2$ for row 3, of Table XXVII by the following schema:

| Source of Variation | $\sum y^2$ | $\sum x^2$ | $\sum xy$ | $(\sum xy)^2$ | Adj. $\sum y^2$ |
|---|---|---|---|---|---|
| 1. Error term | 51 | 122 | 45 | 2025 | $51 - \dfrac{2025}{122} = 34.41$ |
| 2. Interaction: (from row 3) | 10 | 68 | $-1$ | — | 16.40* |
| 3. Total | 61 | 190 | 44 | 1936 | $61 - \dfrac{1936}{190} = 50.81$ |

* After the values of adjusted $\sum y^2$ are determined for the error term and the total, the value of adjusted $\sum y^2$ for the interaction or main effect under consideration is found by subtracting the adjusted $\sum y^2$ value of the error term from that of the Total; in this case: $50.81 - 34.41 = 16.40$.

To clarify the approach, a few examples are provided. The first illustration shows the composition of adjusted $\sum y^2$ for the interaction in row 5 of Table XXVII. The second illustration demonstrates the computation of adjusted $\sum y^2$ for the interaction in row 17 of Table XXVII, and finally, the computation of adjusted $\sum y^2$ for the main effect in row 29 is illustrated in the third example.

*Example 1* (interaction row 5)

| Source of Variation | $\sum y^2$ | $\sum x^2$ | $\sum xy$ | $(\sum xy)^2$ | Adj. $\sum y^2$ |
|---|---|---|---|---|---|
| 1. Error term | 51 | 122 | 45 | 2025 | $51 - \dfrac{2025}{122} = 34.41$ |
| 2. Interaction (row 5) | 66 | 147 | 37 | — | 57.60* |
| 3. Total | 117 | 269 | 82 | 6724 | $117 - \dfrac{6724}{269} = 92.01$ |

* See footnote under general schema example for "row 3."

*Example 2* (interaction row 17)

| Source of Variation | $\sum y^2$ | $\sum x^2$ | $\sum xy$ | $(\sum xy)^2$ | Adj. $\sum y^2$ |
|---|---|---|---|---|---|
| 1. Error term | 51 | 122 | 45 | 2025 | $51 - \dfrac{2025}{122} = 34.41$ |
| 2. Interaction (row 17) | 41 | 31 | 34 | — | 16.80* |
| 3. Total | 92 | 153 | 79 | 6241 | $92 - \dfrac{6241}{153} = 51.21$ |

\* See footnote under general schema example for "row 3."

*Example 3* (main effect row 29)

| Source of Variation | $\sum y^2$ | $\sum x^2$ | $\sum xy$ | $(\sum xy)^2$ | Adj. $\sum y^2$ |
|---|---|---|---|---|---|
| 1. Error term | 51 | 122 | 45 | 2025 | 34.41 |
| 2. Main effect (row 29) | 34 | 4 | 2 | — | 33.06* |
| 3. Total | 85 | 126 | 47 | 2209 | 67.47 |

\* See footnote, general schema for "row 3."

The main effects (factors) considered in the study are: arm strength ($a$), intelligence ($i$), group ($g$), class ($c$), and school ($s$). The factor of arm strength was divided into three levels (categories)—high, average, and low; intelligence into two levels—high and low; group into two levels—mental practice and physical practice; class (experience) into three levels—Varsity, Junior Varsity, and Novice; and schools into four levels. If a multiple comparison was desired, in those cases where a factor included more than two levels, the $t$-test for significant differences between adjusted mean scores was employed. An illustration of the procedures associated with testing the significant difference between the adjusted means for the three levels of class (Varsity, Junior Varsity, and Novice) is presented below:

*Step 1.* Compute the values of the initial score means ($\overline{X}_k$'s), the final score means ($\overline{Y}_k$'s) for the Varsity, Junior Varsity, and Novice classes, the initial total mean score ($\overline{X}_t$).

From "working" Table 3, pages 446–47, the totals necessary to compute the values of the mean scores sought in this step may be found as follows:

Initial score means:

$$\overline{X}_V = \frac{733}{48} = 15.27 \quad \text{(Varsity class, includes 48 members)}$$

$$\overline{X}_{JV} = \frac{583}{48} = 12.14 \quad \text{(Junior Varsity class, includes 48 members)}$$

$$\overline{X}_N = \frac{447}{48} = 9.31 \quad \text{(Novice class, includes 48 members)}$$

Initial total score mean:

$$\overline{X}_t = \frac{733 + 583 + 447}{144} = \frac{1763}{144} = 12.24$$

Final score means:

$$\overline{Y}_V = \frac{848}{48} = 17.66$$

$$\overline{Y}_{JV} = \frac{718}{48} = 14.96$$

$$\overline{Y}_{N} = \frac{602}{48} = 12.54$$

*Step. 2.* Compute the value of the "error term" regression coefficient with appropriate values from Table XXVII, i.e., with the "highest order interaction" values, in this case:

$$b_w = \frac{\sum xy}{\sum x^2} = \frac{45}{122} = .36885$$

*Step 3.* Compute the value of the adjusted mean $(\hat{Y}_k)$ for each class by employing formula (10) page 424.

*Adjusted means:*

$$(\text{varsity}) \quad \hat{Y}_V = \overline{Y}_V - b_w(\overline{X}_V - \overline{X}_t)$$

$$\hat{Y}_V = 17.66 - .36885\,(15.27 - 12.24)$$

$$\hat{Y}_V = 17.66 - 1.12 = 16.54$$

$$(\text{junior varsity}) \quad \hat{Y}_{JV} = \overline{Y}_{JV} - b_w(\overline{X}_{JV} - \overline{X}_t)$$

$$\hat{Y}_{JV} = 14.96 - .36885\,(12.14 - 12.24)$$

$$\hat{Y}_{JV} = 14.96 + .04 = 15.00$$

$$(\text{novice}) \quad \hat{Y}_N = \overline{Y}_N - b_w(\overline{X}_N - \overline{X}_t)$$

$$\hat{Y}_N = 12.54 - .36885\,(9.31 - 12.24)$$

$$\hat{Y}_N = 12.54 + 1.08 = 13.62$$

*Step. 4.* Employ the $t$-test for the significant difference between adjusted means.

Formula (13) is employed to test the significance of the differences: $(\hat{Y}_V - \hat{Y}_{JV})$, $(\hat{Y}_V - \hat{Y}_N)$, and $(\hat{Y}_{JV} - \hat{Y}_N)$. The formula is as follows:

$$t = \frac{\hat{Y}_{k_1} - \hat{Y}_{k_2}}{\sqrt{S_{Y.x}^2\left[\dfrac{1}{n_1} + \dfrac{1}{n_2} + \dfrac{(\overline{X}_{k_1} - \overline{X}_{k_2})^2}{\sum x_w^2}\right]}} \tag{13}$$

where $\hat{Y}_{k_1}$ and $\hat{Y}_{k_2}$ are the adjusted means of the two groups under consideration, $S_{Y.x}^2$ is the adjusted "error" term mean square (variance); $n_1$, is the number of sampling units in one group, and $n_2$ is the number of sampling units in the second group; $\overline{X}_{k_1}$ is the mean of the $k_1$ group in the pre-experimental (pre-test) variable $X$ and $\overline{X}_{k_2}$ is the same type of mean for the $k_2$ group; and $\sum x_w^2$ is the "error" term sum of squares for $X$. In our example, the value of the $t$-test of the significant difference between the respective adjusted means of the Varsity and Junior Varsity classes becomes:

$$t = \frac{\hat{Y}_V - \hat{Y}_{JV}}{\sqrt{S_{Y.x}^2\left[\dfrac{1}{n_V} + \dfrac{1}{n_{JV}} + \dfrac{(\overline{X}_V - \overline{X}_{JV})^2}{\sum x_w^2}\right]}} = \frac{16.54 - 15.00}{\sqrt{3.128\left[\dfrac{1}{48} + \dfrac{1}{48} + \dfrac{(15.27 - 12.14)^2}{122}\right]}}$$

$$t = \frac{1.54}{\sqrt{3.128\left(\dfrac{1}{24} + \dfrac{9.7969}{122}\right)}} = \frac{1.54}{\sqrt{3.128(.12197)}} = \frac{1.54}{.6177}$$

$$\therefore \quad t \approx 2.49$$

Entering the *t*-table with 11 degrees of freedom, the number of *df* associated with the adjusted "error" term mean square (variance, $S^2_{Y.X}$), the critical value of *t* at the .05 level of this two-tailed test is found to be: $t = \pm 2.201$. Since the observed value of $t = 2.49$ falls in the critical region

$$\left\{ \begin{array}{l} t > 2.201 \\ t < -2.201 \end{array} \right\}$$

the null hypothesis of no significant difference between the adjusted means of the Varsity and Junior Varsity classes *is rejected*, and the "alternative" hypothesis (the difference *is* significant) may be accepted.

Testing for the significance of the difference: $(\hat{Y}_V - \hat{Y}_N)$; the adjusted means of the Varsity and the Novice classes, we have:

$$t = \frac{16.54 - 13.62}{\sqrt{3.128 \left[ \dfrac{1}{48} + \dfrac{1}{48} + \dfrac{(15.27 - 9.31)^2}{122} \right]}} = \frac{2.92}{\sqrt{3.128(.04167 + .29311)}} = \frac{2.92}{\sqrt{1.0472}}$$

$$\therefore \quad t = \frac{2.92}{1.023} \approx 2.854$$

Entering the *t*-table with 11 *df* associated with $S^2_{Y.X} = 3.128$, the critical value of *t* at the .05 level of this two-tailed test is found to be $t = \pm 2.201$. Since the observed value of $t = 2.854$ falls in the critical region, the null hypothesis of no significant difference between the adjusted means of the Varsity and Novice classes *is rejected in favor of the "alternative"* hypothesis (the difference *is* significant).

Finally, testing for the significance of the difference: $(\hat{Y}_{JV} - \hat{Y}_N)$ the adjusted means of the Junior Varsity and Novice classes, we find:

$$t = \frac{15.00 - 13.62}{\sqrt{3.128 \left[ \dfrac{1}{48} + \dfrac{1}{48} + \dfrac{(12.14 - 9.31)^2}{122} \right]}} = \frac{1.38}{\sqrt{3.128(.04167 + .06565)}} = \frac{1.38}{\sqrt{.3357}}$$

$$\therefore \quad t = \frac{1.38}{.58} \approx 2.38$$

Since the observed value of $t = 2.38$ is in the critical region of the two-tailed test

$$\left\{ \begin{array}{l} t > +2.201 \\ t < -2.201 \end{array} \right\}$$

the null hypothesis is rejected in favor of the "alternative" hypothesis to the effect that the difference is significant.

The analysis of the multiple comparison of the adjusted means of the respective classes of experience showed that each class adjusted mean was significantly different from the other two. In and of itself, this finding was not unexpected and as such contributed little "new" knowledge about the problem of the research. From the covariance analysis the researcher also found that there was a significant difference between the adjusted means of the mental practice and physical practice groups, respectively. Another "finding" yielded by the analysis of covariance was that of *no significant difference* existing between the adjusted means of the two classifications of intelligence. Finally, by applying the *t*-test for the significance of the differences between the adjusted means of the levels of arm strength and school, a multiple comparison of the respective individual level adjusted means showed significant differences throughout all levels of these two factors.

Although the interaction of *class × group* was found to be "not significant," the amounts of improvement of the *mental* and *physical practice groups* for the *three classes* of *experience* were subjected to the *t*-test of significant differences between the adjusted means of the respective classifications. The findings that resulted from this analysis showed that all groups in each class of experience showed significant *improvement*. In similar fashion, the adjusted means of various classifications existing under the different interactions involved in the analysis were submitted to test by the appropriate *t*-test.

The findings resulting from the covariance and *t*-test analyses are as follows:

1. Both the physical practice and the mental practice groups showed highly significant gains with *t*-test values of 10.5 and 7.7, respectively.

2. The variables of arm strength, school, class (experience), and group (mental and physical practice) were statistically significant.

3. The factor of intelligence was found to be not significant, in the statistical sense of significance.

4. Mental practice was almost as effective as physical practice for the Varsity and Junior Varsity groups, and slightly less effective for the Novice groups under the conditions of the experiment.

5. Under conditions of the experiment the interactions of: arm strength × intelligence × class; arm strength × school × group; arm strength × class × group; school × class × group; arm strength × class; and school × class significantly affected the results of the experiments.

From these findings and those of the introspective analysis the researcher was prepared to draw conclusions concerning the operational hypotheses, and ultimately, the research hypotheses, of the experiment.

In concluding our discussion it should be pointed out that the process of *confounding* was employed in the actual experiment upon which the present example is based. Since the process did not provide any different findings in the analysis associated with the actual experiment, the discussion of *confounding* has been omitted. For those readers interested in the topic, see: W. S. Ray,[143] *An Introduction to Experimental Design* (New York: MacMillan Company, 1960), pp. 171, 231.

## DECISION

*(The "Decision" element of the research model provides for conclusions concerning the hypotheses or answers to general questions posed by the problem of the study.)*

The conclusions of the research could be summarized as follows:

1. The findings of the experiment support the notion that there exists some combination of mental and physical practice periods that will produce an optimum method of instruction which is superior to methods generally employed today in the process of developing (learning) a motor skill.

2. There is a strong relationship between a subject's ability to visualize the motor skill being developed and the amount of improvement experienced.

3. The intelligence of the learner is not necessarily a *significant* factor in the development of a motor skill.

4. Arm strength and experience are significant factors in developing the motor skill known as "the Pacific Coast one-hand foul shot."

5. In this experiment, the factor of school had a significant effect upon the development of the motor skill involved.

6. Although the physical practice group showed a significantly higher adjusted mean score than that of the mental practice group, both groups showed a significant *gain* in the development of the motor skill involved.

7. In this experiment, there was no statistically significant difference between the adjusted group means of the Varsity physical practice group and the Varsity mental practice group; the Junior Varsity physical practice and the Junior Varsity mental practice group and, finally, the Novice physical practice group and the Novice mental practice group.

8. The high degree of improvement from mental practice experienced by the Varsity and Junior Varsity groups suggests that a certain amount of motor skill experience is necessary before mental practice will provide a maximal effect. Further research is indicated.

9. The general improvement of both the mental practice and physical practice groups indicates great potential for the instructional techniques employed in this experiment, especially when used in physical education classes.

Other minor conclusions were drawn in the actual experiment upon which this example was based, but in the interest of time, space, and efficiency of presentation of this illustration of the model and the analysis of covariance technique, they are omitted. For the readers interested in the actual experiment, see: *The Research Quarterly*, 31 : 4 (December, 1960), pp. 560–659.

## Concluding Remarks—Statistical Inference

All the numerical and analytical procedures considered applicable to a model resulting from modifications of the general model of educational research made necessary by a given research problem have been presented in Chapters 14–30. This approach was employed with the hope that a discussion of the underlying rationale of these techniques, along with a discussion of the accompanying mechanics of the analyses and computational procedures, would result in a better understanding of the topics covered, than that which might have resulted from a "formulas presentation" approach.

Obviously, all the computational procedures associated with all the statistical techniques discussed can be programed and submitted to data processing facilities and/or computer analysis. It is safe to say that any computation laboratory can produce the programs necessary to effect the computational processes associated with all the statistical techniques suggested as acceptable numerical and analytical procedures for employment in the "adapted" forms of the general model of educational research.

With this background we are now prepared to discuss three analytical methods that could be employed in those forms of the model of research that call for decision-making in the realms of: "certainty," "risk," or "uncertainty." These subjects: (1) factor analysis; (2) linear programing, and (3) theory of games, are discussed in Chapters 31 and 32.

*Chapter 30—References*
See Bibliography: 38, 49, 53, 54, 65, 66, 67, 76, 77, 104, 112, 113, 141, 143, 148, 159, 175, 183; 31a, 38a, 48a, 72a, 96a, 104a; 1b.

# Numerical Procedures
# (Factor Analysis)

THE ANALOG MODEL designated as the general model of educational research was designed and developed around a method of inquiry composed of elements considered to be common to certain methods of inquiry. In essence, the approach prescribed by the general model is that of the scientific method. The numerical and analytical procedures employed by the scientific method, and hence the general model, are those associated with the fields of mathematics and statistical analysis.

According to Cattell:

> Philosophers of scientific methods have spoken of four kinds of order: (1) constant conjunction of properties, as used in recognizing a chemical element; (2) causal order, i.e., an invariable sequence, as the failure of oxygen supply causes death; (3) numerical relations; and (4) relations among constructs, not all the elements of which can be directly observed, i.e., order among theoretical entities, each an abstraction from observed data.
>
> The methods by which science seeks to establish these relations have been set out by Bacon, Mill, and later students of method under some variety of the principles of agreement, of difference, of residues, and of concomitant variation. They issue in the experimental and statistical research designs we have already mentioned. All are concerned to establish covariation of variables, either without regard to special time sequence as in most numerical laws or constant conjunction of properties, or without regard to time sequence as in causal laws.[1]

Of the four kinds of order listed by Cattell, the suggested general model of educational research concerns itself first with the analysis of type (4), relations among constructs; secondly with type (1), constant conjunction of properties; thirdly with type (2), causal order; and fourthly with type (3), numerical relations. Since the general model was designed primarily to provide an analytical approach to problems involved in types of order (1), (2), and (4), the numerical and analytical procedures associated with statistical analysis are emphasized in those aspects of the model dealing with data processing and decision-making.

Methods of statistical analysis mainly deal with finding measures of central tendency, measures of dispersion, measures of degree of relationship, and measures of difference; and with testing hypotheses of magnitude, difference, and relationship in order to draw inferences of magnitude, differences, relationship, and appraisal. These statistical methods all involve an arbitrary choice of variables, which means that the researcher selects the variables that he believes will provide the best means of testing the hypotheses that have been advanced. A basic risk in this approach to research is the possibility of choosing variables that might produce unclear or misleading indications of the concept, condition, or entity that they are supposed to represent.

A technique which avoids the arbitrary selection of variables and one which can be easily adapted to the suggested general model of educational research is that of *multiple factor analysis*. In addition to avoiding the arbitrary selection of variables, the factor analytic technique provides a method of determining *both* the *degree* of association between the variables involved and the *essential entities* among the influences under study.

## Multiple Factor Analysis

Since it would be impossible to provide adequate space in this book to explain all or even the major methods of multiple factor analysis, only the nature of the technique is discussed here. The reader interested in a detailed exposition of procedures, computational processes, and other related matters associated with the various methods of multiple factor analysis will need to consult resources noted in the bibliography at the end of this chapter.

The basic procedure of the factor analytic process may be outlined as follows:

1. Measurements are taken on an indefinite number of variables in a given problem area.
2. Selecting two variables at a time from the original set, and thus forming all the different combinations of two that are possible, a correlation coefficient is calculated for each of the respective pairs formed.
3. The set of correlation coefficients are placed in a matrix.
4. Employing procedures of matrix algebra, a multiple factor analysis method (centroid, or principle axes, or other methods) is carried out to extract factors from the original set of correlation coefficients.
5. The factor analytic technique shows how some variables might group together because of certain similarities, and at the same time delineates underlying, independent factors that may well be responsible for the groupings.

Through this procedure, factor analytic methods make it possible to identify new entities which result from the synthesis of the original variables. The new entities are then considered to be new variables which can be identified as causes, intervening variables, or independent influences underlying the original set of variables.

Multiple factor analysis may be adapted to those models of educational research that are exploratory and provide foundations for later problems of experimental and action research. This statement does not mean that all experimental and action research in a problem area must begin with factor analysis. On some occasions it is desirable and necessary to carry out experiments in which a priori variables are selected without knowing how they are related to the structure of basic factors underlying the problem situation.

## Clusters and Factors

Although a definitive interpretation of a single correlation coefficient is impossible, the *actual* (basic) sources of variation that account for the correlation can be better defined if they are part of a battery of variables which produce many correlations that can be submitted to study. Actually, as more variables and correlations are brought under investigation, the freedom in finding more sources of variation *which could fit the observed correlations* diminishes. In essence, the greater variety of data tends to produce a perspective which under conditions of fewer available correlations may well not be represented. The simplest definition of a factor then becomes: *a factor is a source of variation spreading over a measured performance in a number of variables.*

Before proceeding to a definition of clusters, we must consider the *vector representation of a correlation coefficient*. A *vector* is a quantity having *both magnitude and direction*. A *scalar* is a quantity having *magnitude only*. Considering the definition of a vector and that of a scalar, we note that a vector could be represented by an arrow—the *length* of the arrow denoting the *magnitude* of the vector and the *arrow head* indicating its direction. The scalar quantity, on the other hand, could be represented by a line segment—the length of the line indicating the magnitude of the quantity. For example, *velocity* is a *vector quantity* because it has both magnitude *and* direction, while speed is a scalar quantity because it indicates *magnitude only*. Geometrically, a velocity of 25 miles per hour toward the east, and a speed of 25 miles per hour could be represented as follows:

$$\frac{\text{25 m.p.h.}}{\text{(velocity)}} \longrightarrow \quad \text{(vector)}$$

$$\frac{\text{25 m.p.h.}}{\text{(speed)}} \quad \text{(scalar)}$$

It is possible to represent geometrically (and trigonometrically) a correlation coefficient as the cosine function of an angle $\theta$ between two vectors, where the two vectors represent the value (magnitude) and direction of action of the two respective variables providing the correlation. The trigonometric function, cosine of $\theta$, is employed because it has been noted that the properties of "cosines" closely parallel those of correlation coefficients.

In a given right triangle, the cosine of $\theta$ (written $\cos \theta$) is defined to be the value of the ratio formed by dividing the magnitude (length) of the side adjacent to the angle by the magnitude (length) of the hypotenuse of the triangle. Employing this trigonometric ratio, correlation coefficients can be represented as shown in Figure 23. It should be pointed out that although the trigonometric function "$\cos \theta$" was originally developed in connection with a right triangle, the law of cosines extended the definition of the function to any type of triangle. Later, "direction cosines" were developed in the discipline of analytical geometry. It is this latter concept of "$\cos \theta$" that is of interest to our discussion.

In statistical analysis, correlation is represented graphically by placing points for each pair of scores on a graph formed by employing, say, two tests as the two coordinate axes. A condition of positive correlation would be shown as in

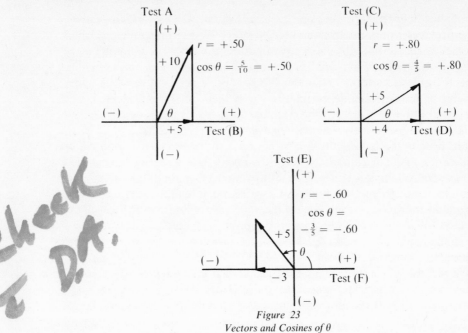

Figure 23
*Vectors and Cosines of θ*

Diagram A of Figure 24, where each point might well represent the pair of scores (formed by the score on Test A combined with that on Test B) for a given person in the sample under consideration. Through this form of representation ("scatter" diagram) the positive correlation is indicated by the oval set of points distributed mainly in quadrants I and III of the graph.

Another representation of the same correlation can be effected by agreeing to "bend" the coordinate axes (Test A and Test B) so that the "rubber sheet" of the graph will be stretched in such a fashion that the former oval distribution

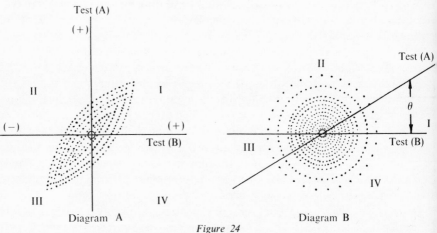

Figure 24
*Scatter Diagram and Vector Representation of Correlation*

of points becomes circular. *When this situation of the circular position of points* (concentric circles of points increasing in density near the origin, *O*) *is reached, the values of the cosine of the angle between the coordinate axes* (Test A and Test B) *equals that of the correlation coefficient.* Therefore, in Diagram B of Figure 24, the cosine of the angle $\theta$ would be equal to the value found for the product-moment correlation coefficient *r* when the values for all the points in Diagram A of Figure 24, are employed in the appropriate statistical formula for *r*. This reasoning explains why the "cos $\theta$" representation of the correlation coefficient can be used.

It should be pointed out that it is not necessary to plot a scatter diagram and "bend" the coordinate axes. All of these geometric manipulations are handled through the employment of appropriate computational procedures. The point being emphasized in our discussion is that the value of the correlation existing between two variables may be found (and represented) by the "cos $\theta$," where $\theta$ is one of the vertical angles between the two vectors representing the respective variables.

If a spatial model of the correlations between many tests were to be employed, as shown in Figure 25, the "test vectors," as they are called, would emanate from the arbitrarily selected origin of the vectors in all directions. Although certain test vectors may be isolated, most of them tend to fall into *clusters*. These clusters are easy to identify in Figure 25. It should be relatively apparent that Test Vectors 4 and 6 are isolated, while 1, 5, 10, and 13 form one cluster; 2, 7, 9, 11 form another cluster; and 3, 8, 12, and 14 form still another cluster.

The construction of Figure 25 is important to understand for further clarification of the theory under discussion. The spatial model is constructed by first

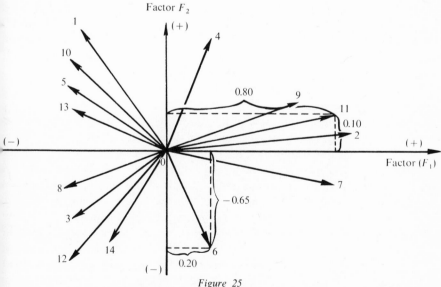

*Figure 25*
*Spatial Model of Test Vectors, Clusters, and Factors*

drawing Test Vector 1 in a randomly selected direction from an arbitrarily chosen origin, $O$. The position of Test Vector 2 is then fixed by the angle it must make with Test Vector 1 in order that the cosine of the "fixed" angle (cos $\theta$) be equal in value to that of the correlation coefficient for these two variables. The appropriate value of the angle between the respective vectors may be found by entering the column of "cos $\theta$" of a table of values of the *natural trigonometric functions* and locating the value of the correlation coefficient of the two variables. The value of the angle found at this point of the table is the one to be employed in laying out Test Vector 2 relative to Test Vector 1. The positions of the test vectors for the remainder of the battery are located in exactly the same fashion, and hence the spatial model is constructed.

It is essential to understand that *the coordinate axes, $OF_1$ and $OF_2$, are placed on the model after all of the test vectors have been drawn in their proper positions.* The respective axes are drawn parallel to the edges of the page purely as a matter of convenience. *The relationship between the rigid system (internally consistent structure) of the test vectors and that of the coordinate axes ($OF_1$ and $OF_2$) is a loose and arbitrary one.* The truth of the latter statement is apparent by the fact that Test Vector 1 may be started anywhere and drawn in any direction.

Through this approach, *multiple factor analysis of a set of correlations among variables becomes essentially the imposition of a framework of coordinate axes (factors) upon the structure of test vectors derived from the correlations.* Figure 25 shows a case where only two factors (coordinate axes, $OF_1$ and $OF_2$) are involved. After the coordinate axes have been rotated about the common fixed point of their own origin and that of the test vectors, and hence the position which provides the most meaningful explanation of the situation is located, it is possible to represent each test of the battery by the numerical value of its projections on the two coordinate axes. For example, Test 6 may be expressed in terms of 0.20 of $F_1$ and $-0.65$ of $F_2$, while Test 11 would be expressed as 0.80 of $F_1$ and 0.10 of $F_2$. In this fashion all fourteen tests can be represented in terms of the two factors, $F_1$ and $F_2$. This parsimony has the advantage of using two measurements to provide essentially the same information that the battery of fourteen tests formerly supplied.

The advantage of the economy of measurement is exemplified in Figure 25 Test 2 is practically a pure measure of factor $F_1$, and for all purposes tends to measure the same dimensions that tests 7, 9, and 11 measure. In similar fashion a reasonably good measure of factor $F_2$ could be realized by averaging the scores on Test 1 and 4. A practical application of this information could be effected by assigning each person scores on the two factors instead of scores on each of the fourteen tests comprising the original battery. From these two scores about as much could be predicted about the person's behavior as could be predicted by the original fourteen test scores. From another point of view, if the projections (loadings) of all fourteen tests on the two factors are determined fairly accurate estimates based upon known two-factor scores can be made for performance on each of the original tests.

RELATIONS OF FACTORS TO VARIABLES

If performance on a given test is measured in terms of standard scores, and the factors are measured in the same units, an individual's performance on that test may be predicted by the *specification equation*. For example, the individual's performances on Tests 6 and 11 would be given by the following specification equations:

$$\text{Performance (Test } 6) = 0.20F_1 - 0.65F_2$$
$$\text{Performance (Test } 11) = 0.80F_1 + 0.10F_2$$

where $F_1$ and $F_2$ indicate the individual's endowments in the factors $F_1$ and $F_2$ previously defined from other sources. The sign of the factor loading in the specification equation indicates the direction in which the factor operates relative to the individual's performance on the test in question. Thus the specification equation for Test 6 shows that the endowment in factor $F_1$ increases performance, while the endowment in factor $F_2$ reduces the individual's performance on that test. If the individual has endowments in factors $F_1$ and $F_2$, his performance will increase on Test 11. In general terms, since a specification equation can be written for each test of the original fourteen, each test performance can be resolved into a function of the same two factors. The particular test performance of a given individual can then be estimated from his particular endowments in those factors included in the specification equation.

In Figure 25 there are three comparatively well-defined groupings of variables. One of the *clusters* is composed of Tests 2, 7, 9, and 11; a second one is composed of Tests 1, 5, 10, and 13; and the third one of Tests 3, 8, 12, and 14. This "natural" alignment might suggest that it would be more convenient to investigate actual clusters than determining hypothetical factors. In fact in the past, especially in the field of psychology, cluster analysis has been used more frequently than factor analysis. In addition to the advantage of working with actual groupings, the computational procedures of inspecting correlations for clusters are much shorter than the prolonged calculations necessary for extracting factors. With the development of the electronic computer, however, the problems of time and difficulty of computational procedures became moot questions, and the decision to conduct either a factor or a cluster analysis had to be based upon other considerations.

At the present time, there are many modified forms of cluster analysis programs being employed in research. Factor analytic approaches, however, are being used much more widely than they were in the past, and at present are continuing to gain in popularity. Reasons for this greater use of factor analysis are: (1) the availability of computer programs for various approaches to factor extraction; (2) usually, the existence of many more clusters than factors (e.g., in personality analysis psychologists have found that individual differences in approximately two hundred variables can be represented either by about sixty clusters or twelve factors); (3) cluster analysis tends to be unable to identify the isolated variables (e.g., Tests 4 and 6 in Figure 25); (4) factors contribute to greater economy of measurement than do clusters; (5) the definition of limits, or criteria, for admission of tests to a cluster is arbitrary (e.g., some investigators insist that only those tests which correlate with each other above $+0.80$ belong to the same cluster, while others use limits as low as $+0.30$); and (6) in any set of real data, clusters are not clearly defined entities, but tend to overlap in the fringe areas, a condition which contributes to the fact that in many cases of analyses the clusters are arbitrarily defined.

## THE CORRELATION MATRIX AND FACTORS

Our discussion to this point has proceeded as if all sets of correlations among tests could be resolved into two factors (coordinate axes). Such is not the case. In practice, where a sufficiently large set of variables is involved, it is found that many more than two general factors are needed to account for the idiosyncrasies of the observations. Since the graphical method previously discussed provides at best a rough estimate of factors, and is limited to the three coordinate axes of Euclidean space (therefore limited to consideration of three factors), it is inadequate for all practical purposes. Mathematical methods have been developed to find, and precisely define, factor loadings. We now discuss briefly certain ramifications of these methods and procedures.

The first problem confronting the analyst is to decide how many factors are at work, or are underlying the system of vectors. Before discussing the mathematical procedures involved in answering the question of *how many*, it might be wise to consider the matter in terms of its geometrical representation. In the example of Figure 25, we chose a situation wherein the angles between the test vectors allowed the vectors to be co-planar, i.e., in the same plane. In practice, such situations are rare. Dimensions under measurement are frequently related in a manner that demands the utilization of hyperspace as opposed to the two dimensions of area or a plane. For example, the situation pictured in Figure 26

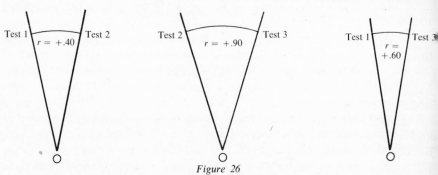

*Figure 26*
*Three Intercorrelations Not Resolvable into the Two Factors (Dimensions) of a Plane Area*

represents cosines equal to the correlations found between two aptitude tests (1 and 2) and a language achievement test (3). If the sectors of a circle with a fixed radius are cut out of paper to simulate the sectors drawn in Figure 26, and are fit together with a fixed origin to form a "vector fan," it is discovered that the fan bends upward into three-dimensional space, i.e., the vectors cannot be put together and still lie in one plane. In order to get the origin $O$, Test Vector 1, Test Vector 2, and Test Vector 3 to be co-planar (in one plane), it would be necessary for angle 102 plus angle 203 to be equal to angle 103 (or the alternative combination to prevail). This special condition rarely occurs in practice.

Since the fan of vectors requires three-dimentional space, three coordinate axes (factors) are necessary to fix the projections (loadings) of the vectors. The general form of the specification equation for performance on any one of the three tests would be:

Performance on Test 1, or 2, or $3 = S_1F_1 + S_2F_2 + S_3F_3$, where $S_1$, $S_2$, and $S_3$ are coefficients in the equation for the factors $F_1$, $F_2$, and $F_3$, respectively.

When a large number of variables are involved, as they are in most educational research problems, correlations are frequently found that cannot be *bounded* by a three-dimensional model. If four dimensions, or more, are demanded, physical models are of limited utility because they only can be constructed in terms of three dimensions at a time while the remaining dimensions are considered to be held constant. This limitation means that a series of three-dimensional models, each model involving a different combination of three, must be constructed to have at best a limited portrayal of the situation. Since mathematical methods have been devised to handle problems involving four, five, and so on through *n-dimensional space*, physical or geometrical models need not be used for such problems.

## HYPERSPACE

Space involving more than three dimensions is called *hyperspace*. It is a mathematically defined space, and is used only to symbolize relationships in which "conventional" spatial representation would not be adequate. Fortunately, the geometrical problems of hyperspace can be worked out by the theorems and corollaries that apply to the familiar three-dimensional space of Euclidean geometry, and can be handled *visually* by considering two or three dimensions (factors) at a time, observing the projections of the test vectors on these axes (factors) while holding the rest of the factors in abeyance.

Considering the definition of a *factor* in relation to hyperspace we find that *factors are the dimensions* (*independent coordinate axes*) *of the n-dimensional space required to contain a certain set of correlations when they are spatially represented.* If the relative magnitudes of the correlations under consideration are such that they can be represented in one plane, then the covariation given by these variables can be expressed by only two independent sources of variation. If the set of correlations demands four dimensions, then there are only four independent variations regardless of the number of tests in the original battery.

## FACTOR LOADINGS

Since we do *not* proceed in factor analysis by constructing a physical model of the test vector structure and then placing coordinates through it, we shall now discuss the mathematical procedures which immediately provide the projections of the vectors on the factors (coordinate axes). Before proceeding with this discussion, however, the relationship of the factor loadings of two variables to their mutual correlation should be presented. If a variable 1 correlates with some constituent of itself, say, $F_1$ a common factor to the degree of $+0.50$; and if another variable 2 correlates with a constituent of itself, also found to be the same common factor $F$, which is a constituent of 1, to the extent of $+0.40$; then the correlation of 1 and 2 will be the product of these separate correlations and $r_{12} = (+0.5)(+0.4) = +0.20$. This rule does not hold for the correlation of any two variables 1 and 2 with a third, 3. *It holds only for orthogonal factors and where the two variables have only the one factor in common.* Expressed in general form, the statement becomes:

$$r_{ab} = r_{aF} \times r_{bF} \tag{1}$$

where $a$ and $b$ have nothing in common but $F$.

Extending the theory, if two tests have *more* than one factor in common, suppose $n$ of them, $F_1, F_2, F_3, \ldots F_n$, the correlation of the two tests is the sum of the products of their corresponding loadings on the common factors, *providing the n factors are independent of each other.* Expressed in a general formula, we have:

$$r_{ab} = (r_{aF_1})(r_{bF_1}) + (r_{aF_2})(r_{bF_2}) + (r_{aF_3})(r_{bF_3}) + \cdots + (r_{aF_n})(r_{bF_n}) \tag{2}$$

Although formulas (1) and (2) provide the means of obtaining correlations from factor loadings, *it is the converse process of obtaining the factor loadings from known correlations which is the important task of factor analysis.*

Considering the converse process, *under the simplified condition of one factor, F,* suppose we originally have a battery of nine tests and the correlations of Test 1 with the eight other tests, *each possessing some amount of the one common factor,* are:

$$r_{12} = (r_{1F})(r_{2F})$$

$$r_{13} = (r_{1F})(r_{3F})$$

$$r_{14} = (r_{1F})(r_{4F})$$

$$\vdots \qquad \vdots \qquad \vdots$$

$$r_{19} = (r_{1F})(r_{9F})$$

Note that the correlation coefficient $(r_{1F})$ is repeated on the right side of each equation, and that the summation of the right side of these equations would result in a "coefficient" multiplied by $r_{1F}$. *The mean correlation of Test 1* (approximately equal to $r_{1F}$) *with all other tests is obtained from this sum, but not by the conventional methods of calculating a mean.* In fact, the mean correlation of Test 1 is found by dividing the sum in question by the square root of the sum of all the columns for $r_{2F}, r_{3F}, r_{4F}, \ldots r_{9F}$, respectively. *This mean value provides part of the definition of the common factor.*

In view of the requirements for computing the mean correlation of Test 1 $(r_{1F})$ from the intercorrelations of the original battery of tests, it is obvious that a factor analysis cannot begin until every possible correlation among the tests has been computed. Thus, every person in the group under consideration must be measured on each of the original tests. The test results are then correlated for all possible pairs, using whatever form of the correlation coefficient is appropriate (e.g., product-moment, point-biserial).

## The Correlation Matrix

In order to insure a systematic approach and analysis of the inter-correlations of the original battery of tests, factor analysis employs the techniques of matrix algebra. The correlation matrix is a convenient arrangement for accounting for all possible correlations of the tests forming the original battery. From earlier discussions (Chapter 14) it may be recalled that the number of different combinations of $n$ different items taken two at a time is:

$$\overset{n}{\underset{2}{C}} = \frac{n!}{2!(n-2)!} = \frac{n(n-1)}{2}$$

The correlation matrix, shown in Table XXVIII, arranges the $n$ test variables along the top and side of the table, and the appropriate value for the correlation coefficient is placed in each cell formed by the intersection of their row and column. Table XXVIII could be considered as the correlation matrix for the nine test variables previously discussed in connection with factor loadings. The data of the matrix are fictitious, and are employed only to

### Table XXVIII

### Correlation Matrix of Nine Test Variables*

| Test Variables | $T_1$ | $T_2$ | $T_3$ | $T_4$ | $T_5$ | $T_6$ | $T_7$ | $T_8$ | $T_9$ | $\Sigma_r$ (entry check) |
|---|---|---|---|---|---|---|---|---|---|---|
| $T_1$ | (.77) | .28 | −.23 | .77 | .23 | .27 | .12 | .15 | .41 | 2.77 |
| $T_2$ | .28 | (.60) | .13 | .28 | −.20 | .60 | .16 | .04 | .42 | 2.31 |
| $T_3$ | −.23 | .13 | (.50) | .10 | −.03 | .35 | .04 | .49 | .50 | 1.85 |
| $T_4$ | .77 | .28 | .10 | (.77) | .23 | .32 | .10 | .33 | .55 | 3.45 |
| $T_5$ | .23 | −.20 | −.03 | .23 | (.32) | −.32 | −.12 | .21 | .08 | .40 |
| $T_6$ | .27 | .60 | .35 | .32 | −.32 | (.81) | .26 | .12 | .81 | 3.22 |
| $T_7$ | .12 | .16 | .04 | .10 | −.12 | .26 | (.26) | −.04 | .20 | .98 |
| $T_8$ | .15 | .04 | .49 | .33 | .21 | .12 | −.04 | (.49) | .40 | 2.19 |
| $T_9$ | .41 | .42 | .50 | .55 | .08 | .81 | .20 | .40 | (.81) | 4.18 |
| $\Sigma r$ | 2.77 | 2.31 | 1.85 | 3.45 | .40 | 3.22 | .98 | 2.19 | 4.18 | $S$ = sum of $\Sigma r$ = 21.35 |
| $r/\sqrt{S}$ | .6000 | .5000 | .4004 | .7467 | .0866 | .6969 | .2121 | .4740 | .9048 | $\sqrt{S} = \sqrt{21.35} = 4.62$ |
| $F_1$ | +.60 | +.50 | +.40 | +.75 | +.09 | +.70 | +.21 | +.47 | +.90 | |

* The positive sign (+) is understood to appear before all values not showing the negative (−) sign.

illustrate our discussion. Applying the formula to the case of nine test variables, we find: $(9)(8)/2 = 36$ correlation coefficients will be needed. Consulting Table XXVIII we note that there are: $(9)(9) = 81$ values in the matrix. The total of 81 is derived from the fact that in addition to the 9 values entered in the cells forming the diagonal of the table, each of the 36 correlation coefficients are entered twice in the matrix; once in the triangular section of values forming the lower left part of the table, and once in the triangular section of values forming the upper right part of the table. To exemplify, the value of the correlation coefficient for Tests 2 and 7 is $r_{27}$ or $r_{72} = .16$, i.e., $r_{27} = r_{72} = .16$. The value ".16" is therefore entered in the cell formed by the intersection of *column $T_2$* and *row $T_7$*, and in the cell formed by the intersection of *column $T_7$* and *row $T_2$*. Thus, 72 of the 81 values in the matrix are accounted for by the "double" entry of the 36 original correlation coefficients. The remaining 9 values found in the diagonal of the table (each one enclosed in parentheses), are called the "*communalities*" of the matrix.

The *communality* of a test variable represents the value of the correlation of the test with itself, *to the extent that this value is due to the common factor, or factors, underlying the original battery of correlations.* The values of the communalities are *not* given by the data of the research, *and should not be confused with the reliability coefficient of a test.* Communalities are estimated, are not exact, and must be supplied in the appropriate cells of the matrix before computations are begun.

There are at least nine different methods of estimating communalities.[2] The simplest method to apply in the majority of cases is the *method of highest correlation*, and is the one employed throughout our illustration and discussion. It should be pointed out that the *best* method for estimating the values of communalities depends upon the situation, but in the majority of cases the method of highest correlation is satisfactory.

The method of highest correlation for estimating communalities is very simple to apply. For example, in *column $T_1$* of the matrix in Table XXVIII we find the highest value of the coefficients in that column to be: $r_{14} = .77$, thus we write it in the diagonal and enclose it in parentheses as the estimated communality. Similarly, in *column $T_5$*, we find the highest magnitude of an $r$ in that column to be associated with a negative sign, namely: $r_{65} = -.32$. Despite the fact that the algebraic sign is negative, we write the value of .32, *with a positive sign*, in the appropriate cell of the diagonal as the estimated communality. The latter example illustrates two facts: (1) in the method of highest correlation, the highest value in the column, *whether it be of positive or negative algebraic sign*, is selected as the estimate of the communality for that column; and (2) *all communalities that are estimated* (not *residual* communalities), *must be positive in sign because they are self correlations.*

After the values of the communalities have been estimated and entered in the appropriate cells of the matrix, we proceed with the process of factor extraction by summing *algebraically* each column of the table. These totals are placed in the row indicated by $\sum r$ at the bottom of the matrix. To check the correctness of entries, both in magnitude and in cell placement, each of the nine *rows* of the matrix is totaled, and the values derived are cross-checked with the totals of the corresponding columns (e.g., $\sum r$ of column $T_1$ equals $\sum r$ of row $T_1$).

In order to find the values of the *first factor loadings*, we find the simple arithmetic mean of each column of the matrix, but not in the customary way, i.e., by dividing the total by the number of elements that were added together (in our example, nine elements). The required factor loadings (arithmetic averages of the respective columns of the matrix) are found by dividing the value of $\sum r$ for each column by the value of $\sqrt{S}$, where $S$ is the grand total of the nine column totals ($\sum r$'s).

The results of the division of each column $\sum r$ by the $\sqrt{S}$ are given correct to two decimal places in the last row of the bottom section of the table. The values found in the row labeled $F_1$ are the first factor loadings, and represent the projections of the points at the end of the original test vectors upon the *first factor coordinate axis*. Before discussing how the first factor loadings are used in the procedures of obtaining the *second factor loadings*, we shall attempt to show geometrically how the algebraic processes that we employed have located the length and direction of the first factor axis by placing it through the center of gravity of the swarm of points defined by the ends of the test vectors.

## Centroid*

The center of gravity of a geometrical figure (e.g., a line, a plane, or a volume) is a centroid. A geometric figure, technically, has no center of gravity. A physical body, on the other hand, has a center of gravity but no centroid. The centroid of a geometrical figure is located at the point where the center of gravity would be if the figure were a physical body.

In Figure 27, we have constructed a geometrical figure composed of points representing the ends of the test vectors, and lines representing the directions of the test vectors from the origin to the points. *The point G is the centroid of the figure.* If a vector were drawn from the origin to point $G$, the direction of the variance common to all test vectors (i.e., the direction of the first factor) would be determined.

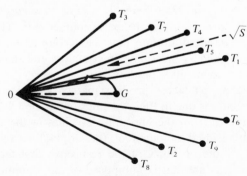

*Figure 27*
*Centroid of a Geometrical Figure of a Set of Correlating Variables*

---

* The term "centroid method" generally refers to developments of factor analysis by L. L. Thurstone,[167] *Multiple Factor Analysis*. It should be recognized, however, that the method does not rely upon Thurstone's techniques of factorization alone. It is a perfectly general method of finding factors which can later be handled by the rotation methods of Thurstone, or by methods of other approaches.

The *length* of the first factor coordinate axis, from the origin $O$ to the centroid $G$, is the amount of the variance which lies in the first factor and is equal in value to the $\sqrt{S}$. By dividing the test projections ($\sum r$ of each column of the matrix) by the $\sqrt{S}$, we express them relative to a coordinate axis of *unit* length. Thus, the value of a factor loading must be fractional, and can never exceed unity. The extent of the need for extracting a *second factor* is indicated by the scatter of the points about the centroid $G$. By our algebraic manipulations employed in extracting the first factor, we have transferred the point of reference from the origin $O$ to the centroid $G$. This action greatly shortens the lengths of the test vectors, but there is still variance in the system as evidenced by the distances between the end points of the vectors and $G$. The only logical explanation for this variance is the existence of other factors in the system. We shall now describe the process of extracting the second factor of the system in our example.

### The Second Factor

After the first factor loadings are determined, a *first factor product matrix* must be constructed. Employing formula (2) (page 468), which shows that the correlation of two variables sharing common factors may be expressed as the product of their respective correlations with the factors (i.e., their factor loadings), the values for the cells of the matrix, shown in Table XXIX, are calculated. For example, the correlation coefficient for Tests 1 and 4 of our illustration, *based upon their respective first factor loadings*, would be:

$$r_{14} = (r_1 F_1)(r_{4F_1}) = (.60)(.75) = .45$$

It should be pointed out immediately that the calculated value of the correlation coefficient for the variables, $T_1$ and $T_4$, read from the correlation matrix of Table XXVIII is: $r_{14} = .77$. Obviously, there is a residual amount of: $= .77 - .45 = .32$ correlation yet to be accounted for. The answer to this problem is that the residual amount must be accounted for by further factors that the variables $T_1$ and $T_4$ must have in common, and the chance errors due to sampling, measurement, and computation.

By constructing a first factor product matrix, we systematically find the values of the correlations due to their loadings on the first factor. These values, in turn, are subtracted from the appropriate values in the correlation matrix to determine the residual amounts of the original correlation coefficients unaccounted for by the products of the respective first factor loadings. We then set up a first residual matrix composed of the aforementioned residuals and begin the extraction of the second factor loadings. This process is discussed in detail later.

The first factor product matrix is constructed by arranging the first factor loadings across the top and down the left side of the table. The *products* formed by the row values (first factor loadings) and the column values of the matrix are entered in the appropriate cells formed by the intersections of the rows and the columns. For example, the product to be entered in the cell formed

Table XXIX
First Factor Product Matrix

| First Factor Loadings | $T_1 = .60$ | $T_2 = .50$ | $T_3 = .40$ | $T_4 = .75$ | $T_5 = .09$ | $T_6 = .70$ | $T_7 = .21$ | $T_8 = .47$ | $T_9 = .90$ |
|---|---|---|---|---|---|---|---|---|---|
| $T_1 = .60$ | (.36) | .30 | .24 | .45 | .05 | .42 | .13 | .28 | .54 |
| $T_2 = .50$ | | (.25) | .20 | .38 | .05 | .35 | .11 | .24 | .45 |
| $T_3 = .40$ | | | (.16) | .30 | .04 | .28 | .08 | .19 | .36 |
| $T_4 = .75$ | | | | (.56) | .07 | .53 | .16 | .35 | .68 |
| $T_5 = .09$ | | | | | (.01) | .06 | .02 | .04 | .08 |
| $T_6 = .70$ | | | | | | (.49) | .15 | .33 | .63 |
| $T_7 = .21$ | | | | | | | (.04) | .10 | .19 |
| $T_8 = .47$ | | | | | | | | (.22) | .42 |
| $T_9 = .90$ | | | | | | | | | (.81) |

by the intersection of row $T_2$ and column $T_3$ is: $(.50)(.40) = .20$. *Since it will not be necessary to find totals of the columns in this table, the values of the "product" r's were only entered in appropriate cells of the upper right section of the table.*

The products found in the first factor product matrix are systematically subtracted from the original r's and the estimated communalities of the correlation matrix. These *algebraic* differences, called *"first residuals,"* are entered in the appropriate cells of the *first residual matrix*, shown in Table XXX.

Table XXX
First Residual Matrix

| Test Variables | $T_1$ | $T_2$ | $T_3$ | $T_4$ | $T_5$ | $T_6$ | $T_7$ | $T_8$ | $T_9$ |
|---|---|---|---|---|---|---|---|---|---|
| $T_1$ | (.41) | −.02 | −.47 | .32 | .18 | −.15 | −.01 | −.13 | −.13 |
| $T_2$ | −.02 | (.35) | −.07 | −.10 | −.25 | .25 | .05 | −.20 | −.03 |
| $T_3$ | −.47 | −.07 | (.34) | −.20 | −.07 | .07 | −.04 | .30 | .14 |
| $T_4$ | .32 | −.10 | −.20 | (.21) | .16 | −.21 | −.06 | −.02 | −.13 |
| $T_5$ | .18 | −.25 | −.07 | .16 | (.31) | −.38 | −.14 | .17 | .00 |
| $T_6$ | −.15 | .25 | .07 | −.21 | −.38 | (.32) | .11 | −.21 | .18 |
| $T_7$ | −.01 | .05 | −.04 | −.06 | −.14 | .11 | (.22) | −.14 | .01 |
| $T_8$ | −.13 | −.20 | .30 | −.02 | .17 | −.21 | −.14 | (.27) | −.02 |
| $T_9$ | −.13 | −.03 | .14 | −.13 | .00 | .18 | .01 | −.02 | (.00) |
| (Totals) $\sum K$ | .00 | −.02 | .00 | −.03 | −.02 | −.02 | .00 | .02 | .02 |

In the residual matrix there frequently appears a negative quantity (e.g., the residual for $T_1$ and $T_2$ is $-.02$) which must be accounted for by further factors. This condition should not cause any undue concern, because a negative residue will occur typically in about one half the r's in a residual matrix. The fact that some variables can be loaded positively on a factor while others are loaded negatively on it can be readily understood by considering, for example, the variable of height which might well be an advantage (positive loading) in some activities (performances) and a disadvantage (negative loading) in other activities.

When an attempt is made to total the columns of the first residual matrix, it is discovered that the sum of each column is very close to zero. In fact, if we had not rounded the original correlation coefficients and the first factor loadings to two places, and used them in the computations for finding the first residuals, we would have obtained precisely zero for each column total. The fact that the column totals should be approximately equal to zero is used as a check procedure of the correctness of the preceding step.

Considering the situation geometrically, the fact that the columns of the first residual matrix each total zero is not surprising. Borrowing the concept of the principle of moments from the field of physics, which states that the "turning moment" (the product formed by the lever arm distance times the weight of the particle in question) of all the particles of a body about its centroid (more precisely, its center of gravity) must *total* zero, we can see that since we have transferred the point of reference of our geometric model (see Figure 27) from the origin $O$ to the centroid $G$, we are at the center of the swarm of points and the sum of the *moments* of the end points of the vectors about $G$ must equal zero.

Although the grand total of the matrix is approximately zero, we are well aware of the fact that at least one more factor of variance exists in the system. In other words, we are aware of the fact that the *positive* moments of the particles of the geometric figure about their centroid are exactly counterbalanced by the negative moments of other particles about the centroid of the body, and this condition tends to camouflage the fact that the swarm of points has at least one more factor of variance in the system. In order to overcome the disadvantages associated with referring the points to their centroid, a mathematical procedure is employed which will *reflect* all the points located on *one side* of the first factor axis to points located as far away on the opposite side of the axis as they were in their original positions. Since the reflection of points occurs after the first factor has been extracted, the test vectors are not reflected about the first origin $O$, but about the first factor axis $OG$.

The process is shown geometrically in Figure 28. The points lying below the first factor axis $OG$, ($T_3$ and $T_5$), in the figure to the reader's left, are reflected

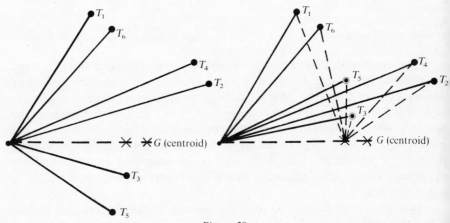

*Figure 28*
*Reflection of Vectors with Respect to First Factor (Centroid)*

to the positions of the small circles in the figure to the reader's right. These "circles" lie as far above the first factor axis *OG* as the original solid points lay below it. The reflected points no longer balance about the first centroid. They now help form a cluster on one side of the first factor axis, and it is possible to find a new centroid and run the axis of the second factor through it.

The mathematical procedures associated with the process of reflection are designed to gain conformity when the sign of the test variable is altered from negative to positive. When the sign is altered on the test number itself (at the same time appropriately altering the naming and meaning of that vector), the algebraic sign of each of its *r*'s with other tests must also be changed. Although this situation of reversing the meaning of the variable when we reverse its sign is easily understood, we can employ more easily in our algebraic processes the method of retaining the *meaning of the variable while we reverse the sign of every loading obtained for it while it is in the reversed condition*. In fact, this latter procedure has been the generally adopted practice in factor analysis.

### The First Residual Matrix and Reflection

Any test score may be positive or negative depending upon the point of reference. If, for example, a positive score means "extroversion," the same score with a negative sign would mean "introversion." It is therefore completely acceptable to imagine all scores on a given test reversed in sign as far as the remaining factors to be extracted are concerned. The fact that in practice the part of the score remaining after extracting the first factor is incapable of actually being reversed need not trouble our thinking, because we make the change in algebraic sign only conceptually and return to the original sign when our purposes are served.

Where in the geometrical model one must think of reflecting the test vector from one side of the first factor to the opposite side of it, algebraically we concern ourselves only with the problem of what would happen if we changed the signs of all the items of one of the variables (tests) when computing a correlation coefficient (*r*) between it and another variable (test). To change the algebraic sign of all scores in one of the sets (tests) will result in changing the algebraic sign of its correlation with each of the other tests (sets). The aim of the process of reflection is to change the signs of those tests that will allow extraction of the largest possible factor loadings from the correlations remaining after the previous factor (in this instance, the first factor) has been removed. In order to illustrate the actual work involved in effecting the method of reflection algebraically, we construct a new first residual matrix, and prepare to estimate *new communalities*. The purpose of estimating communalities *anew* is to avoid the compounding of errors that might have been made in estimating communalities for the original correlation matrix. It should be emphasized at this point that the re-estimating of communalities for the residual matrix does *not* mean that the communality residuals in the first residual matrix of Table XXX should not have been employed as they were. To the contrary, these values are necessary for the computational purposes of checking the subtraction results entered in the product matrix of Table XXIX. *Once the check has been completed* (each column of the first residual matrix should total approximately zero), *the residual communalities should be abandoned in favor of new estimates which should be more in keeping with the pool of that matrix.* If our original estimates of the communalities had been correct, the residual communalities would not only be proper to use, but should be used. But in view of the fact that the first estimates were at best "educated guesses," it is best not to trust them very far, but make new estimates by the "method of the highest inter-function (correlation) residual" for each column of the matrix.

The *"working"* first residual matrix is shown in Table XXXI. The residuals (*r*'s) are written in the appropriate cells of the table, *but instead of writing their algebraic signs immediately beside them* we enter the signs at the *bottom* of the narrow cell, provided for that purpose, directly to the left of the "regular" cell. This action is taken because we shall later wish to make some changes in the temporary signs. This process includes the *residual* communalities, entered in the diagonal in circles. It should be pointed out that the residual communalities may have negative signs, depending upon the results of the subtraction of the *product* communalities (which must be positive) from the *estimated* communalities (which also must be positive) of the previous matrix (in this instance, the correlation matrix). After all reflections are completed, the *final algebraic* signs of the *r*'s are written beside them in the "regular" cells.

The *first step* of the reflection process is to estimate new communalities for the matrix. We re-emphasize the fact that all the new *estimated* communalities must be positive in sign (because they are self-correlations) regardless of whether the inter-function correlations from which they were estimated were negative in algebraic sign.

The *second step* of the process is to sum algebraically the residuals in each of the columns, *not including the communalities*, and to enter the sums in the appropriate cells of the row labeled "$\sum 0$." We now find the highest *negative* sum of that *row*, and prepare to *reflect* the column with which that sum is associated. In the geometric model, the factor axis is passed through the most dense cluster of points. The algebraic equivalent of this action is the choice of the column that aggregates arithmetically large *r*'s because arithmetically high correlations make a clustering of points. The latter fact becomes obvious if it is recalled that the values of the correlations are expressed by cosine ratios of the angle between the test vectors, and that large cosine values (approaching unity) indicate small angles (approaching 0°) between the test vectors. Small angles between the test vectors indicate that a cluster must exist.

The *third step*, after selecting $T_1$ as the test with the highest negative sum in row $\sum 0$, is to place an *a* above the column to indicate we chose it first for "reflection," and reflect Test 1 ($T_1$) by changing all the signs in that column *except the communality, which always remains positive throughout all reflections.*

Table XXXI
First Residual Matrix (With Reflections)

| Test Variables | $a$ $T_1$ | $T_2$ | $T_3$ | $b$ $T_4$ | $c$ $T_5$ | $T_6$ | $T_7$ | $d$ $T_8$ | $T_9$ |
|---|---|---|---|---|---|---|---|---|---|
| $a$ $T_1$ | (.41) / +(.32) | +.02 | +.47 | +.32 | +.18 | +.15 | +.01 | −.13 | +.13 |
| $T_2$ | +.02 | (.35) / +(.25) | −.07 | +.10 | +.25 | +.25 | +.05 | +.20 | −.03 |
| $T_3$ | +.47 | −.07 | (.34) / +(.47) | +.20 | +.07 | +.07 | −.04 | −.30 | +.14 |
| $b$ $T_4$ | +.32 | +.10 | +.20 | (.21) / +(.32) | +.16 / +(.32) | +.21 | +.06 | −.02 | +.13 |
| $c$ $T_5$ | +.18 | +.25 | +.07 | +.16 / +(.38) | (.31) / +(.38) | +.38 | +.11 / +(.14) | +.17 | .00 |
| $T_6$ | +.15 | +.25 | +.07 | +.21 | +.38 | (.32) / +(.38) | +.11 | +.21 | +.18 |
| $T_7$ | +.01 | +.05 | −.04 | +.06 | +.14 | +.11 | (.22) / +(.14) | +.14 | +.01 |
| $d$ $T_8$ | −.13 | +.20 | −.30 | −.02 | +.17 | +.21 | +.14 | (.27) / +(.30) | +.14 / +(.18)? |
| $T_9$ | +.13 | −.03 | +.14 | +.13 | .00 | +.18 | +.01 | +.02 / +(.30) | (.00) / +(.18) |
| $\Sigma k$ | .00 | −.02 | .00 | −.03 | −.02 | −.02 | .00 | +.02 | +.02 |
| $\Sigma 0$ | −.41 | −.37 | −.34 | −.24 | −.33 | −.34 | −.22 | −.25 | +.02 |
| $\Sigma 1$ | +.41 | −.33 | +.60 | −.88 | −.69 | −.04 | −.20 | +.01 | +.28 |
| $\Sigma 2$ | +1.05 | −.13 | +1.00 | +.88 | −1.01 | +.38 | −.08 | +.05 | +.54 |
| $\Sigma 3$ | +1.41 | +.37 | +1.14 | +1.20 | +1.01 | +1.14 | +.20 | −.29 | +.54 |
| $\Sigma 4$ | +1.15 | +.77 | +.54 | +1.16 | +1.35 | +1.56 | +.48 | +.29 | +.58 |
| $\Sigma r_1$ | +1.47 | +1.02 | +1.01 | +1.48 | +1.73 | +1.94 | +.62 | +.59 | +.76 |
| $\Sigma r_1 / \sqrt{S^*}$ | .4509 | .3129 | .3098 | .4540 | .5307 | .5951 | .1902 | .1810 | .2331 |
| $F_2$ | −.45 | +.31 | +.31 | −.45 | −.53 | +.60 | +.19 | −.18 | +.23 |

* $S$ = sum of $\Sigma r$'s = 10.62; therefore: $\sqrt{S} = \sqrt{10.62} = 3.26$.

*We enter the "new" signs just above the original ones in the narrow column immediately to the left of the "regular" column.* Having changed the signs of the $r$'s in *column* $T_1$, we must also change them in *row* $T_1$, and indicate the fact by an *a* placed beside the $T_1$ symbol.

The *fourth step* of the process is to again total the columns with the "new" signs, *disregarding communalities*, to get a new row of sums labeled "$\sum 1$." The highest negative sum in row $\sum 1$ is found in *column* $T_4$, so the signs of all the correlations in that column are changed (using the same procedures as those employed previously with $T_1$) as well as those in *row* $T_4$. This action is indicated by a *b* placed above the $T_4$ of the column and beside the $T_4$ of the row in question. Since all of the column totals are not positive, the reflection process is continued.

The *fifth step* involves totaling the respective columns once again, still disregarding communalities, after the signs have been changed in the column labeled $T_4$ and the $T_4$ row. These totals are entered in the row of the table labeled "$\sum 2$." Since the highest negative sum is $-1.01$ associated with *column* $T_5$, we change the signs of that column and those of the corresponding *row* $T_5$, using the same procedures as those employed in $T_1$ and $T_4$. This action is indicated by a *c*.

The *sixth step* requires that the columns be totaled, disregarding communalities, and that the values derived be entered in the row of the table designated by "$\sum 3$." We note that the only negative sum in row $\sum 3$ is the one associated with column $T_8$. After changing the signs of column $T_8$ and row $T_8$, and designating the action with a *d*, we are prepared to total the columns of the matrix once again.

The *seventh step* of the process is that of totaling the columns, disregarding communalities, and entering the results in the row labeled "$\sum 4$." Since all the sums of the columns entered in row $\sum 4$ are positive, the process of reflection is ended *as far as this table is concerned.*

Upon completing the process of reflection, the matrix is prepared for treatment to extract the loadings of the variables on the second factor of the system. In order to perform this function, the same technique that was employed in deriving the first factor is used again. Stated briefly the procedure involves: (1) totaling each column, *including the new estimate of the communality*, and entering the results in the row of the table designated as "$\sum r_1$"; (2) totaling the values of the $\sum r_1$ row to obtain the value of $S = 10.62$; (3) finding the value of: $\sqrt{S} = 3.26$; (4) dividing each value in the $\sum r_1$ row by $\sqrt{S} = 3.26$ *to obtain the loadings on the second factor of the respective variables*; (5) entering the values derived in (4) in the row of the table designated "$\sum r_1/\sqrt{S}$"; (6) reversing the algebraic sign of each factor loading associated with the tests that were totally reflected (these tests: 1, 4, 5, and 8 are indicated by *a, b, c* and *d*, respectively, above their column headings); and (7) entering the rounded second factor loadings, with correct signs, in the last row of the table indicated by "$F_2$."

*The Third Factor*

Since the magnitudes of the residuals in the first residual matrix of Table XXX are sufficiently large (values larger than those that could be attributed to chance errors resulting from sampling, measurement, and computation) to hypothesize that at least one more common factor exists in the system, we prepare to extract the loadings on the third factor. The *first step* of the process is to construct a *second factor product matrix*. This matrix is constructed in the same fashion used to develop the first factor product matrix of Table XXIX.

The loadings employed across the top and down the side of the second factor product matrix, shown in Table XXXII, are those of the second factor. *All the loadings are considered to be positive for purposes of providing efficient methods of computation.* Those loadings that were found to be negative (Tests 1, 4, 5, and 8) are indicated by $(-)$ placed above the appropriate column and along the side of the appropriate row. Thus, all the entries in the second factor product matrix will be positive, despite the fact that certain factor loadings forming the products (the entries of the table) would produce negative values, *if* algebraic signs were being taken into account. For reasons of computational convenience, however, we shall ignore the signs, i.e., consider all of them to be positive. To illustrate how entries are obtained for the cells of the table, we have:

$$r_{34} = (r_{3F_2})(r_{4F_2}) = (.31)(.45) \approx .14$$

$$r_{22} = (r_{2F_2})(r_{2F_2}) = (.31)(.31) \approx .10$$

All entries for the table are calculated in this fashion.

The second step of the process of finding the third factor loadings is to determine the values of the entries for the second residual matrix, shown in Table XXXIII, by subtracting the "product" values of Table XXXII from values in corresponding cells of the first residual matrix in Table XXX. For example, the residual communality for $T_1$ (circled in the appropriate cell of the diagonal of Table XXXIII would be: $r_{11} = (.32) - (.20) = .12$; while the residual for the cell formed by *row* $T_2$ and column $T_8$ is: $r_{28} = .20 - .06 = .14$; and, finally, the

Table XXXII
Second Factor Product Matrix

| Second Factor Loadings | $(-)$ $T_1 = -.45$ | $T_2 = .31$ | $T_3 = .31$ | $(-)$ $T_4 = -.45$ | $T_5 = -.53$ | $T_6 = .60$ | $T_7 = .19$ | $T_8 = -.18$ | $T_9 = .23$ |
|---|---|---|---|---|---|---|---|---|---|
| $(-)T_1 = -.45$ | (.20) | .14 | .14 | .20 | .24 | .27 | .09 | .08 | .10 |
| $T_2 = .31$ | | (.10) | .10 | .14 | .16 | .19 | .06 | .06 | .07 |
| $T_3 = .31$ | | | (.10) | .14 | .16 | .19 | .06 | .06 | .07 |
| $(-)T_4 = -.45$ | | | | (.20) | .24 | .27 | .09 | .08 | .10 |
| $(-)T_5 = -.53$ | | | | | (.28) | .32 | .10 | .10 | .12 |
| $T_6 = .60$ | | | | | | (.36) | .11 | .11 | .14 |
| $T_7 = .19$ | | | | | | | (.04) | .03 | .04 |
| $(-)T_8 = -.18$ | | | | | | | | (.03) | .04 |
| $T_9 = .23$ | | | | | | | | | (.05) |

entry for cell $T_4 \times T_8$ becomes: $r_{48} = -.02 - .08 = -.10$; where the positive sign $(+)$ before the $(.20)$ in the second example and the negative sign $(-)$ before the $(.02)$ in the last example, *are the final signs of those respective quantities in* the first residual matrix. Since the sign of an estimated communality (such as the one used here in our first numerical example) is always positive, reference need not be made to the "final sign" aspect of such cases.

After all the residuals for the second residual matrix have been determined and entered in Table XXXIII, the computations are checked by summing the columns, including the *residual communalities*. If the computations are correct, all columns will total approximately zero, i.e., within the range of error due to the rounding of numbers to two places. The row of the table designated $\sum k$ contains the sums in question. Since each sum and the grand total of these sums, approximate zero well within the range of "rounding error," we can assume that no biased error has been made in the computations.

The next steps of the process are the same as those that were employed in connection with the first residual matrix of Table XXX. "New" communalities are estimated, the sums of the columns, *excluding the communalities*, are found for the row $\sum 0$; the signs of the values in the column and row of the variable showing the *highest negative* sum in the $\sum 0$ row are reversed, thus reflecting that variable $(T_3)$, and the action is indicated by an $a$ in the appropriate column and row; after the "reflection" the columns are summed again, once again disregarding the communalities; the "new" totals are entered in the row labeled "$\sum 1$." The highest negative sum is found in the $\sum 1$ row, i.e., $T_1$, and the entries in column and row $T_1$, associated with that sum are "reflected." This action is denoted by a $b$ in column $T_1$ and row $T_1$. We proceed with the reflection of tests, achieving all positive signs for the sums of columns after four reflections $(\sum 1, \sum 2, \sum 3,$ and $\sum 4)$. Of course, had it appeared clearly that we would have been unable to reach all positive signs for these sums, we would have stopped the reflection process when we had attained that goal (all positives) as nearly as possible (feasible).

After the reflection process is completed, we once again sum each column of the matrix, this time including the "new" estimate of the communality which is always of positive algebraic sign. The values of these sums are entered in the row of the table designated as "$\sum r_2$." The sums of the respective columns in row $\sum r_2$ are then totaled to produce the value: $S = 8.35$. The square root of $S$ is calculated as: $\sqrt{S} = \sqrt{8.35} \approx 2.89$. Each value in the row labeled "$\sum r_2$" is divided by 2.89, and the resulting value is entered in the row labeled: "$\sum r_2/\sqrt{S}$." These values are rounded and, with appropriate algebraic sign, are entered in the proper cell of the "factor loadings" row, labeled "$F_3$."

It should be noted how the appropriate sign for a factor loading is determined in this matrix. For example, $T_2$ has not been reflected, therefore its loading maintains the positive sign $(+)$ and becomes $+.30$. Because $T_5$ is entered with a $(-)$ sign, to show that it had been reflected in the first matrix (and therefore was still reflected), and since it was *not* reflected in the second residual matrix, the algebraic sign of its loading on the third factor is negative $(-)$. Since $T_1$

Table XXXIII

Second Residual Matrix (With Reflections)

| Test Variables | b (−)T₁ | | T₂ | | a T₃ | | c (−)T₄ | | (−)T₅ | | T₆ | | T₇ | | (−)T₈ | | d T₉ |
|---|---|---|---|---|---|---|---|---|---|---|---|---|---|---|---|---|---|
| (−)T₁ [b] | ⑫ +(.33) | + | +.12 | ± | +.33 | ++ | +.12 | ± | +.06 | ± | +.12 | ± | +.08 | ± | +.21 | ++ | +.03 |
| T₂ | +.12 | ± | ⑮ +(.17) | ± | +.17 | ± | +.04 | + | +.09 | + | +.06 | + | −.01 | − | +.14 | ± | +.10 |
| T₃ [a] | +.33 | ++ | +.17 | ± | ㊲ +(.36) | + | +.06 | ± | +.09 | ± | +.12 | ± | +.10 | ± | +.36 | ++ | +.07 |
| (−)T₄ [c] | +.12 | ++ | +.04 | ± | +.09 | ++ | ⑫ +(.12) | ± | +.08 | ± | +.06 | ± | +.03 | ± | +.10 | ++ | +.03 |
| (−)T₅ | +.06 | ± | +.09 | + | +.09 | ± | +.08 ⑩ +(.12) | ± | | + | +.06 | + | +.04 | + | +.07 | ± | +.12 |
| T₆ | +.12 | ± | +.06 | + | +.12 | ± | +.06 | + | +.06 | + | ⑫ +(.12) | | .00 | | +.10 | ± | −.04 |
| T₇ | +.08 | ± | −.01 | + | +.10 | ± | +.03 | + | +.04 | + | .00 ⑩ +(.11) | | | + | +.11 | + | +.03 |
| (−)T₈ [d] | +.21 | ± | +.14 | + | +.36 | ± | +.10 | + | +.07 | + | +.10 | + | +.11 | + | ㉗ +(.36) | + | +.02 ⑬ +(.12) |
| T₉ | +.03 | ++ | +.10 | ± | +.07 | ++ | +.03 | ± | +.12 | |+ | −.04 | ⊢ | +.03 | ± | +.02 | + | ⑬ +(.12) |
| Σk | +.01 | | .00 | | −.01 | | +.02 | | +.01 | | −.02 | | .00 | | .00 | | +.03 |
| Σ0 | −.11 | | −.15 | | −.38 | | −.10 | | −.09 | | −.04 | | −.10 | | −.27 | | −.10 |
| Σ1 | −.77 | | −.19 | | +.38 | | −.22 | | −.09 | | +.20 | | +.10 | | +.45 | | −.24 |
| Σ2 | +.77 | | +.43 | | +1.04 | | −.46 | | +.21 | | +.44 | | +.26 | | +.87 | | −.30 |
| Σ3 | +1.01 | | +.51 | | +1.16 | | +.46 | | +.37 | | +.56 | | +.32 | | +1.07 | | −.36 |
| Σ4 | +1.07 | | +.71 | | +1.30 | | +.52 | | +.61 | | +.48 | | +.38 | | +1.11 | | +.36 |
| Σr₂ | +1.40 | | +.88 | | +1.66 | | +.64 | | +.73 | | +.60 | | +.49 | | +1.47 | | +.48 |
| Σr₂/√S* | .4844 | | .3045 | | .5744 | | .2214 | | .2526 | | .2076 | | .1695 | | .5086 | | .1661 |
| F₃ | +.48 | | +.30 | | −.57 | | +.22 | | −.25 | | +.21 | | +.17 | | −.51 | | −.17 |

* $S = $ sum of $\sum r = 8.35$; therefore: $\sqrt{S} = \sqrt{8.35} \approx 2.89$

and $T_4$ had been reflected in the first residual matrix, and thus were labeled $(-)$ in the second residual matrix, and then were reflected once again in the second residual matrix (indicated by $b$ and $c$ respectively), they must be returned to their previous orientations and hence must have positive signs $(+)$ for their loadings on the third factor.

The process of factor extraction can be continued until the residuals become so small that they are obviously due to chance. At that point, the extraction of factors should be discontinued. We provide the third factor product matrix in Table XXXIV, and the third residual matrix in Table XXXV, to give the reader a notion of the approximate values of the entries in a residual matrix that could be considered due to chance—a condition indicating that the process of factor extraction should be stopped.

Table XXXIV
Third Factor Product Matrix

| Third Factor Loadings | $T_1 = .48$ | $T_2 = .30$ | $(-)$ $T_3 = -.57$ | $T_4 = .22$ | $(-)$ $T_5 = -.25$ | $T_6 = .21$ | $T_7 = .17$ | $(-)$ $T_8 = -.51$ | $(-)$ $T_9 = -.17$ |
|---|---|---|---|---|---|---|---|---|---|
| $T_1 = .48$ | (.23) | .14 | .27 | .11 | .12 | .10 | .08 | .24 | .08 |
| $T_2 = .30$ | | (.09) | .17 | .07 | .08 | .06 | .05 | .15 | .05 |
| $(-)T_3 = -.57$ | | | (.32) | .13 | .14 | .12 | .10 | .29 | .10 |
| $T_4 = .22$ | | | | (.05) | .06 | .05 | .04 | .11 | .04 |
| $(-)T_5 = -.25$ | | | | | (.06) | .05 | .04 | .13 | .04 |
| $T_6 = .21$ | | | | | | (.04) | .04 | .11 | .04 |
| $T_7 = .17$ | | | | | | | (.03) | .09 | .03 |
| $(-)T_8 = -.51$ | | | | | | | | (.26) | .09 |
| $(-)T_9 = -.17$ | | | | | | | | | (.03) |

Table XXXV
Third Residual Matrix

| Test Variables | $T_1$ | $T_2$ | $T_3$ | $T_4$ | $T_5$ | $T_6$ | $T_7$ | $T_8$ | $T_9$ |
|---|---|---|---|---|---|---|---|---|---|
| $T_1$ | (.10) | −.02 | .06 | .01 | −.06 | .02 | .00 | −.03 | −.05 |
| $T_2$ | −.02 | (.08) | .00 | −.03 | .01 | .00 | −.06 | −.01 | .05 |
| $T_3$ | .06 | .00 | (.04) | −.07 | −.05 | .00 | .00 | .07 | −.03 |
| $T_4$ | .01 | −.03 | −.07 | (.07) | .02 | .01 | −.01 | −.01 | −.01 |
| $T_5$ | −.06 | .01 | −.05 | .02 | (.06) | .01 | .00 | −.06 | .08 |
| $T_6$ | .02 | .00 | .00 | .01 | .01 | (.08) | −.04 | −.01 | −.08 |
| $T_7$ | .00 | −.06 | .00 | −.01 | .00 | −.04 | (.08) | .02 | .00 |
| $T_8$ | −.03 | −.01 | .07 | −.01 | −.06 | −.01 | .02 | (.10) | −.07 |
| $T_9$ | −.05 | .05 | −.03 | −.01 | .08 | −.08 | .00 | −.07 | (.09) |
| $\sum k$ | +.03 | +.02 | +.02 | −.02 | +.01 | −.01 | −.01 | .00 | −.02 |

In bringing our discussion of the factor extraction phase of multiple factor analysis to a close, we should differentiate between the terms: (1) *general factor*, (2) *common factor*, (3) *specific factor*, and (4) *group factor*. The differentiating characteristic of these four types of factor is found in the *extent of influence exercised by the factor on the original set of variables*.

If a factor extends through all the variables, with loadings of reasonable magnitude, it is said to be a *general factor*. For example, general mental capacity is a general factor in a matrix of general measures. A *common factor* is one which exists in two or more, but not in all, of the original variables. To illustrate, a reading factor may be common to language, science, and social studies achievement tests included in a certain battery of examinations, but show a negligible loading for a space perception test belonging to that battery. A *specific* or *unique factor* is one which appears in one test variable only, and emerges only because all of the variance in that one variable cannot be accounted for by common factors. A *group factor* is one which is common to a group of variables but does not extend through all of the members of the battery, i.e., it has approximately zero loadings for tests not included in the "group." Thus, a set of quantitative-intelligence subtests might have a quantitative group factor in common and at the same time share a general ability factor with all the other subtests of the battery comprising the matrix.

In recent years, general and group factors have come to be known as "*common factors of greater or lesser coverage*," and the specific factor is classified as a *narrow common* factor. Through this approach, general, group, and specific factors may be discussed and treated under the pervasive concept of common factors.

With this brief discussion of terminology, and the process of factor extraction explained, we are prepared to discuss the next basic phase of multiple factor analysis—the rotation of factors. The basic purpose of rotation is to make the factors more comparable by establishing a reference system with an origin or zero point common to all of the factors.

## ROTATION OF AXES (FACTORS)*

The first step of the process of rotating axes, whether the method of rotation is graphical or non-graphical is the construction of a *factor matrix*. The factor matrix in Table XXXVI is a summary table of all the factor loadings collected from the last rows of the correlation and reflected residual matrices.

### Table XXXVI
#### Factor Loadings Before Rotation

| Test Variables | $F_1$ | $F_2$ | $F_3$ | $h^2$ |
|---|---|---|---|---|
| $T_1$ | .60 | −.45 | .48 | .79 |
| $T_2$ | .50 | .31 | .30 | .44 |
| $T_3$ | .40 | .31 | −.57 | .58 |
| $T_4$ | .75 | −.45 | .22 | .81 |
| $T_5$ | .09 | −.53 | −.25 | .35 |
| $T_6$ | .70 | .60 | .21 | .89 |
| $T_7$ | .21 | .19 | .17 | .11 |
| $T_8$ | .47 | −.18 | −.51 | .51 |
| $T_9$ | .90 | .23 | −.17 | .89 |

* The algebraic system of transforming loadings presented here is described by C. C. Peters and W. R. Van Voorhis[141] in *Statistical Procedures and Their Mathematical Bases*.

The column labeled "$h^2$" in the matrix is the communality, and represents the amount of the three common factors possessed by a given test variable. The value for the communality of a given row of the matrix is obtained by squaring each of the factor loadings of that row and totaling them across the table. For example, the communality for $T_1$ is:

$$h_1^2 = f_{11}^2 + f_{21}^2 + f_{31}^2 = (.60)^2 + (-.45)^2 + (.48)^2 = .79$$

where $f_{11}$ symbolizes the factor loading of $T_1$ on factor $F_1$, $f_{21}$ denotes the factor loading of $T_1$ on factor $F_2$, and $f_{31}$ denotes the $T_1$ loading on factor $F_3$.

It should be recognized that there is no *unique solution* to a multiple factor problem. Because of the arbitrary selection of an origin for the first test vector, which can be drawn in any direction of the compass, not to mention the large number of different computational methods that may be employed, there is an infinite number of different solutions to a problem of multiple factor dimensions if the values of these solutions maintain the *right* relations between and among themselves.

One method of deriving a unique solution is that of defining the conditions for uniqueness prior to effecting the rotation of the factor axes. On this basis, we shall derive the unique solution that results from imposing the conditions that: (1) all factor loadings shall be positive (to the greatest extent possible), and (2) the number of zero loadings shall be a maximum. Condition (2) can be controlled to the extent that each column except one shall have at least one zero and, if a *positive manifold* (variables loaded only by positive influences of a factor) is possible, the "exceptional" column will have all positive loadings.

Before proceeding with a description of the algebra of the method to be employed in effecting the rotation of orthogonal axes (i.e., the axes are at right angles to each other), we should discuss briefly the matter of communality and common factor space. The spatial model and the fan of test vectors (Figure 25) were constructed with all test vectors being drawn the same length. This *unit length* indicated that the tests had been reduced to comparable standard scores and variances. If we now consider the fact that the square root of the value of $h^2$ in each row of Table XXXVI represents the length of the test vector for that row, we find that the *tests are represented by vectors of various lengths*. Where is the discrepancy? Actually, there is none. Each test is still the same *unit* length, or of variance one, but the *unity* of the length is composed of two parts—the part ascribed *to the loadings of the variables on the common factors* and the part ascribed *to the specific factor present in each test*. The length of the test vector in the *common factor space* is equal to the *square root* of the communality $h^2$ found in the rows of the factor matrix of Table XXXVI, while the length due to the specific factor is equal to $\sqrt{1 - h^2}$. *The test vectors are therefore of different lengths only in the common factor space*, and each vector has a specific factor dimension in addition to that of the common factor space. The projection of the specific factor when squared and added to the communality $h^2$ yields a value of *one*.

   To complete our knowledge of preliminary information vital to a better understanding of the method of rotation of axes which we shall employ, we must consider the coordinate axes (factors) prior to rotation, and the configuration of the test vectors. *There is nothing absolute about the particular position or direction of the orthogonal coordinate axes (factors) found in the unrotated or initial factor extraction process.* The only unchangeable or *absolute* thing about the total system of axes and vectors is the configuration (fan) of the test vectors. In other words, the factor extraction process, the results of which are found in the factor matrix of Table XXXVI, did not start from a fixed position of reference, but rather from whatever chance direction the computational procedures happened to produce. Examples of computational procedures that affect the reference position are : (1) the selection of the combination of variables to be reflected, and (2) the method of analysis (e.g., centroid, bi-factor, principal axes). Although different computational procedures in our example would have provided a different set of loadings on the three factors, they would not have affected the configuration of the vectors. The position of the test vectors in relation to each other would remain the same. The point is illustrated graphically by the two diagrams in Figure 29:

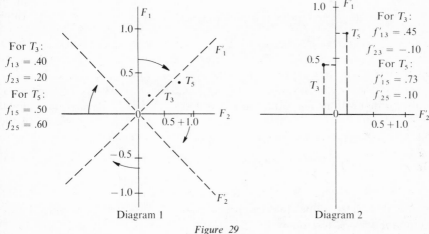

For $T_3$:
$f_{13} = .40$
$f_{23} = .20$
For $T_5$:
$f_{15} = .50$
$f_{25} = .60$

For $T_3$:
$f'_{13} = .45$
$f'_{23} = -.10$
For $T_5$:
$f'_{15} = .73$
$f'_{25} = .10$

Diagram 1                                    Diagram 2

*Figure 29*
*Test Projections Before and After Rotation of Factor Axes*

In Diagram 1, factor axis $F_1$ has been rotated, by visual approximation to the position $F'_1$ to accomplish two facts: (1) to *increase* the loadings of $T_3$ and $T_5$ on $F_1$ ; and (2) to *decrease* the loadings (to zero if possible) of $T_2$ and $T_5$ on factor axis $F_2$. Since factor axes $F_1$ and $F_2$ are orthogonal (at right angles to each other) and are theoretically "fixed" at the origin $O$, when $F_1$ is rotated to $F'_1$, $F_2$ is automatically rotated to position $F'_2$. Diagram 2 shows the factor loadings of the respective test variables *after rotation.* Had the configuration been such that it would have been more feasible to gain heavier loadings on factor $F_2$ and smaller, even zero, loadings on factor $F_1$, a graphical rotation to bring about this result would have been effected. From the two diagrams of Figure 29, it should become clear that the configuration of test vectors (i.e., the relationship of the vectors to each other) remains unchanged regardless of the position to which the coordinate factor axes might be rotated. With this background, we are ready to proceed with an algebraic method for rotating factor axes.

From formula (2) we have the relationship:

$$r_{ab} = (r_{aF_1})(r_{bF_1}) + (r_{aF_2})(r_{bF_2}) + (r_{aF_3})(r_{bF_3}) + \cdots + (r_{aF_n})(r_{bF_n}) \tag{2}$$

If we employ the symbolism that we used in Figure 29, the formula would become:

$$r_{ab} = (f_{1a})(f_{1b}) + (f_{2a})(f_{2b}) + (f_{3a})(f_{3b}) + \cdots + (f_{na})(f_{nb})$$

This formula shows that the value of the original correlation coefficient of two variables can be derived from the loadings of these variables on the common factors involved. Since the configuration of the test vectors is unchangeable, it must be true that:

$$r_{ab} = (f_{1a})(f_{1b}) + (f_{2a})(f_{2b}) + (f_{3a})(f_{3b}) + \cdots$$
$$+ (f_{na})(f_{nb}) = (f'_{1a})(f'_{1b}) + (f'_{2a})(f'_{2b}) + (f'_{3a})(f'_{3b}) + \cdots$$
$$+ (f'_{na})(f'_{nb}) \tag{3}$$

because each of the expressions involving $f$'s, where the primed symbols represent values *after rotation*, must equal $r_{ab}$ which must have a fixed value in the configuration. The situation illustrated in Figure 29 shows that:

$$r_{35} = (f_{13})(f_{15}) + (f_{23})(f_{25}) = (f'_{13})(f'_{15}) + (f'_{23})(f'_{25})$$
$$r_{35} = (.40)(.50) + (.20)(.60) = (-.10)(.10) + (.73)(.45) = .32$$

We also know that the communalities of the various tests in the original battery have fixed values that cannot be changed. The general formula for the communality of a test $k$ over $n$ factors is given in (4):

$$_kh^2_{123\cdots n} = f^2_{1k} + f^2_{2k} + f^2_{3k} + f^2_{4k} + \cdots f^2_{nk} \tag{4}$$

Where $1, 2, 3, \ldots, n$ indicates the $n$ factors involved, and $f$ the value of the factor loading of test $k$ on a given factor.

Since the analysis of the $n$-dimensions (coordinate axes) of hyperspace can be performed by considering them three at a time, the factor matrix of Table XXXVI can be employed to illustrate the algebraic method to be discussed. In order to avoid some complicated algebra, one factor of the three under consideration will be held constant while, in effect, the other two are rotated. Each one of the three factors will be held separate of the transformation at different times while the other two are acted upon. This action, in effect, allows for rotation about one axis at a time.*

Adjusting formula (4) to three variables, we have for a test $k$:

$$_kh^2_{123} = f^2_{1k} + f^2_{2k} + f^2_{3k} = f'^2_{1k} + f'^2_{2k} + f'^2_{3k}$$

If we now hold Factor 3 ($F_3$) constant while we consider $F_1$ and $F_2$ the expression of the communality for a test $k$ would be:

$$_kh^2_{12c} = f^2_{1k} + f^2_{2k} = f'^2_{1k} + f'^2_{2k}$$

Arbitrarily setting the factor loading of test $k$ on factor $F_2$ after rotation equal to zero (i.e., $f_{2k} = 0$), we obtain:

$$_kh^2_{12c} = f'^2_{1k} \tag{5}$$

or

$$_kh_{12c} = f'_{1k} \tag{5}$$

Now considering formula (3) under the same conditions imposed upon (4), we would have for tests 1 and 2:

$$(f'_{11})(f'_{12}) + (f'_{21})(f'_{22}) = (f_{11})(f_{12}) + (f_{21})(f_{22})$$

and since we set $f'_{21} = 0$ (i.e., $k = 1$ in the formula $f'_{2k} = 0$) we find:

$$(f'_{12}) = \frac{(f_{11})(f_{12}) + (f_{21})(f_{22})}{f'_{11}} \tag{6}$$

By arbitrarily setting $f'_{21} = 0$, and employing formulas (5) and (6), we are able to determine the values of the "new" (transformed, or rotated) loadings of $f'_{11}$ and $f'_{12}$, respectively. For the values of other required "rotated" loadings we can construct similar equations involving them.

Formulas (5) and (6) are employed to determine the transformed (rotated) values of factor loadings, $f'_{11}$ and $f'_{12}$. For a *systematic* approach to the problem, we now simplify these equations and write them in generalized form. If, as before, we let $k$ denote any test variable in the battery, and $m$ indicate the test with the lowest negative factor loading after correction for uniqueness (i.e., when the loading has been divided by the square root of the communality, $_kh^2_{12c}$), we have:

$$k'_1 = \frac{m_1k_1 + m_2k_2}{m'_1}$$

---

* Methods are available by which several relations of this type can be made simultaneously. In order to avoid the pitfall of getting lost in a forest of mathematical detail, the method of considering rotation about one axis at a time is presented. Through this approach, the emphasis remains upon the rationale of factor analysis. It is not our intent here to show the reader "how to do" the matrix algebra associated with this phase of factor analysis, but instead to show that one approach to factor analysis is: (1) factor extraction, (2) rotation of the orthogonal axes (factors) for "better" meaning, and (3) "scissoring" of the axes from orthogonal positions to oblique orientations for even further refinement of meaning. With computers available to perform the many computations of the procedures, *programs* have been devised to move immediately from (1) factor extraction to (3) oblique orientations of the factor axes.

Since the values of $m_1$, $m_2$, and $m_1'$ will recur systematically in the computations for finding the "new" loadings in each row, we shall make the required divisions once for the whole battery of tests. Algebraically, we proceed as follows:

$$k_1' = \frac{m_1 k_1 + m_2 k_2}{m_1'} = \frac{m_1 k_1}{m_1'} + \frac{m_2 k_2}{m_1'} = M_1 k_1 + M_2 k_2 \tag{7}$$

where $M_1 = m_1/m_1'$; and $M_2 = m_2/m_1'$. Thus, formula (7) provides a generalized form for determining the "rotated" loading of any test $k$ on Factor 1. For the generalized form of the transformed (rotated) loading of any test $k$ on Factor 2 (i.e., for $k_2'$), we employ the logic that, since we arbitrarily define: $m_2' = 0$, and hence $m_1' = {}_m h_{12c}$; and $m_1^2 + m_2^2 = {}_m h_{12c}^2$; if we were to divide this latter expression by $m_1'^2$, we would have:

$$\frac{m_1^2}{m_1'^2} + \frac{m_2^2}{m_1'^2} = \frac{{}_m h_{12c}^2}{m_1'^2}; \quad \text{or} \quad M_1^2 + M_2^2 = 1 \quad \text{(because } m_1'^2 = {}_m h_{12c}^2) \tag{8}$$

We also know that the unrotated loadings $k_1$ and $k_2$ are related to the communality, ${}_k h_{12c}^2$ as follows:

$$k_1^2 + k_2^2 = {}_k h_{12c}^2 \tag{9}$$

performing the algebra of multiplying equation (8) by equation (9), and then *subtracting* equation (7) squared, we would have

$$M_1^2\, k_1^2 + M_2^2 k_1^2 + M_1^2 k_2^2 + M_2^2 k_2^2 = {}_k h_{12c}^2$$

$$-(M_1^2 k_1^2 + 2M_1 M_2 k_1 k_2 + M_2^2 k_2^2) = -(k_1'^2)$$

$$\overline{M_2^2 k_1^2 - 2M_1 M_2 k_1 k_2 + M_1^2 k_2^2 = {}_k h_{12c}^2 - k_1'^2}$$

or, rewriting:

$$(M_1 k_2 - M_2 k_1)^2 = {}_k h_{12c}^2 - k_1'^2$$

or since,

$$k_2'^2 = {}_k h_{12c}^2 - k_1'^2 = (M_1 k_2 - M_2 k_1)^2$$

If now we find the square root of both sides of the equation, we have:

$$M_1 k_2 - M_2 k_1 = k_2' \tag{10}$$

Formulas (7) and (10) are the ones employed to obtain the new loadings in the rotated system. It should be pointed out that the algebraic system of transforming loadings described here is identical in outcome with the geometric approach of rotation in hyperspace. Usually the rotation of the orthogonal factors is accomplished by rotating two factors (axes) about one of the axes at a time. The parallel algebraic manipulation is the transformation of two columns at a time. If the usual formulas for computing new rotated loadings (usually by matrix algebra) were used, we would have:

$$k_1' = k_1 \cos \phi + k_2 \sin \phi$$
$$k_2' = k_2 \cos \phi - k_1 \sin \phi$$

where $\phi$ is the angle of rotation. If a plotting of points (representing the ends of the test vectors) on a plane of two coordinate (reference) axes is visualized, and then a rotation of the axes is effected so as to make axis $F_1$ pass through the test with the lowest negative loading $m$, it will be discovered that the values of $M_1$ and $\cos \phi$ are the same, and the values of $M_2$ and $\sin \phi$ are equal. In other words, with the substitutions of the values of $\cos \phi$ and $\sin \phi$, resulting from a rotation of the axes through an angle of $\phi$ degrees to effect $F_1$ passing through the test with the lowest negative loading, formulas (7) and (10) become identical with those of the geometrical, rotational system.

We shall now apply formulas (7) and (10) to the factor matrix of Table XXXVI to illustrate the transformation of factor loadings (equivalent to the rotation of two orthogonal factor axes).

In order to satisfy the arbitrarily defined condition that the factor loadings on $F_2$ will be transformed so that they will extend in value from zero through positive $(+)$ values, we must compute first the value of $_k h_{12c}$ for each of the nine tests in the original battery. For example:

$$_1 h_{12c}^2 = (.60)^2 + (-.45)^2 = .3600 + .2025 = .5625$$

and

$$_1 h_{12c} = \sqrt{.5625} = .7500$$

$$_2 h_{12c}^2 = (.50)^2 + (.31)^2 = .2500 + .0961 = .3461$$

and

$$_2 h_{12c} = \sqrt{.3461} = .5883$$

After the nine values of $_k h_{12c}$ have been determined, the factor loading of each test on $F_2$ is corrected for uniqueness by dividing it by the appropriate value of $_k h_{12c}$. To illustrate, the nine factor loadings on $F_2$ when corrected for uniqueness become:

$$\text{corr. } f_{21} = \frac{-.45}{.75} = -.60;$$

$$\text{corr. } f_{22} = \frac{.31}{.5883} = +.5269;$$

$$\text{corr. } f_{23} = \frac{.31}{.5061} = +.6123;$$

$$\text{corr. } f_{24} = \frac{-.45}{.8747} = -.5145;$$

$$\text{corr. } f_{25} = \frac{-.53}{.5376} = -.9858;$$

$$\text{corr. } f_{26} = \frac{.60}{.9220} = +.6508;$$

$$\text{corr. } f_{27} = \frac{.19}{.2832} = +.6709;$$

$$\text{corr. } f_{28} = \frac{-.18}{.5032} = -.3577;$$

$$\text{corr. } f_{29} = \frac{.23}{.9290} = +.2473;$$

Since test variable $T_5$ has the lowest negative loading on factor $F_2$ ($-.9858$), we let it be $m$. Then, by our general procedure: $f'_{25} = 0$; i.e., the new "transformed" loading of Test 5 on factor $F'_2$ (factor $F_2$ after rotation) is zero; and hence:

$$f'_{15} = {}_5h_{12c} = \sqrt{(.09)^2 + (-.53)^2} = \sqrt{.2890} = .5376$$

With the value of $f'_{15}$ determined we can determine the values of $M_1$ and $M_2$ as follows:

$$M_1 = \frac{m_1}{m'_1} = \frac{f_{15}}{f'_{15}} = \frac{.09}{.5376} = .1674$$

and

$$M_2 = \frac{m_2}{m'_1} = \frac{f_{25}}{f'_{15}} = \frac{-.53}{.5376} = -.9858$$

Writing formula (7) and substituting the appropriate values for $M_1$ and $M_2$, we find for each new factor 1 loading:

$$k'_1 = M_1 k_1 + M_2 k_2 = .1674 k_1 + (-.9858)k_2 \approx .167 k_1 - .986 k_2$$

For example:

$$f'_{11} = .167(.60) - .986(-.45) = .1002 + .4437 = .5439$$

$$f'_{12} = .167(.50) - .986(.31) = .0835 - .3057 = -.2222$$

$$f'_{13} = .167(.40) - .986(.31) = .0668 - .3057 = -.2389$$

$$f'_{14} = .167(.75) - .986(-.45) = .1253 + .4437 = .5690$$

The remaining loadings of the respective tests on factor $F_1$ *after one rotation* may be found in the column labeled $F'_1$ of Table XXXVII.

In similar fashion by applying formula (10) after the appropriate values for $M_1$ and $M_2$ have been inserted, we can find the value of each of the new Factor 2 loadings:

$$k'_2 = M_1 k_2 - M_2 k_1 = .167 k_2 - (-.986) k_1 = .167 k_2 + .986 k_1$$

To illustrate how the new Factor 2 loadings are found we have:

$$f'_{21} = .167(-.45) + .986(.60) = -.0752 + .5916 = .5164$$

$$f'_{22} = .167(.31) + .986(.50) = .0518 + .4930 = .5448$$

$$f'_{23} = .167(.31) + .986(.40) = .0518 + .3944 = .4462$$

$$f'_{24} = .167(-.45) + .986(.75) = -.0752 + .7395 = .6643$$

the values of the other loadings on factor $F_2$ *after one rotation* are found in the column headed $F'_2$ in the factor matrix of Table XXXVII. It should be noted that since Factor 3 was held constant the loadings in Table XXXVII, under the column labeled $F_3$ are the same as those in that column of Table XXXVI.

Table XXXVII

Factor Loadings After One Rotation

| Test Variables | Factors | | | |
| --- | --- | --- | --- | --- |
| | $F_1$ | $F_2$ | $F_3$ | $h^2$ |
| $T_1$ | .544 | .516 | .48 | .79 |
| $T_2$ | −.222 | .545 | .30 | .44 |
| $T_3$ | −.239 | .446 | −.57 | .58 |
| $T_4$ | .569 | .664 | .22 | .81 |
| $T_5$ | .538 | .000 | −.25 | .35 |
| $T_6$ | −.475 | .790 | .21 | .89 |
| $T_7$ | −.152 | .239 | .17 | .11 |
| $T_8$ | .256 | .433 | −.51 | .51 |
| $T_9$ | −.076 | .926 | −.17 | .89 |

After transforming the loadings of factors $F_1$ and $F_2$ with factor $F_3$ held constant, we then hold factor $F'_2$ constant and transform the loadings on factors $F'_1$ and $F_3$. This operation is accomplished in a manner similar to the one employed for finding the transformed loadings on factors $F_1$ and $F_2$. We begin our computations by finding the value of $_k h_{13c}$ for each of the nine tests. For example:

$$_1 h^2_{13c} = (.544)^2 + (.48)^2 = .2959 + .2304 = .5263; \quad \text{and}$$

$$_1 h_{13c} = \sqrt{.5263} = .7255$$

$$_2 h^2_{13c} = (-.222)^2 + (.30)^2 = .0493 + .0900 = .1393; \quad \text{and}$$

$$_2 h_{13c} = \sqrt{.1393} = .3732$$

After the nine values of $_k h_{13c}$ have been determined, the factor loading of each test on $F_3$ is corrected for uniqueness by dividing it by the appropriate value of

$_kh_{13c}$. The nine factor loadings on $F_3$ when corrected for uniqueness become:

$$\text{corr. } f_{31} = \frac{.48}{.7255} = .6616;$$

$$\text{corr. } f_{32} = \frac{.30}{.3732} = .8039;$$

$$\text{corr. } f_{33} = \frac{-.57}{.6181} = -.9222;$$

$$\text{corr. } f_{34} = \frac{.22}{.6100} = .3606;$$

$$\text{corr. } f_{35} = \frac{-.25}{.5932} = -.4214;$$

$$\text{corr. } f_{36} = \frac{.21}{.5193} = .4044;$$

$$\text{corr. } f_{37} = \frac{.17}{.2280} = .7456;$$

$$\text{corr. } f_{38} = \frac{-.51}{.5706} = -.8938;$$

$$\text{corr. } f_{39} = \frac{-.17}{.1863} = -.9125$$

Since test variable $T_3$ has the lowest negative loading on factor $F_3$ ($-.9222$), we let it be $m$. Then: $f'_{33} = 0$; i.e., the "new" loading of Test 3 on factor $F'_3$ (factor $F_3$ after rotation) is zero; and $f'_{13} = {}_3h_{13c} = .6181$. Thus, the values of $M_1$ and $M_3$ become:

$$M_1 = \frac{m_1}{m'_1} = \frac{f_{13}}{f'_{13}} = \frac{-.239}{.6181} = -.3867; \quad \text{and}$$

$$M_3 = \frac{m_3}{m'_1} = \frac{f_{33}}{f'_{13}} = \frac{-.57}{.6181} = -.9222$$

Substituting the appropriate values for $M_1$ and $M_2$ in formula (7), we have the equation for determining the value of each new Factor 1 loading:

$$k'_1 = M_1k_1 + M_3k_3 = -.387k_1 - .922k_3$$

To illustrate how the equation is used, we have:

$$f''_{11} = -.387(.544) - .922(.48) = -.2105 - .4426 = -.653$$

$$f''_{12} = -.387(-.222) - .922(.30) = +.0859 - .2799 = -.191$$

$$f''_{13} = -.387(-.239) - .922(-.57) = +.0925 + .5255 = +.618$$

$$f''_{14} = -.387(.569) - .922(.22) = -.2202 - .2028 = -.423$$

the rest of the loadings on factor $F_1$ after *two rotations* are listed in the column labeled "$F_1''$" of Table XXXVIII.

By applying formula (10) with the values of $M_1$ and $M_3$ inserted, we can find the value of each "new" loading on Factor 3:

$$k_3' = M_1 k_3 - M_3 k_1 = -.387k_3 - (-.922)k_1 = -.387k_3 + .922k_1$$

Values of some of the new factor loadings are shown to exemplify the use of the equation:

$$f_{31}' = -.387(.48) + .922(.544) = -.1858 + .5016 = +.316$$

$$f_{32}' = -.387(.30) + .922(-.222) = -.1161 - .2047 = -.321$$

$$f_{33}' = -.387(-.57) + .922(-.239) = +.2206 - .2204 = .000$$

$$f_{34}' = -.387(.22) + .922(.569) = -.0851 + 5246 = +.440$$

the values of the other loadings on factor $F_3$ *after rotation* are found in the column labeled "$F_3'$" in the factor matrix of Table XXXVIII. Since factor $F_2'$ was held constant, its loadings remain constant and therefore are the same in both Table XXXVII and Table XXXVIII, respectively.

Table XXXVIII
Factor Loadings After Rotations

| Test Variables | Factors $F_1''$ | $F_2'$ | $F_3'$ | $h^2$ |
|---|---|---|---|---|
| $T_1$ | −.653 | .516 | .316 | .79 |
| $T_2$ | −.191 | .545 | −.321 | .44 |
| $T_3$ | .618 | .446 | .000 | .58 |
| $T_4$ | −.423 | .664 | .440 | .81 |
| $T_5$ | .022 | .000 | .593 | .35 |
| $T_6$ | −.010 | .790 | −.593 | .89 |
| $T_7$ | −.098 | .239 | −.206 | .11 |
| $T_8$ | .371 | .433 | .433 | .51 |
| $T_9$ | .186 | .926 | −.004 | .89 |

Two points should be noted about the factor matrices shown in Tables XXXVI, XXXVII, and XXXVIII: (1) in all the tables the communalities ($h^2$) remain the same within the limit of accuracy determined by the number of decimal places employed in the computations (summing squares along the rows of the matrix and finding the appropriate values of the $h^2$'s unchanged is a good check on the correctness of the arithmetic); and (2) the design for procuring a zero and all positive loadings on factor $F_3$ in Table XXXVIII was not realized. In regard to the latter point, it should be noted that if the tests of the original battery are of such a nature that some of them are inherently negatively inter-correlated with respect to a given factor, it will be impossible to obtain a positive manifold, i.e., all positive loadings throughout the table. Another condition which prevents the attainment of a positive manifold is that which exists when the tests are short or samples small, so that $r$'s have low reliability and some loadings are negative by chance. When a positive manifold cannot be achieved, the best procedure to follow is that of making the factors comparable in meaning by balancing them against one another, i.e., by attempting to allocate the same number of negative loadings to each of them. In our example, we have allowed factor $F'_2$ to have all positive loadings, and factors $F''_1$ and $F'_3$ to divide nine negative loadings on a five to four basis, respectively.

The difficulty of providing a positive manifold is much more easily resolved in the graphical method of rotation than the algebraic method described here. The graphical method does not hold strictly to the definition of a positive manifold; it accepts as zero small negative loadings, attributing them to chance because of the unreliability of the $r$'s. In fact, loadings of $-.20$, or even $-.40$ if the sample is not large, are accepted as not violating the principle of a positive manifold. The factor axes are rotated until they pass through the densest cluster of points, and the *fit* is effected within the liberal definition of positive manifold just described. Without the aid of the visual adjustment possible in the graphical method, the algebraic method is limited to selecting the test with the lowest negative value for a zero. Actually, it makes little difference, provided the differential rotation is not great, because within reasonable limits the loadings of the tests within each factor remain in the same relative order so that the interpretation of the results is not affected.

The foregoing discussion should make it apparent that when conditions cannot be imposed that determine a unique solution, the arithmetic loadings are of necessity rather than arbitrary. The loadings are equally arbitrary by the algebraic method and by the graphical method. In fact, the exact arithmetic values of the loadings are not important in themselves. The important thing to know is which tests go together and possess the ability to measure one or more factors. Although, for measurement purposes, it would be satisfactory that a given test stand relatively high on all factors, for diagnostic purposes it is desirable to find tests which are high in ability to measure one of the factors while being very low (zero, if possible) in loadings on the other factors.

In order to establish a systematic approach to the rotation procedure for finding the positions that give the best meaning to factors, factor analysts have adopted *simple structure* as a goal. Simple structure in factor analysis means that any one test should have the simplest possible factor constitution and, reciprocally, the estimation of any one factor should require the combination of only *some* of all of the original tests. In terms of the factor matrix, this requirement means that every test should have some *near zeros* in its row, or in other words some factors should not "load" it.

The factor analytic solution rotated to simple structure provides a double application of the parsimony principle. First, many variables are represented by a few common factors, and secondly these factors are so distributed that they give the simplest explanation for that number of factors.

It should be pointed out that the graphical method also incorporates matrix algebra to determine the arithmetic values of the factor loadings. We shall not attempt to discuss the matrix algebra approach in the computations associated with the rotation of factor axes. The interested reader will find an excellent description of these procedures by Fruchter,[72] and is referred to that source. At the same time, no discussion has been accorded the topic of oblique factors, other than to mention that it is possible after factor extraction to proceed to an oblique factor "fit" without first finding an orthogonal factor solution. An excellent discussion is accorded these matters by Raymond Cattell[34] and by Henry F. Kaiser.[64a]

## FACTOR ESTIMATION AND SPECIFICATION EQUATIONS

After the common factors required to account for the correlations have been extracted and rotated to a special position to give them meaning and usefulness, it is necessary to identify these factors and determine how to use them for various kinds of predictions by means of the specification equation. Factor identification, factor estimation, and the specification equation are employed for two different purposes. First, there is the purpose of discovering the nature of the factors at work in a given battery of examinations; and second there is the practical aim of providing an equation for predicting events in specific situations. We now consider these topics in some detail.

### Factor Identification

The nature of a factor is determined on the basis of an inspection of the final factor matrix which shows the results of the total analytical effort. The factor is identified in terms of those variables (tests) which are highly loaded on that factor, and in terms of those which have near zero loadings on it. For example, in Table XXXVIII we note that factor 1 has heavy negative loadings with respect to tests $T_1$ and $T_4$, a heavy positive loading with respect to $T_3$, a moderate positive loading in $T_8$, and near zero loadings in tests $T_5$, $T_6$, and $T_7$. Suppose that tests $T_3$ and $T_8$ deal with mathematical aptitudes, and $T_1$ and $T_4$ with art and music appreciation, and tests $T_5$, $T_6$, and $T_7$ deal with certain aspects of personality and temperament. From this pattern, Factor 1 could be identified as one which measures in its positive direction dimensions of mathematical aptitude, and in its negative direction measures dimensions of art and music appreciation. The fact that personality and temperament have no relationship to this pattern strengthens the use of the factor for measuring the dimensions which loaded heavily upon it.

Factor 2 loads heavily on $T_9$, $T_6$ and $T_4$; moderately on $T_1$, $T_2$, $T_3$, and $T_8$; and $T_5$ is unaffected (.000 loading). If $T_1$ and $T_2$ dealt with measures of scientific concepts and engineering constructs, and $T_9$ was a measure of meticulousness, we could conclude that this factor was (in the positive direction) based upon a pattern of mathematics ($T_3$ and $T_8$), science-engineering ($T_1$ and $T_2$), art ($T_4$), and those personality dimensions contributory to these abilities ($T_6$ and $T_9$). The zero loading of $T_5$ would show that the personality dimension it represents is separate from the pattern of the factor.

Obviously the search for common characteristics in the loaded variables, which give first indications of the nature of a factor, is constantly plagued by the difficulty of what to do when the loadings are either not very high nor very low (near zero). When this condition prevails, further experimentation is necessary, and more knowledge of the population, the sample, and the measuring instruments must be gained. This knowledge can frequently be acquired by constructing a new test or choosing observations that most directly measure the factor presumed to be present. After the results of the new tests or observations are available, we should combine them with the old, and, upon factorization of the "new" complex, ought to find the "new" tests *more highly loaded on the factor* than any of the others that are involved.

*Specification Equation*

After the *meaning* of the factors has been determined, it is possible through the use of the specification equation to calculate the performance of an individual (in standard scores) if his factor endowments (in standard scores) are known. The specification equation of a test is simply its row (excluding the communality) taken from the final factor matrix. Thus, the specification equation for $T_1$ is:

$$P_{T_1} = -.653F_1 + .516F_2 + .316F_3$$

while that for $T_8$ is:

$$P_{T_8} = .371F_1 + .433F_2 + .433F_3$$

The specification equation indicates that the variation in the score of a given test is contributed to by variations in each of the three factors to the degrees shown by the loadings. It should be recalled, however, that the value of the specific factor (determined by subtracting the variance in all the common factors from unity) must be included in the specification equation if *complete* prediction is desired. Thus, for a complete specification for $T_1$, we would have:

$$P_{T_1} = -.653F_1 + .516F_2 + .316F_3 + .485F_s$$

where $F_s$ denotes the specific factor, and the value of (.458) is derived from:

$$\sqrt{1 - {}_1h_{12c}^2} = \sqrt{1 - .79} = .458$$

To illustrate how the specification equation can be used, suppose that a person showed a standard score of: $Z = 50$;* i.e., an *average* standard score, on factor $F_1$; a standard score of: $Z = 60$ on factor $F_2$; and a standard score of: $Z = 45$ on $F_3$. Based upon the construction of the standard score $Z$, these results would mean the person rated *average* on factor $F_1$, i.e., $F_1 = 0$; a standard deviation *above average* on factor $F_2$, or $F_2 = +1.0$; and a half standard deviation *below*

---

* A standard score is a constructed score of the form: $Z = 50 + 10[(X_i - \bar{X})/S]$; where $X_i$ is the individual's score in terms of the original measurement, $\bar{X}$ is the mean score (average) of the set of original measurements, and $S$ is the standard deviation of the set of original measurements. The standard score is constructed so that $\bar{Z}$, the mean (average) standard score is 50, and the standard deviation $S_Z$ is 10. Thus, if a person has a standard score ($Z$) of 60, he is one standard deviation above average; while a score of: $Z = 45$, would be a half standard deviation below the average $\bar{Z} = 50$.

*average* on factor $F_3$; i.e., $F_3 = -.5$. Inserting these values in the specification equation of $T_1$, and assuming the subject has an average ability in the specific factor $F_s$, i.e., $F_s = 0$, we would have;

$$P_{T_1} = -.653F_1 + .516F_2 + .316F_3 + .458F_s$$

substituting:

$$P_{T_1} = -.653(0) + .516(+1.0) + .316(-0.5) + .458(0)$$

or:

$$P_{T_1} = .516 - .158 = .358$$

This result means that the subject would be expected to produce a standard score of .358 standard deviations above average in the performance $P_{T_1}$. Since $T_1$ measures art appreciation, the subject would be expected to produce a Z-score of: $Z = 50 + 10(.358) = 50 + 3.58 = 54$ (rounded). By writing a specific equation for each of the nine test variables, it is possible to predict an *expected* score for the subject on each test, *providing estimates of his capability on each of the factors (F's) can be made.*

## Factor Estimation

The procedure for estimating abilities on factors for a given individual is primarily based upon his performance in those tests that show loadings on a given factor in the region of .5 to .9. The logic of the procedure becomes clear if we consider the situation where a test loads perfectly ($\pm 1.0$) on a factor. Under such circumstances the individual's performance on that test would provide a good indication of his capability in the factor involved. Since the ideal situation rarely, if ever, exists, the tests loading between .5 and .9 on a factor are combined into a sub-battery. The individual's performance on each test of the sub-battery, weighted in terms of the arithmetic values of their loadings on the factor in question, provides the means of estimating the subject's capability in that factor.

Although the procedure is a sound one, the analyst must proceed with caution. The analyst must be alert for those reasonably highly loaded tests for the given factor that *might also load fairly heavily on any other common factors.* Such tests tend to provide unreliable estimates of the subject's abilities on the factors which they share, because they themselves cannot clearly be defined as "belonging" mainly to one factor or the other. In other words, the test variable is distributed over the factors in terms of its *specific variance* in them. Generally, the analyst deals with tests having loadings of about .6, and in most cases five to a dozen tests can give a highly reliable estimate of an individual's abilities in the given factor.

## CONCLUDING REMARKS

The aim of our treatment of factor analysis was to provide the reader with a basic understanding of the total process so that it could be employed as a numerical procedure in those "adapted" forms of the general model of educational research where the use of such procedures might be feasible. In order to realize the objective in question, the fundamental steps of factor analysis: (1) extracting the factors from the correlations, (2) rotating the factors for "best" meaning, (3) estimating an individual's abilities in the factors, and (4) using the specification equations for predictive purposes, were covered in some detail. The remaining topics of importance to a more profound understanding of multiple factor analysis are only mentioned here so that the reader may complete the picture of the total process in a proper context. For detailed discussions of these subjects, the reader is referred to the many excellent treatments found in the materials listed in the bibliography of this chapter.

Of importance to a more profound knowledge of factor analysis is an acquaintance with the *O*-, *P*-, *Q*-, *R*-, *S*-, and *T*-analytic techniques. The *R*-technique is employed most frequently (approximately 95 per cent of the time) and involves the *correlations of test variables* (taken two at a time) *using a set of persons as entries* (scores, or points in a graphical method) *to derive the values of the correlations.* The *Q*-technique, the transpose of the *R*-technique, consists of the *correlations of persons* (taken two at a time) *using the set of scores on the respective test variables belonging to the two persons, to derive the values of the correlations for the correlation matrix.* The *P*-technique begins by measuring a set of variables on *one person over a sufficient number of occasions to provide correlations* for the correlation matrix. The *O*-technique is the *transpose* of the *P*-technique, and analyzes the *correlations of occasions.* For example, after constructing sets of scores by measuring the *same person on,* say, *twenty different tests on each of fifty days, the results associated with days are correlated instead of the tests.* The *S*- and *T*-techniques, the latter being the *transpose* of the former, are logically possible but have been used little, if at all, in experimentation. These designs correlate respectively *two persons* on *one test* on a series of occasions, and *two occasions* on *one test* in a *series of persons.* The *S*-technique would seem to hold promise in *social* psychology; and possibly certain areas of educational sociology. For example, measuring the similarity of response of two people (e.g., two students, two teachers). The *T*-design, since it mainly deals with a set of *test-retest* correlation coefficients, might well be employed in determining what and how many elements in a learning situation affect learners' responses. The technique has immediate value in structuring a population for greater meaning of results garnered by any type of opinion survey or poll.

To complete the systematic view of factor analytic techniques, there are essentially *three* experimental designs which lead to *six* techniques. The three designs are represented by the situations derived from the three pairs (six techniques) of internally transposable techniques, i.e., *R*- and *Q*-; *O*- and *P*-; and *S*- and *T*-techniques. *The pairing of R-Q holds one occasion constant; the pairing of O–P holds one person constant;* and *S–T holds one test constant.* For an excellent discussion of these matters see Cattell.[34]

After rotating *orthogonal* factors, many analysts "scissor" the coordinate factor axes to what is called an *oblique* position for what they consider to be *better* meaning than that which is possible under a condition of orthogonality.* Frequently, oblique factor axes "load" on each other, and thus produce *second-order* factors in the computational results. For a detailed discussion of this and other related matters concerning second-order factors, see Cattell.[34]

Although our discussion was centered upon the centroid method of extraction, here are alternative designs in factorizing a matrix. The principal axes method, the bifactor method, the bipolar system, and the clustering methods—group, grouping, and multigroup—are but a few approaches employed in practice. For further discussion of these methods see Cattell,[34] and for actual computational approaches associated with them, see Fruchter.[72]

For considerations of such problems as sampling, homogeneity and heterogeneity, economy in computing, structuring variables in the controlled experiment, and the difficulties associated with graphical methods of rotation, the reader is referred to the excellent discussion accorded these matters by Cattell.[34] With this recommendation we conclude our discussion of multiple factor analysis and proceed to the topics of linear programing and theory of games as possible further numerical procedures to be employed in "adapted" forms of the suggested general model of educational research.

*Chapter 31—References*
See Bibliography: 34, 41, 72, 89, 97, 107, 130, 141, 144, 147, 162, 164, 166, 167, 172, 175, 187, 201;
39a, 41a, 59a, 60a, 64a, 109a, 111a.

---

* As mentioned in an earlier footnote (p. 487), modern techniques have made it possible to proceed from the originally extracted orthogonal factor axes to oblique positions, thus eliminating the intermediate step of rotating the orthogonal axes, see Henry F. Kaiser.[64a]

*Chapter Thirty-two*

# Numerical Procedures:
# Further Considerations

*(Linear Programing and the Theory of Games)*

THE NUMERICAL and analytical procedures of the suggested general model
of educational research presented in earlier discussions were those associated
with the methods and techniques of *statistical* analysis and multiple factor
analysis. We now consider linear programing and the theory of games as possible
techniques for the general model with the knowledge that both approaches rely
upon *mathematical* analysis as the method of deriving decisions. Mathematically
the two theories can be shown to be highly related, but superficially they are
quite different. Problems employing linear programing are of the type that involve a single person trying to maximize or minimize a function of two or more
variables over a polygonal convex set of values ("certainty" decision). Game
theory deals with situations in which the actions of two or more persons
influence, but do not completely determine, the outcome of an event ("risk"
and "uncertainty" decisions).

## LINEAR PROGRAMING

Linear programing, in the broadest sense, refers to techniques for solving
general class of optimization problems involving many variables that are
subjected to certain restraining conditions. In deriving a solution for these types
of problems, measures of effectiveness are to be obtained in the best possible
fashion subject to restraining conditions. The restraining conditions may arise
from a variety of sources, but despite this situation, an optimal programing
decision can only be made by considering all combinations, and in some cases
permutations, of the variables and conditions involved.

General mathematical techniques for analyzing problems involving large and
complicated sets of interacting variables have been in existence for some time.
With recent developments in electronic computer equipment, the range of
application of the most complicated systematic techniques has been greatly
extended.

Problems calling for analysis by the methods of linear programing usually
involve such terms as: "at least," "at most," "not less than," or "not more
than." These terms can be represented mathematically by inequalities or
systems of inequalities. Iterative techniques of solving systems of inequalities
have been developed, and methods for choosing from a set of solutions the best

ossible (optimal) one(s) in terms of a given condition or objective have also
been perfected.

Industrial problems calling for analysis by the methods of linear programing
are usually so complex that solutions can only be derived through advanced
mathematical procedures and the employment of electronic computers. This
situation should not be interpreted to mean, however, that linear programing
in and of itself is complicated. The basic idea of linear programing is a simple
one which we shall now develop and then apply to certain types of educational
research problems through the use of "adapted" models.

The basic approach of linear programing involves a given system of graphs
of various inequalities. Before moving directly to a discussion of the graph of an
inequality, it might be helpful to recall a few facts about the graphs of equations.

Given a coordinate axes system composed of a horizontal axis (abscissa, or
x-axis) and a vertical axis (ordinate, or y-axis) which intersect at the origin of
the system (point $O$); we define the *graph* or *locus* of a *linear* equation in the
variables $x$ and $y$ to be the set of *all* those points, and *only* those points, whose
coordinates *satisfy* the equation: $ax + by = c$. A pair of values for $x$ and $y$
is said to *satisfy* an equation if the equation becomes a *true* statement when
these values are substituted in it. For example, the locus of the equation $3x + 4y$
= 5 is the straight line plotted in Figure 30. Points which *satisfy* the equation
are located on the line, and some of them are shown in the schedule to the right
of the coordinate axes in Figure 30. To plot the graph of an equation, we usually
substitute arbitrary values for $x$ (or $y$) and calculate corresponding values of $y$
(or $x$) from the equation. So much for a brief discussion of the graph of an
equation.

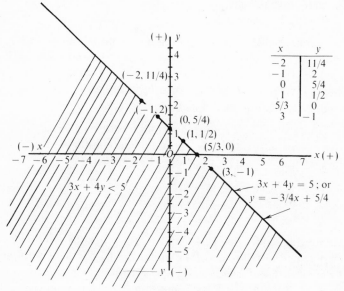

*Figure 30*
*Reference Axes and Graphs*

Suppose now that we were asked to consider *loci* or *inequalities* in the variables $x$ and $y$. Let us locate the set of all points of the plane whose coordinates satisfy the inequality $3x + 4y < 5$ (i.e., $3x + 4y$ is less than 5). There are many points which satisfy this inequality. For example, $(1, 0)$, $(0, 0)$, $(0, 1)$, $(-1, -1)$ and $(-2, 1)$ satisfy the inequality because:

(a) $3(1) + 4(0) < 5$;
(b) $3(0) + 4(0) < 5$;
(c) $3(0) + 4(1) < 5$;
(d) $3(-1) + 4(-1) < 5$; and
(e) $3(-2) + 4(1) < 5$.

On the other hand, the points $(1, 1)$, $(2, 3)$, and $(3, 2)$ are *not* members of the set of points which satisfy the inequality because:

(a) $3(1) + 4(1) \not< 5$;
(b) $3(2) + 4(3) \not< 5$;  and
(c) $3(3) + 4(2) \not< 5$.

We find that the set of points satisfying the inequality $3x + 4y < 5$ are those points of the coordinate plane located *below* the line $3x + 4y = 5$. The set is illustrated by the shaded area shown in Figure 30. Such an area, i.e., one which is on one side of a straight line, is called an "*open half plane.*"

If we were considering the inequality: $3x + 4y \leq 5$ (i.e., $3x + 4y$ is less than or equal to 5), we would find that the set of points satisfying the inequality would be composed not only of those in the area below the line $3x + 4y = 5$, but those *on the line* as well. This area composed of an open half plane *and* its boundary line is called a "*closed half plane.*"

Summarizing our discussion in general terms, we find that:

1. The equation $ax + by = c$ always has a straight line as its graph or locus
2. The inequality $ax + by < c$ (or $ax + by > c$) has an open half plane as its graph or locus; and
3. The inequality $ax + by \leq c$ (or $ax + by \geq c$; i.e., $ax + by$ is *greater than or equal to* $c$) has a closed half plane as its graph.

With this background we can now consider a *system of inequalities*, i.e., *a set of two or more inequalities*, and seek simultaneous solutions to the inequalities forming the system. The system we choose to consider is:

(a) $3x + 4y \leq 5$
(b)    $x \geq 0$
(c)    $y \geq 0$

Without attempting to identify the situation from which the system was derived, we note that constraints (b) and (c) express the fact that it is impossible to produce negative values for either of these situations [i.e., $x$ is greater than or equal to zero by (b), and the same condition holds for $y$ by (c)]. Constraint (a) indicates that under no circumstance can $3x + 4y$ be greater than 5. An point $(x, y)$ in the plane satisfying the constraints (a), (b), (c) is termed a *feasible point*. The set of feasible points consists of the shaded region in Figure 31 including its boundary. The points in this set provide simultaneous solutions of the system of inequalities under consideration and thus are said to form a *polygonal convex set*. Stated in general terms: *The points which are simultaneous solutions of a system of inequalities of the ≤ (or ≥) type, form a polygonal convex set.* This statement is derived from the fact that each inequality of the ≤, rather than < type (or ≥, and > types) has a *closed* half plane as its set of feasible points (solution set), and thus the *system* of such inequalities must have as its set of feasible points, the *intersection* of these closed half planes.

## Maxima and Minima of Linear Functions

The area of a polygonal convex set may be either finite or infinite. Figure 31 shows a set of points forming a *finite* area which consists of a polygon *and* its interior. Henceforth, this entire area is referred to as a polygon. Thus, all polygonal convex sets are called *convex polygons*.

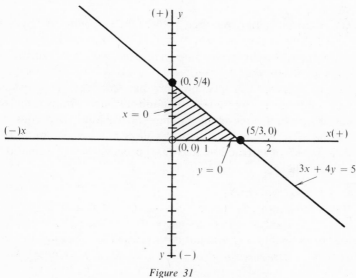

*Figure 31*
*A Polygonal Convex Set of Feasible Points*

A convex polygon with $n$ sides has $n$ corners. For example, the triangle (convex polygon) of Figure 31 has the three corners $(0, \frac{5}{4})$, $(0, 0)$, and $(\frac{5}{3}, 0)$. *A corner is formed by the inter-section of two boundary lines.*

Since a corner point lies on two boundary lines, two of the inequalities in the set of feasible points must actually be equalities. A point on a boundary side of the convex polygon, which is *not* a corner point, must satisfy the equality defining that boundary. Thus, it follows that a feasible point in the interior of the polygon must define an inequality, i.e., not only ≤, but <, holds.

We are now ready to state a theorem of linear programing theory:*

*The linear function, $ax + by = c$, defined over a convex polygon, takes on its maximum (or minimum) value at a corner point of the convex polygon.*

The method of finding the maximum or minimum of the function, $ax + by = c$, over a convex polygon proceeds as follows:

1. Find the corner points of the set; there will be a finite number of them.
2. Substitute the coordinates of each corner point in the function.
3. The largest of the values so obtained will be the maximum of the function and the smallest value will be the minimum of the function.

### Linear Programing Problems in Educational Research

An important class of research problems in education are those which require the determination of the maximum (or minimum) point of a function of the form: $ax + by = c$, defined over a convex set of points. Although the examples presented here are not of the complex type usually encountered in industry, they illustrate how linear programing can be used as a technique of the models of educational research employed in action, descriptive, and survey types of research.†

*Example 1.* In an action research project being conducted by a teaching team, the following problem arises:

There are thirty teaching machines available with programs in spelling; no program is of less than 9 minutes duration, and none is longer than 20 minutes duration. If the team allots no more than 45 minutes per day for spelling and knows that it can accommodate 150 pupils through a transitional approach to spelling instruction, how many minutes of machine instruction, and how many minutes of traditional instruction, will produce a maximum number of "student-minutes" of instruction, if both approaches *must be used* during the 45-minute period?

### Solution by Linear Programing

1. Let $x$ = the number of minutes of machine instruction.
2. Let $y$ = the number of minutes of traditional instruction.
3. Since we know that the amount of time spent in machine instruction plus that spent for traditional instruction must equal 45 minutes, we write the equation:

$$x + y = 45.$$

4. The equation $x + y = 45$ may be written as a system of two inequalities

$$x + y \geq 45$$

$$x + y \leq 45$$

---

* For proof of this theorem, see J. G. Kemeny, J. L. Snell, and G. L. Thompson,[107] *Introduction Finite Mathematics.*

† For an excellent treatment of linear programing techniques employed in certain industrial problems, see chapters on models, iterative techniques, and programing in C. W. Churchman, R. L. Ackoff, and E. L. Arnoff,[36] *Introduction to Operations Research.*

5. Since the time elapsed for each method of instruction must be positive, we have:

$$x \geq 0 \quad \text{and} \quad y \geq 0$$

6. More precisely in the case of $x$ (machine instruction time), we have

$$x \geq 9 \quad \text{and} \quad x \leq 20$$

7. Thus, the system of inequalities to be analyzed is:

(a) $x + y \geq 45$
(b) $x + y \leq 45$
(c) $\quad\quad x \geq 9$
(d) $\quad\quad x \leq 20$
(e) $\quad\quad y \geq 0$

8. The convex polygon of feasible points is the shaded area (including the boundary lines) shown below:

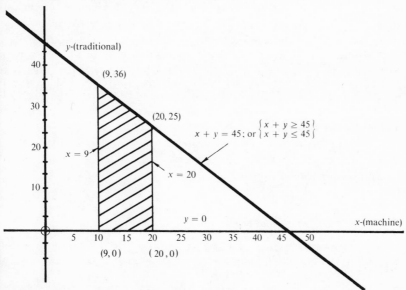

9. If $N$ represents the total number of "student-minutes" of instruction, the function to be maximized is:

$$N = 30x + 150y$$

where the number 30 indicates those students who can be instructed by machine per minute, and 150 denotes the number that can be handled by the traditional approach per minute.

10. Trying the values of the "corner points" of the convex polygon in the function [because these are the values that will determine minimum and maximum values of the function under constraints (a), (b), (c), (d), and (e)],

it is found that:

$$N^{(9,0)} = 30(9) + 150(0) = 270$$
$$N^{(9,36)} = 30(9) + 150(36) = 270 + 5400 = 5670$$
$$N^{(20,25)} = 30(20) + 150(25) = 600 + 3750 = 4350$$
$$N^{(20,0)} = 30(20) + 150(0) = 600$$

11. Since the largest value of the function $N$ occurs at the point $(9, 36)$, the team knows that 9 minutes of machine instruction and 36 minutes of the traditional approach yield the maximum number of "student-minutes" of instruction under these conditions, i.e., if *both* "approaches" must be employed during the 45-minute period of instruction.

*Example 2.* As part of a survey research project being conducted in a comparatively small school system, the following problem occurs:

A bookstore in one of the high school buildings of the system is considering the possibility of stocking two different sizes of loose leaf notebook paper (size A, and size B). A profit of thirty cents per box is made on size A, and a profit of twenty cents per box is realized for size B. From previous experience it is known that at least twice as much size B paper is sold as size A. The bookstore shelf space available for the stocking of loose leaf paper is, at most, 3000 square inches. It requires 80 square inches of shelf space to store a box of size A paper and 100 square inches to store a box of size B. How many boxes of each size paper should the bookstore stock to maximize its profit? How much will the profit be?

*Solution by Linear Programing*
1. Let $x$ = number of boxes of size A paper.
2. Let $y$ = number of boxes of size B paper.
3. It is known by previous experience that:

$$2x \leq y$$

4. From the data pertaining to storage space, it is known that:

$$80x + 100y \leq 3000$$

or:

$$4x + 5y \leq 150$$

5. Since the number of boxes of both sizes of paper must be positive it follows that:

$$x \geq 0 \quad \text{and} \quad y \geq 0$$

6. Thus, the system of inequalities to be analyzed is:

(a) $\qquad 2x \leq y$
(b) $4x + 5y \leq 150$
(c) $\qquad x \geq 0$
(d) $\qquad y \geq 0$

7. The convex polygon of feasible points is the shaded area shown below:

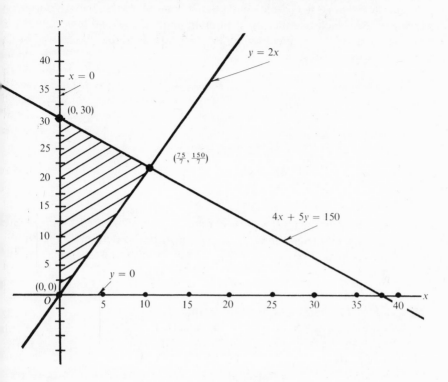

8. If P represents the amount of profit, the function to be maximized is:

$$P = .30x + .20y$$

where .30 is the amount of profit per box for size A paper, and .20 denotes the amount of profit per box for size B paper.

9. Trying the values of the "corner points" of the convex polygon, it is found that:

$$P^{(0,0)} = .30(0) + .20(0) = 0$$
$$P^{(0,30)} = .30(0) + .20(30) = 6.00$$
$$P^{(75/7,150/7)} = .30(75/7) + .20(150/7)$$
$$= \frac{22.50}{7} + \frac{30}{7} = \frac{52.50}{7} = 7.50$$

0. Since the largest value of the function P occurs at the point (75/7, 150/7), the administrative personnel responsible for the operation of the bookstore in question know that approximately 11 boxes of size A paper and approximately 22 boxes of size B paper would provide a maximum profit of $7.50 if all of the paper (both sizes) is sold.

*Example 3.* An action research team is attempting to plan a unit of high schoo mathematics which is to include elements of advanced algebra and trigonometry Three methods, each one placing a different emphasis on the *topics* of algebra and trigonometry to be included in the *unit*, are available. Since one of the methods involves instruction by television, another involves teaching machines and a third demands the employment of a teacher's aid, it is possible for the team to calculate a "cost per unit to be covered." The table below shows the data compiled by the team:

|  | Topics of Algebra | Topics of Trigonometry | Cost per Unit of Method |
|---|---|---|---|
| Method I | 15 | 4 | $1.00 |
| Method II | 10 | 6 | $ .90 |
| Method III | 5 | 20 | $1.50 |

The total unit of mathematics is to contain a minimum of 30 topics of eacl subject (algebra and trigonometry). The team wishes to determine the numbe of units of each method to employ in order to meet this specification at minimum cost.

*Solution by Linear Programing.*
1. Let $x$ = the number of *units* of Method I.
2. Let $y$ = the number of *units* of Method II.
3. Let $z$ = the number of *units* of Method III.
4. The cost equation is: $K = 1.00x + .90y + 1.50z$.
5. It is necessary to find the values of $x$, $y$, and $z$ which minimize the cos $K$, under the following constraints:

   (a) $x \geq 0$
   (b) $y \geq 0$
   (c) $z \geq 0$
   (d) $15x + 10y + 5z \geq 30$
   (e) $4x + 6y + 20z \geq 30$

6. Constraints (a), (b), and (c) indicate that it is impossible to employ "neg ative" units of any method. Constraint (d) assures that the total unit wil contain a minimum of 30 topics of algebra; and constraint (e) insure the same condition for trigonometry.
7. Since there are three variables involved, the constraints are graphed i three dimensional space, as shown below.
8. Constraints (a), (b), and (c) restrict the set of feasible points for the systen of inequalities under consideration to the first octant of the referenc system. The constraints (d) and (e) further delimit the set of feasible point to that portion of the first octant delineated by "heavy" lines.
9. In a three variable problem, which involves three dimensional space the possible cost equations are represented by an infinite set (family) c parallel planes (in problems involving two dimensional space, the possibl

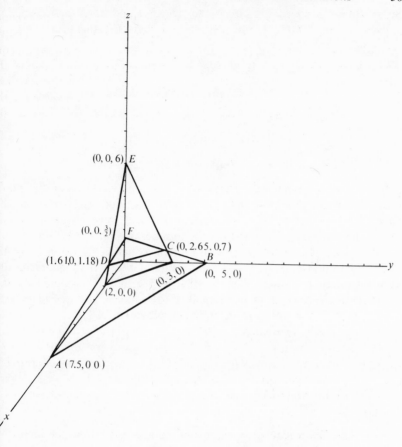

cost equations are represented by an infinite set of parallel lines). Analogous to the two dimensional space problems, in which the maximum and minimum values of the decision functions (e.g., cost, profit or number, equations) are found at the corner points of the convex polygon, the maximum and minimum values of the "function" in three dimensional space problems are found at the vertices of the solid (volume) figure of feasible points formed by the system of inequalities under consideration. In our example, the points (vertices) to be considered for a minimum value of the cost function involved are points $A$, $B$, $C$, $D$, and $E$ with the coordinates:

$$A(7.5, 0, 0)$$
$$B(0, 5, 0)$$
$$C(0, 2.65, 0.7)$$
$$D(1.61, 0, 1.18)$$
$$E(0, 0, 6)$$

10. Substituting the coordinates of points $A$, $B$, $C$, $D$, and $E$ in the cost function (equation): $K = 1.00x + .90y + 1.50z$, we find that the cost values at these points are

$$K_A = 1.00(7.5) + .90(0) + 1.50(0) = \$7.50$$

$$K_B = 1.00(0) + .90(5) + 1.50(0) = \$4.50$$

$$K_C = 1.00(0) + .90(2.65) + 1.50(.7) = \$3.435$$

$$K_D = 1.00(1.61) + .90(0) + 1.50(1.18) = \$3.38$$

$$K_E = 1.00(0) + .90(0) + 1.50(6) = \$9.00$$

11. Since the minimum values of the cost function $K$ occur at the point $(1.6, 0, 1.18)$, the research team should plan to adopt the values of the coordinates at that point. This result means that since $x$ was defined as the number of *units* of Method I, $y$ the number of *units* of Method II, and $z$ the number of *units* of Method III, there would be approximately 1.6 units of Method I (actually 1.61); no units of Method II included, and approximately 1.2 units (actually 1.34) of Method III adopted by the research team. According to inequality (d) which translates units into *topics*, the decision would result in the employment of $15(1.6 = 24$ *topics* of algebra, and by inequality (e): $4(1.6) = 3$ *topics* of trigonometry taught by *Method I* along with $5(1.2) = 6.4$ or 7 topics of algebra, and $20(1.2) = 24$ topics of trigonometry *taught by Method III*. This approach would provide the most economical instruction of the approximate: $23 + 3 = 26$ topics emphasized by Method I plus the $6 + 24 = 30$ topics emphasized by Method III.

Obviously, our discussion of linear programing applications for inclusion in the suggested general model of educational research have been simple ones. The applications would, by their nature, be included in the elements of the general model which deal with data processing and decision-making. This reference to "simple" problems does not mean that linear programing for more complicated problems could *not* be incorporated in the model. Since with each additional constraint there is an increase in the number of corner points to be considered, and with each additional variable an increase in dimensionality occurs, it is readily understandable that the pictorialization of the situation becomes increasingly difficult. For this reason algebraic analytical methods are employed in lieu of geometrical methods as the complexity of the problem increases.*

### The Theory of Games

Games of pure chance (e.g., dice or roulette) can be analyzed by the theory of probability. In contrast to this type of analysis, the theory of games is employed

---

* For a good discussion of such algebraic methods and their applications see Churchman, Ackoff and Arnoff.[36]

to analyze games in which players have the opportunity to make choices and use rational strategies. Examples of such games are: chess, where no chance factors are considered to be at work, and bridge, where a mixture of chance factors and strategy are assumed to be involved.

At the time of this writing, the main applications of the theory of games are found in the business world. In this brief introduction, we shall present only simple applications of the "theory" to selected problems of educational research. For those readers interested in a broader and more profound treatment of the topic, excellent discussions are available in the references noted at the end of this chapter.

The theory of games is applied to those problems dealing with a situation where two or more players with conflicting interests have a comparative freedom of choice of certain game tactics, but whose control over the eventual outcome of the game is at best partial and whose information about the actual situation may be incomplete. This situation allows the player to choose his own actions within the rules of the game, but does not permit him to choose either those of his opponent, or those of chance, if chance factors are involved. The object of the analysis conducted by applying the theory of games is to decide if there are "best" strategies for the players to adopt, and if these strategies do exist, how to determine them.

Games are classified in various ways. If there are *n* numbers of players (or teams, or conflicting interests), an *n-person game* exists. Game theory increases in difficulty as *n* increases, because as *n* becomes greater than 2, the possibility arises of two or more players forming coalitions resulting in the coordination of their strategies to the detriment of the efforts of other players. Obviously, such conditions can occur in business, politics, and war. Under defined conditions, such situations can be considered to occur in certain educational processes and settings. *In our discussion, we shall study only two-person game situations.*

In the terminology of game theory, *positive payoffs* are associated with *winning*, and negative payoffs with losing. If the sum of the payoffs to all players in a game is zero, the game is called a *zero-sum game*. Expressed in another way, if whatever a player wins in the game is lost by other players, so that the sum of the payoffs is zero, the game is a zero-sum game.

*Strictly Determined Games*

We begin our discussion of zero-sum, two-person games by considering a special class of them, namely: *matrix games, or rectangular games.* In matrix games of this type, each of two players, A and B, has only one move which he can make from a finite number of options, and the move is to be made in ignorance of the other player's choice. When the two players reveal their choices, a pre-determined matrix (table) prescribes the payoffs to each of them. Only the payoff to one of the players need be shown, because the game is to be zero-sum, thus if the payoff to, say, player A is $(+)\, x$ units (money, chips, or whatever is contested for), then the payoff to player B must be $(-)\, x$-units.

A rectangular arrangement of *mn* (*m* times *n*) numbers, where *m* indicates the number of *rows* and *n* the number of columns, is called an *m × n* (*m by n*) matrix. For example, "arrangement" (1)

$$
\begin{vmatrix}
-3 & 3 & 1 & 2 & 7 \\
12 & 5 & 6 & 4 & 5 \\
-4 & -3 & 0 & 0 & 1 \\
0 & 2 & -3 & 3 & 2
\end{vmatrix}
\tag{1}
$$

is a 4 × 5 matrix of 20 numbers arranged in 4 rows and 5 columns. Matrix (1) can be used to consider the following game:

Player A chooses a number from the *set of rows* (1, 2, 3, 4). Player B, ignorant of player *A*'s choice, chooses a number from the *set of columns* (1, 2, 3, 4, 5). The choices are then made known and if A has chosen 2, for example, and B has chosen 4, then B pays A the amount in the "cell" formed by the intersection of the second row and the fourth column of the matrix, i.e., B pays A $4.00. If A chooses 3, and B chooses 1, the value appearing in the "cell" formed by the intersection of the third row and first column of the matrix is −4; this choice means that B pays A (−) $4.00, or in actuality, A pays B $4.00. Thus, (1) is called the "*payoff* matrix to player A" of this *matrix game* in which A chooses a *row* and B chooses a *column*, each in ignorance of the other's choice. The choice of a row is a *pure strategy* for player A, and the choice of a column is a *pure strategy* for player B.

Assuming that both players are intelligent, and are attempting to realize the largest possible "payoff" regardless of the choice made by the other player, the players would reason as follows:

Player A reasons that he *could win* 7 by choosing row 1, but at the same time he *could lose* 3, depending upon whether B chooses column 5 or column 1, respectively. Following this line of reasoning for each of the four rows of matrix (1), player A would discover that row 2 is the best choice that he could make. Under the conditions associated with the choice of row 2 the worst that could happen to A would be the selection of column 4 by player B, in which case B would pay A $4.00. If B chooses any other column, A will receive an even greater payoff. Thus, the best strategy for A to pursue in analyzing the game is to search for the minimum payoff in each row, and then select the row which shows the maximum value of the minimum payoffs. In other words, since the minimum payoffs of the rows are called "row minima," A's best strategy is to select the row which includes the *maximum of the row minima*.

In similar fashion, player B reasons that he *could* realize a *winning* of 4 by choosing column 1, but by the same token he *could lose* 12, if player A chooses row 2. Pursuing this line of thought for each of the five columns of the matrix, B would decide that the "safest" choice for him would be column 4. Obviously, under the condition of the selection of column 4 by player B, the best payoff that A could realize would be that of 4 by selecting row 2, and if he should happen to select any other row he would win even less, i.e., 2 (row 1), 0 (row 3), or 3 (row 4). In general terms, the best course of action for B to follow is that of examining the amount of the maximum payoff for each column (*column maxima*), and then choosing the column showing the *minimum of the column maxima*.

Following the "rules" of A choosing the row showing the *maximum value of the row minima*, and B choosing the column that would yield a *minimum value of the column maxima*, player A would choose row 2 and player B would select column 4. By dint of these decisions, A has assured himself of winning at least 4 and B is certain that A can win no more than 4. The choice of *row* 2 is defined as an *optimal pure strategy* for player A, while the choice of *column* 4 is termed an *optimal pure strategy* for player B. The payoff of 4 is defined as the *value* of the game. Since the amount 4 in matrix (1) is the smallest in its row, but the greatest in its column, it is termed the *saddle-value* of the matrix. The position of the saddle-value in the matrix, row 2 and column 5, is called a *saddle-point* of the matrix. The term "saddle-point" is derived from the similarity between the matrix position of the point and the particular point of a saddle which is a maximum point of a curve running in one direction and a minimum point of another curve running at right angles to the first curve (see Figure 32).

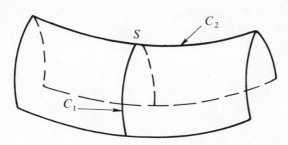

*Figure 32*
*Saddle-point S—Maximum Point of Curve $C_1$, and Minimum Point of Curve $C_2$*

Expressed in general terms, a matrix game is defined by an $m \times n$ payoff matrix of the form:

$$\begin{vmatrix} a_{11} & a_{12} & a_{13} \ldots a_{1n} \\ a_{21} & a_{22} & a_{23} \ldots a_{2n} \\ \cdot & \cdot & \cdot \quad\quad \cdot \\ \cdot & \cdot & \cdot \quad\quad \cdot \\ \cdot & \cdot & \cdot \quad\quad \cdot \\ a_{m1} & a_{m2} & a_{m3} \ldots a_{mn} \end{vmatrix}$$

where each individual entry is of the form $a_{ij}$; $i$ designating the row of entry and $j$ the column of entry (e.g., $a_{23}$ is the entry found at the intersection of row 2 and column 3).

If one player chooses rows the other player must choose columns. The choice of a row (or a column) by a player is made in ignorance of the other player's choice. If the player choosing rows selects row $i$ and the other player chooses column $j$, the first player (the one choosing rows) receives the payoff $a_{ij}$ from the other player.

The *largest* number of the $j$-th column is symbolized as: $\max\limits_{1 \le i \le m} a_{ij}$, and is called the "*$j$-th column maximum.*" The expression: $1 \le i \le m$, in the symbol, indicates that the value of the *row* designator $i$ must lie in the range of values 1 to $m$ inclusive, because there are $m$ rows in the payoff matrix. There is a column maximum value for each of the $j$ $(1, 2, \ldots n)$ columns of the matrix. The smallest value of the column maxima is symbolized as: $\min\limits_{1 \le j \le n} \left( \max\limits_{1 \le i \le m} a_{ij} \right)$, where the expression $1 \le j \le n$, indicates that the value of the column designator $j$ must be in the range of values 1 to $n$ inclusive, because there are $n$ columns in the payoff matrix.

In analogous fashion, the *smallest* number in the $i$-th row is denoted by $\min\limits_{i \le j \le n} a_{ij}$, and is termed the *$i$-th row minimum.* The largest value of these row minima is symbolized as: $\max\limits_{1 \le i \le m} \left( \min\limits_{1 \le j \le n} a_{ij} \right)$, where the symbols employed are as previously defined.

A matrix game is said to be *strictly determined* if the payoff matrix contains an entry $a_{eg}$ which is *simultaneously* the *minimum* of the *row* in which it occurs and the *maximum* of the *column* in which it is entered. Expressed in symbolic form, a strictly determined game exists when:

$$a_{eg} = \max_{1 \le i \le m} \left( \min_{1 \le j \le n} a_{ij} \right) = \min_{1 \le j \le n} \left( \max_{1 \le i \le m} a_{ij} \right)$$

Under this condition, the selection of row $e$ by player A is an *optimal pure strategy* for him, and the choice of column $g$ is an *optimal pure strategy* for B. The value of the payoff $a_{eg}$ is called the "value" of the game. If the value of the game is *zero* (i.e., if $a_{eg} = 0$) the game is called "fair."

Player A can be assured that he will win at least the value of entry $a_{eg}$ by choosing row $e$, and player B can guarantee that A will win no more than the value of $a_{eg}$ by choosing column $g$. It can be shown that these optimal strategies for A and B exist if, and only if, $a_{eg}$ is a *saddle-value*, that is, if $a_{eg}$ satisfies the condition:

$$a_{eg} = \max_{1 \le i \le m} \left( \min_{1 \le j \le n} a_{ij} \right) = \min_{1 \le j \le n} \left( \max_{1 \le i \le m} a_{ij} \right)$$

Using our example to illustrate the discussion, a convenient arrangement of the matrix for conducting a search for a saddle-value (and saddle-point) is as follows:

| Player A \ Player B | 1 | 2 | 3 | 4 | 5 | Values of Row Minima |
|---|---|---|---|---|---|---|
| 1 | −3 | 3 | 1 | 2 | 7 | −3 |
| 2 | 12 | 5 | 6 | ④ | 5 | ④ |
| 3 | −4 | −3 | 0 | 0 | 1 | −4 |
| 4 | 0 | 2 | −3 | 3 | 2 | −3 |
| Values of Column Maxima | 12 | 5 | 6 | ④ | 7 | Saddle-point: Row 2, Column 4. Value of Game = 4 |

The row minima are listed on the right side of the matrix, and the values of the column maxima are entered at the bottom of the matrix. If a saddle-value exists, it is denoted by encirclement. Noting the respective column and row in which the saddle-value occurs, the saddle-point is entered in the lower right corner of the arrangement along with the value of the game. In passing, it might be pointed out that since the value (4) of the game is not zero in our example, the game could not be called a fair one.

With this background, we can now examine a particular type of problem that might occur in connection with an action research project. Suppose that in a given school district a millage campaign is being planned by an action research group. The community has planned a series of "information" meetings to be held throughout the district over a given period of time. On a given date there is to be a meeting held at the same time in each of two different school buildings in the, geographically speaking, large district. The action research group has formed a "team" of four speakers, two of them being excellent orators, the other two being of ordinary caliber. The research team knows that the opposition has two excellent debaters and two ordinary speakers available to express its point of view. The research group and the opposition have agreed to send a team of two speakers to each of the meeting places in order to debate publicly the issues involved in the millage problem. It is known by both "sides" that if debate teams of the same caliber appear at a given meeting, neither "side" will gain the advantage for its point of view as far as that particular meeting is concerned. If, at a given meeting, one of the teams is of significantly higher caliber than the other, any advantage to be gained by the debate will accrue to the element represented by the superior team. The research group (and the opposition group) are faced with the problem of either sending a team of two excellent debaters to one meeting and two ordinary speakers to the other or providing a team composed of one excellent and one ordinary speaker to each meeting place. The research group decides to apply the theory of games in seeking a solution to the problem. The following payoff matrix to the *research group* is constructed:

| Opposition group<br>Research group | I | II | Values of<br>Row Minima |
|---|---|---|---|
| I | ⓪ | 1 | ⓪ |
| II | −1 | 0 | −1 |

| Values of<br>Column Maxima | ⓪ | 1 | Saddle-point:<br>Row 1, Column 1.<br>Value of Game = 0 (fair game) |

*Figure 33*
*Payoff Matrix to the Research Group*

where arrangement I is that of teaming two excellent debaters, and arrangement II is that of teaming an ordinary speaker with an excellent one. It should be noted here that the situation which "matches" team A, composed of an excellent debater and an ordinary one, against team B, composed of two ordinary speakers, is *not* considered a *significant* advantage for team A. This point is discussed in greater detail later in the presentation.

The payoff matrix was constructed as follows:

Since neither "side" would witness an advantage if teams of the same caliber met in debate, a zero was entered at the intersection of the rows and columns denoting the fact that teams of the same caliber were meeting (i.e, 0 was entered for arrangement I at intersection of row 1 and column 1, and for arrangement II at intersection of row 2 and column 2). In the other cases, acknowledging the fact that arrangement I was significantly superior to arrangement II, a payoff of 1 was entered (or −1) according to the advantage *measured in terms of the payoff to the research group*. Thus, when arrangement II of the research group was confronted by arrangement I of the opposition, a (−1) value entry was indicated.

From the analysis of the game, we note that a saddle-value of 0 exists, and the saddle-point is row 1, column 1. Since the value of the game is 0, it is a fair game. From the matrix the research team knows that if it chooses row 1, it cannot lose, and if by chance the opposition makes a "wrong" choice (column 2) it will gain an advantage, indicated by the value 1. Since the diagram could be applied to the situation occurring at each of the two meeting places, if the opposition should happen to choose arrangement II for one meeting place (automatically forcing it to choose the same arrangement for the other meeting, i.e., one good with one ordinary speaker), the search group might gain a "double" advantage (only one of which would be *significant*), so to speak. On the other hand, if after the research team had chosen arrangement I (one team of two good speakers at one meeting place, and a team of two ordinary speakers at the other meeting), the opposition chooses arrangement I, the research group is "guaranteed" that it will not be *disadvantaged*.

*Non-strictly Determined Games (Mixed Strategies)*

Some matrix games have no entry that is simultaneously a row minimum and a column maximum, i.e., some matrix games do not have saddle-values and pure optimal strategies. Such games are called *non-strictly determined games*, or *mixed strategies*.

Non-strictly determined games occur in situations where a mixture of chance and strategy is at work. A game of matching coins can serve as a good example of a non-strictly determined game. In this game, players A and B each choose either "heads" (*H*) or "tails" (*T*) in ignorance of the other player's choice. Suppose player A wins five dollars if the choices of both players "match" when he selects heads (*H*), and seven dollars if the choices match when he selects tails (*T*). Player B wins four dollars if the choices are *not* matched when he selects heads (*H*), and five dollars when he selects tails (*T*) and the coins *do not* match. The payoff matrix to player A then becomes:

| A \ B | H | T | Row Minima |
|-------|-----|-----|-------|
| H | 5 | − 5 | − 5 |
| T | − 4 | 7 | − 4 |
| Column Maxima | 5 | 7 | No Saddle-Value No Saddle-Point |

*Figure 34*
*Payoff Matrix of a Mixed Strategy*

Since the matrix has no saddle-point, players A and B do not have single best plans as their best strategies. Consequently, each player must devise some *mixed strategy* in order to maximize his gain or minimize his loss.

How should a player best proceed to devise a mixed strategy? It must first be recognized that no one choice is clearly optimal for either player. Therefore, a player must not always play the same pure strategy. For example, in playing "matching coins," player A must *avoid playing the same pure strategy repeatedly* (e.g., heads), because player B, always playing the opposite choice (tails) would win. The point of the discussion is illustrated by employing the payoff matrix shown in Figure 34.

Assume that player A decides to play row *H* half of the time, and row *T* half of the time.* Now if player B chooses column *H* all the time, then the expected

---

* Player A must make his choices at *random* so that row *H* is chosen with a frequency of $\frac{1}{2}$ and row *T* with a frequency of $\frac{1}{2}$, because if A should play *H* and *T* in a fixed pattern, say, alternation, player B could learn the pattern and win by merely playing the opposite choice each time. Randomness of play, in this situation, can be insured by basing the next choice of a player on a chance device involving probability $\frac{1}{2}$. The flipping of an unbiased coin would serve the purposes of random choice in this case.

gain of player A will be:

$$\tfrac{1}{2}(5) + \tfrac{1}{2}(-4) = 2.5 - 2 = \$.50$$

On the other hand, if B chooses column $T$ all the time, player A's expected gain will be:

$$\tfrac{1}{2}(-5) + \tfrac{1}{2}(7) = -2.5 + 3.5 = \$1.00$$

If we now assume that player B also has a mixed strategy, and chooses *at random* column $H$ half of the time and column $T$ half of the time, player A's expected gain will be:

$$\tfrac{1}{2}[\tfrac{1}{2}(5) + \tfrac{1}{2}(-4)] + \tfrac{1}{2}[\tfrac{1}{2}(-5) + \tfrac{1}{2}(7)] = .25 + .50 = \$.75$$

In similar fashion, player A's expected gain can be calculated for other mixed strategies. For example, if A plays row $H$ three-fourths of the time and row $T$ one-fourth of the time, while B plays column $H$ one-third of the time and column $T$ two-thirds of the time, then A's expected gain will be:

$$\tfrac{1}{3}[\tfrac{3}{4}(5) + \tfrac{1}{4}(-4)] + \tfrac{2}{3}[\tfrac{3}{4}(-5) + \tfrac{1}{4}(7)] = \tfrac{1}{12}(15 - 4 - 30 + 14) = -\tfrac{5}{12} \approx -\$.42$$

actually, a loss of \$.42.

From the results produced by the different strategies, the question arises: Is there a best mixed strategy for the players? In our first example, wherein player A decided to play row $H$ half of the time and row $T$ half of the time, at random, we note that $A$'s gains varied from fifty cents to one dollar. Can some minimum gain for A be insured, and if so, how much is it? Similarly, can B rest assured that he will not lose more than some maximum amount? All of these questions can be answered in the affirmative. The mathematical theory of games shows that there are always best strategies and a means for finding them.

A general approach of how to determine the best strategies for a given game, and how to find the values of the expected amounts to be gained or lost by the players, is as follows:

Let player A play row $H$ with the frequency $x$, and row $T$ with a frequency $(1 - x)$. Then, if player B selects column $H$ all the time, employing the values of our example, A's gain will be:

$$g(A, H) = x(5) + (1 - x)(-4) = 5x - 4 + 4x = 9x - 4$$

If player B selects column $T$ all the time, A's gain will be:

$$g(A, T) = x(-5) + (1 - x)(7) = -5x + 7 - 7x = 7 - 12x$$

It can be shown mathematically that if player A chooses the frequency of play, $x$, so that $g(A, H) = g(A, T)$, then he will realize the best mixed strategy for him. In our example this would mean:

$$9x - 4 = 7 - 12x$$

$$21x = 11$$

$$x = 11/21$$

Substituting this value of $x$ in the respective value ($g$) equations, we find:

$$g(A, H) = 9x - 4 = 9(\tfrac{11}{21}) - 4 \approx 4.71 - 4 \approx \$.71$$

and

$$g(A, T) = 7 - 12(\tfrac{11}{21}) \approx 7 - 6.29 \approx \$.71$$

Thus, if player A employs the frequency $x = \tfrac{11}{21}$, and, hence $(1 - x) = \tfrac{10}{21}$; i.e., he plays row $H$ *at random* with a frequency of $x = \tfrac{11}{21}$, and row $T$ with frequency $(1 - x) = \tfrac{10}{21}$; regardless of the frequency with which B plays either column $H$ or column $T$, A's gain will be \$.71. For example, suppose B plays column $H$ with a frequency $\tfrac{1}{4}$ and column $T$ with a frequency $\tfrac{3}{4}$, then A's expected gain will be:

$$g(A, \tfrac{11}{21}, \tfrac{10}{21}) = \tfrac{1}{4}[\tfrac{11}{21}(5) + \tfrac{10}{21}(-4)] + \tfrac{3}{4}[\tfrac{11}{21}(-5) + \tfrac{10}{21}(7)]$$

$$= \tfrac{1}{84}(55 - 40 - 165 + 210) = \tfrac{60}{84} = \tfrac{15}{21} \approx \$.71$$

The same method of analysis can be applied for player B. Let the frequency of the choice of column $H$ be denoted by $y$ and that of column $T$ by $1 - y$. The best mixed strategy for player B is determined as follows: If A selects row $H$ all the time, B's gain will be:

$$g(B, H) = y(5) + (1 - y)(-5) = 5y - 5 + 5y = 10y - 5$$

If A selects row $T$ all the time, B's gain will be:

$$g(B, T) = y(-4) + (10y)7 = -4y + 7 - 7y = 7 - 11y$$

Setting $g(B, H)$ equal to $g(B, T)$, we have:

$$10y - 5 = 7 - 11y$$

$$21y = 12$$

$$y = \tfrac{12}{21} \quad \text{and} \quad 1 - y = \tfrac{9}{21}$$

or:

$$y = \tfrac{4}{7} \quad \text{and} \quad 1 - y = \tfrac{3}{7}$$

Thus:

$$g(B, H) = g(B, T) = 10(\tfrac{4}{7}) - 5 = 7 - 11(\tfrac{4}{7}) \approx \$.71$$

We note that $g(A) = g(B)$, as expected for a zero-sum game; and a complete solution of the given game is:

1. Player A should select row $H$ and row $T$ *at random* with frequencies $\tfrac{11}{21}$ and $\tfrac{10}{21}$, respectively.
2. Player B should select column $H$ and column $T$ *at random* with frequencies $\tfrac{4}{7}$ and $\tfrac{3}{7}$, respectively.
3. The value of the game is $g \approx \$.71$

Expressed in general terms, we may summarize our discussions of "strictly determined" and "non-strictly determined" games as follows:

Payoffs for a rectangular game can always be given in $m \times n$ matrix form, where player A has $m$ possible choices of *rows* and player B has $n$ possible choices of *columns*. The payoff matrix, with $a_{ij}$ as the entry in the cell formed by the intersection of the $i$-th row and the $j$-th column, is:

$$
\begin{vmatrix}
a_{11} & a_{12} & a_{13} \cdots a_{1n} \\
a_{21} & a_{22} & a_{23} \cdots a_{2n} \\
a_{31} & a_{32} & a_{33} \cdots a_{3n} \\
\cdot & \cdot & \cdot \quad\quad \cdot \\
\cdot & \cdot & \cdot \quad\quad \cdot \\
\cdot & \cdot & \cdot \quad\quad \cdot \\
a_{m1} & a_{m2} & a_{m3} \quad a_{mn}
\end{vmatrix}
$$

The choice of a *row* is a *pure strategy* for player A, and the choice of a column is a *pure strategy* for player B. If a saddle-value exists, i.e., if *pure optimal strategies* exist, the analysis of the game may be discontinued with its discovery under the assumption that the players, being of normal intelligence, will choose those rows and columns that will result in pure optimal strategies ("best" possible solutions) for themselves. If a saddle-value does not exist in the payoff matrix, i.e., pure optimal strategies do not exist, then the analysis must be continued to determine *optimal mixed strategies*.

The choice of relative frequencies (probabilities), $X = (x_1, x_2, x_3, \ldots x_m)$, wherein the particular probabilities $(x_i)$ must satisfy the conditions:

$$x_i \geq 0 \quad \text{and} \quad x_1 + x_2 + x_3 + x_m = 1,$$

with which to play the *rows* of the payoff matrix is termed a *mixed strategy* for players A. The choice of relative frequencies (probabilities) $Y = (y_1, y_2, y_3, \cdots y_n)$, wherein the particular probabilities $(y_i)$ must satisfy the conditions, $y_i \geq 0$, and $y_1 + y_2 + y_3 + \cdots + y_n = 1$, with which to play columns of the payoff matrix is called a *mixed strategy* for player B.

The *expected gain* of player A for the mixed "frequencies" $(x_1, x_2, x_3, \ldots x_m)$, if player B pursues the strategy of selecting *column j* constantly, is:

$$g(X, j) = x_1 a_{1j} + x_2 a_{2j} + x_3 a_{3j} + \cdots + x_m a_{mj}$$

A mixed strategy of player A which yields the maximum value (maximizes) the quantity $\min_{1 \leq j \leq n} g(X, j)$, where $1 \leq j \leq n$ indicates the value of $j$ must fall somewhere in the set of whole numbers between 1 and $n$ (the total number of columns in the matrix), is termed an *optimal mixed strategy for player A*. If player A employs this optimal mixed strategy, then he assures himself at least an expected gain $g$, where $g$ is the value of the game.

The expected gain of player B for the mixed "frequencies" $(y_1, y_2, y_3, \ldots y_n)$, if player A pursues the strategy of selecting *row i* constantly, is:

$$g(Y, i) = y_1 a_{i1} + y_2 a_{i2} + y_3 a_{i3} + \cdots + y_n a_{in}$$

A mixed strategy of player B which produces the minimum value (minimizes) of the quantity $\max_{1 \le i \le m} g(Y, i)$, where the expression $1 \le i \le m$ indicates the value of $i$ is a whole number between 1 and $m$ (the number of rows in the matrix), is called an *optimal mixed strategy for player B*. When player B employs this optimal mixed strategy he assures himself *at most* a loss of $g$.

The *fundamental minimax theorem* (of von Neumann) states that for any matrix game there exist optimal mixed strategies that produce a value $g$ such that:

$$g = \text{minimum of } \max_{1 \le i \le m} g(Y, i) = \text{maximum of } \min_{1 \le j \le n} g(X, j)$$

for all possible $Y(y_1, y_2, y_3, \ldots, y_n)$ and $X(x_1, x_2, x_3, \ldots x_m)$ values; and the common value $g$ is defined to be the "value" of the game. A game is defined to be "fair" if its value is $g = 0$.

It can be shown that the values of the unknown relative frequencies, $x_1, x_2, x_3, \ldots x_m$ and $y_1, y_2, y_3, \ldots y_n$, and the value of $g$, can be found from the following relations:

$$x_1 + x_2 + x_3 + \cdots + x_m = 1, \qquad x_i \ge 0 \tag{1}$$

$$y_1 + y_2 + y_3 + \cdots + y_n = 1, \qquad y_j \ge 0 \tag{2}$$

$$x_1 a_{1j} + x_2 a_{2j} + \cdots + x_m a_{mj} \ge g; \qquad \text{for } j = 1, 2, 3, \ldots, n \tag{3}$$

$$y_1 a_{i1} + y_2 a_{i2} + \cdots + y_n a_{in} \le g; \qquad \text{for } i = 1, 2, 3, \ldots, m \tag{4}$$

Expression (3) actually represents $n$ inequations, one inequation for each *column* $j$ of the matrix. In similar fashion, (4) represents $m$ inequations, one inequation for each *row* $i$ of the matrix. Thus, we have $m + n + 1$ unknowns with $m + n + 2$ relations (along with $x_i \ge 0$, $y_j \ge 0$, since negative "frequencies" have no meaning). We also note that (3) and (4) may be equalities or inequalities. The minimax theorem insures that there exists a solution to these relations, and that the value of $g$ is unique. It should be noted, however, that a game may have several, and, in some cases, even an infinite number of solutions associated with $x_i$ and $y_j$. Such problems can be solved by "ordinary" algebraic methods, graphic devices, matrix algebra, or iteration.

The ordinary algebraic method is a direct attempt to solve for the unknowns by employing (1), (2), (3), and (4). Fundamental to the solution is the previously stated fact that each rectangular game has a unique value $g$ which exists. Thus, the value of $g$ which satisfies the relations is sought. If this value of $g$ is found, it is known that it is the only $g$, and from that point procedures are invoked to find the values of the remaining unknowns.

A graphical solution may be used whenever one of the players has only two possible plans from which to choose. The matrix solution has wide applications and is easily employed after matrix notations and operations have been mastered. The iterative method is applicable to those problems in which the graphical method cannot be applied, and when the use of the algebraic or matrix methods are not practical. It is a method that provides an approximate solution for the value of the game, and the method is such that one can approach the true value to any desired degree of accuracy.*

Applying the algebraic method to the game represented in Figure 34, the unknowns would become: $x_1, x_2, y_1, y_2$, and $g$. Adapting relations (1), (2), (3), and (4) to the problem, we would have:

$$x_1 + x_2 = 1; \quad x_1 \geq 0, \quad x_2 \geq 0 \tag{1}$$

$$y_1 + y_2 = 1; \quad y_1 \geq 0, \quad y_2 \geq 0 \tag{2}'$$

$$x_1(5) + x_2(-4) \geq g \tag{3}'$$

$$x_1(-5) + x_2(7) \geq g \tag{3}''$$

$$y_1(5) + y_2(-5) \leq g \tag{4}'$$

$$y_1(-4) + y_2(7) \leq g \tag{4}''$$

In this problem we have five unknowns and six equations. We shall therefore solve the "set" using five equations only, and then "check" the results by determining whether the sixth equation is satisfied by the solutions. As a final "check" we note whether $x_1 \geq 0, x_2 \geq 0, y_1 \geq 0$, and $y_2 \geq 0$. If the results are consistent at all these points, then the solution is considered to be complete.

From equations (1)' and (2)', we find that: $x_2 = 1 - x_1$ and $y_2 = 1 - y_1$. Substituting in (3)', (3)'', and (4)', we have:

$$5x_1 + (1 - x_1)(-4) \geq g \tag{3}'a$$

$$-5x_1 + (1 - x_1)(7) \geq g \tag{3}''a$$

$$5y_1 + (1 - y_1)(-5) \leq g \tag{4}'a$$

rewriting these expressions, in equation form, we have:

$$9x_1 - 4 = g \tag{3}'b$$

$$-12x_1 + 7 = g \tag{3}''b$$

$$10y_1 - 5 = g \tag{4}'b$$

Subtracting equation (3)''b from (3)'b, we would have:

$$21x_1 - 11 = 0$$

or

$$21x_1 = 11$$

---

* Since the matrix algebra approach and the iterative method would demand a rather detailed mathematical explanation, they are omitted here. Interested readers are referred to Churchman,[36] Ackoff, and Arnoff, *Introduction to Operation Research*, pp. 540–46, for excellent examples of these methods.

and, therefore:

$$x_1 = \tfrac{11}{21}$$

and, since:

$$x_2 = 1 - x_1$$

thus:

$$x_2 = \tfrac{10}{21}$$

Solving (3)'b for g, we find:

$$9(\tfrac{11}{21}) - 4 = g$$

$$g = 4.71 - 4 \approx .71$$

Substituting the value of g into (4)'b, we get: $10y_1 \approx 5.71$, or $y_1 \approx .571$. Now since $y_1 \approx .571 \approx \tfrac{4}{7}$; thus $y_2 = 1 - \tfrac{4}{7} = \tfrac{3}{7}$. Checking our solution, we employ equation (4)″, and find:

$$-4y_1 + 7y_2 = g$$

$$-4(\tfrac{4}{7}) + 7(\tfrac{3}{7}) = .71$$

$$-2.29 + 3 \approx .71$$

$$.71 = .71 \quad \text{(check)}$$

We also note that since: $x_1 = \tfrac{11}{21} > 0, x_2 = \tfrac{10}{21} > 0, y_1 = \tfrac{4}{7} > 0,$ and $y_2 = \tfrac{3}{7} > 0,$ all check, we have the complete solution:

$$x_1 = \tfrac{11}{21}, \qquad x_2 = \tfrac{10}{21}, \qquad y_1 = \tfrac{4}{7}, \qquad y_2 = \tfrac{3}{7}, \quad \text{and} \quad g \approx \$.71$$

*Graphical Solution*

The solution of a game may be obtained by a graphical method whenever one of the players has but two alternatives from which to make a selection. The method is illustrated by the following fictitious example.

Suppose that a research team is conducting an experiment to determine whether certain selected topics of magnetism, electricity, and heat, usually taught in a high school physical science course, can be taught to certain types of children who are ten to eleven years of age. The pupil-types are established in terms of combinations of the following factors: (1) socio-economic background, (2) reading ability, and (3) quantitative aptitude.

In the first phase of the experimentation, one thousand school children of the appropriate age level were given instruction in the selected topics. Successful performance by a pupil-type was determined on the basis of per cent of topics "mastered" by the learner. The findings of the first phase of the experiment showed that three different pupil-types (I, II, and III) were capable of learning a sufficient per cent of the total number of topics presented to be classified as "successful."

The second phase of the experimentation was concerned with the problem c building a curriculum composed of the selected topics. The team decided tha some of the findings of the first phase of the experiment could be analyzed b methods of the theory of games in order to produce data that could be used t guide further research work on the second phase of the project.

From the first phase of the experiment it was discovered that when topic *A* was presented it was understood very well by the type I pupil, not very well b type II, and only reasonably well by type III. The research team also found tha the understanding of topic B depended in great part on the learner's willingnes to accept pure definition as a point of departure for the discussion of the topic and thus discovered that topic B was exceptionally well-understood by th type II pupil, not very well understood by the type I pupil, and was very difficul for the type III pupil to understand.

Since topics A and B were related, the question arose as to whether a present ation which intermingled the developments of the respective topics might no prove to create a more effective learning situation than the separate presentatio of each topic to a class of students composed of the three basic pupil-types The team decided to employ the theory of games to determine the answer to th question of style of presentation of the topics.

If values could be determined for a payoff matrix to the "player" makin, his choice from one of two topics (A and B), and who is opposed by a "player" who must make his selection from the three pupil-types (I, II, and III), the solu tion to the game could be obtained by a graphical method. With this idea i mind, the team analyzed the data of the first phase of the experiment and decide to assign a positive 3 to the learning of concept A by pupil-type I; a negative to that of pupil-type II; and a positive 1 to the learning of concept A by pupil type III. In similar fashion, the team assigned a negative 2 to the learning c concept B by pupil-type I; a positive 4 to the learning of B by pupil-type II; and finally, a negative 3 to that of pupil-type III. The matrix of the game is show in Figure 35. The team agreed that if a mixed strategy could be found that woul produce a game value of $g \geq 1$, the interchangeable "presentation" of th developments of the two topics (A and B) would be employed.

| Pupil-Type Concept (Topic) Presentation | I | II | III | Row Minima |
|---|---|---|---|---|
| A | 3 | −2 | 1 | −2 |
| B | −2 | 4 | −3 | −3 |
| Column Maxima | 3 | 4 | 1 | No Saddle-Value No Saddle-Point |

*Figure 35*

*Payoff Matrix to "Concept (Topic) Presentation-Player"*

The general relations from the matrix are:

$$x_1 + x_2 = 1 \tag{1}$$
$$y_1 + y_2 + y_3 = 1 \tag{2}$$
$$3x_1 - 2x_2 \geq g \tag{3}$$
$$-2x_1 + 4x_2 \geq g \tag{4}$$
$$x_1 - 3x_2 \geq g \tag{5}$$
$$3y_1 - 2y_2 + y_3 \leq g \tag{6}$$
$$-2y_1 + 4y_2 - 3y_3 \leq g \tag{7}$$

Rewriting and simplifying the equations involving the "concept-player," who has only two possible plans, we find:

$$3x_1 - 2(1 - x_1) \geq g; \quad \text{so that} \quad 5x_1 - 2 \geq g \tag{8}$$
$$-2x_1 + 4(1 - x_1) \geq g; \quad \text{so that} \quad -6x_1 + 4 \geq g \tag{9}$$
$$x_1 - 3(1 - x_1) \geq g; \quad \text{so that} \quad 4x_1 - 3 \geq g \tag{10}$$

Plotting the line $g = 5x_1 - 2$, as shown in Figure 36 we note that the line divides the plane into two regions. For any point $(x_0, g)$ above the line, we have $g > g_0 = 5x_0 - 2$, while for a point below the line, $g < g_0 = 5x_0 - 2$.

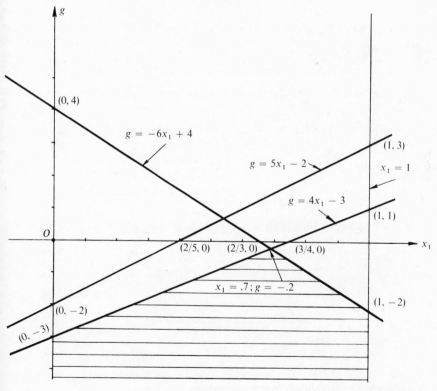

*Figure 36*

*Plots for g in Interval $0 \leq x_1 \leq 1$*

Since the inequality $5x_1 - 2 \geq g$, i.e., $5x_1 - 2$ is *greater than* or *equal to g,* describes the condition in which we are interested, the required solution will be either *on the line* or *below it.* All three lines are plotted in the interval $0 \leq x_1 \leq 1$, and all of the points *below all three lines are indicated by the shaded area.*

We now choose the point in the *shaded area* for which the value of $g$ is highest. The point in question is found at the intersection of the line $g = 4x_1 - 3$ and $g = -6x_1 + 4$. At this point of intersection we find $x_1 = .7$, $x_2 = .3$, and $g = 4x_1 - 3 = 2.8 - 3 = -.2$.

Although the team would (upon discovering the value of the game was $g = -.2$) decide that the mixed strategy of referring to the development of concept A, .7 of the time (at random throughout the discussion of the two topics) and concept B, .3 of the time during the "intermingled" discussion, produces a situation that is actually adverse, (indicated by the *negative* value of $g$) to the "better" learning of the pupil-types involved, it will be instructive if we continue the discussion of the example through the point of deriving a "complete" solution.

In order to make computations easier in progressing to the complete solution of the problem, it will be necessary to invoke a theorem that states:

If

$$x_1 a_{1j} + x_2 a_{2j} + x_3 a_{3j} + \cdots + x_m a_{mj} > g, \text{ then } y_j = 0;$$

and similarly: If

$$y_1 a_{i1} + y_2 a_{i2} + y_3 a_{i3} + \cdots + y_n a_{in} < g, \text{ then } x_i = 0.$$

Applying this theorem, the research team would have proceeded as follows:

1. Since in (3): $3x_1 - 2x_2 = 3(.7) - (2)(.3) = 2.1 - .6 = 1.5 > -.2 = g$; or, in other words, since $3x_1 - 2x_2 > g$; we can set (by the theorem) $y_1 = 0$; and
2. Since in (4): $-2x_1 + 4x_2 = -2(.7) + 4(.3) = -1.4 + 1.2 = -.2 = g$; or since $-2x_1 + 4x_2 = g$, we *cannot* set $y_2 = 0$; and
3. Since in (5): $x_1 - 3x_2 = .7 - 3(.3) = -.2 = g$; or since $x_1 - 3x_2 = g$, we *cannot* set $y_3 = 0$;

we proceed to find from equations (2) and (7), with $y_1$ set equal to 0, that:

$$y_2 + y_3 = 1 \quad \text{or} \quad y_3 = 1 - y_2$$

and, substituting in (7) we have:

$$-2y_1 + 4y_2 - 3y_3 = g$$

$$-2(0) + 4y_2 - 3(1 - y_2) = -.2$$

Solving for $y_2$, we find:

$$7y_2 = 2.8 \quad \text{or} \quad y_2 = .4 \quad \text{and} \quad y_3 = 1 - .4 = .6$$

Now, checking with equation (6), we find:

$$3y_1 - 2y_2 + y_3 = g \quad \text{becomes} \quad 3(0) - 2(.4) + (.6) = -.2$$

Therefore, the complete solution is:

$$x_1 = .7 \qquad x_2 = .3 \qquad y_1 = 0 \qquad y_2 = .4 \qquad y_3 = .6 \quad \text{and} \quad g = -.2$$

The team would interpret these results as follows:

Providing that approximately .4 of the class is type II pupil, approximately .6 of the class is type III pupils, and that there are very few, if any, type I pupils involved, the mixed strategy of presenting the developments of concepts A and B on an interchangeable basis, emphasizing the development of A, .7 of the time and the development of B, .3 of the time, will produce a *maximum* game value of −.2. This result, in turn, means that if such an approach is employed a slightly adverse effect on the learning of the topics by the students involved will result. On this basis, the research team rejects the approach, and can turn its attention to other possible combinations.

Obviously, the algebraic solution, and under certain circumstances, the graphical solution, of a game is quite lengthy. These methods become many times more involved when there are more than three plans for the "payoff player's" two alternatives. The electronic computer can be of great help in problems of this type, and with recent developments in electronic computational devices, there is little if any reason why research problems of the nature described in our example could not be attacked by methods of the theory of games.

Before leaving our example, it should be noted that the application of the theory of games in the example did not overlook the fact that the minimax principle is based on the assumption that the "player" participates in a game for the total reward. The assumption made in applying the theory to the example was that the "teacher-player" would be seeking a *total* payoff in terms of the degree to which the topic was learned by the different pupil-types. The pupil-types present would be responding for a *total* reward on the basis of not being able to inhibit the response if they honestly attempted to learn what was being presented. This situation does not mean that the pupil types would not be, in effect, employing a strategy during the learning situation. Certainly it is not unreasonable to assume that the pupil-types are "players" who are *not* interested in gambling and winning on "long-shots" in the learning situation for the pure "excitement" of the experience. In the absence of this "chance-gambling" orientation, it can be assumed that the learning situation in a classroom is one of a mixture of chance and strategy on the part of the learner. This line of reasoning fits the teacher's role, probably to even a greater degree than it does that of the learner.

In closing our discussion of the theory of games and its potential application in educational research, it might be wise to speculate upon its application in the realm of programed instruction. Theoretically constructed matrix games usually provide only one move for each player. The possibility of learning being of a branching nature, thus providing a realm of many choices, means that the situation through wise programing can be reduced to a form of matrix game that demands the employment of *strategy* on the part of the programmer and the learner. In effect, the programmer is a player *in absentia* who is playing through an agent (the machine, or other instructional device) who can follow instructions but who does not use his own judgment. The programmer accomplishes his purposes as a player by leaving his agent complete instructions as to the choices he (the programmer) wishes to make at each move under all possible circumstances that may arise. This set of instructions is the *pure strategy* of the programmer (player). If "branching" is used in devising the instructions, the game between the "learner-player" and the "programmer-player" will have a finite number of moves with a finite number of optional choices at each move. Thus, there will be only a finite, although perhaps very large, number of possible pure strategies associated with the game. These strategies can be set so as to provide the rows of the payoff matrix. In similar fashion, the pure strategies of the learner will be finite and will provide the columns of the matrix. As a result, a matrix game (perhaps a very large matrix) is derived. Although such a matrix could not be solved by the elementary methods of solution discussed here, it is not unreasonable to assume that such problems could be solved with comparative ease by submitting them to electronic computer analysis employing programs based upon matrix algebra or iterative techniques.

### Chapter 32—References

See Bibliography: 26, 36, 46, 47, 101, 107, 110, 111, 115, 121, 129, 147, 173, 176, 177, 179; 9a, 13a, 60a, 83a, 113a, 119a.

# Notes

CHAPTER ONE

1. Carter V. Good (ed.),[79] *Dictionary of Education* (New York: McGraw-Hill Book Co., 1945), p. 464.
2. C. West Churchman, R. L. Ackoff, E. L. Arnoff,[36] *Introduction to Operations Research* (New York: John Wiley and Sons, 1957), pp. 3–19.

CHAPTER TWO

1. Carter V. Good and Douglas E. Scates,[82] *Methods of Research: Educational, Psychological, Sociological* (New York: Appleton-Century-Crofts, 1954), pp. 74–78.

CHAPTER FOUR

1. Ronald A. Fisher and Frank Yates,[67,1b] *Statistical Tables for Biological Agricultural, and Medical Research* (3rd ed. New York, Oliver & Boyd, 1948).
2. M. C. Kendall and B. Babington-Smith,[26] "Tables of Random Sampling Numbers," *Tracts for Computers*, XXIV (London: Cambridge University Press, 1939).

CHAPTER FIVE

1. M. H. Hansen and W. N. Hurwitz,[54a] "The Problem of Non-Response in Sample Surveys," *Journal of the American Statistical Association*, XLI (December, 1946), p. 517.
2. A. Politz and W. Simmons,[88a] "An Attempt to Get the 'Not-at-Homes' into the Sample Without Callbacks," *Journal of the American Statistical Association*, XLIV (March, 1949), pp. 9–31.
3. Walter Hendricks,[57a] "Adjustment for Bias Caused by Non-Response in Mailed Surveys," *Agricultural Economics Research*, April, 1949, pp. 52–56.
4. J. M. Juren,[63a] "Inspector's Errors in Quality Control," *Mechanical Engineering*, LVII (1935), pp. 643–44.
5. J. Francis Rummel,[150] *An Introduction to Research Procedures in Education* (New York: Harper & Brothers, 1958), pp. 66–67.
6. *Ibid.*, pp. 76–83.

CHAPTER SIX

1. Oscar K. Buros (ed.), *The Fifth Mental Measurement Yearbook* (New Brunswick, N.J.: Rutgers University Press, 1955).
2. Arvil S. Barr, Robert A. Davis, and Palmer O. Johnson,[18] *Educational Research and Appraisal* (Philadelphia: J. B. Lippincott Company, © 1953), pp. 115–16. Reprinted by permission of the publisher.
3. John W. Best,[23] *Research in Education* (Englewood Cliffs, N.J.: Prentice-Hall, Inc., 1959), pp. 151–52.
4. H. A. Greene, A. N. Jorgensen, J. R. Gerberich,[87] *Measurement and Evaluation in the Second School* (New York: Longmans, Green & Co., 1955), pp. 92–93. Permission by David Mackay Company Inc.

CHAPTER SEVEN

1. Sidney Siegel,[155] *Nonparametric Statistics for the Behavioral Sciences* (New York: McGraw-Hill Book Co., 1956), p. 27.


CHAPTER NINE

1. William I. B. Beveridge, *The Art of Scientific Investigation* (New York: W. W. Norton & Co., 1950), p. 13.
2. Ernest Greenwood, *Experimental Sociology* (New York: King's Crown Press of Columbia University Press, 1945), p. 138.
3. *Loc. cit.*
4. *Loc. cit.*
5. Helen F. Christiansen, *The Relation of School Progress to Subsequent Economic Adjustment of Students Attending Four St. Paul High Schools. 1926* (Unpublished Master's thesis, University of Minnesota, 1938).
6. Greenwood, pp. 140–41.


CHAPTER TEN

1. Good and Scates,[82] p. 255.
2. *Ibid.*, p. 726.


CHAPTER ELEVEN

1. Fred H. Blum,[10a] "Action Research: A. Scientific Approach?" *Philosophy of Science*, XXII (January, 1955), pp. 1–7.
2. Stephen M. Corey,[27a] "Fundamental Research, Action Research, and Educational Practices," *Teachers College Record*, L (May, 1949), pp. 509–14.
3. *Loc. cit.*
4. Michigan Association for Supervision and Curriculum Development,[80a] *A Look at Cooperative Action Research in Michigan* (Lansing: Michigan Education Association, 1954), pp. 4–5.
5. Bernard R. Gorman, "Action Research: A Teaching or a Research Method?" *Journal of Educational Research*, XXVII (December, 1957), pp. 544–47.
6. Stephen M. Corey,[39] *Action Research to Improve School Practices* (New York: Bureau of Publications, Teachers College, Columbia University, 1953), pp. 8–16.
7. *Loc. cit.*


CHAPTER TWELVE

1. Good and Scates,[82] pp. 198–201.


CHAPTER THIRTEEN

1. George A. Lundberg, *Social Research: A Study in Methods of Gathering Data* (New York: Longmans, Green & Co., 1949), p. 128.
2. R. L. Schank,[98a] "A Study of a Community and Its Groups and Institutions Conceived of as Behaviors of Individuals," Psychological *Monogram*, II (1932), p. 43.
3. Theodore M. Newcomb,[132] *Personality and Social Change: Attitudes Formation in a Student Community* (New York: Dryden Press, 1943).
4. Robert S. Lynd and Helen Merrell Lynd,[117] *Middletown: A study in Contemporary Culture* (New York: Harcourt, Brace & Co., 1929).
5. Leon Festinger and Daniel Katz (eds.),[63] *Research Methods in the Behavioral Sciences* (New York: Dryden Press, 1953).
6. August B. Hollingshead,[96] *Elmtown's Youth* (New York: John Wiley & Sons, 1949).

CHAPTER FOURTEEN

1. A. C. Rosander,[148] *Elementary Principles of Statistics* (New York: D. Van Nostrand & Co., 1951), pp. 78–79.
2. Elmer B. Mode,[126] *The Elements of Statistics* (Englewood Cliffs, N.J.: Prentice-Hall, Inc., 1941).

CHAPTER SEVENTEEN

1. See Rosander,[148] pp. 277–78 for illustration and discussion of this feature and others pertaining to optimum allocation.

CHAPTER NINETEEN

1. Rosander,[148] pp. 321–24, 370–99.

CHAPTER TWENTY

1. Morris Zelditch, Jr.,[200] *A Basic Course in Sociological Statistics* (New York: Holt, Rinehart & Winston, 1959), pp. 167–69.

CHAPTER TWENTY-ONE

1. Rosander,[148] pp. 372–94.
2. Henry E. Garrett,[77] *Statistics in Psychology and Education* (New York: Longmans, Green & Co., 1958), pp. 372–73.
3. C. C. Peters and W. R. Van Voorhis,[141] *Statistical Procedures and Their Mathematical Basis* (New York: McGraw-Hill Book Co., 1940), pp. 312–49.

CHAPTER TWENTY-TWO

1. Zelditch, Jr.,[200] pp. 201–12.
2. Louis Guttman,[53a] "A Basis for Analyzing Test-Retest Reliability," *Psychometrika*, X (1945), pp. 255–82.
3. P. J. Rulon,[95a] "A Simplified Procedure for Determining the Reliability of a Test by Split-Halves," *Harvard Educational Review*, IX (1939), pp. 99–103.
4. G. F. Kuder and M. W. Richardson,[68a] "The Theory of the Estimation of Test Reliability," *Psychometrika*, III (1937), pp. 156–60.
5. See H. H. Remmers, N. L. Gage, J. F. Rummel,[146] *A Practical Introduction to Measurement and Evaluation* (New York: Harper & Brothers, 1960), pp. 122–26.

CHAPTER TWENTY-THREE

1. See Siegel,[155] pp. 9–10; and Wilfred J. Dixon and Frank J. Massey, Jr.,[49] *Introduction to Statistical Analysis* (New York: McGraw-Hill Book Co., 1957), p. 97.
2. Siegel,[155] p. 14.

CHAPTER TWENTY-FOUR

1. Siegel,[155] pp. 27.
2. *Ibid.*, pp. 47–52.

CHAPTER TWENTY-FIVE

1. Siegel,[155] p. 48.
2. *Ibid.*, p. 128.

CHAPTER TWENTY-SIX

1. Siegel,[155] p. 184.
2. W. H. Kruskal and W. A. Wallis,[67a] "Use of Ranks in One-Criterion Variance Analysis," *Journal of the American Statistical Association*, XLVII (1952), p. 583.

CHAPTER TWENTY-EIGHT

1. Rosander,[148] pp. 595–617.
2. George W. Snedecor,[158] *Analysis of Variance and Covariance* (Ames, Iowa: Iowa State College Press, 1934); also Snedecor,[159] *Statistical Methods Applied to Experiments in Agriculture and Biology* (Ames, Iowa: Iowa State College Press, 1946).
3. Fisher and Yates,[16] *op. cit.*
4. Allen L. Edwards,[54] *Experimental Design in Psychological Research* (New York: Holt Rinehart & Winston, 1960), pp. 125–28.
5. *Loc. cit.*
6. Wilford J. Dixon and Frank J. Massey, Jr.,[49] *Introduction to Statistical Analysis* (New York: McGraw-Hill Book Co., 1957), pp. 179–81.
7. *Ibid.*, pp. 181–82.

CHAPTER TWENTY-NINE

1. Edwards,[54] pp. 125–28.
2. *Ibid.*, pp. 201–10.

CHAPTER THIRTY-ONE

1. Raymond B. Cattell,[34] *Factor Analysis: An Introduction and Manual for the Psychologist and Social Scientist* (New York: Harper & Brothers, 1952), pp. 11–12.
2. Cattell,[34] pp. 158–61.

# Bibliography

1. Abrams, Mark. *Social Surveys and Social Action.* London: William Heinemann, 1951.
2. Ackoff, Russell L. *The Design of Social Research.* Chicago: The University of Chicago Press, 1953.
3. Ackoff, Russell L., and Churchman, C. West. *An Introduction to Experimental Method,* Part I. Detroit: Wayne University Press, 1949.
4. Adams, J. K. *Basic Statistical Concepts.* New York: McGraw-Hill Book Co., 1955.
5. Albig, William. *Public Opinion.* New York: McGraw-Hill Book Co., 1939.
6. Alexander, Carter, and Burke, Arvid J. *How to Locate Educational Information and Data.* New York: Bureau of Publications, Teachers College, Columbia University, 1958.
7. Anastasi, Anne. *Differential Psychology.* 3rd ed. New York: Macmillan Company, 1958.
8. Anderson, R. L., and Bancroft, T. A. *Statistical Theory in Research.* New York: McGraw-Hill Book Co., 1952.
9. Andrews, G. (ed.). *Methods of Psychology.* New York: John Wiley & Sons, 1948.
10. Anstey, E., and Mercer E. O. *Interviewing for the Selection of Staff.* London: George Allen and Unwin, for the Royal Institute of Public Administration, 1956.
11. Association for Supervision and Curriculum Development. *Learning About Learning from Action Research.* Washington, D.C.: National Education Association of the United States, 1959.
12. Association for Supervision and Curriculum Development. *Research for Curriculum Development.* Washington, D.C.: National Education Association of the United States, 1957.
13. Bader, Carolyn F. *The Interviewer's Guide.* St. Louis: Institute of Market Research, 1947.
14. Bales, Robert F. *Interaction Process Analysis.* Cambridge, Mass.: Addison-Wesley Publishing Co., 1950.
15. Barclay, George W. *Techniques of Population Analysis.* New York: John Wiley & Sons, 1958.
16. Barnes, Fred P. *Practical Research Processes—A Guidebook in Research Methods for Practitioners in Education.* Champaign, Ill.: University of Illinois Press, 1958.
17. Barnes, John B. *Educational Research for Classroom Teachers.* New York: G. P. Putnam's Sons, 1960.
18. Barr, Arvil S., Davis, Robert A., and Johnson, Palmer O. *Educational Research and Appraisal.* Philadelphia.: J. B. Lippincott Company, 1953.
19. Bartz, Albert E. *Elementary Statistical Methods for Educational Measurement,* Minneapolis, Minn.: Burgess Publishing Co., 1958.
20. Barzun, Jacques, and Graff, Henry F. *The Modern Researcher.* New York: Harcourt, Brace & Co., 1957.
21. Bergmann, Gustav. *Philosophy of Science.* Madison, Wis.: University of Wisconsin Press, 1957.

22. Berelson, Bernard. *Content Analysis in Communication Research*. Glencoe, Ill.: Free Press, 1952.
23. Best, John W. *Research in Education*. Englewood Cliffs, N.J.: Prentice-Hall, 1959.
24. Beveridge, William I. B. *The Art of Scientific Investigation*. New York: W. W. Norton & Co., 1950.
25. Bingham, Walter Van Dyke, and Moore, Bruce V. *How to Interview*. 3rd ed. New York: Harper & Brothers, 1941.
26. Blackwell, D. H., and Girshick, M. A. *Theory of Games and Statistical Decisions*. New York: John Wiley & Sons, 1954.
27. Blommers, Paul J., and Lindquist, E. F. *Elementary Statistical Methods*. Boston: Houghton Mifflin Co., 1960.
28. Brickman, William W. *Guide to Research in Educational History*. New York: New York University Bookstore, 1949.
29. Brown, Clarence W., and Ghiselli, E. E. *Scientific Method in Psychology*. New York: McGraw-Hill Book Co., 1955.
30. Buros, Oscar K. (ed.). *The Fifth Mental Measurement Yearbook*. New Brunswick, N.J.: Rutgers University Press, 1955.
31. Butsch, R. L. *How to Read Statistics*. Milwaukee: Bruce Publishing Co., 1946.
32. Carnap, Rudolph. "Testability and Meaning," *Readings in the Philosophy of Science*. eds. Herbert Feigl and May Brodbeck. New York: Appleton-Century-Crofts, 1953.
33. Cartwright, Dorwin, and Zander, Alvin. *Group Dynamics, Research and Theory*. Evanston, Ill.: Row, Peterson & Co., 1953.
34. Cattell, Raymond B. *Factor Analysis: An Introduction and Manual for the Psychologist and Social Scientist*. New York: Harper & Brothers, 1952.
35. Chapin, F. Stuart. *Experimental Designs in Sociological Research*. New York: Harper & Brothers, 1947.
36. Churchman, C. West, Ackoff, R. L., and Arnoff, E. L. *Introduction to Operations Research*. New York: John Wiley & Sons, 1957.
37. Cochran, William G. *Sampling Techniques*. New York: John Wiley & Sons, 1953.
38. Cochran, William G., and Cox, G. M. *Experimental Design*. New York: John Wiley & Sons, 1950.
39. Corey, Stephen M. *Action Research to Improve School Practices*. New York: Bureau of Publications, Teachers College, Columbia University, 1953.
40. Cornell, Francis G. *The Essentials of Educational Statistics*. New York: John Wiley & Sons, 1956.
41. Cramer, Harold. *Mathematical Methods of Statistics*. Princeton: Princeton University Press, 1946.
42. Cronbach, Lee J. *Essentials of Psychological Testing*. New York: Harper & Brothers, 1949.
43. ———. *Essentials of Psychology Testing*. New York: Harper & Brothers, 1960.
44. Croxton, Frederick E., and Cowden, Dudley J. *Applied General Statistics*. 2nd ed. New York: Prentice-Hall, Inc., 1955.
45. David, F. N. *Probability Theory for Statistical Methods*. New York: Cambridge University Press, 1949.
46. Davies, Owen L. *Statistical Methods in Research and Production, With Special Reference to the Chemical Industry*. London: Oliver & Boyd, 1949.
47. DeFleur, Melvin L., and Larsen, Otto. *The Flow of Information*. New York: Harper & Brothers, 1958.
48. Deming, William E. *Some Theory of Sampling*. New York: John Wiley & Sons, 1950.
49. Dixon, Wilfred J., and Massey, Frank J. Jr. *Introduction to Statistical Analysis*. New York: McGraw-Hill Book Co., 1957.
50. Doby, John T. (ed.). *An Introduction to Social Research*. Harrisburg, Pa.: The Stackpole Co., 1954.

51. Doll, Ronald. *Organizing for Curriculum Improvement.* New York: Bureau of Public-ations, Teachers College, Columbia University, 1953.
52. Edwards, Allen L. *Statistical Analysis.* New York: Rinehart & Co., 1946.
53. ———. *Statistical Methods for the Behavioral Sciences.* New York: Rinehart & Co., 1954.
54. ———. *Experimental Design in Psychological Research.* New York: Holt, Rinehart & Winston, 1960.
55. Eisenhart, C., Hastay, M. W., and Wallis, W. A. *Techniques of Statistical Analysis.* New York: McGraw-Hill Book Co., 1947.
56. Elmer, Manuel Conrad. *Social Research.* Englewood Cliffs: Prentice-Hall, Inc., 1957.
57. English, Horace and Ava. *A Comprehensive Dictionary of Psychological and Psycho-analytical Terms.* New York: Longmans, Green & Co., 1958.
58. Federer, Walter T. *Experimental Design : Theory and Application.* New York: Mac-millan Company, 1955.
59. Feigl, Herbert, and Brodbeck, May (eds.). *Readings in the Philosophy of Science.* New York: Appleton-Century-Crofts, 1953.
60. Feller, W. *An Introduction to Probability Theory, and Its Applications,* Vol. I. New York: John Wiley & Sons, 1950.
61. Fenlason, Anne F. *Essentials in Interviewing.* New York: Harper & Brothers, 1952.
62. Ferguson, George A. *Statistical Analysis in Psychology and Education.* New York: McGraw-Hill Book Co., 1959.
63. Festinger, Leon, and Katz, Daniel (eds.). *Research Methods in the Behavioral Sciences.* New York: Dryden Press, 1953.
64. Finney, D. J. *Experimental Design and Its Statistical Basis.* Chicago: University of Chicago Press, 1955.
65. Fisher, Ronald A. *Statistical Methods for Research Workers.* Edinburgh: Oliver & Boyd, 1944.
66. Fisher, Ronald A. *The Design of Experiments.* New York: Hafner Publishing Co., 1949.
67. Fisher, Ronald A., and Yates, Frank. *Statistical Tables for Biological, Agricultural and Medical Research.* 3rd ed. New York: Hafner Publishing Co., 1948.
68. Foshay, Arthur W., and Wass, Kenneth D. *Children's Social Values.* New York: Bureau of Publications, Teachers College, Columbia University, 1954.
69. Fraser, D. A. S. *Statistics: An Introduction.* New York: John Wiley & Sons, 1958.
70. Freeman, Frank S. *Theory and Practice of Psychological Testing.* New York: Henry Holt & Co., 1951.
71. Freund, John E. *Modern Elementary Statistics.* Englewood Cliffs, N.J.: Prentice-Hall, 1952.
72. Fruchter, Benjamin. *Introduction to Factor Analysis.* New York: D. Van Nostrand Co., 1954.
73. Furfey, Paul H. *The Scope and Method of Sociology.* New York: Harper & Brothers, 1953.
74. Garraghan, Gilbert J. *A Guide to Historical Method.* 2nd ed. by Jean Delanglez. New York: Fordham University Press, 1946.
75. Garrett, Annette Marie. *Interviewing: Its Principles and Methods.* New York: Family Welfare Association of America, 1942.
76. Garrett, Henry E. *Elementary Statistics.* New York: Longmans, Green & Co., 1956.
77. ———. *Statistics in Psychology and Education.* New York: Longmans, Green & Co., 1958.
78. Gee, Wilson, *Social Science Research Methods.* New York: Appleton-Century-Crofts, 1950.
79. Good, Carter V. (ed.). *Dictionary of Education.* New York: McGraw-Hill-Book Co., 1945.
80. ———. *Introduction to Educational Research.* New York: Appleton-Century-Crofts, 1959.

81. Good, Carter V., Barr, A. S., and Scates, Douglas E. *The Methodology of Educational Research.* New York: Appleton-Century-Crofts, 1941.

82. ———, and Scates, Douglas E. *Methods of Research: Educational, Psychological, Sociological.* New York: Appleton-Century-Crofts, 1954.

83. Goode, William J., and Hatt, Paul K. *Methods in Social Research.* New York: McGraw-Hill Book Co., 1952.

84. Goodenough, F., and Anderson, John. *Experimental Child Study.* New York: Century Co., 1931.

85. Goulden, C. H. *Methods of Statistical Analysis.* 2nd ed. New York: John Wiley & Sons, 1952.

86. Green, Edward B. *Measurement of Human Behavior.* New York: Odyssey Press, 1941.

87. Greene, H. A., Jorgensen, A. N., Gerberich, J. R. *Measurement and Evaluation in the Secondary School.* New York: David MacKay Company, Inc., 1955.

88. Guetzkow, Harold (ed.). *Groups, Leadership, and Men: Research in Human Relations.* Pittsburgh: Carnegie Press, 1951.

89. Guildford, J. P. *Fundamental Statistics in Psychology and Education.* New York: McGraw-Hill Book Co., 1956.

90. Hagood, Margaret Jarman. *Statistics for Sociologists.* New York: Reynal & Hitchcock, 1941.

91. Hansen, Morris H., Hurwitz, William H., and Madow, William G. *Sample Survey Methods and Theory,* Vol. I. New York: John Wiley & Sons, 1953.

92. Harris, Chester W. (ed.). *Encyclopedia of Educational Research.* New York: Macmillan Company, 1960.

93. Hendricks, Walter A. *The Mathematical Theory of Sampling.* New Brunswick: Scarecrow Press, 1956.

94. Hillway, Tyrus. *Introduction to Research.* Boston: Houghton Mifflin Co., 1956.

95. Hirsch, Werner Z. *Introduction to Modern Statistics.* New York: Macmillan Company, 1957.

96. Hollingshead, August B. *Elmtown's Youth.* New York: John Wiley & Sons, 1949.

97. Holzinger, Karl J. *Statistical Methods for Students in Education.* New York: Ginn & Co., 1928.

98. Hull, Clark L. *Principles of Behavior.* New York: Appleton-Century-Crofts, 1943.

99. Hume, D. A. *Treatise of Human Nature.* (1739–1740).

100. Hyman, Herbert H. *Survey Design and Analysis: Principles, Cases and Procedures.* Glencoe, Ill.: Free Press, 1955.

101. Ilserio, A. R. *Statistics and Their Application to Commerce.* London: H. F. L. (Publishers) Ltd., 1956.

102. Jahoda, Marie, Deutsch, Morton, and Cook, Stuart W. *Research Methods in Social Relations, Part One: Basic Processes, Part Two: Selected Techniques.* New York: Dryden Press, 1951.

103. Jerome, Harry. *Statistical Method.* New York: Harper & Brothers, 1924.

104. Johnson, Palmer O. *Statistical Methods in Research.* Englewood Cliffs: Prentice-Hall, Inc., 1940.

105. Johnson, N. L., and Tetley, H. *Statistics,* Vol. I. Cambridge: Cambridge University Press, 1949.

106. Kelley, Truman Lee. *Fundamentals of Statistics.* Cambridge: Cambridge University Press, 1947.

107. Kemeny, U. G., Snell, J. L., and Thompson, G. L. *Introduction to Finite Mathematics.* Englewood Cliffs, N.J.: Prentice-Hall, Inc., 1958.

108. Kendall, Maurice G., and Stuart, Alan. *The Advanced Theory of Statistics,* Vol. II, *Statistical Inference and Statistical Relationship.* New York: Hafner Publishing Co., 1958–61.

109. ———. *The Advanced Theory of Statistics,* Vol. I, New York: Hafner Publishing Co., 1958–61.

10. Kuhn, H. W., and Tucker, A. W. (eds.). *Contributions to the Theory of Games I*. Princeton: Princeton University Press, 1950.

11. ———. *Contributions to the Theory of Games II*. Princeton: Princeton University Press, 1953.

12. Lindquist, Everett F. *A First Course in Statistics*. Boston: Houghton-Mifflin Co., 1942.

13. ———. *Design and Analysis of Experiments in Psychology and Education*. Boston: Houghton Mifflin Co., 1953.

14. Lindsey, Margaret. *Improving Laboratory Experiences in Teacher Education: A Cooperative Action Research Study*. New York: Bureau of Publications, Teachers College, Columbia University, 1955.

115. Luce, R. D., and Raiffa, H. *Games and Decisions—Introduction and Critical Survey*. New York: John Wiley & Sons, 1957.

116. Lundberg, George A. *Social Research: A Study in Methods of Gathering Data*. New York: Longmans, Green & Co., 1949.

117. Lynd, Robert S. and Helen M. *Middletown: A Study in Contemporary Culture*. New York: Harcourt, Brace & Co., 1929.

118. Madge, John. *The Tools of Social Science*. New York: Longmans, Green & Co., 1953.

119. McCormick, Thomas G., and Francis, Roy G. *Methods of Research in the Behavioral Sciences*. New York: Harper & Brothers, 1958.

120. McGrath, G. D., Jelinek, James J., and Wochner, Raymond E. *Educational Research Methods*. New York: Ronald Press Co., 1963.

121. McKinsey, J. *Introduction to the Theory of Games*. New York: McGraw-Hill Book Co., 1952.

122. McMillan, Wayne, *Statistical Methods for Social Workers*. Chicago: University of Chicago Press, 1952.

123. McNemar, Quinn. *Psychological Statistics*. 2nd ed. New York: John Wiley & Sons, 1955.

124. Merton, Robert K., Fiske, Marjorie, and Kendall, Patricia L. *The Focused Interview*. New York: Bureau of Applied Social Research, Columbia University, 1952.

125. Mill, John Stuart. *A System of Logic*. New York: Harper & Brothers, 1872.

126. Mode, Elmer B. *Elements of Statistics*. Englewood Cliffs, N.J.: Prentice-Hall Inc., 1941.

127. Molina, E. C. *Poisson's Exponential Binomial Limit*. New York: D. Van Nostrand & Co., 1942.

128. Mood, A. M. *Introduction to the Theory of Statistics*. New York: McGraw-Hill Book Co., 1950.

129. Morse, Philip M., and Kimball, George E. *Methods of Operations Research*. New York: John Wiley & Sons, 1950.

130. Mowrer, O. Hobart (ed.). *Psychotherapy: Theory and Research*. New York: Ronald Press Co., 1953.

131. Nelson, M. J., Denny, E. C., and Colodarci, Arthur P. *Statistics for Teachers*. New York: Dryden Press, 1956.

132. Newcomb, Theodore M. *Personality and Social Change: Attitudes Formation in a Student Community*. New York: Dryden Press, 1943.

133. Neyman, J. *First Course in Probability and Statistics*. New York: Henry Holt & Co., 1950.

134. Ogle, M. B. Jr., *Public Opinion and Political Dynamics*. New York: Houghton-Mifflin Co., 1950.

135. Oldfield, R. C. *The Psychology of the Interview*. London: Methuen & Co., 1941.

136. Ostle, Bernard. *Statistics in Research*. Ames, Iowa: Iowa State College Press, 1954.

137. Parten, Mildred, *Surveys, Polls, and Samples: Practical Procedures*. New York: Harper & Brothers, 1950.

138. Passow, A. Harry, *et al. Training Curriculum Leaders for Cooperative Research*. New York: Bureau of Publications, Teachers College, Columbia University, 1955.

139. Payne, Stanley L. *The Art of Asking Questions.* Princeton: Princeton University Press, 1951.
140. Peatman, John G. *Descriptive and Sampling Statistics.* New York: Harper & Brothers, 1947.
141. Peters, C. C., and Van Voorhis, W. R. *Statistical Procedures and Their Mathematical Basis.* New York: McGraw-Hill Book Co., 1940.
142. Randall, John Herman, Jr., and Buchler, Justus. *Philosophy: An Introduction.* New York: Barnes & Noble, 1942.
143. Ray, William S. *An Introduction to Experimental Design.* New York: Macmillan Company, 1960.
144. Reitz, Wilhelm. "Higher Mental Processes," *Encyclopedia of Educational Research.* ed. Walter S. Monroe. New York: Macmillan Company, 1950.
145. Remmers, H. H. *Introduction to Opinion and Attitude Measurement.* New York: Harper & Brothers, 1954.
146. ———, Gage, N. L., and Rummel, J. F. A. *A Practical Introduction to Measurement and Evaluation.* New York: Harper & Brothers, 1960.
147. Richardson, M. *Fundamentals of Mathematics.* New York: Macmillan Company, 1958.
148. Rosander, A. C. *Elementary Principles of Statistics.* New York: D. Van Nostrand & Co., 1951.
149. Rose, Arnold M. *Theory and Method in Social Sciences.* Minneapolis: University of Minnesota Press, 1954.
150. Rummel, J. Francis. *An Introduction to Research Procedures in Education.* New York: Harper & Brothers, 1958.
151. Sears, Jesse B. "School Surveys," *Encyclopedia of Educational Research.* New York: Macmillan Company, 1950.
152. Selltiz, Claire, and Others. *Research Methods in Social Relations.* rev. 1 vol. ed. New York: Henry Holt & Co., 1960.
153. Senders, Virginia L. *Measurement and Statistics.* New York: Oxford University Press, 1958.
154. Shumsky, Abraham. *The Action Research Way of Learning.* New York: Bureau of Publications, Teachers College, Columbia University, 1958.
155. Siegel, Sidney. *Nonparametic Statistics for the Behavioral Sciences.* New York: McGraw-Hill Book Co., 1956.
156. Simpson, George, and Kafka, Fritz. *Basic Statistics.* New York: W. W. Norton & Co., 1957.
157. Smith, James G., and Duncan, Acheson J. *Elementary Statistics and Applications.* New York: McGraw-Hill Book Co., 1944.
158. Snedecor, George W. *Analysis of Variance and Covariance.* Ames, Iowa: Iowa State College Press, 1934.
159. ———. *Statistical Methods Applied to Experiments in Agriculture and Biology.* Ames, Iowa: Iowa State College Press, 1946.
160. Sprott, W. J. H. *Science and Social Action.* Glencoe, Ill.: Free Press, 1955.
161. Stephan, F. F., and McCarthy, P. J. *Sampling Opinions: An Analysis of Survey Procedure.* New York: John Wiley & Sons, 1958.
162. Stephenson, William. *The Study of Behavior.* Chicago: University of Chicago Press, 1953.
163. Stouffer, Samuel A., *et al. Measurement and Prediction.* Princeton: Princeton University Press, 1949.
164. Symonds, P. M. *Psychological Diagnosis in Social Adjustment.* New York: American Book Co., 1934.
165. Tate, Merle W., and Clelland, Richard D. *Nonparametric and Shortcut Statistics.* Danville, Ill.: Interstate Printers & Publishers, 1957.

166. Thorndike, Robert L., and Hagen, Elizabeth. *Measurement and Evaluation in Psychology and Education.* New York: John Wiley & Sons, 1955.
167. Thurstone, L. L. *Multiple Factor Analysis.* Chicago: University of Chicago Press, 1947.
168. Toops, Herbert A. "Questionnaires," *Encyclopedia of Educational Research.* New York: Macmillan Company, 1950.
169. Torgerson, Theodore L., and Adams, G. S. *Measurement and Evaluation.* New York: Dryden Press, 1954.
170. Travers, R. M. W. *An Introduction to Educational Research.* New York: Macmillan Company, 1958.
171. Turfey, Paul Hanly. *The Scope and Method of Sociology.* New York: Harper & Brothers, 1953.
172. Underwood, Benton. *Experimental Psychology.* New York: Appleton-Century-Crofts, 1949.
173. Vajda, S. *Theory of Games and Linear Programming.* New York: John Wiley & Sons, 1956.
174. Van Dalen, Deovold B., and Meyer, William J. *Understanding Educational Research.* York, Pa.: Maple Press Co., 1962.
175. Villars, Donald S. *Statistical Design and Analysis of Experiments for Development Research.* Dubuque, Iowa: William C. Brown Co., 1951.
176. Von Neumann, J., and Morgenstern, O. *Theory of Games and Economics Behavior.* Princeton: Princeton University Press, 1944.
177. ———. *Theory of Games and Economics Behavior.* 2nd ed. Princeton: Princeton University Press, 1947.
178. Wald, Abraham. *Sequential Analysis.* New York: John Wiley & Sons, 1947.
179. ———. *Statistical Decision Functions.* New York: John Wiley & Sons, 1950.
180. Walker, Helen M. *Elementary Statistical Methods.* New York: Henry Holt & Co., 1943.
181. ———. *Mathematics Essential for Elementary Statistics.* 2nd ed. New York: Henry Holt & Co., 1951.
182. Walker, Helen M., and Lev, Joseph. *Elementary Statistical Methods.* rev. ed. New York: Henry Holt & Co., 1958.
183. ———. *Statistical Inference.* New York: Henry Holt & Co., 1953.
184. Wallis, W. Allen, and Roberts, Harry V. *Statistics: A New Approach.* Glencoe, Ill.: Free Press, 1956.
185. Wert, James. *Educational Statistics.* New York: McGraw-Hill Book Co., 1958.
186. Wert, James E., Neidt, Charles O., and Ahmann, J. Stanley. *Statistical Methods in Educational and Psychological Research.* New York: Appleton-Century-Crofts, 1954.
187. White, Ralph K. *Value Analysis: The Nature and Use of the Method.* New York: Society for the Psychological Study of Social Issues, Columbia University, 1951.
188. Whitney, Frederick L. *The Elements of Research.* Englewood Cliffs, N.J.: Prentice-Hall, Inc., 1950.
189. Wilcoxon, F. *Some Rapid Approximate Statistical Procedures.* Stamford, Conn.: American Cyanide Co., 1949.
190. Wilks, S. S. *Elementary Statistical Analysis.* Princeton: Princeton University Press, 1958.
191. Wilson, E. Bright. *An Introduction to Scientific Research.* New York: McGraw-Hill Book Co., 1952.
192. Wood, Dorothy Adkins. *Test Construction.* Columbus, Ohio: Charles E. Merrill Books, 1960.
193. Worthing, Archie G., and Geffner, Joseph. *Treatment of Experimental Data.* New York: John Wiley & Sons, 1943.

194. Yates, Frank. *Sampling Methods for Censuses and Surveys.* London: Charles Griffin & Co., 1950.
195. Young, Pauline V. *Scientific Social Surveys and Research.* Englewood Cliffs, N.J.: Prentice-Hall, Inc., 1949.
196. Young, Pauline V., and Schmid, C. *Scientific Social Surveys and Research.* 3rd ed. Englewood Cliffs, N.J.: Prentice-Hall, Inc., 1956.
197. Yule, G. Udny. *An Introduction to the Theory of Statistics.* London: Griffin Book Co., 1929.
198. ———, and Kendall, M. B. *An Introduction to the Theory of Statistics.* 13th ed. London: Charles Griffin & Co., 1947.
199. Zeisel, Hans. *Say It with Figures.* New York: Harper & Brothers, 1947.
200. Zelditch, Morris, Jr. *A Basic Course in Sociological Statistics.* New York: Holt, Rinehart & Winston, 1959.
201. Zipf, George K. *Human Behavior and the Principle of Least Effort.* Cambridge, Mass.: Addison-Wesley Press, 1949.

ARTICLES AND PERIODICALS

1a. Alexander, Carter. "The Place of Instruction in Library Methods in Educational Research," *Journal of Educational Research,* XXIX (September, 1935), 104–10.
2a. Anderson, Robert C. "The Guided Interview as an Evaluative Instrument," *Journal of Educational Research,* XLVIII (November, 1954), 203–09.
3a. Angell, Robert C., and Freedman, Ronald. "Use of Documents, Records, Census Materials and Indices," *Research Methods in the Behavioral Sciences,* ed. Leon Festinger and Daniel Katz, Chapter 7. New York: Holt, Rinehart & Winston, 1953.
4a. Beach, Morton L. "Research Goes Into Action," *Journal of Educational Research,* XLVII (January, 1954), 351–58.
5a. Berelson, Bernard. "Content Analysis in Communication Research," Handbook of Social Psychology, Vol I: *Theory and Method,* 488–522, Cambridge, Mass.: Addison-Wesley Publishing Co., 1954.
6a. Bergmann, Gustav. "Sense and Nonsense in Operationism," *Scientific Monthly,* LXXIX (October, 1954), 210–14.
7a. Birnbaum, Z. W. "Distribution-free Tests of Fit for Continuous Distribution Function," *Annals of Mathematical Statistics,* XXIV (1953), 1–8.
8a. ———. "Numerical Tabulation of the Distribution of Kolmogorov's Statistic, for Finite Sample Values," *Journal of American Statistical Association,* LXVII (1952), 425–41.
9a. Blackwell, D. H. "Game Theory," *Operations Research for Management,* ed. J. F. McCloskey and F. N. Trefethea. Baltimore: Johns Hopkins Press, 1959.
10a. Blum, Fred H. "Action Research: A Scientific Approach?" *Philosophy of Science,* XXII (January, 1955), 1–7.
11a. Blum, Julius R., and Fattu, Nicholas A. "Nonparametric Methods," *Review of Educational Research,* XXIV (December, 1954), 467–87.
12a. Boguslavsky, George W. "Statistical Estimation of the Size of a Small Population," *Science,* CXXIV (August, 1956).
13a. Bohnenblust, H. F. "Theory of Games," *Modern Mathematics for the Engineer,* ed. E. F. Beckenbach. New York: McGraw-Hill Book Co., 1956.
14a. Breitwieser, Joseph V. "Essentials of Good Research," *Phi Delta Kappan,* XXIV (December, 1941), 185.
15a. Brickman, William W. "Reference Aids in Educational Research," *School and Society,* LXXI (May 27, 1950), 324–31.
16a. Bruckner, Leo J. "Research in Education," *Phi Delta Kappan,* XXIV (December, 1941), 186–88.

17a. Buswell, Guy T. "Science and Social Philosophy: The Scientific Point of View in Education," *School and Society*, LXIX (January, 1949), 1–4.

18a. ———. "Structure of Educational Research," *Phi Delta Kappan*, XXIV (December, 1941), 167–69.

19a. Cajal, S. Ramon Y. "Cajal's Suggestions for the Scientific Investigator," *Scientific Monthly*, XXXVI (March, 1933), 225–35.

20a. Cajori, Florian. "Baconian Methods of Scientific Research," *Scientific Monthly*, XX (January, 1952), 85–91.

21a. Clopper, C. J., and Pearson, E. S. "The Use of Confidence on Fiducial Limits Illustrated in the Case of the Binomial," *Biometrika*, XXVI (1934), 404–41.

22a. Cochran, W. G. "Modern Methods in the Sampling of Human Populations," *American Journal of Public Health*, LXI (1951), 647.

23a. ———. "Some Methods for Strengthening the Common Chi-Square Tests," *Biometrics*, X (1954), 417.

24a. Confrey, B. "Checking on Research as It Progresses," *Education*, LIV (October, 1933), 113–15.

25a. Corbally, John E., Jr. "The Critical Incident Technique and Educational Research," *Educational Research Bulletin*, XXXV (March 14, 1956), 57–61.

26a. ———. "A Second Look at the Critical Incident Technique," *Phi Delta Kappan*, XXXVIII (January, 1957), 141–42.

27a. Corey, Stephen M. "Fundamental Research, Action Research, and Educational Practices," *Teachers College Record*, L (May, 1949), 509–14.

28a. Cornell, Francis G. "Sample Surveys in Education," in "Statistical Methodology in Educational Research," *Review of Educational Research*, XXIV (December, 1954), 359–74.

29a. Coxe, W. W. "Wanted: Guessers," *Journal of Educational Research*, XXXVII (November, 1943), 225–27.

30a. Cronbach, L. J., and Meehl, P. B. "Construct Validity in Psychological Tests," *Psychological Bulletin*, LII (July, 1955), 281–302.

31a. Crump. S. L. "The Estimation of Variance Components in Analysis of Variances," *Biometrika*, II (1946), 7.

32a. Davis, Robert A. "Writing a Thesis in Education," *Peabody Journal of Education*, XXVII (March, 1950), 285–95.

33a. DiVesta, F. J. "Problems in the Use of Questionnaires for Studying the Effectiveness of Educational Programs," *Educational and Psychological Measurement*, XIV (Spring, 1954), 138–50.

34a. Dixon, W. J., and Mood, A. M. "The Statistical Sign Test," *Journal of the American Statistical Association*, XLI (1946), 557–66.

35a. Dodd, Stuart C. "Scientific Methods in Human Relations," *American Journal of Economics and Sociology*, X (April, 1951), 221–34.

36a. Duncan, Marie C. "Recording Descriptive Data and Observer Reliability," *Pedagogical Seminary and Journal of Genetic Psychology*, LXXVIII (June, 1951), 159–64.

37a. Dunlap, J. W., and Kroll, A. "Observations on the Methodology of Attitude Scales," *Journal of Social Psychology*. X (1939), 475–87.

38a. Edwards, Allen, "Experiments: Their Planning and Execution," *Handbook of Social Psychology*, Cambridge, Mass.: Addison-Wesley, 1954, I, 259–87.

39a. Edwards, A. L., and Kenney, K. C. "A Comparison on the Thurstone and Likert Techniques of Attitude Scale Construction," *Journal of Applied Psychology*, XXX (1946), 72-83.

40a. *Encyclopedia Britannica*, XVI (1952), p. 798.

41a. Festinger, L. "The Treatment of Qualitative Data by Scale Analysis," *Psychological Bulletin*, XLIV (1947), 146–61.

42a. Fisher, R. A. "The Statistical Utilization of Multiple Measurements," *Annals of Eugenics*, VIII (August, 1938), 376–86.

43a. Flanagan, John C. "General Considerations in the Selection of Test Items and a Short Method of Estimating the Product-Moment from the Data at the Tails of the Distribution," *Journal of Educational Psychology*, XXX (December, 1939), 674–80.

44a. ———. "Methodology in Psychology," *Psychometrika*, XVII, No. 4 (December, 1952), 359–68.

45a. ———. "Critical Requirements: A New Approach to Employee Evaluation," *Personnel Psychology*, II (1949), 419–25.

46a. ———. "The Use of Comprehensive Rationales in Test Development," *Educational Psychology Measurement*, XI (1951), 151–55.

47a. Fowlkes, J. G., and Bardwell, R. W. "What Do You Believe About Public Education? A Scale for Discovering Beliefs in Regard to the Public Schools." Doctoral Dissertation, University of Wisconsin (1939).

48a. Garrett, Henry A. "The Discriminant Function and Its Use in Psychology," *Psychometrika*, VIII (June, 1943), 65–79.

49a. Giedt, F. Harold. "Comparison of Visual Content and Auditory Cues in Interviewing," *Journal of Consulting Psychology*, XIX (December, 1955), 407–16.

50a. Goldhor, Herbert. "How a Librarian Should Do a Field Research Job," *Library Journal*, LXXII (December, 1951), 1677–79.

51a. Good, Carter V. "Educational Research After Fifty Years," *Phi Delta Kappan*, XXXVII (January, 1956), 145–52.

52a. Gorman, Bernard R. "Action Research: A Teaching or a Research Method?" *Journal of Educational Research*, XXVII (December, 1957), 544–47.

53a. Guttman, Louis, "A Basis for Analyzing Test-Retest Reliability," *Psychometrika*, X (1945), 255–82.

54a. Hansen, M. H., and Hurwitz, W. N. "The Problem of Non-response in Sample Surveys," *Journal of American Statistical Association*, XLI (December, 1946), 517–29.

55a. Hardaway, Charles. "Values of and Incentives to Research," *Teachers College Journal*, XXI (November, 1949), 21.

56a. Hart, F. W. "Discussion—Roboting Research," *School and Society*, XXXII (July, 1930), 19–21.

57a. Hendricks, Walter, "Adjustment for Bias Caused by Non-response in Mailed Surveys," *Agricultural Economics Research.* (April, 1949), 52–56.

58a. Herrera, L. "Bias in the Allocation of Treatments by Random Numbers," *Science*, CXX, 3174 (October 28, 1955), 828–29.

59a. Hotelling, H. "Analysis of a Complex of Statistical Variables into Principal Components," *Journal of Educational Psychology*, XXIV (1933), 417–41, 498–520.

60a. ———. "Some New Methods in Matrix Calculation," *Annals of Mathematical Statistics*, XIV (1943), 1–34.

61a. Jersild, Arthur T., and Meigs, M. F. "Direct Observation as a Research Method," *Review of Educational Research*, IX (December, 1939), 472–82.

62a. Johnson, N. L., and Welch, B. L. "Applications of the Non-central *t*-distribution," *Biometrika*, XXXI (1950), 362.

63a. Juren, J. M. "Inspector's Errors in Quality Control," *Mechanical Engineering*, LVII (1935), 643–44.

64a. Kaiser, Henry F. "The Varimax Criterion for Analytic Rotation in Factor Analysis," *Psychometrika*, XXIII (September, 1958), 187–200.

65a. Kaufman, Felix. "The Nature of Scientific Method," *Social Research*, XII (May, 1954), 464–80.

66a. Kolmogorov, A. "Confidence Limits for an Unknown Distribution Function," *Annals of Mathematical Statistics*, XII (1941), 461–63.

67a. Kruskal, W. H., and Wallis, W. A. "Use of Ranks in One-criterion Variance Analysis," *Journal of the American Statistical Association*, XLVII (1952), 583.

68a. Kuder, G. F., and Richardson, M. W. "The Theory of the Estimation of Test Reliability," *Psychometrika*, III (1937), 156–60.

69a. LeChatelier, Henry M. "The Methodology of Scientific Research," *Journal of Chemical Education*, VII (November, 1930), 2584–89.

70a. Lessenberry, D. D. "Research Is No Better Than the Method Used," *National Business Quarterly*, XI (May, 1943), 5–6 ff.

71a. Levin, Harry. "The Influence of Fullness of Interview on the Reliability, Discriminability and Validity of Interview Judgments," *Journal of Consulting Psychology*, XVIII (August, 1954), 303–06.

72a. Lewis, D., and Burke, C. J. "The Use and Misuse of the Chi-Square Test," *Psychology Bulletin*, LXVI, 433–89.

73a. Likert, R. "A Technique for the Measurement of Attitudes," *Archives of Psychology*, CXL 1932, 52–55.

74a. Litwak, Eugene. "Classification of Biased Questions," *American Journal of Sociology*, LXII (September, 1956), 182–86.

75a. Lord, E. "The Use of the Range in Place of the Standard Deviation in the t-test," *Biometrika*, XXXIV (1947), 41.

76a. Lorge, I., and Orden, H. "Trend, Survey and Education Studies," *Review of Educational Research*, XV (December, 1945), 5 : 360–76.

77a. Martz, Velorus. "Philosophy and Science," *Encyclopedia of Educational Research*, New York : Macmillan Co., 1941, pp. 794–97.

78a. Massey, F. J. "The Kolmogorov-Smirnov Test for Goodness of Fit," *Journal of the American Statistical Association*, XLVI (1951), 68–78.

79a. Mauk, Gertrude. *The Development of a Forced Choice Supervisory Performance Report Within a Large Automotive Corporation*. Unpublished Doctoral Dissertation, Wayne State University, Detroit, 1950.

80a. Michigan Association for Supervision and Curriculum Development. *A Look at Cooperative Action Research in Michigan*. Lansing : Michigan Education Association, 1954, pp. 4–5.

81a. Mood, A. M. "On the Asymptotic Efficiency of Certain Nonparametric Two-Sample Tests," *Annals of Mathematical Statistics*, XXV (1954), 514–22.

82a. Moore, G. H., and Wallis, W. A. "Time Series Significance Tests Based on Signs of Differences," *Journal of American Statistical Association*, XXXVIII (1943), 153–64.

83a. Morgenstern, O. "The Theory of Games," *Scientific American*, CLXXX (1949), 22–31.

84a. Moses, L. E. "Nonparametric Statistics for Psychological Research," *Psychology Bulletin*, XLIX (1952), 122–43.

85a. Perdew, Phillip W. "Criteria of Research in Educational History," *Journal of Educational Research*, XLIV (November, 1950), 217–23.

86a. Phillips, William M., Jr. "Weaknesses of the Mail Questionnaire," *Sociology and Social Research*, XXXV (March–April, 1951), 260–67.

87a. Piltz, Albert, and O'Regan, William. "Non-Response and Non-Quantifiable Data in Sample Surveys," *Journal of Educational Research*, LI (October, 1957), 143–47.

88a. Politz, A., and Simons, W. "An Attempt to Get the 'Not at Homes' Into the Sample Without Callbacks," *Journal of the American Statistical Association*, XLIV (March, 1949), 9–31.

89a. Powers, Francis F. "Research as a State of Mind," *Phi Delta Kappan*, XXIV (December, 1941), 173–74.

90a. Quinn, James A. "Concluding Comments, Symposium on Viewpoints, Problems and Methods of Research in Urban Areas," *Scientific Monthly*, LXXIII (July, 1951), 37–50.

91a. Richardson, M. W., and Kuder, F. P. "Making a Rating Scale that Measures," *Personnel Journal*, XII (1933–34), 36–40.

92a. Robinson, Francis P. "The Unit in Interview Analysis," *Educational and Psychological Measurements,* IX (Winter, 1959), 709–16.

93a. Rosander, A. C. "A Researcher Looks at Research," *Educational Record,* XXI (April, 1940), 220–36.

94a. Rosen, Hjalmer, and Hudson, R. A. "The Validity of 'Undecided' Answers in Questionnaire Responses," *Journal of Applied Psychology,* XXXIX (June, 1955), 178–81.

95a. Rulon, P. J. "A Simplified Procedure for Determining the Reliability of a Test by Split-Halves," *Harvard Educational Review,* IX (1939), 99–103.

96a. ———. "Distinctions Between Discriminant and Regression Analysis and a Geometric Interpetation of the Discriminant Function," *Harvard Educational Review,* XXI (1951), 80–90.

97a. Scates, Douglas E. "With the Researchers," *Journal of Teacher Education,* II (March, 1951), 60–63.

98a. Schank, R. L. "A Study of a Community and Its Groups and Institutions Conceived of as Behaviors of Individuals," *Psychological Monogram,* II (1932), 43.

99a. Seashore, R. H., and Havner, K. "A Time Saving Device for the Construction of Attitude Scales," *Journal of Social Psychology,* IV (1933), 366–72.

100a. Seeley, L. C. *Construction of Three Measures for Instructor Technical Reports*— SDC 383-1-5, Office of Naval Research, July 20, 1948.

101a. Sells, Saul B., and Travers, Robert M. W. "Observational Methods of Research," *Review of Educational Research,* XV (December 1945), 394–403.

102a. Shannon, J. R. "Traits of Research Workers," *Journal of Educational Research,* XL (March, 1947), 513–21.

103a. Slocum, W. L., *et al.* "Increasing Response to Questionnaire and Structured Interviews," *American Sociological Review,* XXI (April, 1956), 221–25.

104a. Smirnov, N. V. "Table for Estimating the Goodness of Fit of Empirical Distributions," *Annals of Mathematical Statistics,* XIX (1948), 279–81.

105a. Smith, B. Othanel. "Science of Education," *Encyclopedia of Educational Research.* New York: Macmillan Company, 1950, pp. 1145–51.

106a. Strang, Ruth. "The Interview," *Review of Educational Research,* IX (December, 1939), 201–04.

107a. Swed, Frieda S., and Eisenhart, C. "Tables for Testing Randomness of Grouping in a Sequence of Alternatives," *Annals of Mathematical Statistics,* XIV (1954), 66–87.

108a. Sukhatme, Pandurang B. *Sampling Theory of Surveys with Application,* New Delhi: Indian Society of Agricultural Statistics; Ames: Iowa State College Press, 1954.

109a. Tatscuke, Maurice M., and Tiedman, David B. "Discriminant Analysis," *Review of Educational Research,* XXIV (December, 1954), 402–416.

110a. Thurstone, L. L. "The Method of Paired Comparison for Social Value," *Journal of Abnormal and Social Psychology,* XXI (1927), 384–400.

111a. Tiedman, David V. "The Utility of the Discriminant Function in Psychological and Guidance Investigations," *Harvard Educational Review,* XXI (Spring, 1951), 71–80.

112a. Toops, Herbert A. "Questionnaires," *Encyclopedia of Educational Research,* 2nd ed., New York: Macmillan Company, 1950, pp. 948–51.

113a. United States Office of Education, *Bibliography of Research Studies in Education,* Washington, D.C.

114a. United States Government Printing Office, Dorothy C. Adkins, *Construction and Analysis of Achievement Tests.* Washington, 1947.

115a. Vidich, Arthur J. "Participant Observation and the Collection and Interpretation of Data," *American Journal of Sociology,* LX (January, 1955), 354–60.

116a. Wilcoxon, F. "Individual Comparisons by Ranking Methods," *Biometrika,* I (1945), 80–83.

117a. ———. "Probability Tables for Individual Comparisons by Ranking Methods," *Biometrika*, III (1947), 119–22.
118a. Wiles, Kimball. "Can We Sharpen the Concept of Action Research?" *Educational Leadership*, X (April, 1953), 408–10.
119a. Wrigley, Charles. "Data Processing: Automation in Calculation and in the Methodology of Educational Research," *Review of Educational Research*, XXVII (December, 1957), 538–43.

SPECIAL TABLES

1b. Fisher, Ronald A., and Yates, Frank. *Statistical Tables for Biological, Agricultural, and Medical Research.* Edinburgh: Oliver & Boyd, 1938.
2b. Kendall, M. C., and Babington-Smith, B. "Tables of Random Sampling Numbers," *Tracts for Computers*, XXIV. London: Cambridge University Press, 1939.
3b. Kruskal, W. H., and Wallis, W. A. "Tables for the Distribution of H in the Use of Ranks in One-Criterion Variance Analysis," *Journal of American Statistical Association*, XLVII (1952), 614–17.
4b. Wilcoxon, F. "Table I," *Some Rapid Approximate Statistical Procedures.* New York: American Cyanamid Co., 1949, p. 13.

# Index

Action research, 117–24; cooperative, 118; individual, 118; model of, 120–24

Adjusting, 103–4, 422–24

Alpha $(\alpha)$—Type I error, 33, 294–95

Analog model, 15, 17, 18, 459

Analysis of covariance, 418–58; and adjustment, 422–24; and correlation, 422–24; applied to a factorial experiment, 438–58; examples of, 425–58; and homogeneity of variances, 424–25; and significance of regression, 435–37; sums of products in the, 419

Analysis of variance, 358–417; degrees of freedom, 360, 378, 410–15; examples of, 359–74, 390–404, 415–417; mean squares, 365, 384, 397, 415; multiple bases of classification, 375; outline of, 372; single classification, 358; sums of squares, 361, 376, 392, 395–403, 405–15; testing $H_0 : \mu_1 = \mu_2 = \mu_3 = \cdots = \mu_k$, 359

Analytical procedures of the general model, 145

Basic types of research, 89, 91; action, 117–24; descriptive (survey), 108–16; experimental, 91–107; field, 134–43; historical (documentary), 125–33

Beta $(\beta)$—Type II error, 33, 295–7

Beta coefficients (weights), 283

Case study research, 109

Causes for variation in samples, 44–45

Centroid, 471–72

Chi-square test, 301–10; expected frequency role, 306; goodness-of: fit tests, 302, 304–6; phi coefficient, 309–10; probability table, 303; single classification, 304–5; tests of independence, 302, 306–9

Clusters and factors, 460–64

Coefficient of alienation, 256

Coefficient of determination, 256

Coefficient of equivalent, 62, 288

Coefficient of equivalence and stability, 62

Coefficient of nonlinear relationship, 271

Coefficient of stability, 62, 288

Coefficient of variation, 170

Combinations, 177

Comparative analysis research, 109

Confidence intervals, 187

Confidence limits, 188

Content analysis research, 109

Correlation, 252–57, 263–66, 271–74, 421–22; and covariance, 421–22; correlation-ratio, 271; linear, 252–54; matrix, 469–71; multiple, 275–84; partial, 275–84; Pearson product-moment coefficient, 254–55; interpretation of, 255–57; Phi coefficient, 263–66; test for independence, 257

Correspondence, 60

Covariance, 418, 421–22; and correlation, 421–22

Critical region, 32–33, 297–98

Criticism—synthesis, 7

Cumulative-frequency distribution (Ogive), 153

Data collection, 46–69; error, biased and unbiased, 49–57; history, 46–48; instrumentalities, 61–69; resistance subjects, 49

Data processing, 54, 70–78; errors due to, 54
———— levels of measurement, 71–77; interval scale, 73–74; nominal (categorical) scale, 71–72; ordinal scale, 72–73; ratio-interval scale, 74–75

Decision, research, 79–88

Degrees of freedom, 303, 336–37, 360–61, 378–80

Descriptive (survey) research, 108–16; case study, 109; comparative analysis, 109; content analysis, 109; model of, 110–16; trend analysis, 110

Descriptive statistics, 145

Dichotomous population (binomial probabilities), 197–202

Discrimination, 67–69

Dispersion measures, 165–72

547

Distribution, 30, 41, 152; frequency, 152; sampling, 41

Elements of the general model, 20, 23
Empirical probability, 173–74
Empiricism, 5, 6
Error, 49–57
—— biased, 50, 51–55; data processing, 54; interpreting, 55; interviewing, 53; measuring instruments and techniques, 54; observing, 54; response, 53; sampling, 51–52
—— unbiased, 56–57
Estimation, 146, 240–65, 267–91; linear regression and correlation, 242; multiple correlation and regression, 275; nonlinear regression and correlation, 267; related variates, 146; single variate, 146
Eta ($\eta$)—correlation-ratio, or coefficient of nonlinear relationship, 271–74
Evaluation, 30–31; of experiments, 105–6; of inference, 80–88
Experimental error (estimate), 385, 393, 399
Experimental research, 91–107; before and after, 97–98; cross-sectional, 96–97; ex post facto, 99; formal, 93–94; model of, 438–58; multivariate designs, 101–2; single variable designs, 100–1
Experimentalism, 10–12

$F$-distribution, 355–458; analysis of variance, 358–417; analysis of covariance, 419–58; conditions for employing, 356; degrees of freedom, 360; relationship to z, 355; selected critical values of, 357; test of significance, 366–67
Factorial design, 375, 390–417, 441; applied to a $2 \times 3 \times 5$ table, 390; applied to a five factor table, 441
Factors, 460–98; and clusters, 460–64; and communality, 484; and correlation matrix, 466; common, 482–83; estimation, 497; general, 482–83; group, 482–83; identification, 495–96; loadings, 467, 472; oblique, 487, 498; orthogonal, 484, 498; positive manifold, 484, 494; relations to variables, 465; rotation of, 483–94; simple structure, 494; specific, 382–3; specification equation, 496–97
Field Research, 134–43; cross-cultural, 137, 138; field study, 137; model of, 138–43; survey, 137
Frequency distributions, 152, 153, 154, 156–72, 173–88, 184–85; area of, 156–58; characteristics of, 154, 156–72; cumulative (Ogive),

153; measures of central tendency, 158–64; measures of dispersion, 165–72; probability and, 173–88; stability of, 184–85
Frequency polygon, 152

General model, 20
General questions, 35–36

Hierarchy of hypotheses, 26
Histogram 149–52
Historical (documentary) research, 125–33; criticism, 127, 128; model of, 128–33
Hyperspace, 467
Hypotheses, 26–35, 292, 338–54

Iconic model, 15, 16
Index of forecasting efficiency, 256
Inference, 26, 79–88, 145, 292–99; of appraisal, 30; of difference, 30; of magnitude, 30; and prediction, 79; of relationship, 30; "sound," 79; statistical, 145, 292–99
Inquiry, 3
Instrumentalities, 61–69; discrimination, 67–69; objectivity, 66–67; reliability, 61–65; validity, 65–66
Interactions, 99, 380–84, 395–403, 405–9; error term, 99, 380–84; order of, 395–403, 405–9
Interval scale data, 73, 74, 77, 78
Interviewing, principles of, 59–60
Isomorphism, 14

Judgment or purposive sample, 43

Kolmogorov–Smirnov nonparametric statistical tests, 311–22; one-sample test, 311–17; selected critical values, 312, 318; two-sample test, 317–22
Kruskall–Wallis $H$ test for $k$ independent samples, 328–33; one-way analysis of variance by ranks, 329
Kuder–Richardson formula, 290

Level of significance, 33
Linear programing, 500–10; "closed half plane," 502; convex polygons, 503; equalities, 501; maxima and minima in, 503–4; "open half plane," 502; and problems in educational research, 504–10
Logical positivism, 7, 8

Matching, 102–3, 323–24; paired observations, 324; related samples, 323
Mathematical probability, 174–75

Matrix, 469–71, 473, 479, 481; correlation, 469–71; first factor product, 473; first residual, 473; second factor product, 479; second residual (with reflections), 481

Mean, 159–62, 164, 368–72; arithmetic, 159–62; geometric, 164; harmonic, 164; multiple comparisons of, 368–72

Mean deviation, 166

Mean squares. *See* Analysis of variance and Analysis of covariance

Median, 162–63

Mode, 163–64

Model of action research, 120–24

Model of descriptive (survey) research, 110–16

Model of field research, 138–43

Model of historical (documentary) research, 128–33

Models, 14–20; of action research, 120–24; analog, 15, 17, 18; descriptive (survey) research, 110–16; experimental research, 128–33; field research, 138–43; general, 20; historical (documentary) research, 128–33; iconic, 15, 16; symbolic, 15, 18, 19

Multiple comparisons of means, 368–72

Multiple factor analysis, 460–99

Multivariate experimental designs, 101–2

Nominal (categorical) scale data, 71, 72, 75, 76

Nonlinear regression, 267–70

Nonparametric tests, 300–1, 334–35

Non-random selection, 43

Normal distribution, 186, 187, 188; as an approximation of binomial probabilities, 197–202; as a probability distribution, 189–97

Null hypothesis, 28, 31, 32, 298–99

Numerical procedures of the general model, 145

*O*-factor analytic technique, 498–99

Objectivity, 66–67

Observation, principles of, 58–59

Observational methods, 57–60; correspondence, 60; Rummel's principles of interviewing, 59–60; Rummel's principles of observation, 58–59

One-way analysis of variance by ranks, 329

Operational hypothesis, 27

Operations research, 12–13

Optimum allocation, 215–19; determined total sample size *n*, 215; undetermined total sample size *n*, 216–19

Ordinal scale data, 72, 73, 76, 77

*P*-factor analytic technique, 498–99

Paired observations, 324, 342–43, 348–51

Parameter, 186

Parametric test, 334–35

Pearson product-moment correlation coefficient *r*, 254–55

Percentile, 153

Percentile rank, 153–54

Permutations, 175–77

Phi coefficient, 263–66, 309–10

Population (universe), 30, 37–39, 43, 185; limits, 38; stratification, 38–39

Power of a statistical test, 297

Pragmatism, 9

Principle of least squares, 247–50

Probability, 173–80; of conditional (dependent) events, 180–81; empirical, 173–74; of exactly *x* successes among *n* outcomes, 181–84; of independent events, 177–79; mathematical, 174–75; of mutually exclusive events, 179–80; sampling, 40

Problem, 23–25; evaluation of, 23–24; formulation of, 24–25

*Q*-factor analytic technique, 498–99

Questionnaires, 64–65; characteristics of good, 64

Quota (controlled) sample, 44

*R*-factor analytic technique, 498–99

Random numbers, 40

Randomized-block design, 375

Range, 165

Rank correlation coefficient, 259–62

Ratio-interval scale data, 74, 75, 78

Rationalism, 5

Reflection, 474–80; and first residual matrix, 475; and second residual matrix, 480

Regression, 242–52, 275–84; Beta coefficients (weights), 283; linear, 242–46; multiple, 275–84; nonlinear, 246–47; partial, 275–84; standard error of estimate, 250–52

Related samples, 323

Reliability, 47, 48, 61–65, 287–91; Kuder–Richardson formula, 290; of questionnaires, 64; of rating methods, 64–65; Spearman–Brown prophecy formula, 289; of tests, 63–64

Replication, 104, 375, 378

Research, 4, 33–34, 89; basic types of, 89; "non-hypothesized," 33–34

Research hypothesis, 26

Residual (interaction) term, 380–82, 399

*S*-factor analytic technique, 498–99

Sample, 29, 39, 40, 41, 43–45, 185; allocation of, 43; causes for variation in, 44–45; design of, 43; element of, 39; judgment or purposive, 43; simple random, 40; size, 41
Sampling, 39–41, 51–52, 186–88, 203–39; conditions, 40–41; distribution, 41–42, 186–88; error, 51–52; numerical aspects of, 203–39; probability, 40; with replacement, 40; without replacement, 40; sequential, 41; unit, 39
Sampling distribution, 168–69; of the mean, 186, 187–88; of the standard deviation, 186; of the variance, 186
Scalar, 461
Scheffe Test, 368–72
Scientific method, 91
Semi-interquartile range, 165–66
Sequential sampling, 41, 220–39; methods of processes (dichotomous population), 233–39; numerical aspects of, 220–39; proportions (binomial population), 222–33
Serial samples, 45
Significance of regression, 435–57
Simple random sample, 40, 204–7; size of, 204–7
Single variable experimental designs, 100–1
Skewness, 171–72
Spearman–Brown prophecy formula, 289
Standard deviation, 166–70; population, 166–68; sample, 168, 169, 170
Standard error of estimate, 250–52
Standard error of the mean, 187
Statistic, 29
Statistical alternative hypothesis, 27, 31, 32
Statistical hypotheses of, 29; difference, 29; magnitude, 29; relationship, 29
Statistical inference, 145, 146–47; testing statistical hypotheses, 146–47
Stratified random samples, 207–10, 211–15; design of, 207–10; efficiency of, 215; size of, 211–14
Subsampling, 43
Sums of squares, 361, 376, 392, 395–403, 405–15; equations and degrees of freedom, 410–15; interactions, 395; mechanical method for calculating, 405–9

Symbolic model, 15, 18, 19
Symbols, 154–56
Symmetry (model), 14
Synthesis—Criticism, 7

$T$-distribution, 187, 188, 335–54, 432–35, 455–57; hypotheses of difference, 341–51; hypotheses of magnitude, 338–41; hypotheses of relationship, 351–54; selected percentiles of, 338; test for adjusted group means, 432–35, 455–57
$T$-factor analytic technique, 498–99
Test vectors, 463
Testing statistical hypotheses (inference), 146–47
Theory of games, 510–28; application to problems in education, 515–16, 522–28; best strategies, 518; "fair" game, 514; graphical solution, 523; matrix games (rectangular), 511; negative payoffs, 511; non-strictly determined games, 517–28; optimal pure strategy, 513, 520; positive payoffs, 511; saddle-point, 513; saddle-value, 513; strictly determined games, 511
Translation formula—Pearson $r$ and rank correlation coefficient, 262–63
Trend analysis research, 110
Type I, alpha ($\alpha$) error, 33, 294–95
Type II, beta ($\beta$) error, 33, 295–97

Universe (population), 30, 37–39, 43, 185; limits, 38; stratification, 38–39

Validity, 47, 48, 65, 66, 285–87
Variance, 166–70, 344, 358–87, 415–17; analysis of (single classification), 358; homogeneity of, 344, 367–68; mean squares, 365, 384, 387, 415–17; population, 166–68; sample, 168, 169, 170
Vector, 461

Wilcoxon signed-ranks test, 324–28

Joseph E. Hill, professor of education and associate dean of Graduate Studies at Wayne State University, holds a B.A. from Albion College (1943) and an M.A. from Wayne State University (1948) both in mathematics. His Ed.D. (1957) from Wayne State University was earned in statistics, evaluation, and research design. Dr. Hill served from 1943 to 46 as an aerologist with the U.S. Navy in World War II. He is a consultant to numerous organizations in the fields of research design and statistics.

August Kerber is an associate professor and chairman of the department of Educational Sociology in the College of Education, Wayne State University. He holds a B.S. (1941), an M.A. (1948), and an Ed.D. (1956), all earned at Wayne State University. He was the editor, with Wilfred Smith, of *Educational Issues in a Changing Society*, published by Wayne State University Press in 1962.

The manuscript was edited by Elvin T. Gidley. The book was designed by Edgar Frank. The typeface for the text is Times Roman, designed by Stanley Morrison in 1931 for the London *Times*. The display face is Hellenic italic.

The book is printed on S.D. Warren's Olde Style Antique paper and bound in Interlaken's Pallium cloth. Manufactured in the United States of America.